Metals

Semimetals

Nonmetals

			13 IIIA	14 IVA	15 VA	16 VIA	17 VIIA	18 VIIIA
								2 **He** 4.00 helium
			5 **B** 10.81 boron	6 **C** 12.01 carbon	7 **N** 14.01 nitrogen	8 **O** 16.00 oxygen	9 **F** 19.00 fluorine	10 **Ne** 20.18 neon
10 VIII	11 IB	12 IIB	13 **Al** 26.98 aluminum	14 **Si** 28.09 silicon	15 **P** 30.97 phosphorus	16 **S** 32.07 sulfur	17 **Cl** 35.45 chlorine	18 **Ar** 39.95 argon
28 **Ni** 58.69 nickel	29 **Cu** 63.55 copper	30 **Zn** 65.39 zinc	31 **Ga** 69.72 gallium	32 **Ge** 72.61 germanium	33 **As** 74.92 arsenic	34 **Se** 78.96 selenium	35 **Br** 79.90 bromine	36 **Kr** 83.80 krypton
46 **Pd** 106.42 palladium	47 **Ag** 107.87 silver	48 **Cd** 112.41 cadmium	49 **In** 114.82 indium	50 **Sn** 118.71 tin	51 **Sb** 121.75 antimony	52 **Te** 127.60 tellurium	53 **I** 126.90 iodine	54 **Xe** 131.29 xenon
78 **Pt** 195.08 platinum	79 **Au** 196.97 gold	80 **Hg** 200.59 mercury	81 **Tl** 204.38 thallium	82 **Pb** 207.2 lead	83 **Bi** 208.98 bismuth	84 **Po** (209) polonium	85 **At** (210) astatine	86 **Rn** (222) radon
110 **Ds** (281) darmstadtium	111 **Rg** (280) roentgenium	112 **Cn** (285) copernicium	113 **—** (284)	114 **Fl** (289) flerovium	115 **—** (288)	116 **Lv** (292) livermorium	117* **—** (294)	118 **—** (294)

64 **Gd** 157.25 gadolinium	65 **Tb** 158.93 terbium	66 **Dy** 162.50 dysprosium	67 **Ho** 164.93 holmium	68 **Er** 167.26 erbium	69 **Tm** 168.93 thulium	70 **Yb** 173.04 ytterbium	71 **Lu** 174.97 lutetium
96 **Cm** (247) curium	97 **Bk** (247) berkelium	98 **Cf** (251) californium	99 **Es** (252) einsteinium	100 **Fm** (257) fermium	101 **Md** (258) mendelevium	102 **No** (259) nobelium	103 **Lr** (260) lawrencium

*Element 117 is currently under review by IUPAC.

INTRODUCTORY CHEMISTRY

Charles H. Corwin

Introductory Chemistry: Concepts and Critical Thinking

Second Custom Edition for Houston Community College

Taken from:
Introductory Chemistry: Concepts and Critical Thinking, Seventh Edition
by Charles H. Corwin

Cover photos: Courtesy of Photodisc/Getty Images and Digitalvision.

Taken from:

Introductory Chemistry: Concepts and Critical Thinking, Seventh Edition
by Charles H. Corwin
Copyright © 2014, 2011, 2008, 2005 by Pearson Education, Inc.
Published by Pearson
Upper Saddle River, New Jersey 07458

Pearson Learning Solutions, 501 Boylston Street, Suite 900, Boston, MA 02116
A Pearson Education Company
www.pearsoned.com

Printed in the United States of America

15 16

000200010271776610

AM

ISBN 10: 1-269-32472-1
ISBN 13: 978-1-269-32472-4

Brief Contents

About the Author

CHARLES H. CORWIN has instructed more than 10,000 students in both lecture and laboratory of introductory chemistry. He acknowledges the diversity of basic chemistry students and employs a variety of classroom pedagogies based on Bloom's taxonomy, Myers-Briggs inventory, critical thinking, and algorithmic versus conceptual heuristics. His teaching strategies include learning by objective, collaborative learning, web-based assignments, chemical demonstrations, and multimedia presentations.

The author was awarded degrees from San Jose State University, where he was a member of Tau Delta Phi honor society. He did graduate research at Stanford Research Institute on dialysis membranes, and attended the University of Akron, Institute of Polymer Science. He spent a sabbatical with the chemical education group at Purdue University studying a constructivist approach to cognitive development based on the work of Jean Piaget. Previously, he was visiting professor at Grand Valley State University on an NSF grant, and participated in a self-paced, mastery-learning study. He is currently interested in developing a hybrid online chemistry course with a laboratory component.

Professor Corwin has been recognized as teacher of the year at American River College, and has received a teaching award from Purdue University. In addition, he has been department chair, faculty mentor, academic senate representative, served on the ACS Examinations Committee, judged science projects at California state fairs, and for two decades was an examiner for the greater Sacramento region chemistry contest.

To the Student

A PERSONAL NOTE I have been with you in lecture and answered your questions. I have been with you in lab and given you encouragement. Perhaps I have not spoken to you personally, but I have had countless conversations with students who are trying to juggle college life, financial aid, employment hours, relationship issues, test anxiety, and stress in general. If you are a first-time student, or a reentry student, my advice is to maintain regular student and instructor contacts, and network with others who can help guide you toward your goals.

Introductory chemistry is a subject that builds systematically and culminates in a knowledge base for the physical sciences, life sciences, health sciences, and beyond. Therefore, it is essential that you set aside time each day to study chemistry, and avoid last-minute cramming for exams. On days when you lack motivation, open the textbook to the attractive art that illustrates the topic you are studying; or, go online to the textbook website and view one of the presentations in MasteringChemistry®.

The completion of a basic chemistry course begins to open doors to a rewarding career. A rewarding career is a source of personal satisfaction that spreads to all aspects of your life and helps you avoid making poor life choices. I know you can be successful in your chemistry class. I have seen others like you with different expressions on their faces at the end of the semester. It is a look of confidence after accepting the challenge, doing their best, and knowing they are better prepared for what lies ahead.

Contents

3 Matter and Energy 63

4 Models of the Atom 99

5 The Periodic Table 131

6 Language of Chemistry 160

7 Chemical Reactions 188

11 Liquids and Solids   312

12 Chemical Bonding   341

14 Acids and Bases   403

18 Nuclear Chemistry   526

Appendices

Preface

It is my goal not to repeat mistakes that I have made previously in the classroom and to improve my skill set each semester. Accordingly, I never leave campus without several Post-Its® for improving a presentation. I continually experiment with different topic organizations, employ multimedia and molecular models for visual concepts, and alternate quantitative and qualitative topics to provide a fresh edge.

It is all too obvious from reviewer comments that there is no consensus for the "right way" of presenting introductory chemistry. Each class situation varies with the course objectives and available facilities. In choosing an order of topic presentation in the *Seventh Edition*, I have weighed the arguments and made informed decisions.

Over a decade ago, many chemistry textbooks chose to move atomic theory and chemical bonding to later chapters. The genesis of this decision was based on Piagetian theory and the research evidence that conceptual topics are a higher cognitive task, which dictates descriptive and algorithmic topics be covered early as a foundation. Recently, some chemistry texts have reverted to an "atoms first" approach, which is influenced by innate student interest in the atomic and molecular world.

Experienced instructors may have found that a mathematically "soft" approach resonates with students. In an effort to cultivate student interest, we can first discuss physical and chemical properties and assign easy tasks such as learning the symbols of chemical elements. The downside to this approach is that students who woefully lack basic math skills, will later experience difficulty with calculations, and may not succeed in spite of our best efforts.

The *Seventh Edition* of *Introductory Chemistry: Concepts and Critical Thinking* allows instructors great latitude in choosing their topic presentation. This was mandated by reviewers who argued for the early placement of certain topics, whereas others argued for a later placement. Suggestions for the order of topic presentation were particularly diverse in the following areas: chemical bonding, molar volume, gas stoichiometry, and ionic equations.

We also asked reviewers to assess the rigor to which prerequisite science skills should be covered. The responses ranged from minimal to heavy emphasis; from relegation to an appendix to full chapter coverage. Obviously, a textbook cannot accommodate all views when there is such disparity. After weighing the alternatives, we opted for an interlude on *Prerequisite Science Skills* following Chapter 1. Students with a good preparation will find the material a simple review; whereas students with a weak preparation will find it helpful and improve their confidence.

A related area that was considered at some length was the depth of coverage for chemical calculations. In past editions, problem solving has received high marks by reviewers. Recently, some instructors have asked for more rigorous examples. We responded to this request in two ways: (1) challenge exercises have been added to the end of each chapter; and (2) a new chapter on *Advanced Problem Solving*, has been added that comprehensively covers a broad spectrum of problem-solving techniques.

NEW TO THIS EDITION

In this *Seventh Edition* of *Introductory Chemistry: Concepts and Critical Thinking*, there have been substantial changes including reorganization of chapters. In addition, the *Seventh Edition* includes the following.

- Interlude on **Prerequisite Science Skills** has been added following Chapter 1. The interlude helps students with weak math/science backgrounds prepare for chemical calculations. This brief interlude is an optional assignment at the discretion of the instructor.

- Chapter on **Advanced Problem Solving** has been added. Chapter 15 attacks problem solving comprehensively by applying diverse, proven strategies including: unit analysis, algebraic analysis, visualization, "ballpark" answers, and concept mapping. The new chapter also provides a section on multiconcept problems.

- Featured **Element in the Environment** begins each chapter to heighten student interest. For example, Chapter 5 shows native gold, gold ore, and states its occurrence in seawater. Chapter 9 shows copper and its recovery from an open-pit mine in Utah.

- **Challenge Exercises** have been added to each end-of-chapter exercise. These paired exercises offer questions at a higher level, and often require synthesis of more than one chemical concept.

- http://www **Online Exercises** have been added to each end-of-chapter exercise.

  Web-based learning and incorporation of technology in teaching presentations has rapidly gained momentum. Accordingly, we have added online exercises that students will find both interesting and relevant to keep them engaged.

- A **Learning Objectives table** now appears at the end of each chapter. The learning objectives are correlated to sections and the end-of-chapter exercises for a greater connection between concepts and problems and for ease of assignment.

AN INTEGRATED LEARNING SYSTEM

More than a textbook, *Introductory Chemistry: Concepts and Critical Thinking, Seventh Edition* is a comprehensive learning system that offers print and media resources as well as an extensive website. Unlike other chemistry texts, all the materials are coherently integrated with the textbook by a single author, including the student solutions manual, laboratory manual, instructor's manual, and test item file. Moreover, the genesis of the package is based on considerable classroom experience, student feedback, instructor feedback, and multiple rounds of reviewer feedback from dozens of institutions across the country.

Students are presented with the same topics, in the same sequence, using the same vocabulary, consistently in the textbook and all the supplements. Instructors are presented with a tightly integrated package including an instructor's resource manual and a 3000-question test item file. The media resources include an Instructor Resource DVD, and the Pearson MasteringChemistry® online homework and tutorial system. The Mastering platform provides customizable and automatically graded assessments that provide individualized coaching, and responds to each student's progress.

PROBLEM SOLVING

An important objective of this text is to help students become effective problem solvers. This is accomplished by a walk-through discussion of each new topic, followed by an example exercise, practice exercise, concept exercise, and a problem-solving organizer at the end of each quantitative chapter.

Previous editions have received positive reviews for systematic problem solving. Inasmuch as basic chemistry students often have weak math skills, algebra has been scrupulously avoided in the early chapters in favor of the unit analysis method of problems solving. However, since many instructors prefer an algebraic approach to the gas laws, Chapter 10 offers both an algebraic and unit analysis approach to solving gas law problems.

To assist underprepared students with a weak math/science background, the *Seventh Edition* offers a brief interlude on *Prerequisite Science Skills* that instructors can assign at their discretion.

The *Seventh Edition* offers numerous end-of-chapter exercises correlated to each chapter section, as well as the chapter learning objectives. New to the *Seventh Edition* are Challenge Exercises and Online Exercises. In addition, the *Seventh Edition* has a new chapter on *Advanced Problems Solving* that introduces a comprehensive range of problem-solving techniques.

LANGUAGE OF CHEMISTRY

Another important objective of this text is to help students learn the language of chemistry. To this end, each chapter has a unique matching exercise for all key terms that allows students to verify their definition in Appendix H. The *Study Guide & Student Solutions Manual* has a computer-generated crossword puzzle for each chapter with clues for *key terms* that provide a fun way to learn the language.

CONCEPTUAL LEARNING

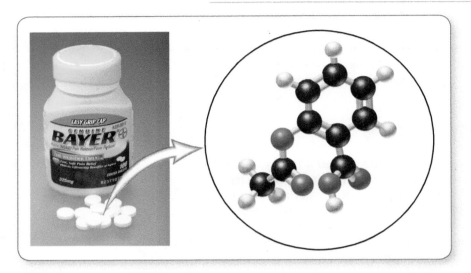

An introductory chemistry student often requires motivation to learn this subject. To this end, in the *Seventh Edition* we have refined the palette of colors and style of rendering to achieve a new level of sophistication in illustrations and photographs. The molecular art program has been enhanced by providing molecular structures for chemical formulas and chemical reactions. Moreover, photographs are enhanced by providing macro/micro molecular art. This visual presentation not only enhances interest in the topics, but adds an effective pedagogical tool for understanding concepts that students find difficult to grasp.

CRITICAL THINKING

Cognitive scientists define *critical thinking* as mental activity associated with three types of thinking: applying reason, making decisions, and problem solving. In this text, critical thinking is introduced within the context of chemical principles. Critical thinking is undertaken specifically in the chapter vignettes and the end-of-chapter self-tests, and generally in problem solving.

In the *Seventh Edition*, we have introduced critical-thinking vignettes on topics ranging from the "World Trade Center" to "Aluminum or Aluminium?" In addition, each end-of-chapter self-test has questions on critical thinking.

FLEXIBLE CHAPTER SEQUENCE

For a variety of reasons, no two introductory chemistry classes present topics in the exact same order. Accordingly, the chapter sequence in *Introductory Chemistry: Concepts and Critical Thinking, Seventh Edition* is constructed in such a way so as to accommodate alternate sequences. For example, chemical bonding (Chapter 12) can immediately follow atomic theory and periodicity (Chapters 4 and 5); ionic equations can follow chemical reactions (Chapter 7); and gas stoichiometry can be deferred to the gas laws (Chapter 10).

ACKNOWLEDGMENTS

I would like to thank the reviewers, instructors, and students who have helped make this learning package so successful. I teach chemistry at a large community college (~40,000 students) with a high introductory chemistry enrollment. I am fortunate to have colleagues who are committed to our mission statement of empowering and preparing students to the full extent of their ability.

From the outset, this textbook has been shaped and honed by instructors who first class-tested the material in module form; and subsequently provided suggestions on a regular basis over six editions. I would be remiss not to specifically recognize my current colleagues: Kristin Casale, Darren Gottke, Ronald Grider, Tamilyn Hong, Jorge Jimenez, Greg Jorgensen, Michael Maddox, Dianne Meador, Chris Meadows, Edmund Niedzinski, Michael Payne, Karen Pesis, Deboleena Roy, Daniel Stewart, Brian Weissbart, Veronica Wheaton, and Linda Zarzana.

I also want to acknowledge a few select individuals for their contribution to the *Seventh Edition*. A most special thank you to Assistant Editor Lisa Pierce, who more than matched my perspicacity for detail and kept everything moving seamlessly and on schedule. Chemistry Editor-in-Chief Adam Jaworski gave broad direction to the *Seventh Edition* based on meetings with instructors around the country who brought issues to his attention. It was once again a pleasure to work with Eric Schrader, photo researcher, who demonstrated tenacity in acquiring high-quality photos to illustrate each topic. Project Manager Jenna Gray at PreMediaGlobal displayed laser focus on the four rounds of page proofs at the ftp website and coordinated the attractive layout and composition. To each of these individuals, singly and collectively, I extend my sincere appreciation.

REVIEWERS OF THE SEVENTH EDITION

The reviewers of this and previous editions of *Introductory Chemistry* continue to define that vague line between the simplifications that students require and the explanations that accuracy and detailed breadth of coverage demand. I thank them for working with me to make this a better learning resource.

Jeff Allison
Austin Community College
Angela Carraway
Meridian Community College
Wanda Davila-Aponte
Valencia Community College
Taiya Fabre
Houston Baptist University
Wendy Fleeman
Shawnee State University
Steven Garber
Front Range Community College
David Holder
Oklahoma State University

Kasem K. Kasem
Indiana University–Kokomo
Kent McCorkle
Fresno City College
Daryl Mincey
Youngstown State University
Barbara Mowery
York College of Pennsylvania
Nancy Mullins
Florida State College at Jacksonville
Christian Ray
University of Illinois at Urbana
Graham Stoner
Houston Community College

REVIEWERS OF PREVIOUS EDITIONS

David Ball
Cleveland State University
Terri Beam
Mount San Antonio College
Karen Bender
Grossmont College
Ralph Benedetto
Wayne Community College
Sean Birke
Jefferson College
Simon Bott
University of Houston
Henry Brenner
New York University
John Brundage
Cuesta College

Nicole K. Carlson
Indiana University
Angela Carraway
Meridian Community College
Kaiguo Chang
University of Arkansas, Fort Smith
Anne Chevalier
Louisiana State University, Alexandria
Bernadette R. Corbett
Metropolitan Community College
Dwaine Davis
Forsyth Technical Community College
John Dolhun
Norwalk Community College
Taiya Fabre
Houston Baptist University

Robert Fremland
Mesa College

Donna Friedman
St. Louis Community College

Wesley Fritz
College of Dupage

Ana Gaillat
Greenfield Community College

David R. Gano
Minot State University

Mary Hadley
Minnesota State University, Mankato

Rebecca K. Hanckel
Charleston Southern University

Helen Haur
Delaware Technical & Community College

Leslie Hersh
Delta College

Mary Hickey
Henry Ford Community College

P. D. Hooker
Colby Community College

Gerald Ittenbach
Fayetteville Technical Community College

Kasem K. Kasem
Indiana University–Kokomo

Ray Kennedy
Massachusetts Bay Community College

Richard Laidlaw
Laramie Community College

Anthony Lazzaro
CA University of Pennsylvania

Jeff Lehman
Grossmont College

Anne Lenhert
Kansas State University

David Lippmann
Southwest Texas State University

Anne Loeb
College of Lake County

Richard Lomneth
University of Nebraska, Omaha

Sharyl Majorski-Briggs
Central Michigan University

Greg J. Maloney
Northland Pioneer College

Jerome Gerard May
Southeastern Louisiana University

Johanna Mazlo
University of North Carolina, Greensboro

Deborah Miller
CNMCC

Richard S. Mitchell
Arkansas State University

Alice Monroe
St. Petersburg College

Robert N. Nelson
Georgia Southern University

Lily Ng
Cleveland State University

Gayle Nicoll
University of Texas, San Antonio

Gita Perkins
Estrella Mountain Community College

Sacha Place
Gonzaga Prep

Jeffrey Rahn
Eastern Washington University

Hussein Samha
Southern Utah University

Scott M. Savage
Northern State University

Mary Setzer
University of Alabama, Huntsville

Julianne M. Smist
Springfield College

Clarissa Sorensen-Unruh
CNMCC

Charles E. Sundin
University of Wisconsin–Platteville

Jerry Swanson
Daytona Beach Community College

Graham Stoner
Houston Community College

Harold Trimm
SUNY Broome Community College

Paul E. Tyner
Schenectady County Community College

Mine Ucak-Astarlioglu
The Pennsylvania State University

Mary Underdown
Montgomery College

Marie Villarba
Glendale Community College

William H. Voige
James Madison University

Charles H. Corwin
Department of Chemistry
American River College
Sacramento, CA 95841
corwinc@arc.losrios.edu

Resources in Print and Online

NAME OF SUPPLEMENT	AVAILABLE IN PRINT	AVAILABLE ONLINE	INSTRUCTOR OR STUDENT SUPPLEMENT	DESCRIPTION
MasteringChemistry®— for Introductory Chemistry: Concepts and Critical Thinking, 7/e 0321804597/ 9780321804594		✓	Supplement for Instructors and Students	The Mastering platform is the most effective and widely used online homework, tutorial, and assessment system for the sciences. It delivers self-paced tutorials that focus on your course objectives, provide individualized coaching, and respond to each student's progress. The Mastering system helps instructors maximize class time with easy-to-assign, customizable, and automatically graded assessments that motivate students to learn outside of class and arrive prepared for lecture or lab.
Study Guide & Selected Solutions Manual for Introductory Chemistry: Concepts and Critical Thinking, 7/e 0321808584/ 9780321808585	✓		Supplement for Students	Written by the author, Charles H. Corwin, this study aid includes diagnostic test questions for each topic covered in the text, crossword puzzles using key terms, and complete solutions to all odd-numbered exercises.
Instructor Manual and Test Bank for Introductory Chemistry: Concepts and Critical Thinking, 7/e 0321807669/ 9780321807663	✓	✓	Supplement for Instructors	The manual features a list of all chapter learning objectives and complete solutions to the even-numbered chapter exercises. This has been updated to reflect the revisions in this text and contains questions in a bank of more than 3000 multiple-choice questions.
Instructor's Resource DVD for Introductory Chemistry: Concepts and Critical Thinking, 7/e 0321821963/ 9780321821966		✓	Supplement for Instructors	This lecture resource contains all art and images from the textbook, three pre-built PowerPoint® presentations, animations, interactive activities, the Instructor's Manual in PDF format, the test item file in Word® format, and the TestGen computerized testing software.
Laboratory Manual for Introductory Chemistry: Concepts and Critical Thinking, 6/e 0321750942/ 9780321750945	✓		Supplement for Laboratory	Emphasizing environmental considerations, Corwin's acclaimed lab manual offers a proven format of a prelaboratory assignment, a stepwise procedure, and a postlaboratory assignment. More than 300,000 students to date in introductory chemistry, preparatory chemistry, and allied health chemistry have used these "bulletproof" experiments successfully. The *Sixth Edition* features environmental icons to alert students to recycle chemical waste, updated prelabs and postlabs, new experimental procedures, a new experiment (Experiment 25), and a new appendix on how to keep a laboratory notebook. Corwin's lab manual can be packaged with any Pearson intro prep chemistry book.
Catalyst: The Pearson Custom Laboratory Program for Chemistry		✓	Supplement for Laboratory	This program allows you to custom-build a chemistry lab manual that matches your content needs and course organization. You can either write your own labs using the Lab Authoring Kit tool or you can select from the hundreds of labs available at http://www.pearsonlearningsolutions.com/custom-library/catalyst. This program also allows you to add your own course notes, syllabi, or other materials.

Inspiring Students to Succeed in Chemistry

PROBLEM-SOLVING STUDY AIDS

Two-Column Example Exercises Using the unit analysis method, these exercises show students a logical way to apply the three-step problem-solving process in the worked-out example problems in each chapter.

Concept Exercises accompany each example exercise and practice exercise. The concept exercise serves to present the related topic at a higher level, whereas the example exercises and practice exercises are specific in nature.

Problem-Solving Organizers An important objective of this text is to help students become effective problem solvers. In the first column is a synopsis of the types of calculations in the chapter. In the second column is the correct procedure for solving each type of problem covered in the chapter. In the third column is an illustrated example of the problem type.

Example Exercise 9.2 Mole–Mole Relationships

Carbon monoxide is produced in a blast furnace by passing oxygen gas over hot coal. How many moles of oxygen react with 2.50 mol of carbon, according to the balanced equation?

$$2\,C(s) + O_2(g) \xrightarrow{\Delta} 2\,CO(g)$$

Strategy Plan

Step 1: What unit is asked for in the answer? **Step 1:** $mol\ O_2$

Step 2: What given value is related to the answer? **Step 2:** $2.50\ mol\ C$

Step 3: What unit factor(s) should we apply? **Step 3:** $\dfrac{2\ mol\ C}{1\ mol\ O_2}$ or $\dfrac{1\ mol\ O_2}{2\ mol\ C}$
Using the balanced equation, we see that $2\ mol\ C = 1\ mol\ O_2$. Thus, the mole ratio and the two unit factors are

given value	unit factor	unit in answer
$2.50\ mol\ C$	$\times\ \dfrac{1\ mol\ O_2}{2\ mol\ C}$	$=\ ?\ mol\ O_2$

Unit Analysis Map

Solution
We select the unit factor that cancels the unit in the given value (mol C). Thus,

$$2.50\ mol\ C \times \frac{1\ mol\ O_2}{2\ mol\ C} = 1.25\ mol\ O_2$$

Practice Exercise
Iron is produced from iron ore in a blast furnace by passing carbon monoxide gas through molten iron(III) oxide. The balanced equation is

$$Fe_2O_3(l) + 3\,CO(g) \xrightarrow{\Delta} 2\,Fe(l) + 3\,CO_2(g)$$

(a) How many moles of carbon monoxide react with 2.50 mol of Fe_2O_3?
(b) How many moles of iron are produced from 2.50 mol of Fe_2O_3?

Answers:
(a) 7.50 mol CO
(b) 5.00 mol Fe

Concept Exercise
How many unit factors are required to solve a mole–mole problem?

Answer: See Appendix G.

Concept Exercise
How many unit factors are required to solve a mole–mole problem?

Answer: See Appendix G.

PROBLEM–SOLVING ORGANIZER

TOPIC	PROCEDURE	EXAMPLE
Avogadro's Number Sec. 8.1	Express the atomic mass of an element in grams to find the mass of Avogadro's number of atoms.	Avogadro's number of Fe atoms has a mass of 55.85 g.
Mole Calculations I Sec. 8.2	1. Write down the unit asked for in the answer. 2. Write down the related given value. 3. Apply a unit factor to convert the given unit to the unit in the answer.	How many iron atoms are in 0.500 mol of Fe? $0.500\ mol \times \dfrac{6.02 \times 10^{23}\ atoms}{1\ mol} = 3.01 \times 10^{23}\ atoms$
Molar Mass Sec. 8.3	Sum the masses of each atom of each element in a compound to calculate the molar mass.	What is the molar mass of iron(III) oxide, Fe_2O_3? $2(55.85\ g/mol) + 3(16.00\ g/mol) = 159.70\ g/mol$
Mole Calculations II Sec. 8.4	1. Write down the unit asked for in the answer. 2. Write down the related given value. 3. Apply a unit factor to convert the given unit to the unit in the answer.	What is the mass of 5.00×10^{23} formula units of Fe_2O_3? $5.00 \times 10^{23}\ formula\ units \times \dfrac{1\ mol}{6.02 \times 10^{23}\ formula\ units}$ $\times \dfrac{159.70\ g\ Fe_2O_3}{1\ mol} = 133\ g\ Fe_2O_3$
Molar Volume Sec. 8.5	The volume occupied by 1 mol of any gas at STP is 22.4 L.	Volume of 1.00 mol of O_2 at STP is 22.4 L.
Mole Calculations III Sec. 8.6	1. Write down the unit asked for in the answer. 2. Write down the related given value. 3. Apply a unit factor to convert the given unit to the unit in the answer.	What is the mass of 2.50 L of O_2 gas at STP? $2.50\ L \times \dfrac{1\ mol}{22.4\ L} \times \dfrac{32.00\ g\ O_2}{1\ mol} = 3.57\ g\ O_2$
Percent Composition Sec. 8.7	Find the mass of each element compared to the total molar mass of the compound, all multiplied by 100%.	What is the percent composition of hydrogen peroxide, H_2O_2 (MM = 34.02 g/mol)? $\dfrac{2(1.01)\ g}{34.02\ g} \times 100\% = 5.94\%\ H$ $\dfrac{2(16.00)\ g}{34.02\ g} \times 100\% = 94.06\%\ O$
Empirical Formula Sec. 8.8	Find the mole ratio of each element in the compound, and simplify to whole numbers.	What is the empirical formula of hydrogen peroxide, given 2.25 mol H and 2.22 mol O? $H\,\dfrac{2.25}{2.22}\,O\,\dfrac{2.22}{2.22} = H_{1.01}O_{1.00}$ thus, H_1O_1
Molecular Formula Sec. 8.9	Find the ratio of the molar mass of the compound to the molar mass of the empirical formula unit. Use this ratio as a multiplier for the subscripts in the empirical formula unit.	What is the molecular formula of hydrogen peroxide, given the molar mass is about 34 g/mol? $\dfrac{(HO)_n}{HO} = \dfrac{34\ g/mol}{17\ g/mol} = 2$ thus, H_2O_2

Conceptual Understanding and Critical Thinking

CRITICAL THINKING Household Chemicals

Q: Is it possible that mixing two common household chemicals can produce a deadly gas?

Salt and sugar are two familiar chemicals on your kitchen table. Vinegar, another kitchen chemical, is a solution of acetic acid. Citrus fruit contains citric acid and is responsible for the sour taste of lemons and limes. Aspirin contains acetylsalicylic acid, which can irritate the lining of the stomach if taken in excess.

Hydrochloric acid, used to acidify swimming pools and clean concrete, is sold in the supermarket as muriatic acid. Sulfuric acid, found in automobile batteries, is a dangerous chemical that should be handled with great caution.

Perhaps the most dangerous chemical in the home is caustic soda, NaOH, which is sold as drain cleaner and as oven cleaner. If it contacts your skin, it gives a slippery sensation and causes redness and irritation. If taken internally, caustic soda could be fatal, especially to an infant. Household ammonia is also potentially dangerous and should not be used with bleach. Together, these two chemicals produce a poisonous gas.

▲ Common Household Chemicals

COMMON HOUSEHOLD CHEMICALS

NAME	FORMULA	PRODUCT/USE	SAFETY
Acids			
acetic acid	$HC_2H_3O_2(aq)$	vinegar	
carbonic acid	$H_2CO_3(aq)$	carbonated drinks	
hydrochloric acid	$HCl(aq)$	swimming pools	avoid contact*
sulfuric acid	$H_2SO_4(aq)$	battery acid	avoid contact*†
Bases			
ammonia	$NH_3(aq)$	window cleaner	
sodium hydrogen carbonate	$NaHCO_3(s)$	baking soda, antacid	
magnesium hydroxide	$Mg(OH)_2(aq)$	milk of magnesia	
sodium hydroxide	$NaOH(aq)$	drain and oven cleaner	avoid contact*†
Miscellaneous			
aluminum hydroxide	$Al(OH)_3(s)$	antacid tablets	
dry ice	$CO_2(s)$	keep items cold	avoid contact
Epsom salts	$MgSO_4 \cdot 7H_2O(s)$	salt bath, laxative	
sodium hypochlorite	$NaClO(aq)$	bleach	avoid contact*
Organic			
ethylene glycol	$C_2H_4(OH)_2(l)$	antifreeze	avoid ingestion†
isopropyl alcohol	$CH_3CHOHCH_3(l)$	rubbing alcohol	avoid ingestion†
naphthalene	$C_{10}H_8(s)$	moth repellent	avoid ingestion†
trichloroethane	$C_2H_3Cl_3(l)$	spot remover	avoid ingestion†

*In the event of contact, flush with water.
†In the event of ingestion, seek medical attention immediately

A: Caution must be exercised when using any chemicals; for example, household ammonia and ordinary bleach, when mixed, release a poisonous gas.

Updated! Critical-Thinking vignettes present relevant topics to help hone students' chemistry skills; they include: **Lower Gasoline Bills, Household Chemicals, Water Fluoridation,** and **Acid Rain.**

---

7 Chapter Self-Test Answers to Self-Test are in Appendix J.

1. Which of the following is evidence for a chemical reaction? (Sec. 7.1)
   (a) a gas is released
   (b) a precipitate is formed
   (c) a permanent color change
   (d) all of the above
   (e) none of the above

2. Which of the following represents an element in its natural state? (Sec. 7.2)
   (a) F_2 (b) Cl_2
   (c) Br_2 (d) I_2
   (e) all of the above

3. What is the coefficient of hydrogen gas after balancing the following equation? (Sec. 7.3)

   $$\_\_N_2(g) + \_\_H_2(g) \longrightarrow \_\_NH_3(g)$$

   (a) 1   (b) 2
   (c) 3   (d) 4
   (e) none of the above

4. Which type of chemical reaction is illustrated in question 3? (Sec. 7.4)
   (a) combination reaction
   (b) decomposition reaction
   (c) single-replacement reaction
   (d) double-replacement reaction
   (e) neutralization reaction

5. Predict the product from the following reaction: (Sec. 7.5)

   $$Mg(s) + O_2 \xrightarrow{\Delta}$$

   (a) MgO   (b) Mg_2O
   (c) MgO_2 (d) Mg_3O_2
   (e) Mg_2O_2

6. Predict the products from the following reaction: (Sec. 7.6)

   $$LiHCO_3(s) \xrightarrow{\Delta}$$

   (a) Li, H_2, and CO_2 (b) Li, H_2O, and CO_2
   (c) Li_2CO_3, H_2, and CO_2 (d) Li_2CO_3, H_2O, and CO_2
   (e) Li_2CO_3 and H_2O

7. Which of the following metals reacts with sulfuric acid? (Sec. 7.7)
   (a) Ag   (b) Cu
   (c) Fe   (d) all of the above
   (e) none of the above

8. What are the products from the following reaction? (Sec. 7.8)

   $$Mg(s) + H_2SO_4(aq) \longrightarrow$$

   (a) MgO and H_2SO_3 (b) MgO and H_2S
   (c) $MgSO_4$ and H_2 (d) $MgSO_4$ and H_2O
   (e) no reaction

9. Which of the following compounds is *insoluble* in water? (Sec. 7.9)
   (a) $(NH_4)_2CO_3$ (b) $BaSO_4$
   (c) K_2CrO_4 (d) Na_2S
   (e) $Sr(OH)_2$

10. What are the products from the following reaction? (Sec. 7.10)

    $$Fe(NO_3)_3(aq) + Na_3PO_4(aq) \longrightarrow$$

    (a) FeP and $NaNO_3$ (b) $FePO_3$ and $NaNO_2$
    (c) $FePO_3$ and $NaNO_3$ (d) $FePO_4$ and $NaNO_2$
    (e) $FePO_4$ and $NaNO_3$

11. What are the predicted products from the following neutralization reaction? (Sec. 7.11)

    $$H_2SO_4(aq) + NH_4OH(aq) \longrightarrow$$

    (a) NH_4SO_3 and H_2O (b) NH_4SO_4 and ...
    (c) $(NH_4)_2SO_4$ and O_2 (d) $(NH_4)_2SO_4$ an...
    (e) no reaction

Key Concepts Questions help students identify the core concepts of chemistry and guide their conceptual understanding of these topics as they learn.

Key Concepts

12. Write a balanced equation for the combination of iron metal with oxygen gas to give solid iron(III) oxide.

13. Write a balanced equation for the decomposition of solid calcium hydrogen carbonate with heat to give calcium carbonate powder, steam, and carbon dioxide gas.

14. Write a balanced equation for the reaction of zinc metal with aqueous nickel(II) nitrate to produce aqueous zinc nitrate and nickel metal.

15. Write a balanced equation for the neutralization of nitric acid with aqueous ammonium hydroxide to give aqueous ammonium nitrate and water.

16. Write a balanced equation for the combustion of ethanol, C_2H_5OH, with oxygen to give carbon dioxide and water.

Critical Thinking

17. Write a balanced equation for the reaction of hydrochloric acid dripping into a test tube containing baking soda, as shown in the illustration.

18. Write a balanced equation for the reaction of potassium iodide solution poured into a beaker containing lead(II) nitrate solution, as shown in the illustration.

Chapter Self-Tests

The final problem set at the end of each chapter is a **Chapter Self-Test**, which includes sample test questions (multiple choice), Key Concepts questions (short answer), and Critical-Thinking questions (short answer).

Chapter Openers Fully redesigned, the *Seventh Edition* now includes photos and descriptions of elements that play a prominent role in the environment for today's visual learners.

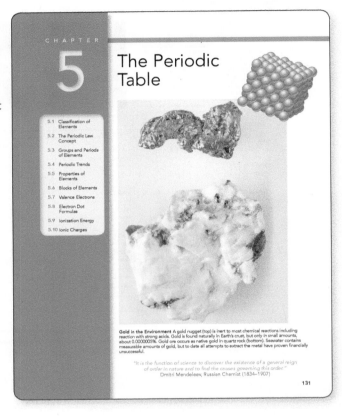

Gold in the Environment A gold nugget (top) is inert to most chemical reactions including reaction with strong acids. Gold is found naturally in Earth's crust, but only in small amounts, about 0.0000005%. Gold ore occurs as native gold in quartz rock (bottom). Seawater contains measurable amounts of gold, but to date all attempts to extract the metal have proven financially unsuccessful.

"It is the function of science to discover the existence of a general reign of order in nature and to find the causes governing this order."
Dmitri Mendeleev, Russian Chemist (1834–1907)

131

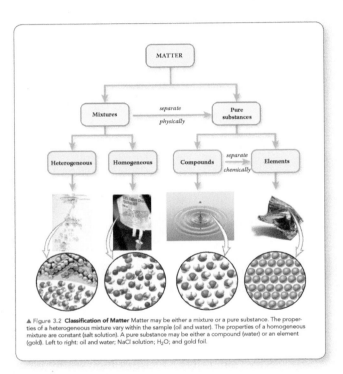

▲ Figure 3.2 **Classification of Matter** Matter may be either a mixture or a pure substance. The properties of a heterogeneous mixture vary within the sample (oil and water). The properties of a homogeneous mixture are constant (salt solution). A pure substance may be either a compound (water) or an element (gold). Left to right: oil and water; NaCl solution; H₂O; and gold foil.

Macro/Micro Art Molecular art is found throughout the text to illustrate chemical compounds on the atomic level. **Macro/Micro Art** helps students connect the the things they encounter in everyday life (the macro view) with depictions of molecules that chemists visualize every day (the micro view). In Corwin's text, the two representations are presented together.

Updated Chemistry Connection Boxes **Chemistry Connection** boxes demonstrate how chemistry is part of students' day-to-day existence. Topics range from the **Olympics**, the **Ozone Hole**, and the **Greenhouse Effect**, to **Forensic Chemistry**, and **Vitamins**.

CHEMISTRY CONNECTION Fireworks

Q: What element is responsible for the red-orange color in the fireworks display?

Have you ever watched a Fourth of July fireworks display and wondered how the colors were produced? The color of fireworks is produced by the chemicals in a rocket shell, which is fitted with a fuse and fired into the air. When the fuse burns, gunpowder ignites and sets off an explosion that shoots chemicals throughout the sky. If the rocket shell is packed with a sodium compound, an orange-yellow color is observed. If the shell is packed with a barium compound, a yellow-green color is observed.

Interestingly, the colors of fireworks and the colors of neon signs are based on the same principle. In a fireworks display an element is energized by heat, whereas in a "neon light" an element is energized by electricity. In either case, electrons are first excited and then immediately lose energy by emitting light. The observed color corresponds to the wavelength of the light emitted. For example, if the emitted light has a wavelength near 650 nm, it is observed as red. If the light has a wavelength near 430 nm, it appears blue.

Chemists can identify an element by the characteristic color of its flame test. In the laboratory, a flame test is performed by placing a small amount of chemical on the tip of a wire and holding the wire in a hot flame. For example, sodium gives an orange-yellow flame test, and barium a yellow-green flame test. Flame-test colors are identical to fireworks colors containing the same element. The red-orange flame-test color of calcium is illustrated.

◄ **Fourth of July Fireworks**

However, not all chemicals produce a colored display. You may recall having seen fireworks that simply produce a shower of white sparks. Powdered aluminum or magnesium metals are used to produce this effect. The following table lists the chemicals used to produce various colors in fireworks:

CHEMICAL	FIREWORKS COLOR
Na compounds	orange-yellow
Ba compounds	yellow-green
Ca compounds	red-orange
Sr compounds	bright red
Li compounds	scarlet-red
Cu compounds	blue-green
Al or Mg metals	white sparks

◄ **Calcium Flame Test** The flame test for calcium is red-orange.

A: The red-orange color suggests that the element is calcium.

Conceptual Understanding and Critical Thinking

Challenge Exercises

87. Iron is prepared industrially by passing carbon monoxide gas through molten iron ore, Fe_2O_3, in a blast furnace at 1500 °C. Assuming the only products are molten iron and carbon dioxide gas, write a balanced chemical equation for the manufacture of iron.

88. Chlorine is prepared industrially by heating hydrogen chloride gas with oxygen gas. Assuming the only products are water and chlorine gas, write a balanced chemical equation for the manufacture of chlorine.

NEW! Challenge Exercises at the end of each chapter are multi-concept questions designed to challenge the student at a higher level.

NEW! Online Exercises are end-of-chapter web-based collaborative activities to help students apply what they have learned in the classroom to different relevant topics.

Online Exercises

Research each of the following using an Internet search engine (e.g., Google.com or Yahoo.com) and cite your URL reference.

55. How many kilograms of lunar samples were brought back from the Moon by the Apollo 11 astronauts?

56. Did the Apollo 11 lunar samples contain water, or show evidence of life?

▶ **Earthrise** This photo, taken from the Moon, shows Earth rising over the lunar horizon.

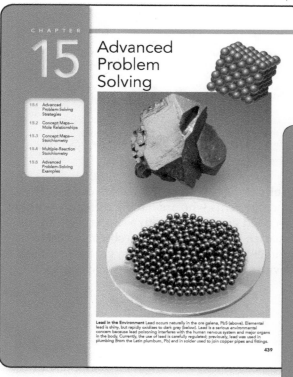

CHAPTER 15

Advanced Problem Solving

15.1 Advanced Problem-Solving Strategies
15.2 Concept Maps—Mole Relationships
15.3 Concept Maps—Stoichiometry
15.4 Multiple-Reaction Stoichiometry
15.5 Advanced Problem-Solving Examples

Lead in the Environment Lead occurs naturally in the ore galena, PbS (above). Elemental lead is shiny, but rapidly oxidizes to dark gray (below). Lead is a serious environmental concern because lead poisoning interferes with the human nervous system and major organs in the body. Currently, the use of lead is carefully regulated; previously, lead was used in plumbing (from the Latin plumbum, Pb) and in solder used to join copper pipes and fittings.

439

NEW! Chapter 15—Advanced Problem Solving provides a comprehensive treatment of problem solving, including unit analysis, algebraic analysis, concept maps, visualization, and "ballpark" answers.

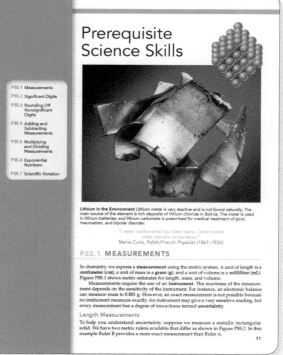

Prerequisite Science Skills

PSS.1 Measurements
PSS.2 Significant Digits
PSS.3 Rounding Off Nonsignificant Digits
PSS.4 Adding and Subtracting Measurements
PSS.5 Multiplying and Dividing Measurements
PSS.6 Exponential Numbers
PSS.7 Scientific Notation

Lithium in the Environment Lithium metal is very reactive and is not found naturally. The main source of the element is rich deposits of lithium chloride in Bolivia. The metal is used in lithium batteries; and lithium carbonate is prescribed for medical treatment of gout, rheumatism, and bipolar disorder.

"I never notice what has been done. I only notice what remains to be done."
Marie Curie, Polish/French Physicist (1867–1934)

PSS.1 MEASUREMENTS

In chemistry, we express a **measurement** using the metric system. A unit of length is a **centimeter (cm)**, a unit of mass is a **gram (g)**, and a unit of volume is a **milliliter (mL)**. Figure PSS.1 shows metric estimates for length, mass, and volume.

Measurements require the use of an **instrument**. The exactness of the measurement depends on the sensitivity of the instrument. For instance, an electronic balance can measure mass to 0.001 g. However, an exact measurement is not possible because no instrument measures exactly. An instrument may give a very sensitive reading, but every measurement has a degree of inexactness termed **uncertainty**.

Length Measurements

To help you understand uncertainty, suppose we measure a metallic rectangular solid. We have two metric rulers available that differ as shown in Figure PSS.2. In this example Ruler B provides a more exact measurement than Ruler A.

11

NEW! Interlude (Prerequisite Science Skills) The interlude helps students with weak math/science backgrounds prepare for chemical calculations. This brief interlude is an optional assignment at the discretion of the instructor.

MasteringChemistry®

The Mastering platform is the most effective and widely used online homework, tutorial, and assessment system for the sciences. It delivers self-paced tutorials that focus on your course objectives, provide individualized coaching, and respond to each student's progress. The Mastering system helps instructors maximize class time with easy-to-assign, customizable, and automatically graded assessments that motivate students to learn outside of class and arrive prepared for lecture or lab.

Chemistry Tutorials
MasteringChemistry® self-paced tutorials are designed to coach students with hints and feedback specific to their individual misconceptions. Tutorials have been created to guide students through the most challenging Introductory Chemistry topics and help them make connections between different concepts.

Unmatched Gradebook Capability MasteringChemistry® is the only system to capture the step-by-step work of each student in your class, including wrong answers submitted, hints requested, and time taken on every step. This data powers an unprecedented gradebook.

Gradebook Diagnostics Instructors can identify at a glance students who are having difficulty with the color-coded gradebook. With a single click, charts summarize the most difficult problems in each assignment, vulnerable students, grade distribution, and even score improvement over the course.

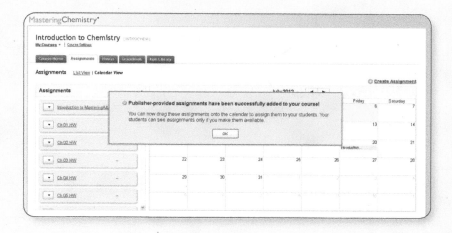

NEW! Calendar Features

The Course Home default page now features a Calendar View displaying upcoming assignments and due dates.

- Instructors can schedule assignments by dragging and dropping the assignment onto a date in the calendar. If the due date of an assignment needs to change, instructors can drag the assignment to the new due date and change the "available from and to dates" accordingly.

- The calendar view gives students a syllabus-style overview of due dates, making it easy to see all assignments due in a given month.

NEW! Coaching Activities

Coaching Activities are interactive, randomizable Example Exercises from the main text, seventh edition. Each example also features hints for the students to utilize if they are having difficulty completing the exercise, and includes the ability to review previous parts of the exercise to reinforce concepts.

INTRODUCTORY CHEMISTRY

Introduction to Chemistry

Sodium in the Environment Sodium (shown left) is a very reactive metal and must be stored in mineral oil to prevent its reaction with oxygen in air. Sodium metal is not found in the environment, but is found combined with chlorine in ordinary table salt, sodium chloride (shown right).

"There are in fact two things, science and opinion; the former begets knowledge, the latter ignorance."
Hippocrates, Greek Physician (ca. 460–377 B.C.)

In the United States, Canada, and other developed countries, we enjoy a standard of living that could not have been imagined a century ago. Owing to the evolution of science and technology, we have abundant harvests; live in comfortable, climate-controlled buildings; and travel the world via automobiles and airplanes. We also have extended life spans free of many diseases that previously ravaged humanity.

The development of technology has provided machinery and equipment to perform tedious tasks, which gives us time for more interesting activities. The arrival of the computer chip has given us electronic appliances that afford ready convenience

▲ Figure 1.1 **Apple iPhone**

▶ To describe the early practice of chemistry.

▶ To identify the three steps in the scientific method.

and dazzling entertainment. We can select from a multitude of audio and video resources that offer remarkable sound and brilliant color. We can access these audio and video resources from the Internet, satellite, a compact disc, or a smartphone that can communicate wirelessly while surfing the Internet (Figure 1.1).

Our present standard of living requires scientists and technicians with educational training in chemistry. The health sciences as well as the life sciences, physical sciences, and earth sciences demand an understanding of chemical principles. In fact, chemistry is sometimes referred to as the central science because it stands at the crossroads of biology, physics, geology, and medicine. Just as personal computers and smartphones are indispensable in our everyday activities, chemistry plays an essential role in our daily lives.

1.1 EVOLUTION OF CHEMISTRY

The earliest concept of science began with the ancient Chinese, Egyptian, and Greek civilizations. The Chinese believed that the universe was created from the interaction of two forces. Yin, the feminine force, was manifested in darkness, cold, and wetness. Yang, the masculine force, was manifested in light, heat, and dryness. When the yin and yang forces interacted, they brought the earthly world into existence and were responsible for everything in nature.

As early as 600 B.C., the Greeks began to speculate that the universe was composed of a single element. Thales, the founder of Greek science, mathematics, and philosophy, suggested that water was the single element. He claimed that Earth was a dense, flat disc floating in a universe of water. He also believed that air and space were less dense forms of water.

A few years later, another Greek philosopher proposed that air was the basic element. This theory was followed by the proposals that fire, and later earth, was the basic element. About 450 B.C., the Greek philosopher Empedocles observed that when wood burned, smoke was released (air), followed by a flame (fire). He also noticed that a cool surface held over a fire collected moisture (water) and that the only remains were ashes (earth). Empedocles interpreted his observations as evidence for air, fire, water, and earth as basic elements. The conclusion was logical based on his observations and he further speculated other substances were examples of these four elements combined in varying proportions, as illustrated in Figure 1.2.

In about 350 B.C., Aristotle adopted the idea that air, earth, fire, and water were basic elements. In addition, he added a fifth element, ether, that he believed filled all space. Aristotle's influence was so great that his opinions dominated other Greek philosophers and shaped our understanding of nature for nearly 2,000 years.

The Scientific Method

In 1661, the English scientist Robert Boyle (1627–1691) published *The Sceptical Chymist*. In his classic book, Boyle stated that theoretical speculation was worthless unless it was supported by experimental evidence. This principle led to the development of the scientific method, which marked a turning point in scientific inquiry and the beginning of modern science.

Science can be defined as the methodical exploration of nature followed by a logical explanation of the observations. The practice of science entails planning an investigation, carefully recording observations, gathering data, and analyzing the results. In an **experiment**, scientists explore nature according to a planned strategy and make observations under controlled conditions.

The **scientific method** is a systematic investigation of nature and requires proposing an explanation for the results of an experiment in the form of a general principle. The initial, tentative proposal of a scientific principle is called a **hypothesis**.

Fire

Hot   Dry

Air   **Earth**

Wet   Cold

Water

▲ Figure 1.2 **The Four Greek Elements** The four elements proposed by the Greeks: air, earth, fire, and water. Notice the properties hot, cold, wet, and dry associated with each element.

After further experimentation, the initial hypothesis may be rejected, modified, or elevated to the status of a scientific principle. However, for a hypothesis to become a scientific principle, many additional experiments must support and verify the original proposal. Only after there is sufficient evidence does a hypothesis rise to the level of a scientific **theory**. We can summarize the three steps in the scientific method as follows:

Applying the Scientific Method

Step 1: Perform a planned experiment, make observations, and record data.

Step 2: Analyze the data and propose a tentative hypothesis to explain the experimental observations.

Step 3: Conduct additional experiments to test the hypothesis. If the evidence supports the initial proposal, the hypothesis may become a scientific theory.

We should note that scientists exercise caution before accepting a theory. Experience has shown that nature reveals its secrets slowly and only after considerable probing. A scientific theory is not accepted until rigorous testing has established that the hypothesis is a valid interpretation of the evidence. For example, in 1803, John Dalton (1766–1844) proposed that all matter was composed of small, indivisible particles called atoms. However, it took nearly 100 years of gathering additional evidence before his proposal was universally accepted and elevated to the status of the atomic theory.

Although the terms *theory* and *law* are related, there is a distinction between the two terms. A theory is a model that explains the behavior of nature. A **natural law** does not explain behavior, but rather states a measurable relationship. To illustrate, it is a *law* that heat flows from a hotter object to a cooler one because we can measure experimentally the change in temperature if we drop an ice cube into water. It is a *theory* that the transfer of heat is due to changes in the motion of molecules in the ice and water.

We can distinguish between a theory and a law by simply asking the question, "Is the proposal measurable?" If the answer is yes, the statement is a law; otherwise, the statement is a theory. Figure 1.3 summarizes the relationship of a hypothesis, a scientific theory, and a natural law.

▲ **Robert Boyle** This stamp honors Boyle for his invention of the vacuum pump in 1659. Boyle's classic textbook, *The Sceptical Chymist*, laid the foundation for the scientific method.

◄ Figure 1.3 **The Scientific Method** The initial observations from an experiment are analyzed and formulated into a hypothesis. Next, additional data is collected from experiments conducted under various conditions and the data is analyzed. If the additional data supports the initial proposal, the hypothesis may be elevated to a scientific theory or a natural law.

1.2 MODERN CHEMISTRY

In the A.D. eighth century, the Arabs introduced the pseudoscience of **alchemy**. Alchemists conducted simple experiments and believed in the existence of a magic potion that had miraculous healing powers and could transmute lead into gold.

▲ **Antoine Lavoisier** This stamp honors Lavoisier for his numerous achievements, including the establishment of a magnificent eighteenth-century laboratory that attracted scientists from around the world.

Although alchemy did not withstand the test of time, it preceded the planned, systematic, scientific experiments that are the cornerstone of modern chemical research.

In the late eighteenth century, the French chemist Antoine Lavoisier (1743–1794) organized chemistry and wrote two important textbooks. Lavoisier also built a magnificent laboratory and invited scientists from around the world to view it; his many visitors included Benjamin Franklin and Thomas Jefferson. Lavoisier was a prolific experimenter and published his work in several languages. For his numerous contributions, he is considered the founder of modern chemistry.

Today, we define **chemistry** as the science that studies the composition of matter and its properties. Chemists have accumulated so much information during the past two centuries that we now divide the subject into several branches or specialties. The branch of chemistry that studies substances containing the element carbon is called **organic chemistry**. The study of all other substances, those that do not contain the element carbon, is called **inorganic chemistry**.

The branch of chemistry that studies substances derived from plants and animals is **biochemistry**. Another branch, analytical chemistry, includes qualitative analysis (what substances are present in a sample) and quantitative analysis (how much of each substance is present). Physical chemistry is a specialty that proposes theoretical and mathematical explanations for chemical behavior. Recently, environmental chemistry has become an important specialty that focuses on the safe disposal of chemical waste. **Green chemistry**, also termed *sustainable chemistry*, refers to the design of chemical products and processes that reduce or eliminate hazardous substances.

Chemistry plays a meaningful role in medicine, especially in the dispensing of pharmaceutical prescriptions. Chemists help ensure agricultural harvests by formulating fertilizers and pesticides. Chemistry is indispensable to many industries including the manufacture of automobiles, electronic components, aluminum, steel, paper, and plastics. One of the largest industries is the petrochemical industry. Petrochemicals are chemicals derived from petroleum and natural gas. They can be used to manufacture a wide assortment of consumer products including paints, plastics, rubber, textiles, dyes, and detergents.

In every chapter you will have example exercises that put learning into action. Each example exercise poses a question and shows the solution. There is also a practice exercise and a concept exercise to further your understanding. Example Exercise 1.1 illustrates a question, practice exercise, and concept exercise.

Example Exercise 1.1 Introduction to Chemistry

What is the difference between ancient chemistry and modern chemistry?

Solution
The principal difference is that modern chemistry is founded on the scientific method. Ancient chemistry was based on speculation, whereas modern chemistry is based on planned experiments.

Practice Exercise
What question can we ask to distinguish a scientific theory from a natural law?

Answer: We can distinguish a theory from a law by asking the question, "Is the proposed statement measurable?" If we take measurements and verify a relationship by a mathematical equation, the statement is a law; if not, it is a theory.

Concept Exercise
Alchemists believed in a magic potion that had what miraculous power?

Answer: See Appendix G.

CHEMISTRY CONNECTION "Worth Your Salt?"

Q: What are the sources of ordinary table salt?

The uses for salt predate modern history. In the ancient world, towns and settlements were near salt reservoirs, as salt is a dietary necessity and a food preservative. Hippocrates, the Greek founder of medicine, urged physicians to soak their patients in salt water as treatment for various ailments. Because most natural salt is not suitable for consumption, pure salt was a rare and valuable commodity. So-called "salt roads" were used by caravans of camels to transport salt long distances in trade for gold and textiles.

The familiar phrases "salt of the earth" and "worth your salt" refer to people who are deserving of respect. The origin of "worth your salt" goes back to Roman times when soldiers were given rations of salt and other necessities. These rations were referred to as *sal* (Latin, meaning "salt"), and when soldiers were paid money, the stipend was called a *salarium*. Our modern term *salary* is derived from the phrase meaning "salt money."

Salt is a necessity in the diet of humans and animals, but toxic to most plants. Table salt comes from three sources:

(1) salt mining, (2) solution mining, and (3) solar evaporation of salt water. The United States and Canada have extensive deposits of salt, and the Great Salt Lake in Utah is so concentrated and dense that humans easily float.

(1) In salt mining, salt is obtained by drilling shafts deep into the earth. The salt is excavated using a "room and pillar" system of mining that offers support while the salt is removed. After crushing, the salt is hauled to the surface on conveyor belts. (2) In solution mining, wells are placed over salt beds and water is injected to dissolve the salt. The resulting salt solution is pumped to a nearby plant for evaporation. The brine is then evaporated to dryness and refined. (3) Salt can also be obtained by the solar evaporation of seawater and salt lakes. The wind and sun evaporate the water in shallow pools, leaving solid salt. The salt is collected when the crust reaches a certain thickness; the salt is then washed and allowed to recrystallize.

Table salt (99% sodium chloride) is necessary in the human diet; however, too much sodium has been linked to high blood pressure that can lead to diabetes and heart problems. A teaspoon of salt contains approximately 2,400 mg of sodium. Surprisingly, most salt in the human diet does not come from table salt, but from processed foods, especially ketchup, pickles, snack foods, and soy sauce. Table salt contains iodine in the form of potassium iodide. Humans require iodine in small quantities for proper function of the thyroid gland. The hormone thyroxine, which contains iodine, is largely responsible for maintaining our metabolic rate. The amount of iodine in one teaspoon of iodized table salt is about 0.3 mg, which is twice the minimum recommended daily allowance (RDA).

◀ The Great Salt Lake was created in prehistoric times and contains far more salt than seawater. Although it provides habitat for brine shrimp and aquatic birds, it is called "America's Dead Sea."

A: Table salt is obtained from mining rock salt, dissolving salt beds, and evaporating salt water.

CHEMISTRY CONNECTION A Student Success Story

Q: Which common inexpensive metal was more valuable than gold in the nineteenth century?

In 1885, Charles Martin Hall (1863–1914) was a 22-year-old student at Oberlin College in Ohio. One day his chemistry teacher told the class that anyone who could discover an inexpensive way to produce aluminum metal would become rich and benefit humanity. At the time, aluminum was a rare and expensive metal. In fact, Napoleon III, a nephew of Napoleon Bonaparte, entertained his most honored guests with utensils made from aluminum while other guests dined with utensils of silver and gold. Although aluminum is the

most abundant metal in Earth's crust, it is not found free in nature; it is usually found combined with oxygen in minerals such as bauxite.

After graduation, Charles Hall set up a laboratory in a woodshed behind his father's church in Oberlin, Ohio. Using homemade batteries, he devised a simple method for producing aluminum by passing electricity through a molten mixture of minerals. After only 8 months of experimenting, he invented a successful method for reducing an aluminum mineral to aluminum metal. In February 1886, Charles Hall walked into his former teacher's office with a handful of metallic aluminum globules.

Just as his chemistry teacher had predicted, within a short period of time, Hall became rich and famous. In 1911, he received the Perkin Medal for achievement in chemistry, and in his will, he donated $5 million to Oberlin College. He also helped to establish the Aluminum Company of America (ALCOA), and the process for making aluminum metal gave rise to a huge industry. Aluminum is now second only to steel as a construction metal.

It is an interesting coincidence that the French chemist Paul Héroult, without knowledge of Hall's work, made a similar discovery at the same time. Thus, the industrial method for obtaining aluminum metal is referred to as the Hall–Héroult process. In 1886, owing to the discovery of this process, the price of aluminum plummeted from over $100,000 a pound. Today, the price of aluminum is less than $1 a pound.

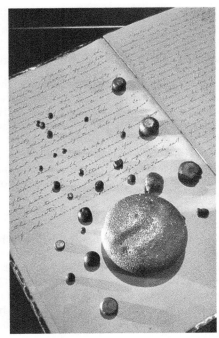

▲ **Aluminum Globules** The notebook of Charles Hall along with globules of aluminum.

A: Before 1885, aluminum was an extremely rare and expensive metal.

1.3 LEARNING CHEMISTRY

LEARNING OBJECTIVE

▶ To appreciate that chemistry is interesting and relevant in our daily lives.

In a survey published by the American Chemical Society, entering college students were asked to express their attitudes about science courses. The students rated chemistry as the most relevant science course, and as highly relevant to their daily lives. Unfortunately, 83% of the students thought chemistry is a difficult subject. In view of the results of the student survey, perhaps we should take a moment to consider perceptions in general, and attitudes about chemistry in particular.

You are probably familiar with the expression that some people see a glass of water as half full, while others see the same glass as half empty. This expression implies that different people can respond to the same experience with optimism or pessimism. Moreover, experimental psychologists have found that they can use abstract visual images to discover underlying attitudes regarding a particular perception. A practical lesson involving two perceptions obtained from the same image is revealed by the following picture.

What do you see? Some students see a white vase on a dark background; others see two dark profiles facing each other. After a short period of time, one image switches to the other. If you concentrate, can you view only one of the images? Can you choose to switch the images back and forth? This exercise is an example of our brains registering dual perceptions from the same image.

Your experience of learning chemistry may be somewhat like the preceding exercise that tests your perspective. Sometimes your perception may be that chemistry is challenging, whereas a short time later your attitude may be that chemistry is easy and fun.

Perception is often affected by unconscious assumptions. Let's consider a type of problem that is slightly different from the vase perception. In the following problem try to connect each of the nine dots using only *four* straight, continuous lines.

We can begin to solve the problem by experimenting. For example, let's start with the upper-left dot and draw a line to the upper-right dot. We can continue to draw straight lines as follows:

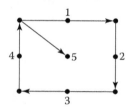

Notice that we connected the nine dots, but that it was necessary to use *five* straight, continuous lines. If we start with a different dot, we find that *five* lines are required no matter where we start. Perhaps we are bringing an underlying assumption to the nine-dot problem. That is, we may be unconsciously framing the nine dots, thus limiting the length of the four straight lines.

What will happen if we start with the upper-left dot and draw a line through the upper-right dot? If we continue, we can complete the problem with *four* straight, continuous lines as follows:

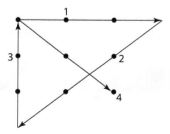

The "secret" to solving this nine-dot problem is to recognize that we may be unconsciously confining our thinking and making it impossible to solve. Similarly, we should not confine our concept of chemistry to a preconceived attitude that learning chemistry will be difficult. Or better yet, we should choose positive associations for our concept of chemistry.

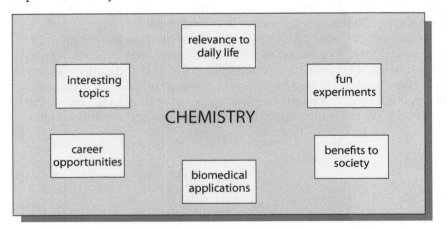

Summary

LEARNING OBJECTIVES

LEARNING OBJECTIVES	SEC	EXERCISES
To describe the early practice of chemistry.	1.1	Exercises 1–4
To identify the three steps in the scientific method.	1.1	Exercises 5–12
To describe the modern practice of chemistry.	1.2	Exercises 13–16
To appreciate that chemistry is interesting and relevant in our daily lives.	1.3	Exercises 17–18

Section 1.1 This chapter traces the development of chemistry from a historical point of view. Beginning in the period 600–350 B.C., the early Greeks used reason and thoughtful mental exercises to understand the laws of nature. Although they often arrived at conclusions based on speculation, they did unveil some of nature's secrets and had a profound influence on Western civilization that lasted for 20 centuries.

The term **science** implies a rigorous, systematic investigation of nature. Moreover, a scientist must accumulate significant evidence before attempting to explain the results. In the seventeenth century, Robert Boyle founded the **scientific method**, and laboratory experimentation became essential to an investigation. After an **experiment**, scientists use their observations to formulate an initial proposal, which is called a **hypothesis**. However, a hypothesis must be tested repeatedly before it is accepted as valid. After a hypothesis has withstood extensive testing, it becomes either a scientific **theory** or a **natural law**. A scientific theory is an accepted explanation for the behavior of nature,

whereas a natural law states a relationship under different experimental conditions and is often expressed as a mathematical equation.

Section 1.2 The pseudoscience of **alchemy** introduced the practice of laboratory experimentation and was the forerunner of modern **chemistry**. Today, chemistry is quite diverse and has several branches, including **inorganic chemistry**, **organic chemistry**, and **biochemistry**. The impact of chemistry is felt in medicine and agriculture, as well as in the electronics, pharmaceutical, petrochemical, and other industries.

Section 1.3 In this section we examined some dual perceptions and pointed out that our brains have the ability to respond to the same image in two ways. Before beginning to learn chemistry, most students have already made associations with the subject. It is hoped that you will be able to focus on chemistry as being an interesting and relevant subject and put aside any preconceived limiting attitudes.

Key Terms   *Answers to Key Terms are in Appendix H.*

Select the key term that corresponds to each of the following definitions.

_____ **1.** the methodical exploration of nature and the logical explanation of the observations

_____ **2.** a scientific procedure for gathering data and recording observations under controlled conditions

(a) alchemy (*Sec. 1.2*)

(b) biochemistry (*Sec. 1.2*)

(c) chemistry (*Sec. 1.2*)

_____ **3.** a systematic investigation that entails performing an experiment, proposing a hypothesis, testing the hypothesis, and stating a theory or law

_____ **4.** a tentative proposal of a scientific principle that attempts to explain the meaning of a set of data collected in an experiment

_____ **5.** an extensively tested proposal of a scientific principle that explains the behavior of nature

_____ **6.** an extensively tested proposal of a scientific principle that states a measurable relationship under different experimental conditions

_____ **7.** a pseudoscience that attempted to convert a base metal, such as lead, to gold; a medieval science that sought to discover a universal cure for disease and a magic potion for immortality

_____ **8.** the branch of science that studies the composition and properties of matter

_____ **9.** the study of chemical substances that contain the element carbon

_____ **10.** the study of chemical substances that do not contain the element carbon

_____ **11.** the study of chemical substances derived from plants and animals

_____ **12.** the design of products and processes that reduce or eliminate hazardous chemical substances

(d) experiment (*Sec. 1.1*)
(e) green chemistry (*Sec. 1.2*)
(f) hypothesis (*Sec. 1.1*)
(g) inorganic chemistry (*Sec. 1.2*)
(h) natural law (*Sec. 1.1*)
(i) organic chemistry (*Sec. 1.2*)
(j) science (*Sec. 1.1*)
(k) scientific method (*Sec. 1.1*)
(l) theory (*Sec. 1.1*)

Exercises *Answers to odd-numbered Exercises are in Appendix I.*

Evolution of Chemistry (Sec. 1.1)

1. According to the Greek philosopher Thales in 600 B.C., what single element composed earth, air, and space?
2. According to ancient Chinese beliefs, what two forces were responsible for bringing the earthly world into existence?
3. According to the Greek philosopher Aristotle in 350 B.C., what five basic elements composed everything in nature?
4. According to the Greek philosopher Empedocles in 450 B.C, what four basic elements composed everything in nature?
5. Who is considered the founder of the scientific method?
6. What is the first step in the scientific method?
7. What is the second step in the scientific method?
8. What is the third step in the scientific method?
9. What is the difference between a hypothesis and a theory?
10. What is the difference between a scientific theory and a natural law?
11. Which of the following statements is a scientific theory?
    (a) The energy in an atomic nucleus is found by $E = mc^2$.
    (b) There is the same number of molecules in equal volumes of gases.
    (c) If the temperature of a gas doubles, the pressure doubles.
    (d) The region surrounding the nucleus of an atom contains electrons.
12. Which of the following statements is a natural law?
    (a) The total mass of reacting substances remains constant after reaction.
    (b) The total energy of two gas molecules remains constant after colliding.
    (c) The volumes of two gases combine in the ratio of small whole numbers.
    (d) The nucleus of an atom contains protons and neutrons.

Modern Chemistry (Sec. 1.2)

13. Who is generally considered the founder of modern chemistry?
14. Why is chemistry considered the central science?
15. Name five industries in which chemistry plays an important role.
16. Name five professions that require a training in chemistry.

Learning Chemistry (Sec. 1.3)

17. It is possible to solve the nine-dot problem with *one* straight, continuous line. Solve the problem and identify the unconscious assumption.

18. It is possible to solve the nine-dot problem with *three* straight, continuous lines. Solve the problem and identify the unconscious assumption.

Challenge Exercises

19. Stare at the image at right and attempt to "flip" the stack of blocks upside down. (*Hint:* If you cannot see the second perception, stare at the point where the three blocks come together and mentally pull the point toward you.)

20. Which of the line segments in the image below appears to be longer, AB or BC?

 Online Exercises

Research each of the following using an Internet search engine (e.g., Google.com or Yahoo.com) and cite your URL reference.

21. Distinguish between the educational requirements for the BSN and AARN degrees.

22. List a few examples of the benefits of "green chemistry."

1 Chapter Self-Test *Answers to Self-Test are in Appendix J.*

1. What is the difference between a scientific theory and a natural law? (Sec. 1.1)
   (a) a theory is a tentative proposal and a law is a tested proposal
   (b) a law is a tentative proposal and a theory is a tested proposal
   (c) a theory explains behavior and a law states a measurable relationship
   (d) a law explains behavior and a theory states a measurable relationship
   (e) none of the above

2. Petrochemicals are derived from which of the following resources? (Sec. 1.2)
   (a) atmosphere   **(b)** petroleum
   (c) seawater   **(d)** trees
   (e) none of the above

3. In a survey by the American Chemical Society, what percent of entering college students thought that chemistry is a difficult subject? (Sec. 1.3)
   (a) 1%   **(b)** 10%
   (c) 50%   **(d)** 83%
   (e) 100%

Key Concept

4. Stare at the box until your first perception changes to a second view. (*Hint:* If you cannot see the second perception, stare at the red dot and mentally "push and pull" the dot.)

Critical Thinking

5. Chemists note the periodic table is arranged by the number of protons in an atom (that is, hydrogen (1), helium (2), lithium (3), etc.) and propose the chemical evolution of elements. Is chemical evolution an example of a scientific theory or a natural law?

6. Biologists note Darwin's principle of natural selection ("survival of the fittest") and propose the biological evolution of species. Is biological evolution an example of a scientific theory or a natural law?

Prerequisite Science Skills

Lithium in the Environment Lithium metal is very reactive and is not found naturally. The main source of the element is rich deposits of lithium chloride in Bolivia. The metal is used in lithium batteries; and lithium carbonate is prescribed for medical treatment of gout, rheumatism, and bipolar disorder.

> *"I never notice what has been done. I only notice what remains to be done."*
> Marie Curie, Polish/French Physicist (1867–1934)

PSS.1 MEASUREMENTS

In chemistry, we express a **measurement** using the metric system. A unit of length is a **centimeter (cm)**, a unit of mass is a **gram (g)**, and a unit of volume is a **milliliter (mL)**. Figure PSS.1 shows metric estimates for length, mass, and volume.

Measurements require the use of an **instrument**. The exactness of the measurement depends on the sensitivity of the instrument. For instance, an electronic balance can measure mass to 0.001 g. However, an exact measurement is not possible because no instrument measures exactly. An instrument may give a very sensitive reading, but every measurement has a degree of inexactness termed **uncertainty**.

Length Measurements

To help you understand uncertainty, suppose we measure a metallic rectangular solid. We have two metric rulers available that differ as shown in Figure PSS.2. In this example Ruler B provides a more exact measurement than Ruler A.

11

▸ To explain why measurements are never exact.

▸ To identify instruments for taking measurements.

Notice that Ruler A has ten 1-cm divisions. Because the divisions are large, we can imagine 10 subdivisions. Thus, we can estimate to one-tenth of a division, that is, ±0.1 cm. On Ruler A, we see that the rectangular solid measures about 4.2 cm. Because the uncertainty is ±0.1 cm, a reading of 4.1 cm or 4.3 cm is also acceptable.

Notice that Ruler B has ten 1-cm divisions and ten 0.1-cm subdivisions. On Ruler B, the subdivisions are smaller. So, with Ruler B we can estimate to one-half of a subdivision, that is, we can estimate to ±0.05 cm. On Ruler B, we see that the rectangular solid measures about 4.25 cm. Because the uncertainty is ±0.05 cm, a reading of 4.20 cm or 4.30 cm is also acceptable.

We can compare the length of the rectangular solid measured with Rulers A and B as follows:

Ruler A: 4.2 ± 0.1 cm   **Ruler B:** 4.25 ± 0.05 cm

In summary, Ruler A has more uncertainty and gives less precise measurements. Conversely, Ruler B has less uncertainty and gives more precise measurements. Example Exercise PSS.1 further illustrates the uncertainty in recorded measurements.

▲ Figure PSS.1 **Estimates for Length, Mass, and Volume** The diameter of a 5¢ coin is about 2 cm, and its mass is about 5 g. The volume of 20 drops from an eye dropper is about 1 mL.

▲ Figure PSS.2 **Metric Rulers** On Ruler A, each division is 1 cm. On Ruler B, each division is 1 cm and each subdivision is 0.1 cm.

Example Exercise PSS.1 Uncertainty in Measurement

Which measurements are consistent with the metric rulers shown in Figure PSS.2?

(a) Ruler A: 2 cm, 2.0 cm, 2.05 cm, 2.5 cm, 2.50 cm
(b) Ruler B: 3.0 cm, 3.3 cm, 3.33 cm, 3.35 cm, 3.50 cm

Solution
Ruler A has an uncertainty of ± 0.1 cm, and Ruler B has an uncertainty of ± 0.05 cm. Thus,

(a) Ruler A can give the measurements 2.0 cm and 2.5 cm.
(b) Ruler B can give the measurements 3.35 cm and 3.50 cm.

Practice Exercise
Which measurements are consistent with the metric rulers shown in Figure PSS.2?

(a) Ruler A: 1.5 cm, 1.50 cm, 1.55 cm, 1.6 cm, 2.00 cm
(b) Ruler B: 0.5 cm, 0.50 cm, 0.055 cm, 0.75 cm, 0.100 cm

Answers:

(a) 1.5 cm, 1.6 cm
(b) 0.50 cm, 0.75 cm

Concept Exercise
What high-tech instrument is capable of making an exact measurement?

Answer: See Appendix G.

Mass Measurements

The **mass** of an object is a measure of the amount of matter it contains. Although the term *weight* is often used instead of *mass*, the two terms are different, as weight is affected by gravity and mass is not. The weight of an astronaut on Earth may be 150 pounds, whereas in space the astronaut is weightless. The mass of the astronaut is the same on Earth and in space.

The measurement of mass always has uncertainty and varies with the balance. A typical balance in a laboratory may weigh a sample to 0.1 of a gram. Thus, the mass has an uncertainty of ± 0.1 g. An electronic balance may weigh a sample to 0.001 of a gram. Thus, its mass has an uncertainty of ± 0.001 g. Figure PSS.3 shows three common laboratory balances.

Volume Measurements

The amount of space occupied by a solid, gas, or liquid is its volume. Many pieces of laboratory equipment are available for measuring the volume of a liquid. Three of the most common are a graduated cylinder, a pipet, and a buret. Figure PSS.4 shows common laboratory equipment used for measuring volume.

A graduated cylinder is routinely used to measure a volume of liquid. The most common sizes of graduated cylinders are 10 mL, 50 mL, and 100 mL. The uncertainty of a graduated cylinder measurement varies, but usually ranges from 1/10 to 1/2 of a milliliter (± 0.1 mL to ± 0.5 mL).

There are many types of pipets. The volumetric pipet shown in Figure PSS.4 is used to deliver a fixed volume of liquid. The liquid is drawn up until it reaches a calibration line etched on the pipet. The tip of the pipet is then placed in a container, and the liquid is allowed to drain from the pipet. The volume delivered varies, but the uncertainty usually ranges from 1/10 to 1/100 of a milliliter. For instance, a 10-mL pipet can deliver 10.0 mL (± 0.1 mL) or 10.00 mL (± 0.01 mL), depending on the uncertainty of the instrument.

A buret is a long, narrow piece of calibrated glass tubing with a valve called a "stopcock" near the tip. The flow of liquid is regulated by opening and closing the

(a)

(b)

(c)

▲ **Figure PSS.3 Laboratory Balances** (a) A balance having an uncertainty of ±0.1 g. (b) A balance having an uncertainty of ±0.01 g. (c) An electronic balance having an uncertainty of ±0.001 g.

Graduated cylinder   Syringe   Buret   Pipet   Volumetric flask

▲ **Figure PSS.4 Laboratory Instruments for Volume** A graduated cylinder, a syringe, and a buret deliver a variable amount of liquid, whereas a volumetric pipet and a volumetric flask contain fixed amounts of liquid, for example, 10 mL and 250 mL.

stopcock, and the initial and final liquid levels in the buret are observed and recorded. The volume delivered is found by subtracting the initial buret reading from the final buret reading. Burets usually have uncertainties ranging from 1/10 to 1/100 of a milliliter. For instance, the liquid level in a buret can read 22.5 mL (± 0.1 mL) or 22.55 mL (± 0.01 mL), depending on the uncertainty of the instrument.

PSS.2 SIGNIFICANT DIGITS

LEARNING OBJECTIVE

▶ To identify significant digits in a measurement.

In a recorded measurement, all numbers are **significant digits**, which can be referred to as a "significant figures" or "sig. figs." For instance, if we weigh a 5¢ nickel coin on different balances, we may record the mass of the coin as 5.0 g, 5.00 g, or 5.000 g. Although the uncertainty varies for the three balances, every digit is significant in all three measurements. Removing the last digit changes the uncertainty of the measurement. In this example, the measurements of mass have two, three, and four significant digits, respectively.

In every measurement, the significant digits express the uncertainty of the instrument. By way of example, refer to Figure PSS.5, which shows a chemical reaction that requires about 35 seconds (s).

Colorless Solution
Stopwatch A: 0 s
Stopwatch B: 0.0 s
Stopwatch C: 0.00 s

Blue Solution
35 s
35.1 s
35.08 s

◀ Figure PSS.5 **Significant Digits and a Timed Reaction** The data demonstrates uncertainty of three different stopwatches. Although each of the measurements is correct, Stopwatch A has the most uncertainty, and Stopwatch C has the least uncertainty.

To determine the number of significant digits in a measurement, we simply count the number of digits from left to right, starting with the first nonzero digit. Therefore, 35 s has two significant digits, 35.1 s has three significant digits, and 35.08 s has four significant digits. We can summarize the rules for determining the number of significant digits with the following rules.

Determining Significant Digits

Rule 1: Count the number of digits in a measurement from left to right.

  (a) Start with the first nonzero digit.
  (b) Do not count placeholder zeros.
     (0.11 g, 0.011 g, and 110 g each have two significant digits.)

Rule 2: The rules for significant digits apply only to measurements and not to exact numbers. Exact numbers can be derived from the following:

  (a) counting items, such as 6 test tubes.
  (b) exact relationships, such as 1 meter = 100 centimeters.
  (c) an equation such as 1 diameter = 2 radii.

Example Exercise PSS.2 illustrates the number of significant digits in a measurement.

Example Exercise PSS.2 Significant Digits

State the number of significant digits in the following measurements:

(a) 12,345 cm   (b) 0.123 g
(c) 0.5 mL   (d) 102.0 s

Solution

In each example, we simply count the number of digits. Thus,

(a) 5   (b) 3
(c) 1   (d) 4

Notice that the leading zero in (b) and (c) is not part of the measurement but is inserted to call attention to the decimal point that follows.

Practice Exercise

State the number of significant digits in the following measurements:

(a) 2005 cm   (b) 25.000 g
(c) 25.0 mL   (d) 0.25 s

Answers:

(a) 4   (b) 5
(c) 3   (d) 2

Concept Exercise

What type of measurement is exact?

Answer: See Appendix G.

Significant Digits and Placeholder Zeros

A measurement may contain placeholder zeros to properly locate the decimal point, for example, 500 cm and 0.005 cm. If the number is less than 1, a placeholder zero is never significant. Thus, 0.5 cm, 0.05 cm, and 0.005 cm each contain only one significant digit.

If the number is greater than 1, we will assume that placeholder zeros are not significant. Thus, 50 cm, 500 cm, and 5000 cm each contain only one significant digit. Example Exercise PSS.3 illustrates how to determine the number of significant digits in a measurement with placeholder zeros.

Example Exercise PSS.3 Significant Digits

State the number of significant digits in the following measurements:

(a) 0.0025 cm   (b) 0.2050 g
(c) 250 mL   (d) 2500 s

Solution

In each example, we count the number of significant digits and disregard placeholder zeros. Thus,

(a) 2   (b) 4
(c) 2   (d) 2

Practice Exercise

State the number of significant digits in the following measurements:

(a) 0.050 cm   (b) 0.055 g
(c) 50.00 mL   (d) 1000 s

Answers:

(a) 2   (b) 2

(c) 4   (d) 1

Concept Exercise

What type of measurement has infinite significant digits?

Answer: See Appendix G.

Note If a placeholder zero is significant, we can express the number using a power of 10. For example, if one zero is significant in 100 cm, we can express the measurement as 1.0×10^2 cm. If both zeros are significant, we can write 1.00×10^2 cm. If neither zero is significant, we can write 1×10^2 cm. The power of 10 does not affect the number of significant digits; thus, 1.1×10^5 cm has two significant digits, and 1.11×10^{-5} cm has three significant digits.

Significant Digits and Exact Numbers

All measurements have uncertainty, so a measurement is never an exact number. However, we can obtain exact numbers when counting items. For instance, a chemistry laboratory may have 24 pipets. Because we have simply counted items, 24 is an exact number. Significant digits do not apply to exact numbers, only to measurements.

▲ **Exact Numbers** We count seven coins in the photo, which is an exact number. This is not a measurement; thus, the concept of significant digits does not apply.

PSS.3 ROUNDING OFF NONSIGNIFICANT DIGITS

LEARNING OBJECTIVE

▶ To round off nonsignificant digits from a calculation.

All digits in a correctly recorded measurement, except placeholder zeros, are significant. However, we often generate **nonsignificant digits** when using a calculator. These nonsignificant digits should not be reported, but they frequently appear in the calculator display and must be eliminated. We eliminate nonsignificant digits through a process of **rounding off**. We round off nonsignificant digits by following three simple rules.

Rounding Off Nonsignificant Digits

Rule 1: If the first nonsignificant digit is less than 5, drop all nonsignificant digits.

Rule 2: If the first nonsignificant digit is greater than 5, or equal to 5, increase the last significant digit by 1 and drop all nonsignificant digits.*

Rule 3: If a calculation has several multiplication or division operations, retain nonsignificant digits in your calculator display until the last operation. Not only is it more convenient, it is also more accurate.

*If the nonsignificant digit is 5, or 5 followed by zeros, an odd–even rule can be applied. That is, if the last significant digit is odd, round up; if it is even, drop the nonsignificant digits.

If a calculator displays 12.846239 and three significant digits are justified, we must round off. Because the first nonsignificant digit is 4 in 12.846239, we follow Rule 1, drop the nonsignificant digits, and round to 12.8. If a calculator displays 12.856239 and three significant digits are justified, we follow Rule 2. In this case, the first nonsignificant digit is 5 in 12.856239, so we round to 12.9.

Rounding Off and Placeholder Zeros

On occasion, rounding off can create a problem. For example, if we round off 151 to two significant digits, we obtain 15. Because 15 is only a fraction of the original value, we must insert a placeholder zero; thus, rounding off 151 to two significant digits gives 150. Similarly, rounding off 1514 to two significant digits gives 1500 or 1.5×10^3. Example Exercise PSS.4 further illustrates how to round off numbers.

▲ **Scientific Calculator** A calculator display often shows nonsignificant digits, which must be rounded off.

> **Example Exercise PSS.4** Rounding Off

Round off the following numbers to three significant digits:

(a) 22.250　　　　　(b) 0.34548　　　　　(c) 0.072038　　　　　(d) 12,267

Solution

To locate the first nonsignificant digit, count three digits from left to right. If the first nonsignificant digit is less than 5, drop all nonsignificant digits. If the first nonsignificant digit is 5 or greater, add 1 to the last significant digit.

(a) 22.3 (Rule 2)　　(b) 0.345 (Rule 1)　　(c) 0.0720 (Rule 1)　　(d) 12,300 (Rule 2)

In (d), notice that two placeholder zeros must be added to 123 to obtain the correct decimal place.

Practice Exercise

Round off the following numbers to three significant digits:

(a) 12.514748　　　　(b) 0.6015261　　　　(c) 192.49032　　　　(d) 14652.832

Answers:

(a) 12.5 (Rule 1)　　(b) 0.602 (Rule 2)　　(c) 192 (Rule 1)　　(d) 14,700 (Rule 2)

Concept Exercise

How many significant digits are in the exact number 155?

Answer: See Appendix G.

PSS.4 ADDING AND SUBTRACTING MEASUREMENTS

When adding or subtracting measurements, *the answer is limited by the value with the most uncertainty;* that is, the answer is limited by the decimal place. Note the decimal place in the following examples:

$$\begin{array}{r} 5 \text{ g} \\ 5.0 \text{ g} \\ +5.00 \text{ g} \\ \hline 15.00 \text{ g} \end{array}$$

The mass of 5 g has the most uncertainty because it measures only ± 1 g. Thus, the sum should be limited to the nearest gram. If we round off the answer to the proper significant digit, the correct answer is **15 g**. In addition and subtraction, the unit (cm, g, mL) in the answer is the same as the unit in each piece of data. Example Exercise PSS.5 illustrates the addition and subtraction of measurements.

PSS.5 MULTIPLYING AND DIVIDING MEASUREMENTS

Significant digits are treated differently in multiplication and division than in addition and subtraction. In multiplication and division, *the answer is limited by the measurement with the least number of significant digits.* Let's multiply the following length measurements:

$$5.15 \text{ cm} \times 2.3 \text{ cm} = 11.845 \text{ cm}^2$$

The measurement of 5.15 cm has three significant digits, and 2.3 cm has two. Thus, the product should be limited to two digits. When we round off to the proper number of significant digits, the correct answer is **12 cm²**. Notice that the units must also be multiplied together, which we have indicated by the superscript 2. Example Exercise PSS.6 illustrates the multiplication and division of measurements.

Example Exercise PSS.5 Addition/Subtraction and Rounding Off

Add or subtract the following measurements and round off your answer:

(a) 106.7 g + 0.25 g + 0.195 g   (b) 35.45 mL − 30.5 mL

Solution

In addition or subtraction operations, the answer is limited by the measurement with the most uncertainty.

(a) Let's align the decimal places and perform the addition.

$$
\begin{array}{r}
106.7 \ \ \text{g} \\
0.25 \ \ \text{g} \\
+ \ 0.195 \ \text{g} \\
\hline
107.145 \ \text{g}
\end{array}
$$

Because 106.7 g has the most uncertainty (± 0.1 g), the answer rounds off to one decimal place. The correct answer is **107.1 g** and is read "**one hundred and seven point one grams**."

(b) Let's align the decimal places and perform the subtraction.

$$
\begin{array}{r}
35.45 \ \text{mL} \\
-30.5 \ \ \text{mL} \\
\hline
4.95 \ \text{mL}
\end{array}
$$

Because 30.5 mL has the most uncertainty (± 0.1 mL), we round off to one decimal place. The answer is **5.0 mL** and is read "**five point zero milliliters**."

Practice Exercise

Add or subtract the following measurements and round off your answer:

(a) 8.6 cm + 50.05 cm   (b) 34.1 s − 0.55 s

Answers:

(a) 58.7 cm   (b) 33.6 s

Concept Exercise

When adding or subtracting measurements, which measurement in a set of data limits the answer?

Answer: See Appendix G.

Example Exercise PSS.6 Multiplication/Division and Rounding Off

Multiply or divide the following measurements and round off your answer:

(a) 50.5 cm × 12 cm   (b) 103.37 g/20.5 mL

Solution

In multiplication and division operations, the answer is limited by the measurement with the least number of significant digits.

(a) In this example, 50.5 cm has three significant digits and 12 cm has two.

$$(50.5 \ \text{cm})(12 \ \text{cm}) = 606 \ \text{cm}^2$$

The answer is limited to two significant digits and rounds off to **610 cm²** after inserting a placeholder zero. The answer is read "**six hundred ten square centimeters**."

(b) In this example, 103.37 g has five significant digits and 20.5 mL has three.

$$\frac{103.37 \ \text{g}}{20.5 \ \text{mL}} = 5.0424 \ \text{g/mL}$$

The answer is limited to three significant digits and rounds off to **5.04 g/mL**. Notice that the unit is a ratio; the answer is read as "**five point zero four grams per milliliter**."

Practice Exercise

Multiply or divide the following measurements and round off your answer.

(a) (359 cm)(0.20 cm)   (b) 73.950 g/25.5 mL

Answers:

(a) 72 cm^2 (b) 2.90 g/mL

Concept Exercise

When multiplying or dividing measurements, which measurement in a set of data limits the answer?

Answer: See Appendix G.

PSS.6 EXPONENTIAL NUMBERS

LEARNING OBJECTIVES

▸ To express an ordinary number as a power of 10.

▸ To express a power of 10 as an ordinary number.

When a value is multiplied times itself, the process is indicated by a number written as a superscript. The superscript indicates the number of times the process is repeated. For example, if the number 2 is multiplied two times, the product is expressed as 2^2. Thus, $(2)(2) = 2^2$. If the number 2 is multiplied three times, the product is expressed as 2^3. Thus, $(2)(2)(2) = 2^3$.

A superscript number indicating that a value is multiplied times itself is called an **exponent**. If 2 has the exponent 2, the value 2^2 is read as "2 to the second power" or "2 squared." The value 2^3 is read as "2 to the third power" or "2 cubed."

Powers of 10

A **power of 10** is a number that results when 10 is raised to an exponential power. You know that an exponent raises any number to a higher power, but we are most interested in the base number 10. A power of 10 has the general form

The number 10 raised to the n power is equal to 10 multiplied times itself n times. For instance, 10 to the second power (10^2) is equal to 10 times 10. When we write 10^2 as an ordinary number, we have 100. Notice that the exponent 2 corresponds to the number of zeros in 100. Similarly, 10^3 has three zeros (1000) and 10^6 has six zeros (1,000,000).

The exponent is positive for all numbers greater than 1. Conversely, the exponent is negative for numbers less than 1. For example, 10 to the negative first power (10^{-1}) is equal to 0.1, 10 to the negative second power (10^{-2}) is equal to 0.01, and 10 to the negative third power (10^{-3}) is equal to 0.001. Table PSS.1 lists some powers of 10, along with the equivalent ordinary number.

TABLE PSS.1 POWERS OF 10

EXPONENTIAL NUMBER	ORDINARY NUMBER
$1 \times 10^6 = 10 \times 10 \times 10 \times 10 \times 10 \times 10$	1,000,000
$1 \times 10^3 = 10 \times 10 \times 10$	1000
$1 \times 10^2 = 10 \times 10$	100
$1 \times 10^1 = 10$	10
$1 \times 10^0 = 1$	1
$1 \times 10^{-1} = \frac{1}{10}$	0.1
$1 \times 10^{-2} = \frac{1}{10} \times \frac{1}{10}$	0.01
$1 \times 10^{-3} = \frac{1}{10} \times \frac{1}{10} \times \frac{1}{10}$	0.001
$1 \times 10^{-6} = \frac{1}{10} \times \frac{1}{10} \times \frac{1}{10} \times \frac{1}{10} \times \frac{1}{10} \times \frac{1}{10}$	0.000 001

Although you can easily carry out operations with exponents using an inexpensive scientific calculator, you will have greater confidence if you understand exponents. Example Exercises PSS.7 and PSS.8 illustrate the relationship between ordinary numbers and exponential numbers.

Example Exercise PSS.7 Converting to Powers of 10

Express each of the following ordinary numbers as a power of 10:

(a) 100,000 (b) 0.000 000 01

Solution

The power of 10 indicates the number of places the decimal point has been moved.

(a) We must move the decimal five places to the left; thus, 1×10^5.

(b) We must move the decimal eight places to the right; thus, 1×10^{-8}.

Practice Exercise

Express each of the following ordinary numbers as a power of 10:

(a) 10,000,000 (b) 0.000 000 000 001

Answers:

(a) 1×10^7
(b) 1×10^{-12}

Concept Exercise

Which of the following lengths is less: 1×10^3 cm or 1×10^{-3} cm?

Answer: See Appendix G.

▲ **Earth** A positive power of 10 can be used to express very large numbers; for example, the diameter of Earth is about 1×10^7 meters.

Example Exercise PSS.8 Converting to Ordinary Numbers

Express each of the following powers of 10 as an ordinary number:

(a) 1×10^4 (b) 1×10^{-9}

Solution

The power of 10 indicates the number of places the decimal point has been moved.

(a) The exponent in 1×10^4 is positive 4, and so we must move the decimal point four places to the right of 1, thus, 10,000.

(b) The exponent in 1×10^{-9} is negative 9, and so we must move the decimal point nine places to the left of 1, thus, 0.000 000 001.

Practice Exercise

Express each of the following powers of 10 as an ordinary number:

(a) 1×10^{10} (b) 1×10^{-5}

Answers:

(a) 10,000,000,000 (b) 0.000 01

Concept Exercise

Which of the following masses is less: 0.000 001 g or 0.000 01 g?

Answer: See Appendix G.

▲ **Red Blood Cells** A negative power of 10 can be used to express very small numbers; for example, the diameter of a red blood cell is about 1×10^{-6} meter.

▶ To express an ordinary number in scientific notation.

▶ To express scientific notation as an ordinary number.

PSS.7 SCIENTIFIC NOTATION

Science often deals with numbers that are very large or very small. These numbers may be awkward and incomprehensible when written with many zeros. The mass of an iron atom, for example, is 0.000 000 000 000 000 000 000 093 g. To overcome this problem, a standard notation has been devised that places the decimal after the first significant digit and sets the size of the number using a power of 10; this method is called **scientific notation**. The scientific notation format is

$$D.DD \times 10^n$$

To use scientific notation, write down the significant digits (D) in the number. Then, move the decimal point to follow the first nonzero digit. Indicate the number of places the decimal is moved using power-of-10 notation. For instance, you can write 555,000 in scientific notation by first moving the decimal five places to the left to give 5.55 and then adding the appropriate power of 10, which is 10^5. Thus, you can express 555,000 in scientific notation as 5.55×10^5.

You can also express numbers smaller than 1 in scientific notation. For example, you can write 0.000 888 in scientific notation by first moving the decimal four places to the right to give 8.88 and then adding the appropriate power of 10, which is 10^{-4}. Thus, 0.000 888 is expressed in scientific notation as 8.88×10^{-4}.

Regardless of the size of the number, in scientific notation the decimal point is always placed after the first nonzero digit. The size of the number is indicated by a power of 10. A positive exponent indicates a very large number, whereas a negative exponent indicates a very small number. To express a number in scientific notation, follow these two steps.

Applying Scientific Notation

Step 1: Place the decimal point after the first nonzero digit in the number, followed by the remaining significant digits.

Step 2: Indicate how many places the decimal is moved by the power of 10. When the decimal is moved to the left, the power of 10 is positive. When the decimal is moved to the right, the power of 10 is negative.

Example Exercise PSS.9 illustrates the conversion between ordinary numbers and exponential numbers.

Example Exercise PSS.9 Scientific Notation

Express each of the following values in scientific notation:

(a) There are 26,800,000,000,000,000,000,000 helium atoms in a 1-liter balloon filled with helium gas.

(b) The mass of one helium atom is 0.000 000 000 000 000 000 000 006 65 g.

Solution

We can write each value in scientific notation as follows:

(a) Place the decimal after the 2, followed by the other significant digits (2.68). Next, count the number of places the decimal has moved. The decimal is moved to the left 22 places, so the exponent is +22. Finally, we have the number of helium atoms in 1.00 L of gas: 2.68×10^{22} atoms.

(b) Place the decimal after the 6, followed by the other significant digits (6.65). Next, count the number of places the decimal has shifted. The decimal has shifted 24 places to the right, so the exponent is −24. Finally, we have the mass of a helium atom: 6.65×10^{-24} g.

Practice Exercise

Express each of the following values as ordinary numbers:

(a) The mass of one mercury atom is 3.33×10^{-22} g.

(b) The number of atoms in 1 mL of liquid mercury is 4.08×10^{22}.

Answers:

(a) 0.000 000 000 000 000 000 000 333 g;

(b) 40,800,000,000,000,000,000,000 atoms

Concept Exercise

Which of the following masses is greater: 1×10^{-6} g or 0.000 01 g?

Answer: See Appendix G.

▶ **Scientific Calculator** A scientific calculator has an exponent key (EXP) for expressing powers of 10.

Calculators and Scientific Notation

A scientific calculator is very helpful in performing calculations that we often encounter in chemistry. Before purchasing a calculator, check with your instructor for a recommended calculator that is appropriate.

Summary

LEARNING OBJECTIVES	SEC	EXERCISES
To explain why measurements are never exact.	PSS.1	Exercises 1–2
To identify instruments for taking measurements.	PSS.1	Exercises 3–8
To identify significant digits in a measurement.	PSS.2	Exercises 9–14
To round off nonsignificant digits from a calculation.	PSS.3	Exercises 15–18
To add or subtract measurements correctly.	PSS.4	Exercises 19–22
To multiply or divide measurements correctly.	PSS.5	Exercises 23–26
To express an ordinary number as a power of 10.	PSS.6	Exercises 31–32
To express a power of 10 as an ordinary number.	PSS.6	Exercises 33–36
To express an ordinary number in scientific notation.	PSS.7	Exercises 37–40
To express scientific notation as an ordinary number.	PSS.7	Exercises 41–42

PSS.1 A **measurement** is obtained using a laboratory **instrument**. A balance is the instrument used to measure **mass**. We can record length, mass, and volume measurements in metric units of **centimeter (cm)**, **gram (g)**, and **milliliter (mL)**. No measurement is exact because every instrument has **uncertainty**.

PSS.2 The **significant digits** in a measurement are those digits known with certainty, plus one digit that is estimated.

PSS.3 **Nonsignificant digits** are obtained from a calculator. The process of eliminating nonsignificant digits is called **rounding off**.

PSS.4 When adding or subtracting measurements, the answer is limited by the measurement having the most uncertainty. If the uncertainties of three mass measurements are ± 0.1 g, ± 0.01 g, and ± 0.001 g, the measurement with the most uncertainty, ± 0.1 g, limits the answer.

PSS.5 When multiplying or dividing measurements, the answer is limited by the least number of significant digits in the data. Every calculated answer must include the correct number of significant digits, as well as the proper units.

PSS.6 A number written as a superscript indicating that a value is multiplied by itself is called an **exponent**. If the value is 10, the exponent is a **power of 10**. A power of 10 can be positive or negative. If the exponent is positive (10^3), the number is greater than 1; if the exponent is negative (10^{-3}), the number is less than 1.

PSS.7 In science we use **scientific notation** to express numbers that are very large or very small. Scientific notation uses the following format to express a number with three significant digits: D.DD $\times$ 10^n. The three significant digits (D.DD) are multiplied by a power of 10 (10^n) to set the decimal point.

PROBLEM–SOLVING ORGANIZER

TOPIC	PROCEDURE	EXAMPLE
Measurements PSS.1	State the measurement and indicate the uncertainty.	11.50 cm $\pm$ 0.05 cm 0.545 g $\pm$ 0.001 g 10.0 mL $\pm$ 0.5 mL
Significant Digits PSS.2	Count the significant digits in a measurement from left to right: (a) start with the first nonzero digit, (b) do not count placeholder zeros.	0.05 g (1 significant digit) 50.0 g (3 significant digits) 505 g (3 significant digits) 50,000 g (1 significant digit)
Rounding Off Nonsignificant Digits PSS.3	1. If the first nonsignificant digit is less than 5, drop all nonsignificant digits. 2. If the first nonsignificant digit is 5 or greater, add 1 to the last significant digit. 3. If a calculation involves several steps, retain nonsignificant digits until the final step.	505.05 g rounds to 505 g (3 significant digits) 505.50 g rounds to 506 g (3 significant digits)
Adding and Subtracting Measurements PSS.4	The answer is limited by the least certain measurement in a set of data.	5.05 g + 5.005 g = 10.06 g 5.05 mL − 2.1 mL = 3.0 mL
Multiplying and Dividing Measurements PSS.5	The answer is limited by the least number of significant digits in the given data.	5.05 cm $\times$ 5.005 cm = 25.3 cm^2 5.0 g /10.0 mL = 0.50 g/mL
Exponential Numbers PSS.6	(a) Numbers greater than 1 have a positive exponent. (b) Numbers less than 1 have a negative exponent.	1,000,000 = 1 $\times$ 10^6 0.000 001 = 1 $\times$ 10^{-6}
Scientific Notation PSS.7	Place the decimal point after the first nonzero digit. Using an exponent, indicate how many places the decimal is moved.	55,500 g = 5.55 $\times$ 10^4 g 0.000 555 g = 5.55 $\times$ 10^{-4} g

Key Terms   *Answers to Key Terms are in Appendix H.*

Select the key term that corresponds to each of the following definitions.

_____ 1. a numerical value and unit that expresses length, mass, or volume

_____ 2. a common metric unit of length

_____ 3. a common metric unit of mass

_____ 4. a common metric unit of volume

_____ 5. a device for recording a measurement such as length, mass, or volume

_____ 6. the degree of inexactness in an instrumental measurement

_____ 7. the quantity of matter in an object

_____ 8. the certain digits in a measurement plus one estimated digit

_____ 9. the digits in a measurement that exceed the certainty of the instrument

_____ 10. the process of eliminating digits that are not significant

_____ 11. a number written as a superscript that indicates a value is multiplied by itself, for example, $10^4 = 10 \times 10 \times 10 \times 10$, and cm^3 = cm $\times$ cm $\times$ cm

_____ 12. a positive or negative exponent of 10

_____ 13. a method for expressing numbers by moving the decimal place after the first significant digit and indicating the number of decimal moves by a power of 10

(a) centimeter (cm) *(PSS.1)*
(b) exponent *(PSS.6)*
(c) gram (g) *(PSS.1)*
(d) instrument *(PSS.1)*
(e) mass *(PSS.1)*
(f) measurement *(PSS.1)*
(g) milliliter (mL) *(PSS.1)*
(h) nonsignificant digits *(PSS.3)*
(i) power of 10 *(PSS.6)*
(j) rounding off *(PSS.3)*
(k) scientific notation *(PSS.7)*
(l) significant digits *(PSS.2)*
(m) uncertainty *(PSS.1)*

Exercises *Answers to odd-numbered Exercises are in Appendix I.*

Uncertainty in Measurements (PSS.1)

1. What quantity (length, mass, volume, time) is expressed by the following units?
   (a) centimeter   (b) gram
   (c) milliliter   (d) second

2. What quantity (length, mass, volume, time) is expressed by the following units?
   (a) kilometer   (b) microgram
   (c) liter   (d) nanosecond

3. Which of the following measurements corresponds to metric Ruler A shown in Figure PSS.2?
   (a) 2.0 cm   (b) 2.00 cm
   (c) 2.05 cm   (d) 2.5 cm

4. Which of the following measurements corresponds to metric Ruler B shown in Figure PSS.2?
   (a) 50.0 cm   (b) 50.00 cm
   (c) 50.05 cm   (d) 50.5 cm

5. Which of the following measurements corresponds to the electronic balance shown in Figure PSS.3?
   (a) 25 g   (b) 25.0 g
   (c) 25.00 g   (d) 25.000 g

6. Which of the following measurements corresponds to the electronic balance shown in Figure PSS.3?
   (a) 75 g   (b) 75.0 g
   (c) 75.22 g   (d) 75.518 g

7. Which of the following measurements corresponds to the graduated cylinder shown in Figure PSS.4 having an uncertainty of ± 0.5 mL?
   (a) 25 mL   (b) 25.0 mL
   (c) 25.5 mL   (d) 25.50 mL

8. Which of the following measurements corresponds to the buret shown in Figure PSS.4 having an uncertainty of ± 0.05 mL?
   (a) 32.0 mL   (b) 32.00 mL
   (c) 32.05 mL   (d) 32.58 mL

Significant Digits (PSS.2)

9. State the number of significant digits in each of the following:
   (a) 0.05 cm   (b) 0.50 cm
   (c) 25.0 cm   (d) 20.50 cm

10. State the number of significant digits in each of the following:
    (a) 1.050×10^2 cm   (b) 2×10^3 cm
    (c) 3.00×10^{-4} cm   (d) 5.0×10^{-5} cm

11. State the number of significant digits in each of the following:
    (a) 5.0 g   (b) 5.05 g
    (c) 0.5 g   (d) 1055 g

12. State the number of significant digits in each of the following:
    (a) 1.2×10^0 g   (b) 4.50×10^1 g
    (c) 5.02×10^{-1} g   (d) 100×10^{-2} g

13. State the number of significant digits in each of the following:
    (a) 0.5 mL   (b) 0.50 mL
    (c) 5.00 mL   (d) 500 mL

14. State the number of significant digits in each of the following:
    (a) 1×10^{-1} mL   (b) 1.0×10^{-2} mL
    (c) 1.00×10^1 mL   (d) 1.000×10^3 mL

Rounding Off Nonsignificant Digits (PSS.3)

15. Round off the following to three significant digits:
    (a) 20.155   (b) 0.204 500   (c) 2055   (d) 0.2065

16. Round off the following to three significant digits:
    (a) 10.25   (b) 10.20   (c) 0.01029   (d) 10,248

17. Round off the following to three significant digits:
    (a) 1.454×10^1 (b) 1.455×10^2
    (c) 1.508×10^{-3} (d) 1.503×10^{-4}

18. Round off the following to three significant digits:
    (a) 9.123×10^5 (b) 9.456×10^{10}
    (c) 9.000×10^{-7} (d) 9.075×10^{-12}

Adding and Subtracting Measurements (PSS.4)

19. Add the following measurements and round off the answer:
    (a)   0.4 g   (b)   15.5 g
            0.44 g   7.50 g
        $+$ 0.444 g $+$ 0.050 g

20. Add the following measurements and round off the answer:
    (a)   1.55 cm   (b)   5.0 cm
            36.15 cm   16.3 cm
        $+$ 17.3 cm $+$ 0.95 cm

21. Subtract the following measurements and round off the answer:
    (a)   242.197 g   (b)   27.55 g
        $-$ 175   g $-$ 14.545 g

22. Subtract the following measurements and round off the answer:
    (a)   22.10 cm   (b)   10.0 cm
        $-$ 10.5 cm $-$ 0.15 cm

Multiplying and Dividing Measurements (PSS.5)

23. Multiply the following measurements and round off the answer:
    (a) 3.65 cm $\times$ 2.10 cm   (b) 8.75 cm $\times$ 1.15 cm
    (c) 16.5 cm $\times$ 1.7 cm   (d) 21.1 cm $\times$ 20 cm

24. Multiply the following measurements and round off the answer:
    (a) 1.25 cm $\times$ 0.5 cm   (b) 2.55 cm $\times$ 1.1 cm
    (c) 12.0 cm^2 $\times$ 1.00 cm   (d) 22.1 cm^2 $\times$ 0.75 cm

25. Divide the following measurements and round off the answer:
    (a) 26.0 cm^2/10.1 cm   (b) 9.95 cm^3/0.15 cm^2
    (c) 131.78 cm^3/19.25 cm   (d) 131.78 cm^3/19.2 cm

26. Divide the following measurements and round off the answer:
    (a) 66.3 g/7.5 mL   (b) 12.5 g/4.1 mL
    (c) 42.620 g/10.0 mL   (d) 91.235 g/10.00 mL

Exponential Numbers (PSS.6)

27. Express each of the following products as a power of 10:
    (a) $10 \times 10 \times 10$
    (b) $1/10 \times 1/10 \times 1/10$
28. Express each of the following products as a power of 10:
    (a) $10 \times 10 \times 10 \times 10$
    (b) $1/10 \times 1/10 \times 1/10 \times 1/10$
29. Express each of the following products in exponential form:
    (a) $2 \times 2 \times 2$
    (b) $1/2 \times 1/2 \times 1/2$
30. Express each of the following products in exponential form:
    (a) $3 \times 3 \times 3 \times 3$
    (b) $1/3 \times 1/3 \times 1/3 \times 1/3$
31. Express each of the following ordinary numbers as a power of 10:
    (a) 1,000,000,000
    (b) 0.000 000 01
32. Express each of the following ordinary numbers as a power of 10:
    (a) 100,000,000,000,000,000
    (b) 0.000 000 000 000 001
33. Express each of the following powers of 10 as an ordinary number:
    (a) 1×10^3
    (b) 1×10^{-7}
34. Express each of the following powers of 10 as an ordinary number:
    (a) 1×10^{12}
    (b) 1×10^{-22}
35. Express each of the following powers of 10 as an ordinary number:
    (a) 1×10^1
    (b) 1×10^{-1}
36. Express each of the following powers of 10 as an ordinary number:
    (a) 1×10^0
    (b) 1×10^{-10}

Scientific Notation (PSS.7)

37. Express the following ordinary numbers in scientific notation:
    (a) 80,916,000
    (b) 0.000 000 015
    (c) 335,600,000,000,000
    (d) 0.000 000 000 000 927
38. Express the following ordinary numbers in scientific notation:
    (a) 1,010,000,000,000,000
    (b) 0.000 000 000 000 456
    (c) 94,500,000,000,000,000
    (d) 0.000 000 000 000 000 019 50
39. There are 26,900,000,000,000,000,000,000 atoms in 1 liter of argon gas at standard temperature and pressure. Express this number in scientific notation.

40. There are 269,000,000,000,000,000,000,000 molecules in 10 liters of oxygen gas at standard temperature and pressure. Express this number in scientific notation.
41. The mass of a neon atom is 3.35×10^{-23} g. Express the mass as an ordinary number.
42. The mass of a chlorine molecule is 1.18×10^{-22} g. Express the mass as an ordinary number.

General Exercises

43. A Class A 10-mL pipet has an uncertainty of ± 0.01 mL. Express the volume of the pipet as an ordinary number.
44. A student 10-mL pipet has an uncertainty of ± 0.1 mL. Express the volume of the pipet as an ordinary number.
45. The velocity of light is 186,282.397 miles per second. Round off this value to three significant digits.
46. The velocity of light is 299,792,458 meters per second. Round off this value to three significant digits.
47. Find the total mass of two brass cylinders, which weigh 126.457 g and 131.6 g.
48. Find the length of magnesium metal ribbon that remains after two 25.0-cm strips are cut from 255 cm of the ribbon.
49. Convert the following exponential numbers to scientific notation.
    (a) 352×10^4
    (b) 0.191×10^{-5}
50. Convert the following exponential numbers to scientific notation.
    (a) 0.170×10^2
    (b) 0.00350×10^{-1}

Challenge Exercises

51. The mass of a neutron is 1.6749×10^{-24} g, and the mass of a proton is 1.6726×10^{-24} g. What is the total mass of a neutron and a proton?
52. The mass of a neutron is 1.6749×10^{-24} g, and the mass of a proton is 1.6726×10^{-24} g. What is the mass difference of a neutron and a proton?
53. A metric ton is defined as 1000 kg, or 2.200×10^3 lb. An English ton is defined as 2000 lb, or 2.000×10^3 lb. What is the difference in mass between a metric ton and an English ton expressed in pounds?
54. The distance from Earth to the Moon is 2.39×10^5 miles, whereas the distance from the Moon to Mars is 4.84×10^7 miles. What is the total distance from Earth to the Moon to Mars?

Online Exercises

Research each of the following using an Internet search engine (e.g., Google.com or Yahoo.com) and cite your URL reference.

55. How many kilograms of lunar samples were brought back from the Moon by the Apollo 11 astronauts?
56. Did the Apollo 11 lunar samples contain water, or show evidence of life?

▶ **Earthrise** This photo, taken from the Moon, shows Earth rising over the lunar horizon.

PSS Self-Test   *Answers to Self-Test are in Appendix J.*

1. Which of the following balances has the least uncertainty? (PSS.1)
   (a) platform balance, ± 0.1 g
   (b) triple-beam balance, ± 0.01 g
   (c) electronic balance, ± 0.001 g
   (d) analytical balance, ± 0.0001 g
   (e) all balances have the same uncertainty

2. State the number of significant digits in a mass of 0.050 g. (PSS.2)
   (a) 1   (b) 2
   (c) 3   (d) 4
   (e) none of the above

3. Round off the following measurement to three significant digits: 7268 mL. (PSS.3)
   (a) 720 mL   (b) 726 mL
   (c) 727 mL   (d) 7260 mL
   (e) 7270 mL

4. Add 55.5 cm to 0.50 cm and round off the answer. (PSS.4)
   (a) 56 cm   (b) 56.0 cm
   (c) 56.05 cm   (d) 56.1 cm
   (e) 57 cm

5. Multiply 7.2 cm by 3.75 cm by 1.555 cm and round off the answer. (PSS.5)
   (a) 41.9 cm^3 (b) 41.99 cm^3
   (c) 42 cm^3 (d) 42.0 cm^3
   (e) 42.00 cm^3

6. Express 5.55×10^{-2} as an ordinary number. (PSS.6)
   (a) 0.055 5   (b) 0.005 55
   (c) 0.000 555   (d) 5,550
   (e) none of the above

7. Express 55,500,000,000,000,000,000,000 in scientific notation. (PSS.7)
   (a) 5.55×10^{-22} (b) 5.55×10^{-23}
   (c) 5.55×10^{22} (d) 5.55×10^{23}
   (e) none of the above

Key Concept

8. When using a scientific calculator to perform multistep multiplication or division, is it better to round off after each step, or round off the final answer in the calculator display?

Critical Thinking

9. The mass of an alpha particle is 6.64×10^{-24} g, and the mass of a beta particle is 9.11×10^{-28} g. Which is heavier: an alpha particle or a beta particle?

10. An ounce of iron weighs 28.4 g, and an ounce of gold weighs 31.1 g. Which is heavier: an ounce of iron or an ounce of gold?

The Metric System

Platinum in the Environment Platinum is a precious metal that is inert to chemical reaction even at high temperatures. Platinum is found naturally in Earth's crust, but only in tiny amounts, about 0.0000005%. Platinum ore often occurs with nickel and copper. Platinum is mined in South Africa, which accounts for most of the world production.

"Never has anything more grand and more simple, more coherent in all of its parts, issued from the hand of man."
Antoine Lavoisier, French Chemist (1743–1794)

Since the beginning of civilization there has been the need to convey measurement. When exchanging goods, traders had to agree on standards for length, weight, and volume. Historically, length was often defined in terms of hands and feet because it was convenient. For instance, a digit was defined as the thickness of the index finger, a span was the width of four fingers, and a cubit was the distance from the elbow to the end of the middle finger.

The Greeks proposed the foot as a unit of length and divided it into 12 parts. The Romans in turn adopted the unit and referred to 1/12 of a foot as an *uncia.* The Anglo-Saxons pronounced *uncia* as "inch," which is how it entered into the English language.

The English system of measurement originated in 1215 with the signing of the Magna Carta. The Magna Carta attempted to bring uniform measurements to world trade and decreed, "Throughout the kingdom there shall be standard measures of wine, ale, and corn." To ensure uniform measurements, the English used reference standards. An inch was defined as the length of three barleycorns, and a pound and a gallon were similarly referenced to barley.

2.1 BASIC UNITS AND SYMBOLS

LEARNING OBJECTIVES

▶ To list the basic units and symbols of the metric system.

▶ To list the prefixes for multiples and fractions of basic units.

Discontent over the lack of worldwide standards in measurement reached a peak in the late 1700s. Although the **English system** was common, it was used primarily within the British Empire. In 1790, the French government appointed a committee of scientists to investigate the possibility of a universal measuring system.

The committee spent nearly 10 years devising and agreeing on a new system. The resulting **metric system** offers simplicity and basic units. The basic unit of length is the **meter** (symbol **m**), the basic unit of mass is the **gram** (symbol **g**), the basic unit of volume is the **liter** (symbol **L**), and the basic unit of time is the **second** (symbol **s**). The basic units and symbols of the metric system are shown in Table 2.1.

TABLE 2.1 THE METRIC SYSTEM

PHYSICAL QUANTITY	BASIC UNIT	SYMBOL
length	meter*	m
mass	gram	g
volume	liter*	L
time	second	s

*The U.S. Metric Association recommends the spellings "meter" and "liter." All other English-speaking nations use the spellings "metre" and "litre."

The metric system is simple and coherent for two reasons: First, it uses a single basic unit for each quantity measured, that is, meter, gram, and liter. Second, it is a decimal system that uses prefixes to enlarge or reduce a basic unit. For instance, a kilometer is 1000 meters and a centimeter is 1/100 meter.

The metric committee defined a meter, kilogram, and liter as follows. A meter was defined as one ten-millionth of the distance from the North Pole to the equator. A kilogram was defined as the mass of a cube of water one-tenth of a meter on a side. A liter was equal to the volume occupied by a kilogram of water (at 4 °C).

▲ The Original Metric References A meter was originally defined as one ten-millionth of the distance from the North Pole to the equator. A kilogram was equal to the mass of a cube of water one-tenth of a meter on each side. A liter was equal to the volume of one kilogram of water at 4 °C.

In addition, the metric committee members made reference standards for the meter, kilogram, and liter. They cast a platinum bar (alloyed with 10% iridium metal) as the reference standard for one meter. They cast a solid platinum cylinder as the reference for one kilogram and a platinum container as the standard for one liter. These platinum castings became the reference standards for world measurement. In 1875 all the major nations of the world, including the United States, signed the Treaty of the Meter. Duplicates of the original castings were made and distributed to all member nations. The original casting of the standard reference meter is shown in Figure 2.1.

▶ Figure 2.1 **The Meter** The official reference meter was cast from platinum and iridium metals in 1790. The original casting is kept at the International Bureau of Weights and Measures outside Paris, France.

Metric Prefixes

The United States uses the dollar ($1.00) as the basic unit of currency. In our monetary system we move the decimal to express a multiple or fraction of a dollar ($10.00 and $0.10). Similarly, the metric system is a decimal system, but it uses a prefix to express a multiple or a fraction of a basic unit. A metric prefix increases or decreases a basic unit by a factor of 10. For instance, the prefix *kilo-* increases a basic unit by 1000, whereas the prefix *centi-* decreases a basic unit by 100. Thus, a kilometer is 1000 m, and a centimeter is 0.01 m. Table 2.2 lists some common prefixes for basic metric units.

TABLE 2.2 METRIC PREFIXES

PREFIX	SYMBOL	MULTIPLE/FRACTION
tera-	T	$1{,}000{,}000{,}000{,}000 = 1 \times 10^{12}$
giga-	G	$1{,}000{,}000{,}000 = 1 \times 10^{9}$
mega-	M	$1{,}000{,}000 = 1 \times 10^{6}$
kilo-	k	$1000 = 1 \times 10^{3}$
Basic unit: meter, gram, liter, second		
deci-	d	$0.1 = 1 \times 10^{-1}$
centi-	c	$0.01 = 1 \times 10^{-2}$
milli-	m	$0.001 = 1 \times 10^{-3}$
micro-	μ*	$0.000\ 001 = 1 \times 10^{-6}$
nano-	n	$0.000\ 000\ 001 = 1 \times 10^{-9}$
pico-	p	$0.000\ 000\ 000\ 001 = 1 \times 10^{-12}$

*The Greek letter mu (μ) is the symbol for micro.

The names of metric units can be abbreviated using symbols. We can illustrate this by writing symbols for the following metric units: kilometer (km), milligram (mg), microliter (μL), and nanosecond (ns). Example Exercise 2.1 further illustrates how to write names of metric units and symbols.

Example Exercise 2.1 Metric Basic Units and Prefixes

Give the symbol for each of the following metric units and state the quantity measured by each unit:

(a) gigameter

(b) kilogram

(c) centiliter

(d) microsecond

Solution

We compose the symbol for each unit by combining the prefix symbol and the basic unit symbol. If we refer to Tables 2.1 and 2.2, we have the following:

(a) Gm, length

(b) kg, mass

(c) cL, volume

(d) μs, time

Practice Exercise

Give the symbol for each of the following metric units and state the quantity measured by each unit:

(a) nanosecond

(b) milliliter

(c) decigram

(d) megameter

Answers:

(a) ns, time

(b) mL, volume

(c) dg, mass

(d) Mm, length

Concept Exercise

What is the basic unit of length, mass, and volume in the metric system?

Answer: See Appendix G.

Note The metric system is sometimes referred to as the International System of measurement. Although the **International System** (symbol **SI**) is similar to the metric system, SI is much more comprehensive. In this text, we will use the metric system and utilize SI units only in special instances.

CRITICAL THINKING The International System of Units (SI)

Q: What is the only reference standard that is identical in the metric system and SI?

In 1875, representatives of several nations, including the United States, signed a pact creating the International Bureau of Weights and Measures. This organization was given authority to establish worldwide standards of measurement, and in 1960, it approved a resolution to establish an international system of units.

The International System of Units (abbreviated SI for the French *Système International d' Unités*) is an extension of the metric system. SI has seven base units and numerous derived units. The base unit of length remains the meter, but the base unit of mass is the kilogram—not the gram. The five other SI quantities are time, temperature, electric current, light intensity, and amount of substance.

The Official Standard Kilogram

It is important to note that SI units have been defined in terms of natural phenomena so that measurements can

THE INTERNATIONAL SYSTEM OF UNITS (SI)

QUANTITY	BASE UNIT	SYMBOL
length	meter	m
mass	kilogram	kg
time	second	s
temperature	Kelvin	K
electric current	ampere	A
light intensity	candela	cd
amount of substance	mole	mol

◀ **The Kilogram** The official reference kilogram was cast from platinum and iridium metals in 1790. The original casting is kept at the International Bureau of Weights and Measures outside Paris, France.

be reproduced anywhere in the world without the need for physical reference standards. A meter is defined as 1,650,763.73 wavelengths of the orange-red light emitted from excited atoms of krypton gas. Mass is the sole exception and still relies on the original international prototype kilogram in France.

Currently, the U.S. Bureau of Weights and Measures is encouraging the use of SI units. In practice, however, scientists do not always follow SI conventions. It requires considerable effort to apply the system correctly, and many instruments are not calibrated in SI units. Moreover, SI disallows use of the familiar term "liter" and discourages use of the common prefixes *deci-* and *centi-*.

A: The original prototype kilogram is the reference standard for mass in both the metric system and SI.

2.2 METRIC CONVERSION FACTORS

In the next section we will tackle our single most important task: problem solving. We will learn a simple but powerful method called unit analysis. To use the unit analysis method of problem solving, we must understand equivalent relationships and unit equations.

A **unit equation** relates two quantities that are equal. As an example, let's find a unit equation for kilometers and meters. Since the metric prefix *kilo-* means 1000 basic units, 1 kilometer equals 1000 meters. We can write the **exact equivalent** as 1 kilometer = 1000 meters, or simply 1 km = 1000 m.

A centimeter is 1/100 of a meter, and we can write the relationship as 1 cm = 0.01 m. However, working with fractions is more confusing than working with multiples of basic units. Fortunately, we can avoid decimal fractions by simply restating the relationship. Because there are 100 cm in a meter, we can write the exact equivalent as 1 m = 100 cm. Example Exercise 2.2 further illustrates how to write unit equations for metric relationships.

Example Exercise 2.2 Metric Unit Equations

Complete the unit equation for each of the following exact metric equivalents:

(a) 1 Mm = ? m
(b) 1 kg = ? g
(c) 1 L = ? dL
(d) 1 s = ? ns

Solution

We can refer to Table 2.2 as necessary.

(a) The prefix *mega-* means 1,000,000 basic units; thus, 1 Mm = 1,000,000 m.
(b) The prefix *kilo-* means 1000 basic units; thus, 1 kg = 1000 g.
(c) The prefix *deci-* means 0.1 of a basic unit; thus, 1 L = 10 dL.
(d) The prefix *nano-* means 0.000 000 001 of a basic unit; thus, 1 s = 1,000,000,000 ns.

Alternatively, we can express the unit equation using exponential numbers:

(a) 1 Mm = 1×10^6 m
(b) 1 kg = 1×10^3 g
(c) 1 L = 1×10^1 dL
(d) 1 s = 1×10^9 ns

Practice Exercise

Complete the unit equation for each of the following exact metric equivalents:

(a) 1 Gm = ? m
(b) 1 g = ? cg
(c) 1 L = ?μL
(d) 1 s = ? ms

Answers:

(a) 1 Gm = 1×10^9 m
(b) 1 g = 1×10^2 cg
(c) 1 L = 1×10^6 μL
(d) 1 s = 1×10^3 ms

Concept Exercise

How many significant digits are in the following unit equation: 1 m = 1000 mm?

Answer: See Appendix G.

Writing Metric Unit Factors

Once we are able to write unit equations, we can easily generate two unit factors. A **unit factor** is the ratio of the two equivalent quantities. That is, the quantity in the numerator is equal to the quantity in the denominator.

It is helpful to consistently write the larger metric unit first and the smaller metric unit second in a unit equation; for example, 1 m = 100 cm, 1 kg = 1000 g, and 1 L = 1000 mL.

The numerator and the denominator are equivalent, so we can generate a second unit factor by inverting the ratio and writing the **reciprocal**. As an example, consider the unit equation 1 m = 100 cm. The two associated unit factors are

$$\frac{1 \text{ m}}{100 \text{ cm}} \quad \text{and} \quad \frac{100 \text{ cm}}{1 \text{ m}}$$

Example Exercise 2.3 further illustrates how to write unit factors corresponding to a given metric relationship:

> It is helpful to consistently write the larger metric unit first and the smaller metric unit second in a unit equation; for example, 1 m = 100 cm, 1 kg = 1000 g, and 1 L = 1000 mL.

Example Exercise 2.3 | Metric Unit Factors

Write two unit factors for each of the following metric relationships:

(a) kilometers and meters (b) grams and decigrams

Solution

We start by writing the unit equation to generate the two unit factors.

(a) The prefix *kilo-* means 1000 basic units; thus, 1 km = 1000 m. The two unit factors are

$$\frac{1 \text{ km}}{1000 \text{ m}} \quad \text{and} \quad \frac{1000 \text{ m}}{1 \text{ km}}$$

(b) The prefix *deci-* means 0.1 basic unit; thus, 1 g = 10 dg. The two unit factors are

$$\frac{1 \text{ g}}{10 \text{ dg}} \quad \text{and} \quad \frac{10 \text{ dg}}{1 \text{ g}'}$$

Practice Exercise

Write two unit factors for each of the following metric relationships:

(a) liters and milliliters (b) megaseconds and seconds

Answers:

(a) 1 L/1000 mL and 1000 mL/1 L (b) 1 Ms/1,000,000 s and 1,000,000 s/1 Ms

Concept Exercise

How many significant digits are in the following unit factor: 1 L/1000 mL?

Answer: See Appendix G.

2.3 METRIC–METRIC CONVERSIONS

LEARNING OBJECTIVE

▶ To express a given metric measurement using a different metric prefix.

Science has the reputation for tackling difficult problems. Fortunately, you are about to learn a powerful technique for solving problems. It is called the **unit analysis method**. This approach to problem solving is also referred to as *dimensional analysis,* or the *factor-label method.* Unit analysis cannot solve every problem, but it is very effective for the problems we encounter in introductory chemistry.

Solving problems by unit analysis is a simple three-step process. Step 1: Read the problem and determine the unit required in the answer. Step 2: Analyze the problem and determine the given value that is related to the answer. Step 3: Write one or more unit factors to convert the unit in the given value to the unit in the answer. You should follow these three steps consistently and systematically when using the unit analysis method of problem solving.

Applying the Unit Analysis Method

Step 1: Write down the unit asked for in the answer.

Step 2: Write down the given value related to the answer.

Step 3: Apply unit factor(s) to convert the unit in the given value to the unit in the answer.

given value	*unit factor(s)*	*unit in answer*
(Step 2)	× (Step 3)	= (Step 1)

Let's begin with a simple problem and find the mass in grams of a 325 mg aspirin tablet. *First*, we write down the unit asked for in the answer (g). *Second*, we write down the related given value (325 mg). *Third*, we apply a unit factor using the following format:

$$325 \text{ mg} \quad \times \quad \frac{\text{unit}}{\text{factor}} \quad = \quad \text{g}$$

$$\text{(Step 2)} \quad \text{(Step 3)} \quad \text{(Step 1)}$$

The unit equation that relates Steps 1 and 2 is 1 g = 1000 mg. Therefore, the two associated unit factors are

$$\frac{1 \text{ g}}{1000 \text{ mg}} \quad \text{and} \quad \frac{1000 \text{ mg}}{1 \text{ g}}$$

To cancel the unit in the given value (325 mg), we should select the unit factor 1 g/1000 mg. After substituting, we have

$$325 \text{ mg} \times \frac{1 \text{ g}}{1000 \text{ mg}} = 0.325 \text{ g}$$

The given value has three significant digits, and the unit factor is an exact equivalent. Thus, the answer has three significant digits.

Example Exercises 2.4 and 2.5 further illustrate the unit analysis method of problem solving for metric–metric conversions.

Example Exercise 2.4 Metric–Metric Conversion

A hospital has 125 deciliter bags of blood plasma. What is the volume of plasma expressed in milliliters?

Strategy Plan

Step 1: What unit is asked for in the answer?

Step 1: mL

Step 2: What given value is related to the answer?

Step 2: 125 dL

Step 3: What unit factor(s) should we apply?

Given that 1 L = 10 dL, and 1 L = 1000 mL, the two pairs of unit factors are

Step 3:

$$\frac{1 \text{ L}}{10 \text{ dL}} \quad \text{or} \quad \frac{10 \text{ dL}}{1 \text{ L}}$$

$$\frac{1 \text{ L}}{1000 \text{ mL}} \quad \text{or} \quad \frac{1000 \text{ mL}}{1 \text{ L}}$$

Unit Analysis Map

given value	unit factor 1	unit factor 2	unit in answer
125 dL	$\times$ $\dfrac{1\ L}{10\ dL}$ or $\dfrac{10\ dL}{1\ L}$	$\times$ $\dfrac{1\ L}{1000\ mL}$ or $\dfrac{1000\ mL}{1\ L}$	= ? mL

Solution

We apply the unit factor 1 L/10 dL to cancel deciliters (dL), and 1000 mL/1 L to cancel liters (L).

$$125\ \cancel{dL} \times \frac{1\ \cancel{L}}{10\ \cancel{dL}} \times \frac{1000\ mL}{1\ \cancel{L}} = 1.25 \times 10^4\ mL$$

The given value, 125 dL, limits the answer to three significant digits. Each unit factor is derived from an exact equivalent, so neither affects the number of significant digits in the answer.

Practice Exercise

A dermatology patient is treated with ultraviolet light having a wavelength of 375 nm. What is the wavelength expressed in centimeters?

Answer: 0.0000375 cm (3.75×10^{-5} cm)

Concept Exercise

Express the volume of a cube 1 cm on a side in milliliters.

Answer: See Appendix G.

▲ **Blood Plasma** A blood plasma bag has a volume of 1 deciliter, that is, 0.1 liter.

Example Exercise 2.5 Metric–Metric Conversion

The mass of Earth is 5.98×10^{24} kg. What is the mass expressed in megagrams?

Strategy Plan

Step1: What unit is asked for in the answer?	**Step 1:** Mg
Step 2: What given value is related to the answer?	**Step 2:** 5.98×10^{24} kg
Step 3: What unit factor(s) should we apply? Given that 1 kg = 1000 g, and 1 Mg = 1,000,000 g, the two pairs of unit factors are	**Step 3:** $\dfrac{1\ kg}{1000\ g}$ or $\dfrac{1000\ g}{1\ kg}$
	$\dfrac{1\ Mg}{1,000,000\ g}$ or $\dfrac{1,000,000\ g}{1\ Mg}$

Earth

◀ **Earth** The mass of Earth is about 6,000,000,000,000,000,000,000,000 kilograms.

Unit Analysis Map

given value	unit factor 1	unit factor 2	unit in answer
5.98×10^{24} kg	$\times$ $\dfrac{1\ kg}{1000\ g}$ or $\dfrac{1000\ g}{1\ kg}$	$\times$ $\dfrac{1\ Mg}{1,000,000\ g}$ or $\dfrac{1,000,000\ g}{1\ Mg}$	= ? Mg

Solution

We apply the unit factor 1000 g/1 kg to cancel kilograms (kg), and 1 Mg/1,000,000 g to cancel grams (g).

$$5.98 \times 10^{24} \, kg \times \frac{1000 \, g}{1 \, kg} \times \frac{1 \, Mg}{1,000,000 \, g} = 5.98 \times 10^{21} \, Mg$$

The given value limits the answer to three significant digits. Because each unit factor is derived from an exact equivalent, neither affects the number of significant digits in the answer.

Practice Exercise

Light travels through the universe at a velocity of 3.00×10^{10} cm/s. How many gigameters does light travel in one second?

Answer: 0.300 Gm $(3.00 \times 10^{-1} \, Gm)$

Concept Exercise

How many significant digits are in the following unit factor: 1 g/1000 mg?

Answer: See Appendix G.

LEARNING OBJECTIVES

▶ To state the metric equivalent for inch, pound, quart, and second.

▶ To express a given measurement in metric units or English units.

2.4 METRIC–ENGLISH CONVERSIONS

Despite the superiority of the metric system, its adoption has been resisted from its inception. When the French asked the Americans and the British for their cooperation in creating a worldwide system of measurement, both countries declined. The initial objection, interestingly, was political rather than scientific. The meter was defined by a longitude passing through Dunkirk, France, and the original metric standards were kept in a special vault outside of Paris.

In 1975, President Gerald Ford signed an official metric conversion act. Thus, the United States became the last major nation in the world to formally adopt the metric system. Although the metric system is now taught in public schools, the United States is making slow progress in achieving full compliance.

In science, we regularly record measurements in metric units. In everyday activities, you may be more familiar with inches, pounds, and quarts. Therefore, let's compare the two systems to gain a practical awareness of metric sizes. Table 2.3 contrasts some common English and metric units.

TABLE 2.3 ENGLISH–METRIC EQUIVALENTS

PHYSICAL QUANTITY	ENGLISH UNIT	METRIC EQUIVALENT
length	1 inch (in.)	1 in. = 2.54 cm
mass	1 pound (lb)	1 lb = 454 g
volume	1 quart (qt)	1 qt = 946 mL
time	1 second (sec)	1 sec = 1.00 s

When applying these metric equivalents, assume three significant digits. Because the metric and English systems have different reference standards, these are not exact equivalents; however, the U.S. Bureau of Weights and Measures has redefined 1 in. as exactly equal to 2.54 cm.

Which race do you think is run faster: 100 meters or 100 yards? Obviously, it is the shorter race distance that is run faster. Given that 1 yd = 0.914 m, we can calculate the distance in yards for a 100.0-meter race.

First, we write down the unit asked for in the answer (yd). *Second*, we write down the related given value (100.0 m). *Third*, we apply a unit factor using the following format:

$$100.0 \, m \quad \times \quad \frac{unit}{factor} \quad = \quad yd$$

$$(Step \, 2) \qquad\qquad (Step \, 3) \qquad (Step \, 1)$$

The unit equation that relates Steps 1 and 2 is 1 yd = 0.914 m. Therefore, the two unit factors are

$$\frac{1\text{ yd}}{0.914\text{ m}} \quad \text{and} \quad \frac{0.914\text{ m}}{1\text{ yd}}$$

To cancel the unit in the given value (100.0 m), we select the unit factor (1 yd/0.914 m). After substituting, we have

$$100.0\text{ m} \times \frac{1\text{ yd}}{0.914\text{ m}} = 109\text{ yd}$$

Although the given value (100.0 m) has four significant digits, the unit factor has only three because 1 yd = 0.914 m is not an exact equivalent. Thus, the answer is rounded to three significant digits. Because 100 meters is a longer distance than 100 yards, the 100-yard race is run faster. In fact, the world record for 100 meters is more than 9 seconds, whereas the world record for 100 yards is less than 9 seconds!

Example Exercises 2.6 and 2.7 further illustrate the unit analysis method of problem solving.

Example Exercise 2.6 Metric–English Conversion

A can of soda contains 12.0 fl oz (1 quart = 32 fluid ounces). What is the volume of soda in milliliters?

Strategy Plan

Step 1: What unit is asked for in the answer?	**Step 1:**	mL
Step 2: What given value is related to the answer?	**Step 2:**	12.0 fl oz
Step 3: What unit factor(s) should we apply? Given that 1 qt = 32 fl oz; and in Table 2.3 we find that 1 qt = 946 mL. The two pairs of unit factors are	**Step 3:**	$\dfrac{32\text{ fl oz}}{1\text{ qt}}$ or $\dfrac{1\text{ qt}}{32\text{ fl oz}}$
		$\dfrac{1\text{ qt}}{946\text{ mL}}$ or $\dfrac{946\text{ mL}}{1\text{ qt}}$

Unit Analysis Map

given value		unit factor 1		unit factor 2		unit in answer
12 fl oz	×	$\dfrac{32\text{ fl oz}}{1\text{ qt}}$ or $\dfrac{1\text{ qt}}{32\text{ fl oz}}$	×	$\dfrac{1\text{ qt}}{946\text{ mL}}$ or $\dfrac{946\text{ mL}}{1\text{ qt}}$		= ? mL

Solution
We apply the unit factor 1 qt/32 fl oz to cancel ounces (fl oz), and 946 mL/1 qt to cancel quarts (qt).

$$12.0\text{ fl oz} \times \frac{1\text{ qt}}{32\text{ fl oz}} \times \frac{946\text{ mL}}{1\text{ qt}} = 355\text{ mL}$$

The given value, 12.0 fl oz, limits the answer to three significant digits. Unit factor 1 has no effect as it is an exact equivalent, and unit factor 2 has three significant digits.

Practice Exercise
A can of soda contains 12.0 fl oz. What is the volume in liters (given that 1 L = 1000 mL)?

Answer: 0.355 L

Concept Exercise
How many significant digits are in the following unit equation: 1 L = 1000 mL?

Answer: See Appendix G.

▲ **Dr. Pepper** A 12 fl oz can of soda contains 355 mL.

Example Exercise 2.7 · Metric–English Conversion

If a tennis ball weighs 2.0 oz, what is the mass of the tennis ball in grams?

◀ **Tennis Balls** A tennis ball weighs about 2.0 ounces, and has a diameter of 2.5 inches.

Strategy Plan

Step 1: What unit is asked for in the answer?	**Step 1:**	g
Step 2: What given value is related to the answer?	**Step 2:**	2.0 oz
Step 3: What unit factor(s) should we apply? Given that 1 lb = 16 oz and that in Table 2.3 we find that 1 lb = 454 g. The two pairs of unit factors are	**Step 3:**	$\dfrac{1\ lb}{16\ oz}$ or $\dfrac{16\ oz}{1\ lb}$ $\dfrac{1\ lb}{454\ g}$ or $\dfrac{454\ g}{1\ lb}$

Unit Analysis Map

given value	*unit factor 1*	*unit factor 2*	*unit in answer*
2.0 oz	$\times\ \dfrac{1\ lb}{16\ oz}$ or $\dfrac{16\ oz}{1\ lb}$	$\times\ \dfrac{1\ lb}{454\ g}$ or $\dfrac{454\ g}{1\ lb}$	= ? g

Solution

We apply the unit factor 1 lb/16 oz to cancel ounces (oz), and 454 g/1 lb to cancel pounds (lb).

$$2.0\ oz \times \frac{1\ lb}{16\ oz} \times \frac{454\ g}{1\ lb} = 57\ g$$

The given value, 2.0 oz, limits the answer to two significant digits. Unit factor 1 has no effect as it is derived from an exact equivalent, and unit factor 2 has three significant digits.

Practice Exercise

If a tennis ball has a diameter of 2.5 inches, what is the diameter in millimeters?

Answer: 64 mm

Concept Exercise

How many significant digits are in the following unit factor: 1 kg/2.20 lb?

Answer: See Appendix G.

CHEMISTRY CONNECTION The Olympics

Q: Which Olympic race is nearly equal in length to a quarter mile, that is, 440 yards?

The Olympics began in 776 B.C. with a single event, a 200-yard dash called a *stadion*. In time, a 2-stadia dash and a 24-stadia event were added, and wrestling appeared in 708 B.C. Eventually, participation in the games declined, and the ancient Olympics were discontinued in A.D. 394.

In the summer of 1896, the modern Olympic Games were initiated and held in Greece. The games attracted about 500 athletes from 13 nations. Since then, the games have been held every four years in various cities around the world.

The games have steadily increased in number of participants, as well as in number of events. In 1896, 311 men from 13 nations competed, and the United States won gold medals in 9 of the 12 events. In 2004, over 10,000 men and women athletes from 197 nations competed.

U.S. track and field competitions have been conducted using the English system of measurement. That is, American runners compete at distances of 100 yards, 440 yards, and 1 mile. In Olympic competitions, events are conducted using the metric system owing to its international acceptance. Olympic runners compete at comparable distances such as 100, 400, and 1500 meters. The marathon, however, is an exception. It corresponds to the distance run by the Greek messenger who carried news of the Athenian victory on the plains of Marathon in 490 B.C. That legendary distance is 26 miles, 385 yards.

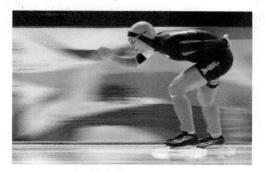

▲ **Olympic Speed Skater** Olympic speed skaters compete in events measured in metric distances including 500, 1000, and 5000 meters.

In 1924, the Olympic Winter Games were introduced at Chamonix, France, and have been held four times in the United States, twice at Lake Placid, once at Squaw Valley, and in 2002 at Salt Lake City. The winter games feature skating, skiing, bobsledding, luge, tobogganing, and ice hockey. In Nordic cross-country skiing, the races are 10, 20, 30, and 50 kilometers; in ski jumping, the ramps are 70 and 90 meters. Thus, Olympic competitions—winter and summer—employ the metric system of measurement.

A: The 400-meter Olympic race is nearly identical to 440 yards, and the world records for the two races are within tenths of a second.

CRITICAL THINKING World Trade Center

Q: What is the difference between a building that has an area footprint of 150 square feet, versus 150 feet square?

When the architect's proposal was accepted for the new World Trade Center building in New York City, a national daily newspaper stated that the building "footprint" was to be 150 square feet. Given that Freedom Tower will be one of the tallest structures in the world, does this statement reflect critical thinking?

If the building footprint is 150 square feet, the structure would measure only about 12 feet per side! Given that the building will be 1776 feet high, it is unreasonable that the base would be only 12 feet per side. It makes more sense that the footprint would be 150 feet square; that is, 150 feet per side.

Another example reflecting a lack of critical thinking occurred when NASA engineers mixed up English and metric units in the navigation program for the Mars Climate Orbiter. The Orbiter was to sample the Martian atmosphere and a navigation error caused a $100 million loss of the Orbiter as it approached the planet's atmosphere too closely.

The minimal safe approach distance to the planet was estimated to be 53 miles. When NASA engineers mixed up English and metric units, the Orbiter approached within

60 kilometers (*37 miles*) and burned up in the Martian atmosphere.

◀ **One World Trade Center** The structure dubbed "Freedom Tower" will be completed in 2013 at a cost in excess of $3 billion.

A: An area footprint of 150 square feet is only 12 feet per side; whereas, 150 feet square, is 150 feet per side.

LEARNING OBJECTIVES

▶ To express a quantity in a sample as a percent.

▶ To apply percent as a unit factor.

2.5 THE PERCENT CONCEPT

A **percent** (symbol %) expresses the amount a single quantity compared to an entire sample. For example, a dime is 10% of a dollar, and a quarter is 25% of a dollar. The percent symbol (%) is derived from the ratio sign (/) and the two zeros in 100.

A percent expresses a ratio and can be referred to as parts per 100 parts. To calculate a percent, divide a single quantity by the total sample, and multiply that ratio by 100%.

$$\frac{\text{one quantity}}{\text{total sample}} \times 100\% = \%$$

As an example, consider that 5¢ coins minted after 1971 are composed of the two metals copper and nickel. If a 5¢ coin contains 3.80 g copper and 1.27 g nickel, what is the percent of copper in the coin? We can calculate the percent of copper as follows:

$$\frac{3.80 \text{ g}}{(3.80 + 1.27) \text{ g}} \times 100\% = 75.0\%$$

Example Exercise 2.8 The Percent Concept

Sterling silver contains silver and copper metals. If a sterling silver chain contains 18.5 g of silver and 1.5 g of copper, what is the percent of silver?

◀ **Sterling Silver** Sterling silver has a high luster and is found in fine utensils and jewelry.

Strategy Plan

Step 1: What is asked for in the answer?	**Step 1:** %
Step 2: What given value is related to the answer?	**Step 2:** 18.5 g and 1.5 g
Step 3: What unit factor should we apply? No unit factor is required.	**Step 3:** none

Solution

To find percent, we compare the mass of silver metal to the total mass of the silver and copper in the chain, and multiply by 100%.

$$\frac{18.5 \text{ g}}{(18.5 + 1.5) \text{ g}} \times 100\% = 92.5\%$$

Genuine sterling silver is cast from 92.5% silver and 7.5% copper. If you carefully examine a piece of sterling silver, you may see the jeweler's notation .925, which indicates the item is genuine sterling silver.

Practice Exercise

A 14-karat gold ring contains 7.45 g of gold, 2.66 g of silver, and 2.66 g of copper. Calculate the percent of gold in the 14-karat ring.

Answer: 58.3%

Concept Exercise

If a gold alloy contains 20% silver and 5% copper, what is the percent of gold in the alloy?

Answer: See Appendix G.

Percent Unit Factors

A percent can be expressed as parts per 100 parts. For instance, 10% and 25% correspond to 10 and 25 parts per 100 parts, respectively. Thus, we can write a percent as a ratio fraction; that is, we can write 10% as 10/100, and 25% as 25/100.

Let's try a type of problem in which the percent is given. *Apollo 11* traveled 394,000 km from Earth to land the first astronaut on the Moon. How many kilometers had the astronauts traveled when they had gone 15.5% of the distance? By definition, 15.5% means 15.5 parts per 100 parts. In this example, 15.5% is 15.5 km per 100 km. Thus, we can write the ratio as a unit factor and apply the unit analysis method.

$$394{,}000 \text{ km} \times \frac{15.5 \text{ km}}{100 \text{ km}} = 61{,}100 \text{ km}$$

In this problem, notice that we used percent as a unit factor. Example Exercise 2.9 further illustrates the application of percent as a unit factor.

▲ **Moon** The Moon and Earth have a similar composition.

Example Exercise 2.9	Percent as a Unit Factor

The Moon and Earth have a similar composition and each contains 4.70% iron, which supports the theory that the Moon and Earth were originally a single planet. What is the mass of iron in a lunar sample that weighs 235 g?

Strategy Plan

Step 1: What unit is asked for in the answer?

Step 1:	g iron

Step 2: What given value is related to the answer?

Step 2:	235 g sample

Step 3: What unit factor should we apply? From the definition of percent, 4.70 g iron = 100 g sample; the two unit factors are 4.70 g iron/100 g sample, and its reciprocal 100 g sample/4.70 g iron.

Step 3:	$\dfrac{4.70 \text{ g iron}}{100 \text{ g sample}}$ or $\dfrac{100 \text{ g sample}}{4.70 \text{ g iron}}$

Unit Analysis Map

given value	*unit factor*	*unit in answer*
235 g sample	$\times \dfrac{4.70 \text{ g iron}}{100 \text{ g sample}}$ or $\dfrac{100 \text{ g sample}}{4.70 \text{ g iron}}$	= g iron

Solution

We should apply the unit factor 4.70 g iron/100 g sample to cancel grams sample (g sample), which appears in the denominator.

$$235 \text{ g sample} \times \frac{4.70 \text{ g iron}}{100 \text{ g sample}} = 11.0 \text{ g iron}$$

The given value and unit factor each have three digits and limit the answer to three significant digits.

Practice Exercise

A Moon sample is found to contain 7.50% aluminum. What is the mass of the lunar sample if the amount of aluminum is 5.25 g?

Answer: 70.0 g sample

Concept Exercise

Water is 11.2% hydrogen by mass. What two unit factors express the percent hydrogen in water?

Answer: See Appendix G.

2.6 VOLUME BY CALCULATION

LEARNING OBJECTIVES

▶ To perform calculations that relate length, width, thickness, and volume of a rectangular solid.

▶ To perform calculations that express a given volume in milliliters, cubic centimeters, or cubic inches.

▲ **Volume by Calculation** The volume of a rectangular solid is equal to its length (*l*) times width (*w*) times thickness (*t*) or height.

Have you ever wondered how a building contractor arrives at the costs for a new home? For example, how does one estimate the cost of pouring a foundation? The cost is based on the volume of concrete that is poured. If the foundation is rectangular, the volume of concrete is found by multiplying length (*l*) times width (*w*) times thickness (*t*). We can express this relationship by the following equation:

$$l \times w \times t = \text{volume}$$

Before calculating a volume, we must express each of the measurements in the same units. If we express length, width, and thickness in centimeters, the volume of the solid has the units of **cubic centimeters** (symbol cm^3). For example, if a rectangular solid measures 3 cm by 2 cm by 1 cm, we find the volume is 6 cm^3. Example Exercise 2.10 further illustrates how to determine the volume of a rectangular solid by calculation.

Example Exercise 2.10   Volume Calculation for a Rectangular Solid

If a stainless steel rectangular solid measures 5.55 cm long, 3.75 cm wide, and 2.25 cm thick, what is the volume in cubic centimeters?

Strategy Plan

Step 1: What unit is asked for in the answer?

| Step 1: | cm^3 |

Step 2: What given value is related to the answer?

| Step 2: | **5.55 cm, 3.75 cm, and 2.25 cm** |

Step 3: What unit factor(s) should we apply? No unit factor is required.

| Step 3: | **none** |

Solution

We can calculate the volume of the rectangular solid by multiplying length times width times thickness: $l \times w \times t$.

$$5.55 \text{ cm} \times 3.75 \text{ cm} \times 2.25 \text{ cm} = 46.8 \text{ cm}^3$$

The answer is rounded off to three significant digits because each given value has three significant digits.

Practice Exercise

If a rectangular brass solid measures 52.0 mm by 25.0 mm by 15.0 mm, what is the volume in cubic millimeters?

Answer: 19,500 mm^3 (1.95×10^4 mm^3)

Concept Exercise

Express the volume of a cube 10 cm on a side in liters.

Answer: See Appendix G.

Let's now consider a rectangular solid with a length of 4 cm, a width of 3 cm, and a volume of 24 cm^3. Given the length, width, and volume, we can calculate the thickness of the rectangular solid by dividing the volume by its length and its width; that is, we divide 24 cm^3 by 4 cm and 3 cm. In this example, the thickness of the solid is 2 cm. Example Exercise 2.11 illustrates finding the thickness of rectangular solid.

Example Exercise 2.11   Thickness Calculation for a Rectangular Solid

A sheet of aluminum foil measures 25.0 mm by 10.0 mm, and the volume is 3.75 mm^3. What is the thickness of the foil in millimeters?

Strategy Plan

Step 1: What unit is asked for in the answer?	**Step 1:**	mm
Step 2: What given value is related to the answer?	**Step 2:**	3.75 mm^3, 25.0 mm, and 10.0 mm
Step 3: What unit factor(s) should we apply? No unit factor is required.	**Step 3:**	none

Solution

We can calculate the thickness of the foil by dividing the volume by length and width. Because the unit of volume is mm^3, we obtain the thickness in mm by unit cancellation.

$$3.75 \text{ mm}^3 \times \frac{1}{25.0 \text{ mm}} \times \frac{1}{10.0 \text{ mm}} = \frac{3.75 \text{ mm} \times \text{mm} \times \text{mm}}{25.0 \text{ mm} \times 10.0 \text{ mm}} = 0.0150 \text{ mm}$$

The answer is rounded off to three significant digits because each given value has three significant digits.

Practice Exercise

A sheet of aluminum foil measures 35.0 cm by 25.0 cm, and the volume is 1.36 cm^3. What is the thickness of the foil in centimeters?

Answer: 0.00155 cm (1.55×10^{-3} cm)

Concept Exercise

Which of the following is the greatest thickness?

$$1 \text{ mm}, 0.1 \text{ cm, or } 0.001 \text{ m}$$

Answer: See Appendix G.

▲ **Aluminum Foil** A thin sheet of aluminum foil.

Volumes of Solids, Liquids, and Gases

In the metric system, the basic unit of liquid volume is the liter. A liter is equivalent to the volume occupied by a cube exactly 10 cm on a side.

A cube is a regular solid with its length, width, and thickness being equal. We calculate the volume of the cube by multiplying length by width by thickness.

$$10 \text{ cm} \times 10 \text{ cm} \times 10 \text{ cm} = 1000 \text{ cm}^3$$

The calculated volume of 1 L is 1000 cm³. Moreover, we recall the exact equivalent: 1 L = 1000 mL. We can combine the two equivalents as follows.

$$1000 \text{ cm}^3 = 1 \text{ L} = 1000 \text{ mL}$$

Simplifying, we have

$$1 \text{ cm}^3 = 1 \text{ mL}$$

We see that 1 cm³ is exactly equivalent to 1 mL. Example Exercise 2.12 further illustrates the calculation of volume.

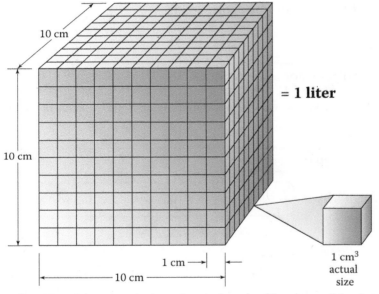

▲ **One Liter** A liter equals the volume of a cube 10 cm on a side, that is, 1000 cm³.

▲ **1-Liter Bottle** A 1-liter bottle contains 1000 mL of liquid.

Example Exercise 2.12 Metric–English Volume Conversion

Given that an automobile engine has a volume displacement of 498 cm³ in each cylinder, express the volume in cubic inches.

Strategy Plan

Step 1: What unit is asked for in the answer?	**Step 1:** in.³
Step 2: What given value is related to the answer?	**Step 2:** 498 cm³
Step 3: What unit factor(s) should we apply?	**Step 3:** $\dfrac{1 \text{ in.}}{2.54 \text{ cm}}$ or $\dfrac{2.54 \text{ cm}}{1 \text{ in.}}$

Unit Analysis Map

given value	unit factor 1	unit factor 2	unit factor 3	unit in answer
498 cm^3	$\times \dfrac{1 \text{ in.}}{2.54 \text{ cm}}$	$\times \dfrac{1 \text{ in.}}{2.54 \text{ cm}}$	$\times \dfrac{1 \text{ in.}}{2.54 \text{ cm}}$	$= \; ? \text{ in.}^3$

Solution

We can calculate the volume in cubic inches by converting the volume given in cubic centimeters. Notice that cm units do not cancel cm^3. To obtain cubic inches, we must apply the unit factor, 1 in. /2.54 cm, three times. Thus,

$$498 \text{ cm}^3 \times \frac{1 \text{ in.}}{2.54 \text{ cm}} \times \frac{1 \text{ in.}}{2.54 \text{ cm}} \times \frac{1 \text{ in.}}{2.54 \text{ cm}} = 30.4 \text{ in.}^3$$

The given value, and unit factors, each limits the answer to three significant digits.

Practice Exercise

Given that an SUV has a 244 in.^{3} engine, express the engine volume in liters.

Answer: 4.00 L

Concept Exercise

Which of the following is the greater volume: 500 mL or 500 cm^3?

Answer: See Appendix G.

▲ **Mini Cooper** The Mini Cooper is built in England and marketed in the United States by BMW.

Note A cubic centimeter is sometimes abbreviated "cc," as in a 1 cc medical injection. It is not obvious that cc stands for cubic centimeters, so use of this abbreviation is discouraged in science, even though it is common in medicine.

2.7 VOLUME BY DISPLACEMENT

LEARNING OBJECTIVE

▸ To determine the volume of a solid and gas by the displacement of water.

The volumes of liquids and solids can be determined by several methods. The volumes of liquids can be determined directly with calibrated glassware, such as graduated cylinders, pipets, and burets. The volumes of regular solids (cubes, cylinders, spheres) can be calculated from measurements.

The volume of an irregular solid cannot be determined directly by multiplying its measurements. However, the volume can be determined *indirectly* by measuring the amount of water the solid displaces. This technique is called determination of **volume by displacement**.

Suppose we wish to determine the volume of a piece of jade. Because it is an irregular solid object, we cannot measure its volume directly. We have to use the technique of determining volume by displacement. We first fill a graduated cylinder halfway with water (Figure 2.2) and record the water level. Next, we carefully slip the piece of jade into the graduated cylinder and record the new water level. The difference between the final and the initial water levels represents the volume of the piece of jade.

We can also use the volume by displacement method to determine the volume of a gas. When a gas is produced from a chemical reaction, its volume is equal to the amount of water it displaces. This technique provides good results for gases that do not dissolve, or only slightly dissolve, in water. For instance, heating a solid sample may release oxygen gas, which displaces water from a closed container. Because oxygen dissolves only slightly in water, the volume of water displaced is equal to the volume of gas released. Determining the volume of a gas by displacement is referred to as *collecting a gas over water* and is illustrated in Figure 2.3.

◀ Figure 2.2 **Volume of a Solid by Displacement** The difference between the final water level and the initial water level in the graduated cylinder (10.5 mL) is equal to the volume of the solid piece of jade.

50.0 mL

60.5 mL

Green jade sample

Gas

H_2O

Gas

Water

◀ Figure 2.3 **Volume of a Gas by Displacement** A flask is filled with water, and a sample is placed in the test tube. After heating, the sample decomposes and produces oxygen gas, which in turn displaces water from the flask. The volume of water displaced into the beaker equals the volume of oxygen gas produced by the sample.

Example Exercise 2.13   Volume by Displacement

A quartz stone weighing 30.475 g is carefully placed into a graduated cylinder. If the water level increases from 25.0 mL to 36.5 mL, what is the volume of the quartz stone?

Strategy Plan

Step 1: What unit is asked for in the answer?

Step 1: | mL

Step 2: What given value is related to the answer?

Step 2: | 25.0 mL and 36.5 mL

Step 3: What unit factor(s) should we apply?
No unit factor is required.

Step 3: | none

Solution
We can calculate the displaced volume in milliliters by subtracting the initial volume from the final volume.

$$36.5 \text{ mL} - 25.0 \text{ mL} = 11.5 \text{ mL}$$

Practice Exercise
Hydrogen peroxide decomposes to give oxygen gas, which displaces a volume of water into a beaker. If the water level in the beaker increases from 50.0 mL to 105.5 mL, what is the volume of oxygen gas?

Answer: 55.5 mL

Concept Exercise
Which of the following has the greater volume: 1 mL or 1 cm^3 ?

Answer: See Appendix G.

2.8 THE DENSITY CONCEPT

If we hold a piece of wood in one hand and a piece of metal in the other (each having the same mass), the piece of metal may feel heavier. This contradiction is explained by the term **density** (symbol d), which expresses the concentration of mass. The more concentrated the mass is in a sample, the greater its density. We sometimes say an object is heavy when we are trying to convey density. A 1 kg block of lead and a 1 kg block of ice have the same mass, but the lead is much more dense.

We define density as the amount of mass per unit volume. The term *per* indicates a ratio, as in "miles per hour." Thus, mass divided by volume equals density. We can write this relationship mathematically as

$$\frac{\text{mass}}{\text{volume}} = \text{density}$$

Density is expressed in different units. For solids and liquids, it is usually expressed in grams per cubic centimeter (g/cm^3) or grams per milliliter (g/mL). For gases, density is usually expressed in grams per liter (g/L). Figure 2.4 illustrates the concept of density.

Ice	Water	Lead	Osmium
1 cm³	1 cm³	1 cm³	1 cm³
0.917 g	1.00 g	11.3 g	22.5 g

◀ Figure 2.4 **An Illustration of Density** Each cube represents a volume of 1 cm³. Notice the mass of each cube increases as its density becomes greater. Osmium has the greatest density of any metal, 22.5 g/cm³.

Recall that the original metric standards for mass and volume were based on water. A mass of 1 kg was set equal to a 1 L volume of water. Therefore, the density of water is 1 kg/L. A density of 1 kg/L is exactly equivalent to 1 g/mL.

Although the density of solids and liquids varies slightly with temperature, we will ignore this small effect. For our purposes, we will consider the density of water to be 1.00 g/mL. The density of gases, however, is an exception. The density of a gas varies greatly with changes in temperature and pressure. Table 2.4 lists the density for selected solids, liquids, and gases.

We can drop a solid object into water and estimate its density. An object that sinks in water has a density greater than 1.00 g/mL. An object that floats on water has a density less than 1.00 g/mL.

Consider the following experiment. Water, chloroform, and ethyl ether are poured into a tall glass cylinder. The liquids form three layers as shown in Figure 2.5. Identify liquids L1 and L2 by referring to the density of the liquids listed in Table 2.4. Next, ice, rubber, and aluminum cubes are dropped into the cylinder. Identify solids S_1, S_2, and S_3 by referring to the density of the solids listed in Table 2.4.

We know that liquid L_1 must be less dense than water ($d = 1.00$ g/mL) because it floats; liquid L_2 must be more dense than water because it sinks. Thus, liquid L_1 is ethyl ether ($d = 0.714$ g/mL), which is less dense than water, and liquid L_2 is chloroform ($d = 1.48$ g/mL), which is more dense than water.

We see in Figure 2.5 that S_1 floats on water, S_2 floats on chloroform, and S_3 sinks in chloroform. Table 2.4 indicates the densities of ice, rubber, and aluminum are 0.917, 1.19, and 2.70 g/cm³, respectively. Thus, S_1 must be ice because it sinks in ether and floats on water, S_2 must be rubber because it sinks in water and floats on chloroform, and S_3 must be aluminum because it sinks in chloroform.

Now that we understand the concept of density, let's try some calculations. We can find the density of a sample by simply dividing its mass by its volume. Example Exercise 2.14 illustrates the calculation of density.

▲ Figure 2.5 **The Concept of Density** In a tall glass cylinder, liquid L_1 is shown floating on water, which is floating on liquid L_2. Solid S_1 is floating on water, solid S_2 is floating on liquid L_2, and solid S_3 has sunk to the bottom of the glass cylinder.

TABLE 2.4 DENSITY OF SELECTED SOLIDS, LIQUIDS, AND GASES

EXAMPLE	DENSITY (d)
Solids	
ice	0.917 g/cm³ or g/mL
rubber	1.19
magnesium	1.74
aluminum	2.70
iron	7.87
lead	11.3
gold	19.3
Liquids	
ethyl ether	0.714 g/cm³ or g/mL
ethyl alcohol	0.789
water	0.789
chloroform	1.48
mercury	13.6
Gases*	
hydrogen	0.090 g/L
helium	0.179
ammonia	0.760
air	1.29
oxygen	1.43

*The density value for each gas is given at 0 °C and a pressure equal to normal atmospheric pressure.

Example Exercise 2.14   Density Calculation

If a platinum nugget has a mass of 214.50 g and a volume of 10.0 cm³, what is the density of the metal?

Strategy Plan

Step 1: What unit is asked for in the answer?	**Step 1:**	g/cm^3
Step 2: What given value is related to the answer?	**Step 2:**	214.50 g and 10.0 cm³
Step 3: What unit factor(s) should we apply? No unit factor is required.	**Step 3:**	none

Solution

We can calculate the density of the platinum nugget by comparing the mass of metal, 214.50 g, to its volume, 10.0 cm³.

$$\frac{214.50 \text{ g}}{10.0 \text{ cm}^3} = 21.5 \text{ g/cm}^3$$

The given volume has three significant digits, so the answer is rounded off to three digits. It is interesting to note that platinum metal is more dense than lead ($d = 11.3\,\text{g/cm}^3$), and more valuable than gold.

▲ **Platinum Nugget** A nugget of precious platinum metal.

Practice Exercise

Carbon tetrachloride is a solvent used for degreasing electronic parts. If 25.0 mL of carbon tetrachloride has a mass of 39.75 g, what is the density of the liquid?

Answer: 1.59 g/mL

Concept Exercise

Which of the following has the greater density: ice or water?

Answer: See Appendix G.

Applying Density as a Unit Factor

We can also solve problems that ask for the mass or volume of a sample by applying the unit analysis method of problem solving. The secret to solving these problems is to realize that density can be used as a unit factor because it relates mass and volume. For example, the density of mercury is 13.6 g/mL, and so we can write

$$\frac{13.6 \text{ g}}{1 \text{ mL}} \quad \text{and} \quad \frac{1 \text{ mL}}{13.6 \text{ g}}$$

Let's calculate the milliliter volume of 75.5 g of liquid mercury. *First*, we write down the unit asked for in the answer (mL). *Second*, we write down the related given value (75.5 g). *Third*, we apply a unit factor using the following format:

$$\underset{(\text{Step 2})}{75.5 \text{ g}} \quad \times \quad \underset{(\text{Step 3})}{\frac{\text{unit}}{\text{factor}}} \quad = \quad \underset{(\text{Step 1})}{\text{mL}}$$

To cancel the units in the given value (75.5 g), we select the unit factor 1 mL/13.6 g. After substituting, we have

$$75.5 \text{ g} \times \frac{1 \text{ mL}}{13.6 \text{ g}} = 5.55 \text{ mL}$$

The given value and the unit factor each have three significant digits; thus, the answer is rounded to three digits. Example Exercise 2.15 further illustrates the use of density as a unit factor.

Example Exercise 2.15   Density as a Unit Factor

A 1.00-in. cube of copper measures 2.54 cm on a side. What is the mass of the copper cube (given that *d* of copper = 8.96 g/cm^3)?

Strategy Plan

Step 1: What unit is asked for in the answer?	**Step 1:** $\quad$ g
Step 2: What given value is related to the answer?	**Step 2:** $\quad$ 2.54 cm cube
Step 3: What unit factor(s) should we apply? From the definition of density, 8.96 g = 1 cm^3; thus, the two unit factors are 8.96 g/1 cm^3, and its reciprocal 1 cm^3/8.96 g.	**Step 3:** $\quad \dfrac{8.96 \text{ g}}{1 \text{ cm}^3} \quad \text{or} \quad \dfrac{1 \text{ cm}^3}{8.96 \text{ g}}$

Unit Analysis Map

Copper

given value	unit factor	unit in answer
2.54 cm cube	$\times \dfrac{8.96\ \text{g}}{1\ \text{cm}^3}$ or $\dfrac{1\ \text{cm}^3}{8.96\ \text{g}}$	= g

▲ **Copper Metal** A 1.00-inch cube of copper metal.

Solution

First, we find the volume of the copper cube. We obtain the volume of the cube, 16.4 cm³, by multiplying (2.54 cm) (2.54 cm) (2.54 cm). We use the given density, 8.96 g/1 cm³, as a unit factor to cancel cubic centimeters (cm³), which appears in the denominator.

$$16.4\ \text{cm}^3 \times \frac{8.96\ \text{g}}{1\ \text{cm}^3} = 147\ \text{g}$$

The given value and unit factor each has three significant digits, so the answer is rounded off to three significant digits.

Practice Exercise

A cube of silver is 5.00 cm on a side and has a mass of 1312.5 g. What is the density of silver?

Answer: 10.5 g/cm³

Concept Exercise

If some humans float in water and others sink, what is the approximate density of the human body?

Answer: See Appendix G.

Specific Gravity

The ratio of the density of a liquid to the density of water at 4 °C is called **specific gravity** (symbol **sp gr**). Because specific gravity is a ratio of two densities, the units cancel and specific gravity is a unitless quantity. The density of water is 1.00 g/mL, and the specific gravity of water is 1.00.

Diagnostic medical testing often includes the specific gravity of body fluids. For instance, the specific gravity of urine may be 1.02, and the specific gravity of blood may be 1.06. Both of these values are considered to be in the normal range.

LEARNING OBJECTIVES

▸ To state the freezing point and boiling point of water on the Fahrenheit, Celsius, and Kelvin scales.

▸ To express a given temperature in degrees Fahrenheit (°F), degrees Celsius (°C), or Kelvin units (K).

2.9 TEMPERATURE

The "hotness" or "coolness" of the atmosphere is determined by how fast the tiny air molecules are moving. If the temperature is warmer, molecules move faster and have more energy. If the temperature is cooler, molecules move slower and have less energy. **Temperature** is the average kinetic energy of individual particles in motion; for example, the average energy of air molecules in the atmosphere. We measure temperature using a thermometer.

In 1724 Daniel Gabriel Fahrenheit (1686–1736), a German physicist, invented the mercury thermometer. In attempting to produce as cold a temperature as possible, Fahrenheit prepared an ice bath to which he added salt to lower the temperature further. He then assigned a value of zero to that temperature and marked his Fahrenheit scale accordingly.

Fahrenheit obtained a second reference point by recording his underarm body temperature; he assigned that temperature a value of 96. He divided the distance between the two reference points into 96 equal units, and each division was termed a **Fahrenheit degree** (symbol **°F**). Later, the freezing and boiling points of water were selected as the standard reference points. The freezing point of water was assigned a value of 32 °F, and the boiling point a value of 212 °F. The Fahrenheit degree eventually became a basic unit in the English system of measurement.

In 1742 Anders Celsius (1701–1744), a Swedish astronomer, proposed a scale similar in principle to the Fahrenheit scale. On the Celsius scale, the freezing point of water was assigned a value of 0 °C and the boiling point of water a value of 100 °C. The scale was then divided into 100 equal divisions, each division representing a **Celsius degree** (symbol **°C**). The Celsius degree is sometimes referred to as a centigrade degree, but the use of degrees centigrade is discouraged.

In 1848 William Thomson (1824–1907), an English physicist also known as Lord Kelvin, proposed a scale based on the lowest possible temperature. The unit of temperature was the **Kelvin unit** (symbol **K**), which is a basic unit in the SI system. On the Kelvin scale, the coldest temperature was assigned a value of 0 K, and each division on the scale is equal to one Celsius degree. The lowest temperature is referred to as absolute zero and corresponds to −273.15 °C. Although there is no highest temperature on the Kelvin scale, the interior of the Sun reaches about 10,000,000 K.

Fahrenheit and Celsius Temperature Conversions

One division on the Kelvin scale is equivalent to 1° on the Celsius scale. Because 0 K is equivalent to −273 °C, the freezing point of water is 273 K, and the boiling point of water is 373 K. Figure 2.6 illustrates how the three temperature scales are related.

32 °F 0 °C 273 K   212 °F 100 °C 373 K

(a)   (b)

◀ Figure 2.6 **Temperature Scales** A Fahrenheit, a Celsius, and a Kelvin thermometer are placed in (a) ice water and (b) boiling water. Notice the freezing point and boiling point on each scale. The number of divisions is 180 units on the Fahrenheit scale, 100 units on the Celsius scale, and 100 units on the Kelvin scale.

Notice that 180 Fahrenheit units are equivalent to 100 Celsius units. Therefore, to convert from °F to °C, we first subtract 32 (the difference between the freezing point of water on the two scales) and then multiply by 100 °C/180 °F. That is,

$$(°F - 32 \; °F) \times \frac{100 \; °C}{180 \; °F} = °C$$

To convert from °C to °F, we reverse the procedure of converting °F to °C. We first multiply the Celsius temperature by the ratio 180 °F/100 °C, and then add 32 °F. That is,

$$\left(°C \times \frac{180 \; °F}{100 \; °C}\right) + 32 \; °F = °F$$

Example Exercise 2.16 illustrates the conversion of Fahrenheit and Celsius temperatures.

Example Exercise 2.16 °F and °C Temperature Conversions

Normal body temperature is 98.6 °F. What is normal body temperature in degrees Celsius?

Strategy Plan

Step 1: What unit is asked for in the answer?	**Step 1:**	°C
Step 2: What given value is related to the answer?	**Step 2:**	98.6 °F
Step 3: What unit factor(s) should we apply? No unit factor is required.	**Step 3:**	none

Solution

To calculate °C, we refer to Figure 2.6 and compare the Celsius and Fahrenheit temperature scales. The conversion from °F to °C is as follows.

$$(98.6\ °F - 32\ °F) \times \frac{100\ °C}{180\ °F} = °C$$

Simplifying and canceling units gives

$$66.6\ °F \times \frac{100\ °C}{180\ °F} = 37.0\ °C$$

The given value, 98.6 °F, has three significant digits, so the answer is rounded off to three digits. Because 32 °F and 100 °C/180 °F are exact numbers, neither affects the significant digits in the answer.

▲ **Australian Stamp** The cartoon illustrates that 38 °C is approximately equal to 100 °F.

Practice Exercise

The average surface temperature of Mars is –55 °C. What is the average temperature in degrees Fahrenheit?

Answer: −67 °F

Concept Exercise

What is the relationship between the Celsius and centigrade temperature scales?

Answer: See Appendix G.

Celsius and Kelvin Temperature Conversions

Let's reexamine the temperature scales in Figure 2.6. Notice that the Kelvin scale is 273 units above the Celsius scale. Therefore, to convert from °C to K, we must add 273 units to the Celsius temperature.

$$°C + 273 = K$$

Conversely, to convert from K to °C, we subtract 273 units from the Kelvin temperature. It is helpful to remember that negative Kelvin temperatures are nonexistent. By definition, the lowest possible temperature is assigned a value of 0 K. Example Exercise 2.17 illustrates the conversion of Celsius and Kelvin temperatures.

Example Exercise 2.17	°C and K Temperature Conversions

Dermatologists use liquid nitrogen to freeze skin tissue. If the Celsius temperature of liquid nitrogen is −196 °C, what is the Kelvin temperature?

Strategy Plan

Step 1: What unit is asked for in the answer?	**Step 1:**	K
Step 2: What given value is related to the answer?	**Step 2:**	− 196 °C
Step 3: What unit factor(s) should we apply? No unit factor is required.	**Step 3:**	none

Solution

Given the Celsius temperature, we add 273 units to find the corresponding Kelvin temperature.

$$-196\,°C + 273 = 77\,K$$

Practice Exercise

The secret to "fire-walking" is to first walk barefoot through damp grass and then step lively on the red-hot coals. If the bed of coals is 1475 K, what is the Celsius temperature?.

Answer: 1202 °C

Concept Exercise

Which of the following temperatures does not exist?

−100 °F, −100 °C, −100 K

Answer: See Appendix G.

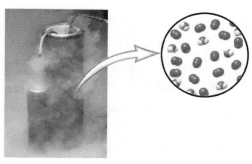

▲ **Liquid Nitrogen** Although nitrogen is normally a gas, it liquefies at −196 °C. When liquid nitrogen is poured from a Thermos, it is cold enough to freeze the moisture in air and form a white mist.

Note We can convert Fahrenheit and Celsius temperatures by understanding the relationship of the two temperature scales (see Figure 2.6). In practice, nurses and other professionals may have a reference chart showing equivalent Fahrenheit and Celsius temperatures. Moreover, students can convert Fahrenheit and Celsius temperatures with a single keystroke using an inexpensive scientific calculator.

2.10 THE HEAT CONCEPT

Scientists define *heat* differently depending on context. In this text, we will define heat as the flow of energy from an object at a higher temperature to an object at a lower temperature. For example, if you hold an ice cube, the heat from your hand (higher temperature) flows into the ice cube (lower temperature) and your hand feels cold.

Heat and temperature are both a measure of energy. However, **heat** is a measure of total energy, and temperature is a measure of average energy. To distinguish heat from temperature, consider a cup of hot tea and a teaspoon of hot tea, each of which is at 100 °C. Which feels hotter: quickly drinking a cup of hot tea, or sipping a teaspoon of hot tea? Obviously, the cup of hot tea is more likely to burn your mouth than the teaspoon of hot tea. The cup of tea has more heat than the teaspoon of tea, even though each is at the same temperature, 100 °C. Figure 2.7 further illustrates the concepts of heat and temperature.

Heat energy is often expressed in units of calories or kilocalories. A **calorie** (symbol **cal**) is the amount of heat necessary to raise 1 gram of water 1 degree on the Celsius scale. A kilocalorie (kcal) is the amount of heat necessary to raise 1000 grams of water 1 degree on the Celsius scale. A nutritional Calorie (Cal) is spelled with a capital letter to distinguish it from a metric calorie. One nutritional Calorie is equal to 1 kilocalorie, that is, 1000 calories.

LEARNING OBJECTIVES

▶ To distinguish between heat and temperature.

▶ To perform calculations that express heat energy in calories, kilocalories, joules, and kilojoules.

▶ To state the value for the specific heat of water.

▶ Figure 2.7 **Heat versus Temperature** In (a) 500 mL of water is heated to 100 °C, and in (b) 1000 mL is heated to 100 °C. Although the temperatures are the same, the second beaker has twice the amount of heat.

(a)   (b)

The SI unit of energy is the **joule** (symbol **J**), where 1 cal = 4.184 J. The heat produced by chemical reactions is often expressed in kilocalories, as well as in kilojoules (kJ), where 1 kcal = 4.184 kJ. Example Exercise 2.18 illustrates the conversion of calories, kilocalories, and joules.

Example Exercise 2.18 Energy Conversion

Burning one liter of natural gas produces 9.46 kcal of heat energy. Express the energy in kilojoules (given that 1 kcal = 4.184 kJ).

Strategy Plan

Step 1: What unit is asked for in the answer?

Step 1: | kJ |

Step 2: What given value is related to the answer?

Step 2: | 9.46 kcal |

Step 3: What unit factor(s) should we apply?

Step 3: | $\dfrac{1\ kcal}{4.184\ kJ}$ or $\dfrac{4.184\ kJ}{1\ kcal}$ |

The unit equation is 1 kcal = 4.184 kJ, so the two unit factors are 1 kcal/4.184 kJ, and its reciprocal 4.184 kJ/1 kcal.

Unit Analysis Map

| *given value* | *unit factor* | *unit in answer* |
| 9.46 kcal | $\times\ \dfrac{1\ kcal}{4.184\ kJ}$ or $\dfrac{4.184\ kJ}{1\ kcal}$ | = kJ |

Solution

We apply the unit factor 4.184 kJ/1 kcal to cancel kilocalories (kcal), which appears in the denominator.

$$9.46\ kcal \times \frac{4.184\ kJ}{1\ kcal} = 39.6\ kJ$$

The given value has three significant digits, and the unit factor has four digits. Thus, we round off the answer to three significant digits.

Practice Exercise

Burning one gram of gasoline produces 47.9 kJ of energy. Express the heat energy in kilocalories (given that 1 kcal = 4.184 kJ).

Answer: 11.4 kcal

Concept Exercise

If an aerosol can feels cold after releasing the spray, is heat flowing from the can or from your hand?

Answer: See Appendix G.

▲ **Bunsen Burner** A laboratory burner that uses natural gas for fuel.

Specific Heat

The specific heat of a substance is the amount of heat required to bring about a given change in temperature. It is observed that the amount of heat necessary is unique for each substance. The specific heat of water is relatively high, and the change in temperature is minimal as water gains or loses heat. The surface of Earth is covered with water, and fortunately its high specific heat helps to regulate climates and maintain moderate temperatures. Figure 2.8 illustrates the increase in temperature for four substances each receiving 1 cal of heat.

◀Figure 2.8 **An Illustration of Specific Heat** Each cube represents a volume of 1 gram of substance receiving 1 calorie of heat. Notice the temperature change increases as the specific heat decreases. Silver has a low specific heat and is a good conductor of heat.

We can define **specific heat** as the amount of heat required to raise the temperature of one gram of substance one degree Celsius; the units of specific heat are often given in calories per gram per degree Celsius. For reference, the specific heat of water has a value of $1.00 \, cal/(g \times °C)$.

Water has an unusually high specific heat and requires more energy to raise its temperature 1 °C than ice or steam. The high specific heat of water is responsible for maintaining Earth's climate as our oceans resist wide swings in temperature. Table 2.5 lists the specific heat for selected solids, liquids, and gases.

TABLE 2.5 SPECIFIC HEAT FOR SELECTED SOLIDS, LIQUIDS, AND GASES

EXAMPLE	SPECIFIC HEAT
Solids	
ice	$0.492 \, cal/(g \times °C)$
aluminum	0.215
carbon (graphite)	0.170
carbon (diamond)	0.124
iron	0.108
copper	0.0920
silver	0.0566
gold	0.0305
Liquids	
water	$1.00 \, cal/(g \times °C)$
ethyl alcohol (ethanol)	0.587
methyl alcohol (methanol)	0.424
freon (CFC refrigerant)	0.232
mercury	0.0331
Gases	
steam	$0.485 \, cal/(g \times °C)$
nitrogen	0.249
oxygen	0.219
argon	0.124
radon	0.0224

Summary

LEARNING OBJECTIVES	SEC	EXERCISES
To list the basic units and symbols of the metric system.	2.1	Exercises 1–6
To list the prefixes for multiples and fractions of basic units.	2.1	Exercises 7–10
To write the unit equation for a basic metric unit and a prefix unit.	2.2	Exercises 11–12
To write the two unit factors derived from a metric unit equation.	2.2	Exercises 13–14
To express a given metric measurement using a different metric prefix.	2.3	Exercises 15–18
To state the metric equivalent for inch, pound, quart, and second.	2.4	Exercises 19–20
To express a given measurement in metric units or English units.	2.4	Exercises 21–26
To express a quantity in a sample as a percent.	2.5	Exercises 27–30
To apply percent as a unit factor.	2.5	Exercises 31–34
To perform calculations that relate length, width, thickness, and volume of a rectangular solid.	2.6	Exercises 35–38
To perform calculations that express a given volume in milliliters, cubic centimeters, or cubic inches.	2.6	Exercises 39–42
To determine the volume of a solid and gas by the displacement of water.	2.7	Exercises 43–46
To apply the concept of density.	2.8	Exercises 47–50
To state the value for the density of water.	2.8	Exercises 51–52
To perform calculations that relate density, mass, and volume.	2.8	Exercises 53–58
To state the freezing point and boiling point of water on the Fahrenheit, Celsius, and Kelvin scales.	2.9	Exercises 59–60
To express a given temperature in degrees Fahrenheit (°F), degrees Celsius (°C), or Kelvin units (K).	2.9	Exercises 61–66
To distinguish between heat and temperature.	2.10	Exercise 67
To state the value for the specific heat of water:	2.10	Exercises 68–70
To perform calculations that express heat energy in calories, kilocalories, joules, and kilojoules.	2.10	Exercises 71–72

Section 2.1 The **English system** of measurement has many unrelated units. On the other hand, the **metric system** of measurement is a decimal system with basic units: **meter (m)**, **gram (g)**, **liter (L)**, and **second (s)**. Metric prefixes provide multiples and fractions of basic units. The common prefixes include *giga-* (G), *mega-* (M), *kilo-* (k), *deci-* (d), *centi-* (c), *milli-* (m), *micro-* (μ), and *nano-* (n). The **International System** (**SI**) is based on the metric system but is more comprehensive.

Section 2.2 Metric conversion problems are solved by systematically writing a **unit equation** or an **exact equivalent** (1 m = 100 cm). An equal or equivalent relationship generates a **unit factor** and its **reciprocal** (1 m/100 cm and 100 cm/1 m).

Section 2.3 Metric problems are solved systematically by applying the **unit analysis method.** Step 1: Write down the units of the unknown. Step 2: Write down a given value that is related to the unknown. Step 3: Apply one or more unit factors to convert the units of the given value to the units asked for in the answer.

Section 2.4 Every nation in the world uses the metric system of measurement; however, the English system is still common in the United States. Therefore, we will relate the two systems and memorize the following: 2.54 cm = 1 in., 454 g = 1 lb, and 946 mL = 1 qt. These equivalents will be used for metric–English conversions.

Section 2.5 A **percent** (%) expresses the amount of a single quantity compared to an entire sample. Percent is a ratio, so we can apply percent unit factors to perform calculations using the unit analysis method.

Section 2.6 The volume of a rectangular solid is equal to length times width times thickness. The calculated volume is reported in cubic units, such as **cubic centimeters** (cm^3). You should memorize the exact equivalent 1 mL = 1 cm^3.

Section 2.7 For irregularly shaped objects, as well as gases, we must determine volume indirectly. We can find the volume of an object or a gas from the amount of water it displaces; this technique involves **volume by displacement**.

Section 2.8 The **density** of water is 1.00 g/mL. A liquid or solid that floats on water is less dense than water; if it sinks, it is more dense. Density can be used as a unit factor, for example, 1.00 g/1 mL or 1 mL/1.00 g. **Specific gravity (sp gr)** is unitless and expresses the ratio of the density of a liquid to the density of water.

Section 2.9 **Temperature** is the average energy of molecules in motion. The **Fahrenheit**, **Celsius**, and **Kelvin** scales have re-

lated reference points. The freezing point of water is 32 °F, 0 °C, or 273 K; and the boiling point is 212 °F, 100 °C, or 373 K.

Section 2.10 **Heat** is the total energy of molecules in motion. Heat changes are expressed in **calories (cal)** or kilocalories (kcal). Heat changes can also be expressed in the SI unit **joule (J)**, where 1 cal = 4.184 J. **Specific heat** is the amount of heat necessary to raise the temperature of 1 g of substance 1 °C; for water, the value is 1.00 cal/(g × °C).

PROBLEM–SOLVING ORGANIZER

TOPIC	PROCEDURE	EXAMPLE
Basic Units and Symbols Sec. 2.1	Combine basic metric units and prefixes using symbols.	centimeter, cm (length); kilogram, kg (mass); milliliter, mL (volume)
Metric Conversion Factors Sec. 2.2	(a) Write a unit equation involving basic metric units and prefix units. (b) Write two unit factors for a metric relationship. 1 m = 100 cm	$\dfrac{1\ m}{100\ cm}$ and $\dfrac{100\ cm}{1\ m}$
Metric–Metric Conversions Sec. 2.3	1. Write down the unit asked for in the answer. 2. Write down the related given value. 3. Apply a unit factor to convert the given unit to the unit in the answer.	What is the decigram mass of a wheel of cheese that weighs 0.515 kg? $0.515\ kg \times \dfrac{1000\ g}{1\ kg} \times \dfrac{10\ dg}{1\ g} = 5150\ dg$
Metric–English Conversions Sec. 2.4	1. Write down the unit asked for in the answer. 2. Write down the related given value. 3. Apply a unit factor to convert the given unit to the unit in the answer.	What is the pound mass of a wheel of cheese that weighs 0.515 kg? $0.515\ kg \times \dfrac{1000\ g}{1\ kg} \times \dfrac{1\ lb}{454\ g} = 1.13\ lb$
The Percent Concept Sec. 2.5	Compare the amount of a single quantity to the total sample, and multiply by 100%.	If a 14-karat ring contains 20.0 g gold and 14.3 g silver, what is the percent of gold? $\dfrac{20.0\ g}{(20.0 + 14.3)g} \times 100\% = 58.3\%$
Volume by Calculation Sec. 2.6	To calculate the volume of a rectangular solid, multiply length by width by thickness: $V = l \times w \times t$.	What is the volume of a rectangular solid measuring 65 mm by 35 mm by 12 mm? $65\ mm \times 35\ mm \times 12\ mm = 27{,}000\ mm^3$
Volume by Displacement Sec. 2.7	The volume by displacement is the difference between the initial and final readings in a calibrated container.	What is the volume of a gold nugget if the water level in a graduated cylinder increases from 25.0 mL to 42.5 mL? 42.5 mL − 25.0 mL = 17.5 mL
The Density Concept Sec. 2.8	The density of a sample is equal to its mass divided by its volume: density = mass/volume.	What is the density of 10.0 mL of ether if its mass is 7.142 g? $\dfrac{7.142\ g}{10.0\ mL} = 0.714\ g/mL$
Temperature Sec. 2.9	(a) To convert from Celsius to Kelvin, add 273 units. (b) To convert from Kelvin to Celsius, subtract 273 units.	−88 °C + 273 = 185 K 1265 K − 273 = 992 °C

PROBLEM–SOLVING ORGANIZER (Continued)

TOPIC	PROCEDURE	EXAMPLE
The Heat Concept Sec. 2.10	1. Write down the unit asked for in the answer. 2. Write down the related given value. 3. Apply a unit factor to convert units.	What is the heat energy of 10.0 cal expressed in joules? $10.0 \text{ cal} \times \dfrac{4.184\text{J}}{1 \text{ cal}} = 41.8 \text{ J}$

Key Terms   *Answers to Key Terms are in Appendix H.*

Select the key term that corresponds to each of the following definitions.

_____ **1.** a nondecimal system of measurement without basic units

_____ **2.** a decimal system of measurement with basic units

_____ **3.** the basic unit of length in the metric system

_____ **4.** the basic unit of mass in the metric system

_____ **5.** the basic unit of volume in the metric system

_____ **6.** the basic unit of time in the metric system

_____ **7.** a comprehensive system of measurement with seven base units

_____ **8.** a statement of two equivalent values, for example, 1 m = 39.4 in.

_____ **9.** a statement of two exactly equal values, for example, 1 m = 100 cm

_____ **10.** a ratio of two quantities that are equivalent, for example, 1 lb/454 g

_____ **11.** the relationship between a fraction and its inverse, for example, 1 qt/946 mL and 946 mL/1 qt

_____ **12.** a procedure for solving problems that proceeds from a given value to a related answer by the conversion of units

_____ **13.** an expression for the amount of a single quantity compared to an entire sample

_____ **14.** the volume occupied by a cube 1 cm on a side

_____ **15.** a technique for determining volume from the amount of water displaced

_____ **16.** the amount of mass in one unit of volume

_____ **17.** the ratio of the density of a liquid compared to the density of water at 4 °C

_____ **18.** the flow of energy from an object at a higher temperature to an object at a lower temperature

_____ **19.** the average energy of molecules in motion

_____ **20.** the basic unit of temperature in the English system

_____ **21.** the basic unit of temperature in the metric system

_____ **22.** the basic unit of temperature in the SI system

_____ **23.** the amount of heat required to raise 1 g of substance 1 °C

_____ **24.** the amount of heat required to raise 1 g of water 1 °C

_____ **25.** a unit of energy in the SI system

(a) calorie (cal) (*Sec. 2.10*)

(b) Celsius degree (°C) (*Sec. 2.9*)

(c) cubic centimeter (cm³) (*Sec. 2.6*)

(d) density (*d*) (*Sec. 2.8*)

(e) English system (*Sec. 2.1*)

(f) exact equivalent (*Sec. 2.2*)

(g) Fahrenheit degree (°F) (*Sec. 2.9*)

(h) gram (g) (*Sec. 2.1*)

(i) heat (*Sec. 2.10*)

(j) International System (SI) (*Sec. 2.1*)

(k) joule (J) (*Sec. 2.10*)

(l) Kelvin unit (K) (*Sec. 2.9*)

(m) liter (L) (*Sec. 2.1*)

(n) meter (m) (*Sec. 2.1*)

(o) metric system (*Sec. 2.1*)

(p) percent (%) (*Sec. 2.5*)

(q) reciprocal (*Sec. 2.2*)

(r) second (s) (*Sec. 2.1*)

(s) specific gravity (sp gr) (*Sec. 2.8*)

(t) specific heat (*Sec. 2.10*)

(u) temperature (*Sec. 2.9*)

(v) unit analysis method (*Sec. 2.3*)

(w) unit equation (*Sec. 2.2*)

(x) unit factor (*Sec. 2.2*)

(y) volume by displacement (*Sec. 2.7*)

Exercises *Answers to odd-numbered Exercises are in Appendix I.*

Basic Units and Symbols (Sec. 2.1)

1. What is the basic unit for each of the following quantities in the metric system?
   (a) length   (b) mass
   (c) volume   (d) time

2. What is the basic unit for each of the following quantities in SI?
   (a) length   (b) mass
   (c) volume   (d) time

3. Write the symbol for the following metric units.
   (a) terameter   (b) gigagram
   (c) nanoliter   (d) picosecond

4. Write the symbol for the following metric units.
   (a) megameter   (b) kilogram
   (c) milliliter   (d) microsecond

5. State the physical quantity that is measured using the following instruments.
   (a) metric ruler   (b) electronic balance
   (c) graduated cylinder (d) stopwatch

6. State the physical quantity that is measured using the following instruments.
   (a) micrometer   (b) beam balance
   (c) syringe   (d) atomic clock

7. State the name and symbol for the metric prefix that represents the following:
   (a) 1×10^{12} (b) 1×10^{9}
   (c) 1×10^{-3} (d) 1×10^{-6}

8. State the name and symbol for the metric prefix that represents the following:
   (a) 1×10^{6} (b) 1×10^{3}
   (c) 1×10^{-9} (d) 1×10^{-12}

9. Write the name of the metric unit indicated by the following symbols:
   (a) Tm   (b) Gg
   (c) mL   (d) μs

10. Write the name of the metric unit indicated by the following symbols:
    (a) Mm   (b) kg
    (c) nL   (d) ps

Metric Conversion Factors (Sec. 2.2)

11. Write a unit equation for each of the following metric equivalents:
    (a) m and Tm   (b) g and Gg
    (c) L and mL   (d) s and μs

12. Write a unit equation for each of the following metric equivalents:
    (a) m and Mm   (b) g and kg
    (c) L and nL   (d) s and ps

13. Write two unit factors for each of the following metric relationships:
    (a) m and Tm   (b) g and Gg
    (c) L and mL   (d) s and μs

14. Write two unit factors for each of the following metric relationships:
    (a) m and Mm   (b) g and kg
    (c) L and nL   (d) s and ps

Metric–Metric Conversions (Sec. 2.3)

15. Perform the following metric–metric conversions.
    (a) 5.00 m to km   (b) 5.00 g to cg
    (c) 5.00 L to dL   (d) 5.00 s to ns

16. Perform the following metric–metric conversions.
    (a) 5.00 Mm to m   (b) 5.00 μg to g
    (c) 5.00 mL to L   (d) 5.00 ds to s

17. Perform the following metric–metric conversions:
    (a) 6.50 Tm to Mm   (b) 650 Gg to kg
    (c) 0.650 cL to dL   (d) 0.000 650 ns to ps

18. Perform the following metric–metric conversions:
    (a) 7.50 km to Gm   (b) 750 Mg to Tg
    (c) 0.750 pL to μL   (d) 0.000 750 ms to ns

Metric–English Conversions (Sec. 2.4)

19. State the following metric–English equivalents:
    (a) ? cm = 1 in.   (b) ? g = 1 lb
    (c) ? mL = 1 qt   (d) ? s = 1 sec

20. State the following metric–English equivalents:
    (a) 1 m = ? yd   (b) 1 kg = ? lb
    (c) 1 L = ? qt   (d) 1 s = ? sec

21. Perform the following metric–English conversions.
    (a) 25 cm to in.   (b) 25 g to lb
    (c) 2.50 qt to mL   (d) 2.50 sec to s

22. Perform the following metric–English conversions.
    (a) 65 in. to cm   (b) 65 lb to g
    (c) 65.0 mL to qt   (d) 6.50×10^{-3} s to sec

23. Perform the following metric–English conversions.
    (a) 72 in. to m   (b) 175 lb to kg
    (c) 0.500 qt to L   (d) 4.55×10^{-4} min to ds

24. Perform the following metric–English conversions.
    (a) 800.0 m to yards (b) 0.375 kg to lb
    (c) 1250 mL to gallons (d) 1.52×10^{3} ds to min

25. A Toyota Prius hybrid gets 23 kilometers per liter in city driving. What is the mileage in miles per gallon? (Given: 1 km = 0.621 mi and 1 L = 0.264 gal)

26. A Toyota Prius hybrid gets 21 kilometers per liter in highway driving. What is the mileage in miles per gallon? (Given: 1 km = 0.621 mi and 1 L = 0.264 gal)

The Percent Concept (Sec. 2.5)

27. A sterling silver spoon has a mass of 65.5 g and contains 7.50% copper. Find the mass of copper in the spoon.

28. A stainless steel spoon has a mass of 55.5 g and contains 10.5% chromium. Find the mass of chromium in the spoon.

29. If a solution contains 255 mL of ethanol and 375 mL of water, what is the percent of ethanol in the solution?

30. If 20.0 gallons of gasohol contains 2.40 gal of ethanol, what is the percent of alcohol in the gasohol?

31. Water is composed of 11.2% hydrogen and 88.8% oxygen. What mass of water contains 50.0 g of oxygen?

32. Sodium chloride, table salt, is composed of 39.3% sodium and 60.7% chlorine. Calculate the mass of sodium in 0.375 g of salt.

33. Before 1982 the U.S. Mint cast penny coins from a copper and zinc mixture. If a 1980 penny weighs 3.051 g and contains 0.153 g zinc, what is the percent of copper in the coin?

34. In 1982 the U.S. Mint stopped making copper pennies and began phasing in pennies made of zinc plated with a thin layer of copper. If a 1990 penny weighs 2.554 g and contains 2.490 g zinc, what is the percent of copper in the coin?

Volume by Calculation (Sec. 2.6)

35. A piece of black onyx was cut into a rectangular solid measuring 5.00 cm by 5.00 cm by 2.50 mm. What is the volume in cubic centimeters?

36. A piece of green jade was cut into a rectangular solid measuring 2.50 cm by 1.25 cm by 3.50 mm. What is the volume in cubic centimeters?

37. A brass rectangular solid measures 4.95 cm by 2.45 cm. What is the thickness of the brass solid if the volume is 10.0 cm^3?

38. A rectangular sheet of aluminum foil measures 75.0 cm by 35.0 cm. What is the thickness of the foil if the volume is 5.00 cm^3?

39. Complete the following volume equivalents:
    (a) 1 L = ? mL   (b) 1 L = ? cm^3

40. Complete the following volume equivalents:
    (a) 1 mL = ? cm^3 (b) 1 in.^{3} = ? cm^3

41. A motorcycle engine is 0.750L. Express the volume in cubic inches.

42. An automobile engine is 355-in.^{3}. Express the volume in liters.

Volume by Displacement (Sec. 2.7)

43. The initial water level in a 10-mL graduated cylinder reads 4.5 mL. After a ruby gemstone is dropped into the cylinder, the water level reads 7.0 mL. What is the volume of the ruby?

44. The initial water level in a 10-mL graduated cylinder is 5.0 mL. After a sapphire gemstone is added into the cylinder, the water level is 6.5 mL. What is the volume of the sapphire?

45. Magnesium metal reacts with acid to produce hydrogen gas. The gas displaces water from a graduated cylinder, and the water level decreases from 95.0 mL to 32.5 mL. What is the volume of gas produced by the reaction?

46. Calcium metal reacts with water to produce hydrogen gas. The gas displaces water from a graduated cylinder, and the water level decreases from 75.5 mL to 43.0 mL. What is the volume of gas produced by the reaction?

The Density Concept (Sec. 2.8)

47. State whether the following will sink or float when dropped into water.
    (a) wax (d = 0.90 g/cm^3)
    (b) marble (d = 3.5 g/cm^3)

48. State whether the following will sink or float when dropped into water.
    (a) redwood (d = 1.2 g/mL)
    (b) bamboo (d = 0.40 g/mL)

49. Will a balloon filled with the given gas rise in the air or drop to the ground?

(Assume the mass of the balloon is negligible and the density of air is 1.29 g/L.)
    (a) helium (d = 0.178 g/L)
    (b) argon (d = 1.78 g/L)

50. Will a balloon filled with the given gas rise in the air or drop to the ground?
    (Assume the mass of the balloon is negligible and the density of air is 1.29 g/L.)
    (a) laughing gas (d = 1.96 g/L)
    (b) ammonia (d = 0.759 g/L)

51. State the density of water in grams per milliliter.

52. State the density of water in kilograms per liter.

53. Calculate the mass in grams for each of the following liquids.
    (a) 250 mL of gasoline (d = 0.69 g/mL)
    (b) 150 mL of ethanol (d = 0.79 g/mL)

54. Calculate the volume in milliliters for each of the following liquids.
    (a) 25.0 g of ether (d = 0.714 g/mL)
    (b) 15.0 g of acetone (d = 0.792 g/mL)

55. Calculate the mass in grams for each of the following solids.
    (a) 5.00 cm^3 of table salt (d = 2.18 g/cm^3)
    (b) 2.50 cm^3 of table sugar (d = 1.59 g/cm^3)

56. Calculate the volume in milliliters for each of the following solids.
    (a) 1.00 kg of silicon (d = 2.33 g/cm^3)
    (b) 1.00 kg of titanium (d = 4.51 g/cm^3)

57. Calculate the density in grams per milliliter for each of the following.
    (a) 25.0 mL of ethyl alcohol having a mass of 19.7 g
    (b) 10.0 g of ethyl ether having a volume of 14.0 mL

58. Calculate the density in grams per milliliter for each of the following.
    (a) 25.5-g solid whose volume is found by displacement to be 4.5 mL
    (b) 95.5-g rectangular solid measuring 3.55 cm × 2.50 cm × 1.75 cm

Temperature (Sec. 2.9)

59. State the freezing point of water on the following temperature scales:
    (a) Fahrenheit   (b) Celsius   (c) Kelvin

60. State the boiling point of water on the following temperature scales:
    (a) Fahrenheit   (b) Celsius   (c) Kelvin

61. Express the following Fahrenheit temperatures in degrees Celsius:
    (a) 101 °F   (b) −215 °F

62. Express the following Celsius temperatures in degrees Fahrenheit:
    (a) 19 °C   (b) −175 °C

63. Express the following Celsius temperatures in Kelvin units:
    (a) 495 °C   (b) −185 °C

64. Express the following Kelvin temperatures in degrees Celsius:
    (a) 273 K   (b) 100 K

65. The space shuttle uses liquefied hydrogen at a temperature of −422 °F. What is the Kelvin temperature?

66. The temperature in the Mojave Desert in California has reached 324 K. What is the Fahrenheit temperature?

The Heat Concept (Sec. 2.10)

67. Distinguish between the terms *temperature* and *heat*.

68. State the metric value for the specific heat of water.

69. State the solid listed in Table 2.5 that is the best conductor of heat.

70. State the liquid listed in Table 2.5 that is the worst conductor of heat.

71. If a gas furnace releases 450 kcal of heat energy, what is the energy in kilojoules? (1 cal = 4.184 J)

72. If a gas stove releases 120 kJ of heat energy, what is the energy in kilocalories? (1 cal = 4.184 J)

General Exercises

73. If a computer hard disk has 1.5 terabytes (TB) of memory, what is the storage capacity in megabytes (MB)?

◀ **Personal Computer** A personal computer may have a hard disk memory greater than 1000 gigabytes (GB). That is, some personal computers can store terabytes (TB) of information.

74. If a computer hard disk has 850 gigabytes (GB) of memory, what is the storage capacity in megabytes (MB)?

75. If a DVD can store 4.7 gigabytes (GB) of data, and a computer hard disk has a capacity of 1.5 terabytes (TB), how many DVDs of data can be loaded onto the hard disk?

▲ **Digital Videodisc** DVDs have generally replaced CDs and have about 10 times the memory.

76. If a USB flash drive can store 16 gigabytes (GB) of data, and a computer hard disk has a capacity of 2.0 terabytes (TB), how many flash drives of data can be loaded onto the hard disk?

77. Which of the following are exact equivalent relationships?
    (a) 1 m = 10 dm   (b) 1 lb = 454 g
    (c) 1 L = 1000 mL   (d) 1 qt = 946 mL

78. How many significant digits are in the following unit factors?
    (a) 1 m/10 dm   (b) 1 lb/454 g
    (c) 1 L/1000 mL   (d) 1 qt/946 mL

79. An automobile airbag inflates in 35 ms. What is the time of inflation in microseconds?

80. An automobile antilock brake system (ABS) operates the brakes at 30 pulses per second. How many times do the brakes pulse in 1.00 ds?

81. A light year is the distance light travels in 1.00 year. Given the velocity of light, 1.86×10^5 mi/s, how many miles does light travel in a light year?

82. A parsec is the distance light travels in 3.26 years. Given the velocity of light, 3.00×10^8 m/s, how many kilometers does light travel in a parsec?

83. A basketball court measures 94.0 feet by 50.0 feet. Calculate the area in square meters. (Given: 1 yd = 0.914 m)

84. A football field measures 120.0 yards by 160.0 feet including end zones. Calculate the area in square meters. (Given: 1 yd = 0.914 m)

85. Olympic athletes compete in a 1500-meter event, but not in a mile event.
    Which race is shorter: 1500 meters or 1 mile? (Given: 1 mi = 1.61 km)

86. An oxygen molecule travels 975 miles per hour at room temperature. What is the velocity in meters per second? (Given: 1 mi = 1.61 km)

87. How many 325-mg tablets can be produced from 2.50 kg of powdered aspirin?

88. How many molecules are in one drop of water if 1.00 g of water contains 3.34×10^{22} molecules? (Given: 1 mL = 20 drops)

89. What is the density of a metal sample if a 37.51-g sample placed into a graduated cylinder increased the liquid level from 50.0 mL to 57.5 mL?

90. What is the mass of 275 L of seawater if the density is 1.025 g/cm³?

91. What is the specific gravity of gasohol if the density is 0.801 g/mL?

92. What is the density of jet fuel if the specific gravity is 0.775?

Challenge Exercises

93. Express the density of water in the English units of pounds per cubic foot.

94. Express the density of water in the English units of pounds per gallon.

95. The density of mercury is 13.6 g/mL. Express the density in SI units (kg/m³).

96. The radius (r) of the international reference kilogram cylinder is 1.95 cm. Assuming the density of the kilogram is 21.50 g/cm³, calculate its height (h). The volume of a cylinder equals $\pi r^2 h$, where π is the constant 3.14.

Online Exercises

Research each of the following using an Internet search engine (e.g., Google.com or Yahoo.com) and cite your URL reference.

97. Research photos of the official metric reference standards for the meter and kilogram and describe the reference prototypes.

98. Distinguish the metric system from the International System (SI) of measurement according to base units.

2

Chapter Self-Test *Answers to Self-Test are in Appendix J.*

1. Which of the following is a basic unit and symbol in the metric system? (Sec. 2.1)
   (a) centimeter (cm)   (b) kilogram (kg)
   (c) milliliter (mL)   (d) all of the above
   (e) none of the above

2. What are the two unit factors that relate meters and millimeters? (Sec. 2.2)
   (a) 1000 mm/1 m and 1 m/1000 mm
   (b) 1000 mm/1 m and 1000 m/1 mm
   (c) 1 mm/1000 m and 1 m/1000 mm
   (d) 1 mm/1000 m and 1000 m/1 mm
   (e) none of the above

3. What is the three-step sequence in applying the unit analysis method of problem solving? (Sec. 2.3)
   (a) 1–unknown unit, 2–unit factor, 3–relevant given value
   (b) 1–unknown unit, 2–relevant given value, 3–unit factor
   (c) 1–relevant given value, 2–unknown unit, 3–unit factor
   (d) 1–unit factor, 2–unknown unit, 3–relevant given value
   (e) 1–unit factor, 2–relevant given value, 3–unknown unit

4. If a chemistry student weighs 155 pounds, what is the mass in kilograms? (Sec. 2.4)
   (a) 0.341 kg   (b) 0.394 kg
   (c) 70.4 kg   (d) 341 kg
   (e) 70,400 kg

5. A sample of 18K gold contains the following by mass: 18.0 grams gold, 3.0 grams silver, and 3.0 grams copper. What is the percent gold? (Sec. 2.5)
   (a) 18%   (b) 25%   (c) 33%   (d) 75%   (e) 90%

6. If a rectangular aluminum block measures 3.80 cm by 2.55 cm by 1.25 cm, what is the volume of the rectangular solid? (Sec. 2.6)
   (a) 0.0826 cm^3 (b) 1.19 cm^3
   (c) 1.86 cm^3 (d) 7.75 cm^3
   (e) 12.1 cm^3

7. What is the volume of a sample of fool's gold that displaces the water level from 25.5 mL to 35.0 mL in a graduated cylinder? (Sec. 2.7)
   (a) 9.5 mL   (b) 11.5 mL
   (c) 25.5 mL   (d) 35.0 mL
   (e) 60.5 mL

◀ **Fool's Gold** Iron pyrite, FeS$_2$, is commonly referred to as fool's gold because of its yellow metallic luster.

8. If a 50.0 mL of gasohol has a mass of 37.5 g, what is the density of the gasohol in grams per cubic centimeter? (Sec. 2.8)
   (a) 0.00750 g/cm^3 (b) 0.0750 g/cm^3
   (c) 0.750 g/cm^3 (d) 7.50 g/cm^3
   (e) 10.0 g/cm^3

9. A rare metal alloy is a superconductor at 55 K. What is the temperature on the Celsius scale? (Sec. 2.9)
   (a) −328 °C   (b) −218 °C
   (c) −55 °C   (d) 218 °C
   (e) 328 °C

10. Which of the following expresses the total heat energy in a sealed capsule? (Sec. 2.10)
    (a) 20 °C   (b) 68 °F
    (c) 293 K   (d) 20 kcal
    (e) all of the above

Key Concepts

11. A tall glass cylinder contains water ($d = 1.00$ g/mL) floating on liquid mercury ($d = 13.6$ g/mL). If a piece of fool's gold ($d = 5.00$ g/mL) and a gold nugget ($d = 18.3$ g/mL) are dropped into the cylinder, where does each come to rest?

12. Which of the following temperatures is the coldest: 0 °F, 0 °C, or 0 K?

Water ———

Mercury ———

◀ **The Density Concept** A glass cylinder is shown containing water and liquid mercury.

Critical Thinking

13. Given two organic liquids, hexane ($d = 0.70$ g/mL) and chloroform ($d = 1.5$ g/mL), how could you identify each liquid given only a beaker of water?

14. A 10¢ silver dime is smaller and thinner than a 1¢ zinc penny. Why is the mass of the 10¢ coin heavier than the larger 1¢ coin?

Matter and Energy

Aluminum in the Environment Aluminum is the most common metal in Earth's crust, constituting about 8% by mass of Earth's surface. However, aluminum metal is too reactive to be found naturally, but is found combined in various compounds. Aluminum is found naturally in minerals such as garnet and turquoise, as well as ruby and sapphire gemstones.

"Matter is discontinuous and cannot be infinitely divided."
Democritus, Greek Philosopher (450–370 B.C.)

"Matter is continuous and can be infinitely divided."
Aristotle, Greek Philosopher (384–322 B.C.)

In the seventeenth century, British scientist Robert Boyle (1627–1691) established the importance of experiments in the study of science. Boyle realized the value of laboratory research and described his work thoroughly so that other scientists could repeat his procedures and confirm his observations. In 1661, he published *The Sceptical Chymist*, which marked a turning point in science by suggesting that theories were no better than the experimental methods that supported them.

Boyle rejected the Greek notion that air, earth, fire, and water were basic elements. Instead, he proposed that an element was a substance that could not be broken down further. Thus, an element must gain weight when it undergoes a chemical change and combines with another element. This was a practical proposal that could be tested in the laboratory.

Following the lead of Boyle, others established scientific principles by performing experiments that could be verified by fellow scientists. Although scientists continued to propose theories about the behavior of matter, their theories were now based on laboratory evidence.

3.1 PHYSICAL STATES OF MATTER

Matter is defined as a substance that has mass and occupies volume. It exists in one of three **physical states**: solid, liquid, or gas. In the solid state, matter has a fixed shape and a fixed volume. The particles in a solid are tightly packed, held in rigid positions, and cannot be compressed together. In the liquid state, matter has a variable shape, but a fixed volume. The particles in a liquid are loosely packed, free to move around, and compress only slightly.

In the gaseous state, tiny particles of matter are widely spaced apart and uniformly distributed throughout its container. If the volume increases, the gas expands and the particles move farther away from each other. If the volume decreases, the gas compresses and the particles move closer to one another. Table 3.1 summarizes the properties of the three states of matter.

TABLE 3.1 PHYSICAL STATES OF MATTER

PROPERTY	SOLID	LIQUID	GAS
shape	fixed	variable	variable
volume	fixed	fixed	variable
compressibility	negligible	negligible	significant

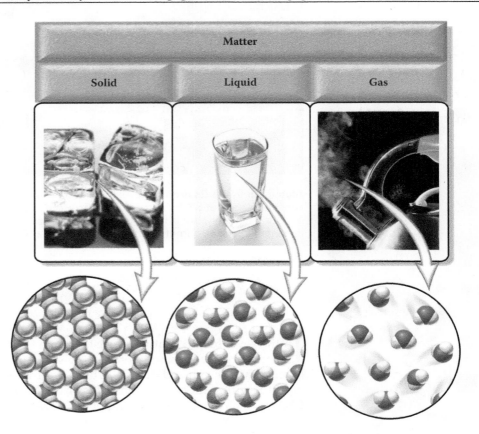

▶ **Physical States of Matter**
Ice, water, and steam represent the three states of matter: solid, liquid, and gas.

◀ **Sublimation and Deposition** Iodine crystals in a heated beaker undergo sublimation to a purple gas. As the gas cools, it undergoes deposition to a solid on the upper rim of the beaker.

Even though we may describe a substance as being a solid, every substance can exist as a solid, liquid, or gas. We can change the physical state of a substance by changing the temperature. Water, for example, can be changed from a liquid to solid ice at 0 °C, and from a liquid to gaseous steam at 100 °C. Other substances behave similarly at different temperatures. Iron, for example, can be changed to a molten liquid at 1535 °C and to a gas at 2750 °C.

We can describe changes of physical state as follows. As temperature increases, a solid *melts* to a liquid, and then the liquid *vaporizes* to a gas. A direct change of state from a solid to a gas is called **sublimation**. Dry ice, for example, undergoes sublimation and disappears as it changes directly from a solid to a gas.

Conversely, as temperature decreases, a gas *condenses* to a liquid, and the liquid then *freezes* to a solid. A direct change of state from a gas to a solid is called **deposition**. The freezer compartment in a refrigerator may demonstrate deposition by collecting ice. Opening the refrigerator door allows moist air to enter, which deposits frost without a trace of liquid water. Figure 3.1 shows the relationship of temperature and physical state.

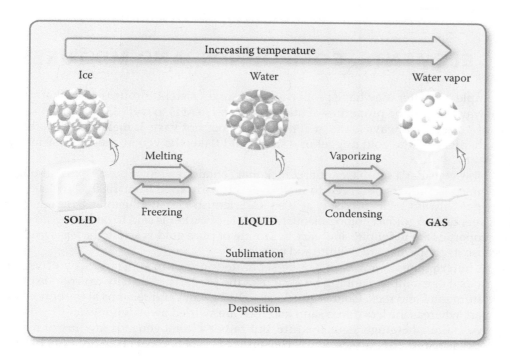

◀ Figure 3.1 **Changes in Physical State** As temperature increases, a solid melts to a liquid and then vaporizes into a gas. As temperature decreases, a gas condenses to a liquid and then freezes to a solid.

> **Example Exercise 3.1** Change of Physical State

State the term that applies to each of the following changes of physical state:

(a) Snow changes from a solid to a liquid.
(b) Gasoline changes from a liquid to a gas.
(c) Dry ice changes from a solid to a gas.

Solution
Refer to Figure 3.1 for the changes of physical state.

(a) The change from solid to liquid is called *melting.*
(b) The change from liquid to gas is called *vaporizing.*
(c) The change from solid to gas is called *sublimation.*

Practice Exercise
State the term that applies to each of the following changes of physical state:

(a) A refrigerant changes from a gas to a liquid.
(b) Water changes from a liquid to a solid.
(c) Iodine vapor changes from a gas to a solid.

Answers:

(a) condensing   (b) freezing   (c) deposition

Concept Exercise
Identify the physical state (solid, liquid, gas) that corresponds to each of the following pictorial representations:

Answer: See Appendix G.

LEARNING OBJECTIVE

▶ To classify a sample of matter as an element, compound, or mixture.

3.2 ELEMENTS, COMPOUNDS, AND MIXTURES

A sample of matter may have properties that are consistent throughout or that vary. One way to tell if the properties of matter are consistent is to melt the sample. A sample of pure gold always melts at 1064 °C and does not vary. It makes no difference whether it is a large gold nugget or a small gold flake; the yellow metal consistently melts at 1064 °C.

Now consider a sample of quartz rock that contains a vein of pure gold. Although the quartz sample is observed to melt over a broad range from 1000 °C to 1600 °C, pure gold always melts precisely at 1064 °C. Scientists classify the quartz rock as heterogeneous and gold as homogeneous. A sample of matter is said to be *heterogeneous* if its properties are indefinite and vary. A sample of pure gold is said to be *homogeneous* because its properties are definite and constant.

A **heterogeneous mixture** can be separated into pure substances by physical methods. For example, panning for gold uses the property of density to separate pure gold from sand and rock. Gold is quite dense, 19.3 g/cm^3, and remains at the bottom of the pan, whereas the less dense sand and rock are swirled away with water.

Air is not a heterogeneous mixture, but rather a homogeneous mixture of nitrogen, oxygen, and other gases. Similarly, salt water is a homogeneous mixture of salt and water. Unlike those of a heterogeneous mixture, the properties of a **homogeneous mixture** are constant for a given sample. However, a homogeneous mixture may have properties that vary from sample to sample. For example, samples of salt water from the Pacific Ocean and from the Dead Sea have different properties. Salt water from the Dead Sea has a higher density and a greater concentration of dissolved minerals.

▲ **Heterogeneous Mixture** Sand and water are each pure substances. However, they form a heterogeneous mixture when added together, and the properties vary throughout the sample.

An **alloy** is a homogeneous mixture of two or more metals. Examples of alloys include 10K, 14K, and 18K gold jewelry. Although 10K, 14K, and 18K jewelry may contain only gold, silver, and copper metals, the amount of gold varies from 42% to 75%. Gold alloy is a homogeneous mixture; therefore the properties from different samples can vary. For instance, 10K gold is a harder alloy and is more scratch resistant than 18K gold.

A **substance** is matter that has definite composition and constant properties. A substance is either a compound or an element. A **compound** has predictable properties, but can be broken down into elements by an ordinary chemical reaction. Table sugar is an example of a compound that can be broken down into carbon, hydrogen, and oxygen.

An **element** is a substance that cannot be broken down further by a chemical reaction. For example, table salt is a compound composed of the elements sodium and chlorine, which cannot be broken down any further. Figure 3.2 shows the overall classification of matter.

▶ **Compound, Element, Mixture**
The orange compound, mercury oxide, decomposes to give the element mercury, which is a silver liquid. Adding the orange powder and the metallic liquid together produces a heterogeneous mixture.

▲ Figure 3.2 **Classification of Matter** Matter may be either a mixture or a pure substance. The properties of a heterogeneous mixture vary within the sample (oil and water). The properties of a homogeneous mixture are constant (salt solution). A pure substance may be either a compound (water) or an element (gold). Left to right: oil and water; NaCl solution; H_2O; and gold foil.

Example Exercise 3.2 Element, Compound, or Mixture

Consider the following properties of the element copper:

(a) Copper metal cannot be broken down by a chemical change.
(b) Copper reacts with oxygen in air to give copper oxide.
(c) Copper, in the form of malachite ore, is found worldwide.
(d) Copper and tin compose bronze alloy.

Classify each of the following copper samples as an element, a compound, a homogeneous mixture, or a heterogeneous mixture:

(a) copper wire   (b) copper oxide
(c) malachite ore   (d) bronze alloy

Solution
Refer to Figure 3.2 to classify each sample.

(a) Copper wire is a metallic *element*.
(b) Copper oxide is a *compound* of the elements copper and oxygen.
(c) Malachite ore is a *heterogeneous mixture* of copper and other substances.
(d) Bronze alloy is a *homogeneous mixture* of copper and tin.

Practice Exercise

Consider the following properties of the element mercury:

(a) Mercury liquid cannot be broken down by a chemical change.
(b) Mercury oxide can be heated to give mercury and oxygen gas.
(c) Mercury, in form of cinnabar ore, is found in Spain and Italy.
(d) Mercury and silver compose the alloy used for dental fillings.

Classify each of the following mercury samples as an element, a compound, a homogeneous mixture, or a heterogeneous mixture:

(a) mercury liquid   (b) mercury oxide
(c) cinnabar ore   (d) dental alloy

Answers:

(a) element   (b) compound   (c) heterogeneous mixture   (d) homogeneous mixture

Concept Exercise

Classify each of the following gases as an element, a compound, or a mixture of gases, as shown in the illustration:

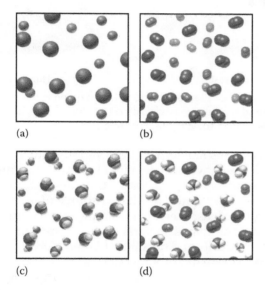

(a)   (b)

(c)   (d)

Answer: See Appendix G.

3.3 NAMES AND SYMBOLS OF THE ELEMENTS

There are 81 stable elements that occur in nature. In addition, there are a few other naturally occurring elements, such as uranium, which are unstable. In total, there are over 100 elements, but only 10 account for 95% of the mass of Earth's crust, water, and atmosphere.

Oxygen is the most abundant element on Earth. It is found combined with hydrogen in water and with silicon in sand and rocks. Oxygen is found in air and constitutes about 21% of our atmosphere. The mass of oxygen in Earth's crust, water, and atmosphere is about equal to the total mass of all other elements. Table 3.2 lists the 10 most abundant elements.

Oxygen, silicon, and aluminum are the three most abundant elements on Earth. The elements oxygen, carbon, hydrogen, nitrogen, calcium, and phosphorus account for over 99% of the mass of the human body. The remaining 1% consists of trace elements, many of which are essential to human life. For example, a trace of iron is necessary to bind oxygen to hemoglobin in blood. Figure 3.3 compares the distribution of elements in Earth's crust and in the human body.

TABLE 3.2 ELEMENTS IN EARTH'S CRUST, WATER, AND ATMOSPHERE

ELEMENT	MASS PERCENT	ELEMENT MASS	PERCENT
oxygen	49.5%	sodium	2.6%
silicon	25.7%	potassium	2.4%
aluminum	7.5%	magnesium	1.9%
iron	4.7%	hydrogen	0.9%
calcium	3.4%	titanium	0.6%
		all other elements	0.5%

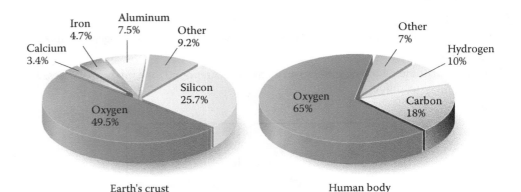

Earth's crust   Human body

▲ **Figure 3.3 Abundance of Elements** Notice that oxygen is the most abundant element in both Earth's crust and the human body. Although aluminum is abundant in Earth, there is evidence that this element is toxic to the human body.

The names of elements are derived from various sources. For example, hydrogen is derived from the Greek word *hydro* meaning "water former." Carbon is derived from the Latin word *carbo*, meaning "coal." Calcium is derived from the Latin word *calcis*, which translates as "lime," a mineral source of calcium. Some elements are named for their region of discovery. For example, germanium comes from Germany, and scandium from Scandinavia. Several elements are named for famous scientists, such as curium (Marie Curie) and nobelium (Alfred Nobel).

The name of each element is abbreviated using a **chemical symbol**. In 1803, the English chemist John Dalton (1766–1844) proposed that elements are composed of indivisible, spherical particles. Dalton referred to each of these individual particles as an **atom**, from the Greek word *atomos* meaning "indivisible." He suggested the use of circles with enclosed markings as symbols for the elements. Figure 3.4 shows selected symbols chosen by Dalton to represent elements.

▶ **Figure 3.4 Dalton's Symbols for Selected Elements** Dalton symbolized each element using a circle with an inscribed marking. Dalton's system was not practical, but it did convey the idea that elements were composed of atomic spheres.

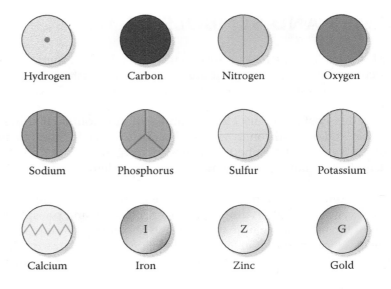

CRITICAL THINKING **Aluminum or Aluminium?**

Q: **What suffix is commonly attached to the name of an element to indicate the element is a metal?**

At the turn of the nineteenth century, many new elements were isolated and added to a growing list. For example, sodium, potassium, magnesium, calcium, strontium, and barium were all discovered in the period from 1807 to 1808 by the English chemist Humphry Davy (1778–1829). Metallic elements were systematically named by adding an *–ium* suffix to its root name. The nonmetal selenium was discovered a few years later in 1817, and named for the Greek word *selene*, which means "moon." The semimetal tellurium had been previously discovered in 1782, and named for the Latin word *tellus*, which means "earth."

In 1808, Davy proposed the name *alumium* for an element that he was attempting to isolate from the mineral alumina. A couple of years later he changed the name to *aluminium* for the element that was not isolated until Charles Martin Hall accomplished the feat in 1885 (see Chemistry Connection in Chapter 1).

Today, the official IUPAC name for the element is *aluminium*; however, both Americans and Canadians refer to it as aluminum. The name *aluminum* has been explained in a couple of ways. According to Oberlin College in Ohio, the name of the element was misspelled on a notice that publicized Charles Martin Hall's discovery of the process that separated the metal from its ore. Another account is that a spelling error on the stationery of the Aluminum Company of America (ALCOA), a company that Charles Hall helped to found, was instrumental in dictating the name. In either case, it appears that a spelling error was responsible for the irregular ending for the name of the element that is extremely important today, and second only to steel as a construction metal.

For most of the nineteenth century, Americans used the *–ium* suffix and *aluminium* appeared in Webster's dictionary in 1828. However, the misspelling of the metal was common, and in 1926 the American Chemical Society decided officially to call the metal *aluminum*. Meantime, in Europe the *–ium* ending was the accepted spelling. In 1990, IUPAC adopted aluminium as the official international name for the metal, which is used by French, German, Danish, Dutch, Norwegian, and Swedish scientists. In 1993, IUPAC officially approved the alternate spelling aluminum, but stated a preference for the name *aluminium*.

◀ **Aluminum Cap on the Washington Monument**
The Washington Monument, in Washington, D.C., is capped by a shiny metal pyramid. The thin metal pyramid weighing 2.85 kilograms is composed of aluminum, which was an expensive metal at the time of its construction in 1884.

A: An *–ium* suffix is the most common ending for metallic elements, although there are a few exceptions such as platinum (Pt), molybdenum (Mo), and tantalum (Ta). In addition, the Latin names of elements known since ancient times such as cuprum (Cu), argentum (Ag), and aurum (Au) are exceptions.

In 1813, the Swedish chemist J. J. Berzelius (1779–1848) proposed our current system of symbols for the elements. He suggested that a symbol correspond to the first letter of the name of the element; for example, H for hydrogen, O for oxygen, and C for carbon. Furthermore, when elements start with the same letter, he recommended using two letters in the name, for example, Ca for calcium, Cd for cadmium, and Cl for chlorine.

In some instances, the chemical symbol is derived from the original Latin name of the element. For example, the symbol Pb for lead is derived from the Latin *plumbum*. Interestingly, the Romans used lead pipe to transport water, which explains the derivation of our word "plumbing." The symbol Hg for mercury is derived from the Greek *hydrargyro*, meaning "liquid silver." Similarly, the symbols for gold (Au), copper (Cu), iron (Fe), mercury (Hg), potassium (K), sodium (Na), antimony (Sb), and tin (Sn), are derived from the original Latin and Greek names.

When writing symbols for the names of elements, it is important to follow convention to avoid confusion. The first letter is always capitalized, and the second is lowercase. For example, the symbol for the metallic element cobalt is Co. In contrast, notice that the formula for the deadly gas carbon monoxide is CO. Table 3.3 lists the names and symbols of selected elements.

TABLE 3.3 NAMES AND SYMBOLS OF SELECTED ELEMENTS

NAME OF ELEMENT	SYMBOL	NAME OF ELEMENT	SYMBOL	NAME OF ELEMENT	SYMBOL	NAME OF ELEMENT	SYMBOL
aluminum	Al	chlorine	Cl	lead	Pb	radium	Ra
antimony	Sb	chromium	Cr	lithium	Li	selenium	Se
argon	Ar	cobalt	Co	magnesium	Mg	silicon	Si
arsenic	As	copper	Cu	manganese	Mn	silver	Ag
barium	Ba	fluorine	F	mercury	Hg	sodium	Na
beryllium	Be	germanium	Ge	neon	Ne	strontium	Sr
bismuth	Bi	gold	Au	nickel	Ni	sulfur	S
boron	B	helium	He	nitrogen	N	tellurium	Te
bromine	Br	hydrogen	H	oxygen	O	tin	Sn
cadmium	Cd	iodine	I	phosphorus	P	titanium	Ti
calcium	Ca	iron	Fe	platinum	Pt	xenon	Xe
carbon	C	krypton	Kr	potassium	K	zinc	Zn

LEARNING OBJECTIVES

▸ To distinguish between the properties of metals and nonmetals.

▸ To predict whether an element is a metal, nonmetal, or semimetal given its position in the periodic table.

▸ To predict whether an element is a solid, liquid, or gas at 25 °C and normal atmospheric pressure.

3.4 METALS, NONMETALS, AND SEMIMETALS

An element is a pure substance that cannot be broken down further and still maintain its unique properties. A **metal** is an element that typically is a solid, has a bright metallic luster, a high density, a high melting point, and is a good conductor of heat and electricity. A metal can usually be hammered into a thin sheet of foil and is said to be **malleable**. If it can be drawn into a fine wire, it is said to be **ductile**. Aluminum, copper, and silver are familiar examples of metals.

A **nonmetal** is an element that usually has a low density, a low melting point, and is a poor conductor of heat and electricity. Many nonmetals occur naturally in the solid state and have a dull appearance, for example, phosphorus and sulfur. These solid nonmetals are neither malleable nor ductile and crush to a powder if hammered. Eleven nonmetals occur naturally in the gaseous state; hydrogen and oxygen are familiar examples of colorless, gaseous nonmetals. Table 3.4 summarizes the properties of metals and nonmetals.

TABLE 3.4 GENERAL CHARACTERISTICS OF METALS AND NONMETALS*

PROPERTY	METALS	NONMETALS
physical state	solid	solid, gas
appearance	metallic luster	dull
pliability	malleable, ductile	brittle
conductivity	heat, electricity	nonconductor
density	usually high	usually low
melting point	usually high	usually low
chemical reactivity	react with nonmetals	react with metals and nonmetals

*There are numerous exceptions to these general characteristics. For example, mercury and bromine are liquids, magnesium metal has a low density, and gallium metal has a melting point below 30 °C.

A **semimetal** (or metalloid) is an element that typically has properties midway between those of metals and nonmetals. Silicon is a familiar semimetal used in the semiconductor industry for making transistors and integrated circuits. Example Exercise 3.3 further illustrates the identification of properties of metals and nonmetals.

Example Exercise 3.3 Properties of Metals

Which of the following properties is *not* characteristic of a metal?

(a) good conductor of heat   (b) malleable
(c) high melting point   (d) reacts with other metals

Solution

Refer to Table 3.4 to classify each of the following properties:

(a) Metals are good conductors of heat.
(b) Metals are malleable.
(c) Metals usually have high melting points.
(d) Metals do *not* react with other metals; they mix to form alloys.

Practice Exercise

Which of the following properties is *not* characteristic of a nonmetal?

(a) insulator of electricity
(b) ductile
(c) low density
(d) reacts with nonmetals

Answer:

(b) Nonmetals crush to a powder and are not malleable or ductile.

Concept Exercise

Which of the following is a solid metal under normal conditions: calcium, phosphorus, mercury, or silicon? (Refer to Figure 3.6.)

Answer: See Appendix G.

Periodic Table of the Elements

In Chapter 5, we will devote our entire discussion to the chemical elements. For now, realize that each element is assigned a number. The number that identifies a particular element is called the **atomic number**. For example, the atomic number of hydrogen is 1, helium is 2, lithium is 3, and so on, and the atomic number of uranium is 92.

All the elements have been arranged by atomic number and placed in a special chart. This chart is called the *periodic table of the elements*, or simply the **periodic table**. Metals are placed on the left side of the table, and nonmetals are placed on the right side. Hydrogen is an exception. Although it is a nonmetal, hydrogen has unusual properties and has been placed by itself at the top center of the periodic tables in this text.

Metals and nonmetals are separated by semimetals that include boron, silicon, germanium, arsenic, antimony, and tellurium. The unstable elements polonium and astatine are also considered semimetals. Figure 3.5 shows the overall arrangement of metals, nonmetals, and semimetals in the periodic table of the elements.

▲ Figure 3.5 **Metals, Nonmetals, and Semimetals** The symbols of elements having metallic properties are on the left side of the periodic table, nonmetallic are on the right side, and semimetallic are in between. Notice the special placement of hydrogen, a nonmetallic element.

Physical States of the Elements

The periodic table can help you master a large amount of information. With little effort, you can correctly predict the physical state of most elements. Excluding mercury, all the metals are in the solid state at normal conditions of 25 °C and normal atmospheric pressure. All semimetals are also in the solid state at normal temperature and pressure.

Nonmetals, on the other hand, show great diversity in physical state. At 25 °C and normal pressure, 5 nonmetals are solids, 1 is a liquid, and 11 are gases. The solids are carbon, phosphorus, sulfur, selenium, and iodine. The only nonmetal liquid is reddish-brown bromine. The 11 gases are hydrogen, nitrogen, oxygen, fluorine, chlorine, helium, neon, argon, krypton, xenon, and radon. All these gases are colorless except fluorine and chlorine, which are greenish-yellow. Figure 3.6 illustrates the normal physical state of each element.

PERIODIC TABLE OF THE ELEMENTS

▲ **Figure 3.6 Physical States of the Elements** At 25 °C and normal atmospheric pressure, all metals are in the solid state except Hg. Most nonmetals are gases except C, P, S, Se, and I, which are solids. The only elements in the liquid state at normal conditions are Hg and Br.

CHEMISTRY CONNECTION Elements 104 and Beyond

Q: Element 112 was recently officially named for which sixteenth-century astronomer?

In 1964, a team of Russian scientists reported the first synthesis of element 104. The Russians proposed the name "kurchatovium" for Igor Kurchatov, a Soviet physicist. American scientists could not confirm the results, however, and denied the Russian claim of discovery. In 1969, a heavy-element team at the University of California, Berkeley, synthesized element 104 and proposed the name "rutherfordium" after the English physicist Ernest Rutherford. A few years later, a similar disagreement arose over element 105. Russian and American scientists each claimed they had discovered element 105, and each team proposed different names and symbols.

In 1985, the International Union of Pure and Applied Chemistry (IUPAC) attempted to resolve the controversy by recommending systematic names based on the atomic numbers of the elements. According to IUPAC, the names for elements 104 and beyond were to be formed from Latin prefixes plus the suffix –ium. The name for element 104, for example, was to be unnilquadium. Interestingly, there was a strong objection to the IUPAC recommendation because it did not honor scientists who had made significant contributions to our understanding of heavy elements.

In 1997, IUPAC issued a new set of official names. Element 104 is named *rutherfordium* for Ernest Rutherford. Element 105 is named *dubnium* for the Russian nuclear research facility at Dubna. Element 106 is named *seaborgium* for the American chemist, Glenn Seaborg. Element 107 is named *bohrium* in honor of the Danish physicist Niels Bohr. Element 108 is named *hassium* for the province of Hesse in Germany. Element 109 is named *meitnerium* in honor of the Austrian nuclear physicist Lise Meitner. Element 110 is named *darmstadtium* for the

German nuclear research facility at Darmstadt. Element 111 is named *roentgenium* for William Roentgen, the German physicist who discovered X-rays. Recently, element 112 was officially named *copernicium* for Nicolas Copernicus, the sixteenth-century astronomer who first proposed a heliocentric model with the Sun (not Earth) at the center of our solar system.

ELEMENT	DISCOVERY	PROPOSED NAME	IUPAC NAME
104	Russia, 1964 United States, 1969	kurchatovium, Ku rutherfordium, Rf	rutherfordium, Rf
105	Russia, 1967 United States, 1970	nielsbohrium, Ns hahnium, Ha	dubnium, Db
106	United States, 1974	seaborgium, Sg	seaborgium, Sg
107	Germany, 1974	bohrium, Bh	bohrium, Bh
108	Germany, 1984	hassium, Hs	hassium, Hs
109	Germany, 1982	meitnerium, Mt	meitnerium, Mt
110	Germany, 1994	darmstadtium, Ds	darmstadtium, Ds
111	Germany, 1994	roentgenium, Rg	roentgenium, Rg
112	Germany, 1996	copernicium, Cn	copernicium, Cn
113	Russia, 2003		
114	Russia, 1999	flerovium, Fl	flerovium, Fl
115	Russia, 2004		
116	Russia, 2001	livermorium, Lv	livermorium, Lv
117	Russia, 2010		
118	Russia, 2002		

A: Element 112 was officially named *copernicium* for Nicolas Copernicus, the sixteenth-century astronomer who first proposed that the Sun, not Earth, was at the center of our solar system.

Example Exercise 3.4   Physical States of the Elements

Indicate the physical state for each of the following elements at 25 °C and normal pressure. Classify each element as a metal, nonmetal, or semimetal:

(a) barium   (b) boron
(c) bismuth   (d) bromine

Solution

Referring to Figures 3.5 and 3.6, we observe the following:

(a) Barium (Ba) is on the left side of the periodic table; it is a *solid metal* under normal conditions.
(b) Boron (B) is in the middle of the periodic table; it is a *solid semimetal*.
(c) Bismuth (Bi) is to the right, but below the semimetals in the periodic table, it is a *solid metal*.
(d) Bromine (Br) is on the right side of the periodic table; it is a *liquid nonmetal* at normal conditions.

Practice Exercise

Indicate the physical state for each of the following elements at 25 °C and normal pressure. Classify each element as a metal, nonmetal, or semimetal:

(a) aluminum   (b) hydrogen
(c) helium   (d) radium

Answers:

(a) solid metal   (b) gaseous nonmetal
(c) gaseous nonmetal   (d) solid metal

Concept Exercise

Which of the following is a liquid nonmetal under normal conditions: sodium, mercury, bromine, or sulfur? (Refer to Figure 3.7.)

Answer: See Appendix G.

▲ **Figure 3.7 Pictorial Periodic Table of the Elements** The natural abundance is the percent by mass of an element in Earth's crust, oceans, and atmosphere. The natural abundance of an element listed as rare is less than 1 mg per metric ton (1000 kg). An element listed as synthetic is made artificially and does not occur naturally. An element listed as unstable often disintegrates in a fraction of a second.

Malleable metallic solid

Gray, metal-like crystals

Dull powder or crystals

Liquid at 25 °C and normal pressure

Gas at 25 °C and normal pressure

Essential for a biological species

Radioactive element

			13 IIIA	14 IVA	15 VA	16 VIA	17 VIIA	18 VIIIA

He 1895 — 0.0000004%

B 1808 — 0.001%
C ancient — 0.09%
N 1772 — 0.03%
O 1774 — 49.5%
F 1886 — 0.03%
Ne 1898 — 0.0000005%

Al 1825 — 7.54%
Si 1823 — 25.7%
P 1669 — 0.09%
S ancient — 0.05%
Cl 1806 — 0.19%
Ar 1894 — 0.0004%

10 VIII	11 IB	12 IIB						

Ni 1750 — 0.01%
Cu ancient — 0.01%
Zn ancient — 0.01%
Ga 1875 — 0.001%
Ge 1886 — 0.0006%
As 13th century — 0.0006%
Se 1817 — 0.00008%
Br 1826 — 0.0006%
Kr 1898 — rare

Pd 1803 — 0.000001%
Ag ancient — 0.00001%
Cd 1817 — 0.00003%
In 1863 — 0.000001%
Sn ancient — 0.003%
Sb 15th century — 0.00007%
Te 1782 — 0.000001%
I 1811 — 0.000006%
Xe 1898 — rare

Pt 1735 — 0.0000005%
Au ancient — 0.0000005%
Hg ancient — 0.00004%
Tl 1862 — 0.00003%
Pb ancient — 0.002%
Bi 15th century — 0.00002%
Po 1898 — rare
At 1940 — rare
Rn 1899 — rare

Ds 1994 — unstable synthetic
Rg 1994 — unstable synthetic
Cn 1996 — unstable synthetic
— 2003 — unstable synthetic
Fl 1999 — unstable synthetic
— 2004 — unstable synthetic
Lv 2001 — unstable synthetic
— 2010 — unstable synthetic
— 2002 — unstable synthetic

Gd 1886 — 0.0006%
Tb 1843 — 0.00009%
Dy 1886 — 0.0004%
Ho 1879 — 0.0001%
Er 1843 — 0.0002%
Tm 1879 — 0.00002%
Yb 1905 — 0.0003%
Lu 1905 — 0.00007%

Cm 1944 — synthetic
Bk 1949 — synthetic
Cf 1950 — synthetic
Es 1952 — synthetic
Fm 1953 — synthetic
Md 1955 — synthetic
No 1957 — synthetic
Lr 1960 — synthetic

▸ To state the number of atoms of each element in a compound given the chemical formula.

▸ To apply the law of definite composition to a compound.

3.5 COMPOUNDS AND CHEMICAL FORMULAS

In the late 1700s, the French chemist Joseph Louis Proust (1754–1826) painstakingly analyzed the compound copper carbonate. No matter how he prepared the compound, he found that the elements copper, carbon, and oxygen were always present in the same proportion by mass. Proust studied many other compounds and obtained similar constant proportions for the elements. In 1799, Proust stated that "compounds always contain the same elements in a constant proportion by mass." This statement is now called the **law of definite composition** or the law of constant proportion.

Ordinary table salt is the compound sodium chloride, NaCl. According to the law of definite composition, salt contains sodium and chlorine in a constant proportion by mass. For NaCl, the ratio is 39.3% sodium and 60.7% chlorine. Moreover, the proportion of sodium and chlorine is the same whether we have a tiny crystal of salt, a block of salt, or a mountain of salt.

Similarly, the compound water contains 11.2% hydrogen and 88.8% oxygen by mass. Regardless of the amount, water always contains hydrogen and oxygen in a constant proportion by mass. Figure 3.8 illustrates the law of definite composition with water as an example.

▲ Figure 3.8 **Law of Definite Composition** A drop of water, a glass of water, and a lake of water all contain hydrogen and oxygen in the same percent by mass, that is, 11.2% hydrogen and 88.8% oxygen.

Chemical Formulas

Most elements occur naturally as a collection of individual atoms. A few nonmetal elements, such as hydrogen and oxygen, occur naturally as two atoms of the element in a single unit. A unit of matter composed of two or more nonmetal atoms is called a **molecule**. Hydrogen, H_2, and oxygen, O_2, occur naturally as molecules containing two atoms.

We have learned to use chemical symbols for the names of elements. In a similar fashion, we use chemical formulas for the names of compounds. A **chemical formula** expresses the number of atoms of each element in a compound. The number of atoms is indicated with a subscript, unless the number is 1, in which case the subscript is omitted. A molecule of water contains two atoms of hydrogen and one atom of oxygen. Therefore, its chemical formula is H_2O. A molecule of ammonia has one atom of nitrogen and three atoms of hydrogen; its chemical formula is NH_3. The chemical formula of sulfuric acid, H_2SO_4, is interpreted in Figure 3.9.

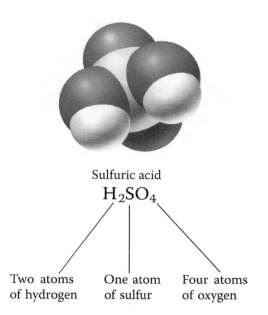

◄ Figure 3.9 **Interpretation of a Chemical Formula** The chemical formula of sulfuric acid, H_2SO_4, indicates 2 hydrogen atoms, 1 sulfur atom, and 4 oxygen atoms. Thus, sulfuric acid has a total of 7 atoms.

Sulfuric acid

$$H_2SO_4$$

Two atoms of hydrogen   One atom of sulfur   Four atoms of oxygen

---

Example Exercise 3.5   Composition of Chemical Formulas

State the total number of atoms in a molecule of vitamin B_3, $C_6H_6N_2O$.

Solution

The chemical formula for vitamin B_3 indicates 6 carbon atoms, 6 hydrogen atoms, 2 nitrogen atoms, and 1 oxygen atom. Thus, $C_6H_6N_2O$ has a total of 15 atoms.

Practice Exercise

Write the chemical formula for vitamin B_6, which is composed of 8 carbon atoms, 11 hydrogen atoms, 1 nitrogen atom, and 3 oxygen atoms.

Answer: $C_8H_{11}NO_3$ (total of 23 atoms)

Concept Exercise

Examine the model for vitamin C and determine the molecular formula. In the model shown, the black sphere = C atom, white = H atom, and red = O atom.

Answer: See Appendix G.

Some chemical formulas use parentheses to clarify the chemical composition. For example, antifreeze is ethylene glycol and has the chemical formula $C_2H_4(OH)_2$. A molecule of ethylene glycol is composed of 2 atoms of carbon, 4 atoms of hydrogen, and 2 units of OH. The parentheses around (OH) in the chemical formula indicate that OH is a two-atom unit. The chemical formula of ethylene glycol, $C_2H_4(OH)_2$, is interpreted in Figure 3.10.

▶ Figure 3.10 **Interpretation of a Chemical Formula** The chemical formula of ethylene glycol, $C_2H_4(OH)_2$, indicates 2 carbon atoms, 4 hydrogen atoms, and 2 OH units. The oxygen atom and hydrogen atom are a single unit that appear twice in a single molecule. Thus, ethylene glycol has a total of 10 atoms.

Ethylene glycol
$$C_2H_4(OH)_2$$

| Two atoms of carbon | Four atoms of hydrogen | One atom of oxygen | One atom of hydrogen | Two units of OH |

Example Exercise 3.6 Composition of Chemical Formulas

State the total number of atoms in a molecule of glycerin, $C_3H_5(OH)_3$.

Solution
The chemical formula for glycerin indicates 3 carbon atoms, 5 hydrogen atoms, and 3 OH units. Thus, $C_3H_5(OH)_3$ has a total of 14 atoms.

Practice Exercise
Write the chemical formula for nitroglycerin if a molecule is composed of 3 carbon atoms, 5 hydrogen atoms, 3 oxygen atoms, and 3 NO_2 units.

Answer: $C_3H_5O_3(NO_2)_3$

Concept Exercise
State the total number of atoms in a molecule of nitroglycerin, $C_3H_5O_3(NO_2)_3$.

Answer: See Appendix G.

Note In Chapter 6 we will learn how to systematically name compounds. It is helpful to begin referring to compounds by pronouncing their chemical formulas. Even professional chemists pronounce chemical formulas of compounds; for instance, water is H_2O and is referred to as "H two O." Sulfuric acid is H_2SO_4 and is referred to as "H two, S, O four." We can pronounce the chemical formula for milk of magnesia, $Mg(OH)_2$, as "Mg, OH taken twice."

LEARNING OBJECTIVE

▶ To classify a property of a substance as physical or chemical.

3.6 PHYSICAL AND CHEMICAL PROPERTIES

Previously, we classified matter as either a mixture or a pure substance. Recall that the physical and chemical properties of a pure substance are consistent throughout a sample. Moreover, no two substances have the same physical and chemical properties.

Furthermore, we said that a pure substance is either a compound or an element. However, the physical and chemical properties of a compound are never the same as the properties of its constituent elements. For example, sodium is a soft, silver metal, and chlorine is a poisonous, yellow gas. In a reaction, these two elements combine to form white crystals of table salt, NaCl (Figure 3.11).

A **physical property** refers to those characteristics of a pure substance that we can observe without changing the composition of the substance. The list of physical properties is extensive, but those considered important are appearance, melting and boiling points, density, heat and electrical conductivity, solubility, and physical state under

▲ Figure 3.11 **Sodium, Chlorine, and Sodium Chloride** (a) Sodium is a shiny metal, (b) chlorine is a yellow gas, and (c) table salt is white crystals. (d) A salt crystal, NaCl is composed of sodium (purple) and chloride (green).

(a) Sodium metal, Na atoms

(b) Chlorine gas, Cl_2 molecules

(c) Table salt, NaCl

(d) Salt crystal, NaCl

normal conditions. Table 3.5 lists some of the physical properties of sodium, chlorine, and sodium chloride at 25 °C and normal atmospheric pressure.

A **chemical property** of a pure substance describes its chemical reactions with other substances. The chemical properties of sodium, for example, include its reaction with oxygen to form sodium oxide and its reaction with water to produce hydrogen gas. There are many reactions for the elements, more than we can possibly consider. We can, however, use the periodic table of elements to predict chemical behavior.

TABLE 3.5 PHYSICAL PROPERTIES OF SODIUM, CHLORINE, AND SODIUM CHLORIDE AT NORMAL CONDITIONS (25 °C AND 1.00 ATM)

PROPERTY	SODIUM	CHLORINE	SODIUM CHLORIDE
appearance	silver metal	yellowish gas	white crystals
melting point	98 °C	−101 °C	801 °C
boiling point	883 °C	−35 °C	1413 °C
density	0.97 g/cm³	2.90 g/L	2.17 g/cm³
solubility in 100 g water	reacts with water	0.51 g at 30 °C	35.7 g at 0 °C

The periodic table is arranged according to families of elements that in general give similar reactions. For instance, the metals in Group IA/1 on the far left side of the periodic table react with oxygen gas to give products with similar chemical formulas, namely, Li_2O, Na_2O, K_2O, Rb_2O, and Cs_2O. Notice that in each case, the number of metal to oxygen atoms is in the ratio of 2 to 1.

In Chapter 5 we will study families of elements. For now, review Table 3.6, which illustrates that elements in the same family have similar chemical properties and give products with similar chemical formulas.

TABLE 3.6 CHEMICAL PROPERTIES FOR FAMILIES OF ELEMENTS

FAMILY AND ELEMENT	REACTION WITH OXYGEN	REACTION WITH WATER	REACTION WITH HCl ACID
Group IA/1			
lithium	Li_2O	H_2 + LiOH	H_2 + LiCl
sodium	Na_2O	H_2 + NaOH	H_2 + NaCl
potassium	K_2O	H_2 + KOH	H_2 + KCl
Group IIA/2			
calcium	CaO	H_2 + Ca(OH)$_2$	H_2 + CaCl$_2$
strontium	SrO	H_2 + Sr(OH)$_2$	H_2 + SrCl$_2$
barium	BaO	H_2 + Ba(OH)$_2$	H_2 + BaCl$_2$
Group IVA/14			
carbon	CO_2	no reaction	no reaction
silicon	SiO_2	no reaction	no reaction
germanium	GeO_2	no reaction	no reaction
Group VIIIA/18			
helium	no reaction	no reaction	no reaction
neon	no reaction	no reaction	no reaction
argon	no reaction	no reaction	no reaction

Classifying Physical and Chemical Properties

We can distinguish between a physical and a chemical property as follows. Physical properties are observed without altering the composition of the substance, whereas chemical properties always involve a chemical change. When a chemical change occurs, the composition of a substance changes and another substance is formed. Example Exercise 3.7 illustrates the distinction between physical and chemical properties.

Example Exercise 3.7 Physical and Chemical Properties

Classify each of the following as a physical property or a chemical property.

(a) Water appears colorless and odorless at 20 °C.
(b) Water dissolves sugar crystals.
(c) Water produces a gas with calcium metal.
(d) Water exists as ice at −10 °C.

Solution

If a reaction occurs, there is a change in composition and the property is chemical. Otherwise, the property is physical.

(a) Color and odor are *physical properties*.
(b) Solubility is a *physical property*.
(c) A reaction producing a gas is a *chemical property*.
(d) Physical state is a *physical property*.

Practice Exercise

Classify each of the following as a physical property or a chemical property.

(a) Water appears hard and crystalline at 0 °C.   (b) Water is insoluble in gasoline.
(c) Water is a very weak conductor of electricity.   (d) Water produces a gas with sodium metal.

Answers:

(a) physical property   (b) physical property
(c) physical property   (d) chemical property

Concept Exercise
Copper melts at 1083 °C, has a density of 8.92 g/mL, is a good conductor of electricity, and turns black when heated. Which of these is an example of a chemical property?

Answer: See Appendix G.

3.7 PHYSICAL AND CHEMICAL CHANGES

LEARNING OBJECTIVE

▸ To classify a change in a substance as physical or chemical.

When a pure substance is altered, the alteration is classified as a physical or a chemical change. In a **physical change**, the chemical composition of the sample does not change. If we melt ice to water, heat alcohol to a vapor, or recycle aluminum cans into aluminum foil, we are performing a physical change. The chemical composition of the ice, alcohol, and aluminum is the same before and after the change. In other words, the formula of each substance (H_2O, C_2H_5OH, and Al) remains constant. Thus, altering the shape or physical state of a pure substance is an indication of a physical change.

In a **chemical change**, there is a chemical reaction. The composition of the sample changes, and we observe a new set of properties. If a banana ripens from green to yellow, an antacid tablet in water evolves gas bubbles, or fireworks display a shower of colorful lights, we are observing a chemical change. The composition of the banana, antacid tablet, and fireworks are different before and after the change.

Classifying Physical and Chemical Changes

We can distinguish between a physical and a chemical change as follows: a physical change can be observed without altering the composition of the substance, whereas a chemical change involves the formation of a new substance. When a new substance is formed, we usually observe one of the following: a permanent color change, an odor or bubbles from the release of a gas, or light or heat from the release of energy.

In the laboratory, we may observe that two solutions added together produce an insoluble substance. The formation of a solid substance in a solution is a practical observation that indicates a chemical change. Figure 3.12 illustrates three examples of chemical changes.

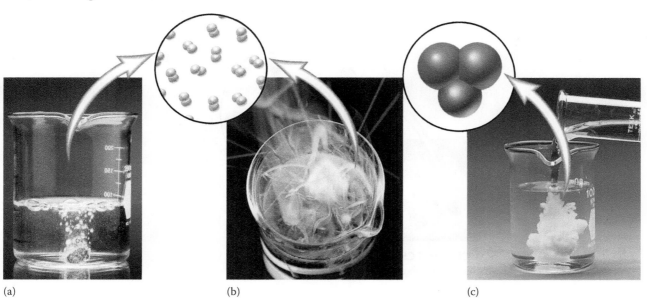

(a)   (b)   (c)

▲ **Figure 3.12 Evidence of Chemical Change** The evidence for a chemical change includes (a) gas bubbles from the reaction of calcium metal in water, (b) heat and light energy from the reaction of potassium metal in water, and (c) a colorful, insoluble substance from the reaction of two solutions.

Example Exercise 3.8 further illustrates the distinction between physical and chemical changes.

Example Exercise 3.8 Physical and Chemical Changes

Classify each of the following as a physical change or a chemical change.

(a) Touching a lit candle to hydrogen soap bubbles gives an explosion.
(b) Heating water in a flask produces moisture on the glass.
(c) Combining two colorless solutions gives a yellow solid.
(d) Pouring vinegar on baking soda produces gas bubbles.

Solution
An observation that indicates a physical change is a change of physical state. The observations that suggest a chemical change include burning, fizzing, changing color, or forming an insoluble substance in solution.

(a) Hydrogen explodes; thus, it is a *chemical change*.
(b) Water is boiled; thus, it is a *physical change*.
(c) Two solutions give an insoluble substance; thus, it is a *chemical change*.
(d) Baking soda fizzes; thus, it is a *chemical change*.

Practice Exercise
Classify each of the following as a physical change or a chemical change.

(a) Freezing water in a refrigerator makes cubes of ice.
(b) Adding silver nitrate to tap water gives a cloudy solution.
(c) Burning sulfur gives a light blue flame.
(d) Grinding aspirin tablets produces a powder.

Answers:

(a) physical change
(b) chemical change
(c) chemical change
(d) physical change

Concept Exercise
An Alka-Seltzer tablet dissolves in water and produces gas bubbles. Is this an example of a physical change or a chemical change?

Answer: See Appendix G.

▲ **Alka-Seltzer** An Alka-Seltzer tablet in water releases carbon dioxide gas bubbles.

▲ **Chemical Change** Hydrogen and oxygen gases react explosively when ignited by a candle.

3.8 CONSERVATION OF MASS

LEARNING OBJECTIVE

▶ To apply the conservation of mass law to chemical changes.

In the late 1700s, the French chemist Antoine Lavoisier (1743–1794) performed exacting laboratory experiments and found that the mass of reactants before a chemical change was always equal to the mass of products after the change. He concluded that matter was neither created nor destroyed during a chemical reaction. In 1789, he announced the conservation of mass principle. This principle has become known as the **law of conservation of mass**.

As an example of conservation of mass, consider the reaction of hydrogen and oxygen. Hydrogen and oxygen always combine in the same ratio by mass to form water. That is, if 1 g of hydrogen combines with 8 g of oxygen, then 2 g of hydrogen combines with 16 g of oxygen, 3 g of hydrogen reacts with 24 g of oxygen, and so on. We can predict the mass of water produced by each of these reactions. From the conservation of mass law, we know that the mass of hydrogen plus the mass of oxygen must equal the mass of water produced. That is,

$$1.0 \text{ g hydrogen} + 8.0 \text{ g oxygen} = 9.0 \text{ g water}$$

Conversely, we can predict the masses of hydrogen and oxygen produced by the decomposition of water. Passing an electric current through water produces hydrogen gas and oxygen gas. This process is called *electrolysis*. If the electrolysis of 45.0 g of water produces 5.0 g of hydrogen, how many grams of oxygen are evolved?

The conservation of mass law states that the mass of the hydrogen and oxygen is equal to the mass of the water, 45.0 g. Therefore, the mass of oxygen must equal the mass of the water minus the mass of the hydrogen. That is,

$$45.0 \text{ g water} - 5.0 \text{ g hydrogen} = 40.0 \text{ g oxygen}$$

The conservation of mass law is one of the most important principles in chemistry. Historically, it was used to determine the formulas of compounds and to develop the first periodic table of elements. As we will discuss in Chapter 9, it is the cornerstone of all quantitative relationships in chemistry. Example Exercise 3.9 further illustrates the conservation of mass law.

Example Exercise 3.9 Conservation of Mass Law

In an experiment, 2.430 g of magnesium metal was ignited and burned with oxygen in the air. If 4.030 g of white magnesium oxide powder, MgO, was collected, what was the mass of oxygen gas that reacted?

Solution

Applying the conservation of mass law, we find that the mass of the magnesium metal plus the mass of the oxygen gas equals the mass of the magnesium oxide powder. That is,

$$2.430 \text{ g Mg} + \text{mass of oxygen} = 4.030 \text{ g MgO}$$
$$\text{mass of oxygen} = 4.030 \text{ g MgO} - 2.430 \text{ g Mg}$$
$$\text{mass of oxygen} = 1.600 \text{ g}$$

Practice Exercise

If 0.654 g of zinc metal reacts with 0.321 g of yellow powdered sulfur, what is the mass of the zinc sulfide produced?

Answer: 0.975 g

Concept Exercise

Heating 1.000 g copper metal with yellow sulfur produces 1.252 g of black copper sulfide. What is the mass of sulfur that reacted with the copper metal?

Answer: See Appendix G.

▸ To distinguish between potential and kinetic energy.

▸ To relate kinetic energy, temperature, and physical state.

3.9 POTENTIAL AND KINETIC ENERGY

Energy makes things happen and is often defined as the ability to do work. There are two types of energy: potential and kinetic. **Potential energy (PE)** is stored energy that matter possesses as a result of its position or composition. **Kinetic energy (KE)** is the energy matter has as a result of its motion. A boulder perched at the top of a mountain has potential energy. If the boulder rolls down the mountain, it loses potential energy, but gains kinetic energy. In the process of rolling down the mountain, the potential energy of the boulder is converted to kinetic energy. Figure 3.13 illustrates the conversion from potential to kinetic energy.

▶ Figure 3.13 **Potential Energy and Kinetic Energy** A cannonball shot into the air loses kinetic energy while gaining potential energy. At the top of its flight, the potential energy is at a maximum and the kinetic energy is at a minimum. As the cannonball falls to Earth, the potential energy decreases as the kinetic energy increases.

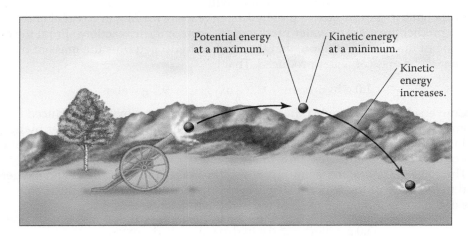

In our study of chemistry, we are usually interested in the potential energy associated with the chemical composition of a pure substance. For example, gasoline has potential energy that is converted to kinetic energy when it undergoes combustion. As gasoline burns, the potential energy of the cool liquid is converted to the kinetic energy of the hot, expanding gas mixture.

Kinetic Energy, Temperature, and Physical State

We can view a sample of matter as a large collection of very small particles. The attraction between particles is one of the criteria that influences the physical state. In solids, this force of attraction holds particles in fixed positions and allows little or no movement.

When a substance in the *solid state* is heated, the temperature increases and particles begin to randomly vibrate in fixed positions. As a solid acquires more heat energy, particles vibrate so intensely that the force of attraction is overcome and the particles break free from each other. This is a description of the *liquid state*.

A liquid is, therefore, a state of matter in which particles possess sufficient energy to overcome their mutual attraction and have limited movement. When a liquid has enough energy to completely overcome the force of attraction, the particles are free to fly about and strike the walls of the container. At this point, the liquid has changed to the *gaseous state.* Table 3.7 summarizes the relationship between the properties of particles and the physical state.

We can review the relationship between kinetic energy and physical state as follows. If we heat a solid, it acquires enough energy to overcome the attraction between particles and melts to a liquid. As the temperature increases, particles gradually gain more energy and demonstrate increasing motion. If we continue to heat the liquid, it

TABLE 3.7 PROPERTIES AND PHYSICAL STATES

PROPERTY OF PARTICLES	SOLID	LIQUID	GAS
kinetic energy	very low	high	very high
movement	negligible	restricted	unrestricted

◀ Figure 3.14 **Kinetic Energy and Physical State** The energy of individual H_2O molecules increases as solid ice is heated. As the attraction between molecules is overcome, solid ice changes to liquid water and then to gaseous steam.

Gas

Liquid

Solid

acquires enough energy to vaporize to a gas. Figure 3.14 illustrates the relationship between increasing energy and physical state.

The kinetic energy of a gas is directly related to its temperature. If the temperature increases, the kinetic energy increases; if the temperature decreases, the kinetic energy decreases. Moreover, if the temperature increases, the motion of the particles increases; if the temperature decreases, the motion decreases.

Example Exercise 3.10 further illustrates how temperature, kinetic energy, and the motion of gas particles are related.

Example Exercise 3.10   Kinetic Energy and Molecular Motion

A balloon filled with helium gas is cooled from 25 °C to −25 °C. State the change in each of the following:

(a) kinetic energy of the gas   (b) motion of helium atoms

Solution

Temperature, kinetic energy, and velocity are related as follows:

(a) As the temperature cools from 25 °C to −25 °C, the kinetic energy of helium atoms *decreases.*

(b) Because a drop in temperature produces a decrease in kinetic energy, the motion of helium atoms *decreases.*

Practice Exercise

A steel cylinder containing air is heated from 25 °C to 50 °C. State the change in each of the following:

(a) kinetic energy of the gas   (b) motion of air molecules

Answers:

(a) increases   (b) increases

Concept Exercise

What happens to the kinetic energy and velocity of air molecules when the temperature increases?

Answer: See Appendix G.

▸ To apply the conservation of energy law to physical and chemical changes.

▸ To identify the following forms of energy: chemical, electrical, mechanical, nuclear, heat, and light.

3.10 CONSERVATION OF ENERGY

In the middle of the nineteenth century, several English and German scientists proposed that the total energy in the universe is constant. This proposal was worded in different ways, but it essentially stated that energy cannot be created nor destroyed. Energy can, however, be converted from one form to another. This principle is known as the **law of conservation of energy**. This principle applies experimentally, and we can make energy predictions for physical and chemical changes.

Energy and Physical Changes

Let's consider the conservation of energy law applied to a change of physical state. When water is converted to steam, a given amount of heat energy is required. Energy cannot be destroyed, so the same amount of heat must be released if the steam condenses to a liquid. In practice, it requires 540 cal of heat energy to convert 1 g of water at 100 °C to steam at 100 °C. It therefore follows that 540 cal of heat are released when 1 g of steam at 100 °C condenses to water. Figure 3.15 illustrates the conservation of energy for a physical change.

▸ **Figure 3.15 Conservation of Energy for a Physical Change** The physical change of state from water to steam, and the reverse process, involve the same amount of heat energy.

Heat energy absorbed

1 g water + 540 cal $\xrightarrow{100\ °C}$ 1 g steam

1 g steam $\xrightarrow{100\ °C}$ 1 g water + 540 cal

Heat energy released

The conservation of energy law states the following:
heat energy absorbed (540 cal) = heat energy released (540 cal)

Energy and Chemical Changes

The conservation of energy law applied to a chemical change is analogous to the conservation of mass law. That is, the total energy before a reaction is the same as the total energy after the reaction. It is important to understand, however, that some chemical changes release energy, whereas others absorb energy. Yet, the total energy before and after a reaction must always be constant.

How can the energy be constant for a reaction that involves a change in heat? The explanation is that a reaction involves the two types of energy discussed previously, *potential* chemical energy and *kinetic* heat energy. In a reaction, the initial reactants may lose potential energy, but the resulting products gain kinetic energy. In reactions that produce heat, the initial reactants have more potential energy than the products. Conversely, in reactions that absorb heat, the initial reactants have less potential energy than the products.

If we consider the conservation of energy law, we can say that the energy released from a given change is equal to the energy required for the reverse change. For example, we know from experiments that 3200 cal of heat is released when hydrogen gas and oxygen gas react to produce 1 g of water. Thus, 3200 cal of heat is required for the reverse process of decomposing 1 g of water into hydrogen gas and oxygen gas. If we decompose water into the two gases using an electric current, the electrical energy required is equivalent to 3200 cal. Figure 3.16 illustrates the conservation of energy for a chemical change.

Energy absorbed

Water + electrical energy ⟶ Hydrogen gas + oxygen gas

Hydrogen gas + oxygen gas ⟶ Water + heat energy

Energy released

The conservation of energy law states the following:
electrical energy absorbed = heat energy released

◀ **Figure 3.16 Conservation of Energy for a Chemical Change** The chemical change from water to hydrogen and oxygen gases, and the reverse process, involve the same amount of energy.

Forms of Energy

There are six forms of energy: heat, light, chemical, electrical, mechanical, and nuclear. Each of these can be converted from one form of energy to another. For example, we can use solar energy panels to convert light energy from the Sun to heat energy, which we can store as hot water.

Although we can convert sunlight to electrical energy, the current process is only 15% efficient. We can also convert mechanical energy to electrical energy, which is a more efficient process. For example, the mechanical energy of water spilling over a dam is used to spin a turbine that in turn drives an electrical generator. This hydroelectric process operates at nearly 90% efficiency. Example Exercise 3.11 illustrates the conversion of various forms of energy.

Example Exercise 3.11   Forms of Energy

Identify two forms of energy that are involved in each of the following conversions:

(a) Radioactive emissions vaporize water to steam.
(b) Steam drives a turbine.
(c) A turbine spins and drives an electrical generator.

Solution
We can refer to the six forms of energy listed above. It follows that

(a) *Nuclear* energy is converted to *heat* energy.
(b) *Heat* energy is converted to *mechanical* energy.
(c) *Mechanical* energy is converted to *electrical* energy.

Practice Exercise
Identify two forms of energy that are involved in each of the following devices:

(a) flashlight
(b) solar calculator
(c) lead–acid battery

Answers:

(a) chemical and light

(b) light and electrical

(c) chemical and electrical

Concept Exercise

Which of the following is *not* a basic form of energy: chemical, electrical, heat, light, mechanical, nuclear, solar?

Answer: See Appendix G.

CRITICAL THINKING Lower Gasoline Bills

Q: In terms of expense, is it better to fill a gas tank in the cool morning, or in the warm afternoon?

Interestingly, you can reduce your automobile fuel bills by applying the density concept discussed in this chapter. The density of most liquids decreases as the temperature warms, and increases as the temperature cools. Thus, the density of gasoline decreases in the warm afternoon, and increases in the cool morning.

Gasoline is sold at the pump by the volume delivered (gallons), and not by the mass, which is greater when the density increases. Although $50.00 of fuel contains the *same volume* at different temperatures, $50.00 of fuel contains a *greater mass* of gasoline at 40 °F than at 70 °F because the density increases. Thus, filling up with gas in the cool morning saves money.

Two liquids violate the principle of greater density at a lower temperature. The liquids are water and ammonia. At temperatures near their freezing points (0 °C and −77 °C, respectively), each of these liquids expands to form a crystalline solid. Consequently, the density of water decreases and solid ice demonstrates the unusual property of floating in water. Similarly, solid ammonia floats in liquid ammonia. All other solid substances are more dense and sink in their corresponding liquids.

▲ Lower Gasoline Bills

A: Although it is more economical to fill a gas tank in the cool morning, the density change is small and the mass of gasoline is only about 1% greater at 40 °F than at 70 °F.

▲ **Albert Einstein** The relationship between mass and energy is expressed by Einstein's famous equation: $E = mc^2$.

Conservation of Mass and Energy

In 1905, Albert Einstein (1879–1955) presented a paper on the special theory of relativity that proposed that matter and energy are interrelated, stating this relationship in the form $E = mc^2$. In this famous equation, Einstein showed that energy (E) and mass (m) are related by the velocity of light (c) squared.

Because mass and energy are related, it naturally follows that the conservation of mass and the conservation of energy are related. Thus, a more accurate statement combines these two principles into the **law of conservation of mass and energy**. The combined law states that the total mass and energy in the universe is constant. When applied to a chemical reaction, the law indicates that the total mass and energy before and after a chemical change is constant.

By applying the combined law, we realize that any decrease in mass corresponds to an increase in energy. Even a slight decrease in mass, however, corresponds to an enormous amount of energy. For instance, a mass loss of 0.001 g produces enough heat energy to raise the temperature of a large swimming pool about 30 °C. Because the mass loss for ordinary chemical reactions is undetectable from a practical laboratory point of view, the original conservation of mass law is still valid.

Summary

LEARNING OBJECTIVES	SEC	EXERCISES
To describe the motion of particles in the solid, liquid, and gaseous states of matter.	3.1	Exercises 1–6
To describe the effect of temperature on the solid, liquid, and gaseous states of matter.	3.1	Exercises 7–12
To classify a sample of matter as an element, compound, or mixture.	3.2	Exercises 13–16
To relate the names and symbols of 48 common elements.	3.3	Exercises 17–22
To distinguish between the properties of metals and nonmetals.	3.4	Exercises 23–26
To predict whether an element is a metal, nonmetal, or semimetal given its position in the periodic table.	3.4	Exercises 27–30
To predict whether an element is a solid, liquid, or gas at 25 °C and normal atmospheric pressure.	3.4	Exercises 31–34
To state the number of atoms of each element in a compound given the chemical formula.	3.5	Exercises 35–40
To apply the law of definite composition to a compound.	3.5	Exercises 41–42
To classify a property of a substance as physical or chemical.	3.6	Exercises 43–50
To classify a change in a substance as physical or chemical.	3.7	Exercises 51–58
To apply the conservation of mass law to chemical changes.	3.8	Exercises 59–62
To distinguish between potential and kinetic energy.	3.9	Exercises 63–64
To relate kinetic energy, temperature, and physical state.	3.9	Exercises 65–68
To apply the conservation of energy law to physical and chemical changes.	3.10	Exercises 69–74
To identify the following forms of energy: chemical, electrical, mechanical, nuclear, heat, and light.	3.10	Exercises 75–78

Section 3.1 Matter exists in three **physical states**: solid, liquid, and gas. A *solid* is characterized by a fixed shape and fixed volume. A *liquid* has a variable shape, but a fixed volume. A *gas* has a variable shape and a variable volume.

As temperature increases, a solid *melts* to a liquid and then *vaporizes* to a gas. A direct change of state from a solid to a gas is called **sublimation**. Conversely, as temperature decreases, a gas *condenses* to a liquid and then *freezes* to a solid. A direct change of state from a gas to a solid is called **deposition**.

Section 3.2 We can classify matter according to its properties. A **heterogeneous mixture** has an indefinite composition and variable properties. A **homogeneous mixture** has a definite composition, but variable properties from sample to sample; examples include **alloys**, solutions, and mixtures of gases. A **substance** can be either an **element** or a **compound**. A substance has a definite composition and constant properties.

Section 3.3 In 1803, the English chemist John Dalton proposed that elements are composed of indivisible spherical particles called **atoms**. In 1813, the Swedish chemist J. J. Berzelius suggested that the name of an element be abbreviated with a **chemical symbol** corresponding to the first letter of the name of the element, for instance, N for nitrogen. If two or more names began with the same letter, he recommended using two letters in the name, for example, Ni for nickel.

Section 3.4 An element can be classified as a **metal** or a **nonmetal**. If an element can be hammered into a thin sheet, it is said to be **malleable**. If it can be drawn into a fine wire, it is said to be **ductile**. An element having properties between those of a metal and a nonmetal is termed a **semimetal**, or *metalloid*. All elements can be ordered by **atomic number** and arranged in a **periodic table**. The periodic table shows a general trend in properties, with metals on the left side and nonmetals on the right side.

Section 3.5 The **law of definite composition** states that a compound always contains the same elements in the same proportion by mass. The composition of a compound is given by its **chemical formula**. Vitamin C has the formula $C_6H_8O_6$; one **molecule** contains 6 carbon atoms, 8 hydrogen atoms, and 6 oxygen atoms. Thus, the total number of atoms in the chemical formula of vitamin C is 20.

Section 3.6 The properties of substances are classified as physical or chemical. A **physical property** refers to a characteristic such as color, density, melting point, conductivity of heat and electricity, solubility, and physical state. A **chemical property** describes a chemical reaction of a substance with another substance.

Section 3.7 The changes in substances are classified as physical or chemical. A **physical change** does not alter the chemical composition and involves a change in mass, volume, or physical state. A **chemical change** involves a change in chemical composition. Evidence for a chemical change includes burning, producing a gas, forming a solid substance in solution, and releasing heat or light energy.

Section 3.8 The **law of conservation of mass** states that matter is neither created nor destroyed. This fundamental principle has practical applications in the chemistry laboratory; that is, the total mass of substances produced from a reaction can be calculated because the mass of the products must equal the mass of the reactants.

Section 3.9 The **potential energy (PE)** of a substance is related to its chemical composition, whereas the **kinetic energy (KE)** of a substance is related to the motion of its particles. Kinetic energy is directly related to temperature. That is, when we heat a solid substance and increase its temperature, we also increase its kinetic energy. As the temperature increases,

the particles gain more energy and begin to overcome their attraction for each other. If we continue heating, we will eventually produce a change of state from a solid to a liquid, and from a liquid to a gas.

Section 3.10 The six forms of energy are heat, light, chemical, electrical, mechanical, and nuclear. The **law of conservation of energy** states that energy is neither created nor destroyed. Energy may be converted, however, from one form to another. In practice, chemical energy is used to provide heat and electrical energy. The laws of conservation of mass and conservation of energy can be treated as a single principle—the **law of conservation of mass and energy**. For ordinary chemical reactions, energy changes are sufficiently small that we can ignore this principle and apply conservation of mass and conservation of energy individually.

Key Terms   *Answers to Key Terms are in Appendix H.*

Select the key term that corresponds to each of the following definitions.

_____ **1.** the condition of matter existing as a solid, liquid, or gas

_____ **2.** a direct change of state from a solid to a gas

_____ **3.** a direct change of state from a gas to a solid

_____ **4.** matter having an indefinite composition and variable properties

_____ **5.** matter having a definite composition, but variable properties from sample to sample; for example, alloys and solutions

_____ **6.** matter having a definite composition and constant properties; for example, an element or compound

_____ **7.** a homogeneous mixture of two or more metals

_____ **8.** a substance that can be broken down into simpler substances

_____ **9.** a substance that cannot be broken down by chemical reaction

_____ **10.** the smallest particle that represents an element

_____ **11.** an abbreviation for the name of a chemical element

_____ **12.** an element that is generally shiny in appearance, has a high density, high melting point, and is a good conductor of heat and electricity

_____ **13.** the property of a metal that allows it to be machined into a foil

_____ **14.** the property of a metal that allows it to be drawn into a wire

_____ **15.** an element that is generally dull in appearance, has a low density, low melting point, and is not a good conductor of heat and electricity

_____ **16.** an element that is generally metallic in appearance and has properties midway between those of a metal and a nonmetal

_____ **17.** a number that identifies a particular element

_____ **18.** a chart that arranges elements according to their properties

_____ **19.** the principle that states a compound always contains the same elements in the same proportion by mass

_____ **20.** a single particle composed of two or more nonmetal atoms

_____ **21.** an abbreviation for the name of a chemical compound that indicates the number of atoms of each element

(a) alloy (*Sec. 3.2*)

(b) atom (*Sec. 3.3*)

(c) atomic number (*Sec. 3.4*)

(d) chemical change (*Sec. 3.7*)

(e) chemical formula (*Sec. 3.5*)

(f) chemical property (*Sec. 3.6*)

(g) chemical symbol (*Sec. 3.3*)

(h) compound (*Sec. 3.2*)

(i) deposition (*Sec. 3.1*)

(j) ductile (*Sec. 3.4*)

(k) element (*Sec. 3.2*)

(l) heterogeneous mixture (*Sec. 3.2*)

(m) homogeneous mixture (*Sec. 3.2*)

(n) kinetic energy (KE) (*Sec. 3.9*)

(o) law of conservation of energy (*Sec. 3.10*)

(p) law of conservation of mass (*Sec. 3.8*)

(q) law of conservation of mass and energy (*Sec. 3.10*)

(r) law of definite composition (*Sec. 3.5*)

(s) malleable (*Sec. 3.4*)

(t) metal (*Sec. 3.4*)

(u) molecule (*Sec. 3.5*)

_____ **22.** a characteristic of a substance that can be observed without changing the chemical composition

_____ **23.** a characteristic of a substance that cannot be observed without changing the chemical formula

_____ **24.** a modification of a substance that alters its chemical composition

_____ **25.** a modification of a substance that does not alter its chemical composition

_____ **26.** the stored energy that matter possesses owing to its position or composition

_____ **27.** the energy associated with the mass and velocity of a particle

_____ **28.** the law that states mass cannot be created or destroyed

_____ **29.** the law that states energy cannot be created or destroyed

_____ **30.** the law that states the total mass and energy in the universe is constant

(v) nonmetal (_Sec. 3.4_)

(w) periodic table (_Sec. 3.4_)

(x) physical change (_Sec. 3.7_)

(y) physical property (_Sec. 3.6_)

(z) physical state (_Sec. 3.1_)

(aa) potential energy (PE) (_Sec. 3.9_)

(bb) semimetal (_Sec. 3.4_)

(cc) sublimation (_Sec. 3.1_)

(dd) substance (_Sec. 3.2_)

Exercises _Answers to odd-numbered Exercises are in Appendix I._

Physical States of Matter (Sec. 3.1)

1. Which physical state is described as having a variable shape and variable volume?

2. Which physical state is described as having a fixed shape and fixed volume?

3. Which physical state is described as having a variable shape and compresses negligibly?

4. Which physical state is described as having a variable shape and compresses significantly?

5. Which physical state is described as having particles closely packed and held rigidly in position?

6. Which physical state is described as having particles closely packed and free to move around?

7. Supply the term that describes each of the following changes of physical state:
   (a) solid to liquid   **(b)** liquid to gas

8. Supply the term that describes each of the following changes of physical state:
   (a) gas to liquid   **(b)** liquid to solid

9. Indicate whether the following changes of physical state require heating or cooling:
   (a) solid to liquid   **(b)** gas to liquid

10. Indicate whether the following changes of physical state require heating or cooling:
    (a) liquid to solid   **(b)** liquid to gas

11. State whether the process of sublimation requires heating or cooling.

12. State whether the process of deposition requires heating or cooling.

Elements, Compounds, and Mixtures (Sec. 3.2)

13. Classify each of the following as an element, compound, or mixture:
    (a) iron metal   **(b)** oxygen gas
    (c) iron oxide   **(d)** iron ore

14. Classify each of the following as an element, compound, or mixture:
    (a) sodium metal   **(b)** chlorine gas
    (c) sodium chloride   **(d)** salt water

15. Classify each of the following as an element, compound, homogeneous mixture, or heterogeneous mixture:
    (a) copper wire   **(b)** copper ore
    (c) copper oxide   **(d)** brass alloy

◀ **Copper Wire** Copper metal is ductile and can be drawn into a thin wire.

16. Classify each of the following as an element, compound, homogeneous mixture, or heterogeneous mixture:
    (a) silver ingot   **(b)** silver ore
    (c) silver oxide   **(d)** silver alloy

Names and Symbols of the Elements (Sec. 3.3)

17. Write the chemical symbol for each of the following elements:
    (a) strontium   **(b)** xenon
    (c) oxygen   **(d)** zinc
    (e) fluorine   **(f)** sodium
    (g) copper   **(h)** nickel

18. Write the chemical symbol for each of the following elements:
    (a) lithium   **(b)** argon
    (c) magnesium   **(d)** manganese
    (e) beryllium   **(f)** silicon
    (g) mercury   **(h)** titanium

19. Write the name of the element for each of the following chemical symbols:
    (a) P   **(b)** S
    (c) Kr   **(d)** Fe
    (e) Sb   **(f)** N
    (g) Pt   **(h)** Ag

20. Write the name of the element for each of the following chemical symbols:
    (a) Cl   (b) Ne
    (c) Cd   (d) Ge
    (e) Co   (f) Ra
    (g) Cr   (h) Te

21. Refer to the periodic table and find the atomic number for each of the following:
    (a) hydrogen   (b) boron
    (c) aluminum   (d) titanium
    (e) arsenic   (f) strontium
    (g) tin   (h) bismuth

22. Refer to the periodic table and find the atomic number for each of the following:
    (a) helium   (b) carbon
    (c) potassium   (d) copper
    (e) selenium   (f) silver
    (g) lead   (h) radon

Metals, Nonmetals, and Semimetals (Sec. 3.4)

23. State whether each of the following properties is more typical of a metal or a nonmetal:
    (a) dense solid
    (b) low boiling point
    (c) ductile
    (d) reacts with metals

24. State whether each of the following properties is more typical of a metal or a nonmetal:
    (a) shiny luster
    (b) low melting point
    (c) malleable
    (d) reacts with metals and nonmetals

25. State whether each of the following properties is more typical of a metal or a nonmetal:
    (a) shiny solid   (b) brittle solid
    (c) low density   (d) forms alloys

26. State whether each of the following properties is more typical of a metal or a nonmetal:
    (a) dull powder   (b) colorless gas
    (c) high density   (d) reacts with metals

27. Refer to the periodic table and classify each of the following elements as a metal, nonmetal, or semimetal
    (a) C   (b) Ca
    (c) Cl   (d) Cu

28. Refer to the periodic table and classify each of the following elements as a metal, nonmetal, or semimetal:
    (a) H   (b) He
    (c) Hf   (d) Ho

29. Refer to the periodic table and classify each of the following elements as a metal, nonmetal, or semimetal:
    (a) boron   (b) barium
    (c) beryllium   (d) bismuth

30. Refer to the periodic table and classify each of the following elements as a metal, nonmetal, or semimetal:
    (a) argon   (b) antimony
    (c) arsenic   (d) astatine

31. Refer to the periodic table and indicate the physical state for each of the following elements at 25 °C and normal pressure:
    (a) N   (b) Na
    (c) Ne   (d) Ni

32. Refer to the periodic table and indicate the physical state for each of the following elements at 25 °C and normal pressure:
    (a) S   (b) Se
    (c) Si   (d) Sn

33. Refer to the periodic table and indicate the physical state for each of the following elements at 25 °C and normal pressure:
    (a) hydrogen   (b) titanium
    (c) fluorine   (d) bromine

34. Refer to the periodic table and indicate the physical state for each of the following elements at 25 °C and normal pressure:
    (a) helium   (b) manganese
    (c) iodine   (d) mercury

Compounds and Chemical Formulas (Sec. 3.5)

35. State the composition for a molecule of each of the following vitamins:
    (a) vitamin B_1, $C_{12}H_{17}N_4OS$
    (b) vitamin B_2, $C_{17}H_{20}N_4O_6$

36. State the composition for a molecule of each of the following compounds:
    (a) cholesterol, $C_{27}H_{45}OH$
    (b) quinine, $C_{20}H_{24}N_2O_2$

37. Write the chemical formula for each of the following compounds:
    (a) vitamin A: 20 carbon, 30 hydrogen, and 1 oxygen atom
    (b) vitamin K: 31 carbon, 46 hydrogen, and 2 oxygen atoms

38. Write the chemical formula for each of the following compounds:
    (a) lysine (an amino acid): 6 carbon, 14 hydrogen, 2 nitrogen, and 2 oxygen atoms
    (b) methionine (an amino acid): 5 carbon, 11 hydrogen, 1 nitrogen, 2 oxygen, and 1 sulfur atom

39. What is the total number of atoms in a molecule of each of the following compounds?
    (a) stearic acid (in animal fat), $CH_3(CH_2)_{16}COOH$
    (b) triolein (in vegetable oil), $C_3H_5(C_{17}H_{33}COO)_3$

40. What is the total number of atoms in a molecule of each of the following compounds?
    (a) citric acid (in citrus fruit), $C_3H_4OH(COOH)_3$
    (b) lactic acid (in sore muscles), $C_2H_4(OH)COOH$

41. The mass ratio of H:O in a bottle of water is 1:8. Predict the mass ratio of water in 10 bottles of water.

42. The mass ratio of C:H:O in natural vitamin C found in rose hips is 9:1:12. Predict the mass ratio of synthetic vitamin C synthesized in the laboratory.

Physical and Chemical Properties (Sec. 3.6)

43. State whether each of the following is a physical or a chemical property of gold:
    (a) yellow color   (b) high density
    (c) conducts electricity   (d) reacts with nitric acid

▲ **Gold Foil and Copper Rods** Gold and copper are both malleable and ductile metals; that is, each can be hammered into a foil and drawn into thin rods.

44. State whether each of the following is a physical or a chemical property of copper:
(a) shiny metallic luster   (b) high melting point
(c) conducts heat   (d) reacts with oxygen

45. State whether each of the following is a physical or a chemical property:
(a) Titanium is ductile.
(b) Zinc generates a gas in acid.
(c) Yellow phosphorus ignites in air.
(d) Chromium conducts heat.

46. State whether each of the following is a physical or a chemical property:
(a) Manganese bubbles in acid.
(b) Silver is malleable.
(c) Calcium turns dark in air.
(d) Carbon grinds to a powder.

47. State whether each of the following is a physical or a chemical property:
(a) Ether is flammable.
(b) Bromine is a reddish-orange liquid.
(c) Ethanol vaporizes at 78 °C.
(d) Steam condenses to water at 100 °C.

48. State whether each of the following is a physical or a chemical property:
(a) Electricity decomposes water.
(b) Ice floats on water.
(c) Potassium metal fizzes in water.
(d) Acetone dissolves in water.

49. State whether each of the following is a physical or a chemical property:
(a) Sugar ferments to ethanol.
(b) Ethanol dissolves in gasoline.
(c) Ethylene glycol freezes at −12 °C.
(d) Ethanol burns with a light blue flame.

50. State whether each of the following is a physical or a chemical property:
(a) Iron oxidizes to rust.
(b) Dry ice undergoes sublimation.
(c) Lithium metal turns gray in air.
(d) Plutonium radioactively decays.

Physical and Chemical Changes (Sec. 3.7)

51. State whether each of the following is a physical or a chemical change:
(a) combustion   (b) vaporization
(c) sublimation   (d) oxidation

52. State whether each of the following is a physical or a chemical change:
(a) burning   (b) condensing
(c) freezing   (d) rusting

53. State whether each of the following is a physical or a chemical change:
(a) slicing an orange into wedges
(b) fermenting apples into apple cider
(c) grinding sugar crystals into powder
(d) digesting carbohydrates for energy

54. State whether each of the following is a physical or a chemical change:
(a) cutting aluminum foil   (b) caramelizing sugar
(c) adding air to a tire   (d) igniting a sparkler

55. State whether each of the following is a physical or a chemical change:
(a) steam condenses and freezes to ice.
(b) hydrogen and oxygen gases explode.
(c) bromine vaporizes to a brown gas.
(d) sodium metal changes to a white powder.

56. State whether each of the following is a physical or a chemical change:
(a) zinc metal produces a colorless gas in acid.
(b) nickel alloys with copper in a 5¢ coin.
(c) liquid helium boils at −269 °C.
(d) sodium metal reacts with chlorine gas.

57. State whether each of the following is a physical or a chemical change:
(a) baking soda fizzes in vinegar.
(b) vinegar and oil separate into two layers.
(c) a flaming wood log releases heat.
(d) a helium balloon decreases in size.

58. State whether each of the following is a physical or a chemical change:
(a) mercury cools to a silvery solid.
(b) natural gas burns with a blue flame.
(c) ammonia and copper solution turns deep blue.
(d) sugar crystals dissolve in water.

Conservation of Mass (Sec. 3.8)

59. If 5.00 g of gray iron powder reacts with 2.77 g of red phosphorus powder, what is the mass of the iron phosphide product?

60. If 1.00 g of gray zinc powder reacts with 0.49 g of yellow sulfur powder, what is the mass of the zinc sulfide product?

61. If 0.750 g of orange mercury oxide decomposes to 0.695 g of liquid mercury and oxygen gas, what is the mass of oxygen produced?

62. If 10.11 g of limestone decomposes by heat to give 8.51 g of solid calcium oxide and carbon dioxide gas, what is the mass of carbon dioxide produced?

Potential and Kinetic Energy (Sec. 3.9)

63. Which physical state has particles with the highest kinetic energy?

64. Which physical state has particles with the most restricted movement?

65. If the temperature increases, does the kinetic energy increase or decrease?

66. If the temperature increases, does the motion of particles increase or decrease?

67. If a steel cylinder of helium gas is heated from 50 °C to 100 °C, does the motion of helium atoms increase or decrease?

68. If a steel cylinder of hydrogen gas is cooled from 50 °C to 0 °C, does the motion of hydrogen molecules increase or decrease?

Conservation of Energy (Sec. 3.10)

69. Steam at 100 °C passing through a radiator condenses to water and releases heat. If 1500 kcal of heat are released, how much energy is required to vaporize the water, at 100 °C, to steam?

70. An ice cube at 0 °C melts to water by absorbing heat. If 10.5 kcal of heat are required to melt the ice, how much energy must be lost to freeze the water, at 0 °C, to ice?

71. A 10.0 g sample of mercury absorbs 110 cal as it is heated from 25 °C to its boiling point at 356 °C. It then requires an additional 697 cal to vaporize. How much energy is released as the mercury vapor cools from 356 °C to 25 °C?

72. A 25.0 g sample of molten iron releases 1230 cal as it cools from 2000 °C to its freezing point, 1535 °C. It then releases an additional 1590 cal as it solidifies. How much energy is required to heat the solid iron from 1535 °C to 2000 °C?

73. The reaction of hydrogen and oxygen gases produces 15.0 g of water and releases 48.0 kcal of heat. How much energy is required to decompose 15.0 g of water into hydrogen and oxygen gases?

74. The electrolysis of 25.0 g of water requires 335 kJ of energy to produce hydrogen and oxygen gases. How much energy is released when hydrogen and oxygen gases react to produce 25.0 g of water?

75. Identify two forms of energy that are involved in each of the following energy conversions relating to a fossil fuel power plant:
    (a) Burning coal converts water to steam.
    (b) Steam drives a turbine.
    (c) A turbine turns a generator.
    (d) A generator makes electricity.

76. Identify two forms of energy that are involved in each of the following energy conversions relating to a nuclear power plant:
    (a) Uranium converts water to steam.
    (b) Steam drives a turbine.
    (c) A turbine turns a generator.
    (d) A generator makes electricity.

77. Identify two forms of energy that are involved in each of the following energy conversions relating to an automobile:
    (a) hot gases moving pistons
    (b) pistons powering the crankshaft
    (c) crankshaft turning the generator
    (d) generator charging the battery

78. Identify two forms of energy that are involved in each of the following energy conversions relating to an automobile:
    (a) lead–acid battery making electricity
    (b) electricity turning a starter motor
    (c) starter motor turning a flywheel
    (d) gasoline exploding into hot gases

General Exercises

79. A pre-1982 penny was minted from an alloy of copper and zinc. Is a pre-1982 penny an example of a homogeneous or heterogeneous mixture?

80. A post-1982 penny is minted by plating copper onto a zinc disk. Is a post-1982 penny an example of a homogeneous or heterogeneous mixture?

81. Gasoline contains a complex mixture of hydrocarbons. Is gasoline an example of a heterogeneous or a homogeneous mixture?

82. A dry cleaning solvent contains chlorofluorocarbons (CFCs). Is this dry cleaning solvent an example of a homogeneous mixture or a pure substance?

83. The electronics industry manufactures semiconductor chips from silicon. Refer to the periodic table and predict an element that may substitute for silicon.

84. The electronics industry manufactures transistors using arsenic diffusion. Refer to the periodic table and predict an element that may substitute for arsenic.

85. Name the three most abundant elements in Earth's crust.

86. Name the three most abundant elements in the human body.

87. State the atomic number for each of the following elements:
    (a) argentum   (b) plumbum
    (c) stannum   (d) aurum

88. State the atomic number for each of the following elements:
    (a) rutherfordium   (b) seaborgium
    (c) bohrium   (d) copernicium

89. The reaction of hydrogen and nitrogen gases produces 5.00 g of ammonia and releases 3250 cal of heat. How much energy is required to decompose 5.00 g of ammonia into hydrogen and nitrogen gases?

90. The decomposition of 10.0 g of ammonia requires 27,200 J of energy to give hydrogen and nitrogen gases. How much energy is released when hydrogen and nitrogen gases react to produce 10.0 g of ammonia?

91. Iron and sulfur react to produce iron sulfide and heat energy. An experiment shows that the mass of iron and sulfur is equal to the mass of the iron sulfide. In theory, should the products weigh slightly more or slightly less than the reactants?

92. Hydrogen and iodine react to give hydrogen iodide while absorbing heat energy. An experiment shows that the total mass of the reactants is equal to the product. In theory, should the product weigh slightly more or slightly less than the reactants?

93. Define each symbol in Einstein's equation: $E = mc^2$.

94. State the law of conservation of mass and energy as it applies to a chemical reaction.

Challenge Exercises

95. State whether the following describes a physical or a chemical change: changing physical state, but not chemical formula.

96. State whether the following describes a physical or a chemical change: changing chemical formula, but not physical state.

 ## Online Exercises

Research each of the following using an Internet search engine (e.g., Google.com or Yahoo.com) and cite your URL reference.

97. Who first discovered oxygen?

98. Who first discovered hydrogen?

99. What is the boiling point of liquid oxygen in °F? °C? K?

100. What is the boiling point of liquid hydrogen in °F? °C? K?

3

Chapter Self-Test   *Answers to Self-Test are in Appendix J.*

1. Which of the following describes a substance in the solid physical state? (Sec. 3.1)
   (a) The substance has a variable shape.
   (b) The substance has a fixed volume.
   (c) The substance compresses negligibly.
   (d) all of the above
   (e) none of the above

2. Water contains hydrogen and oxygen. Which of the following describes water? (Sec. 3.2)
   (a) compound
   (b) element
   (c) heterogeneous mixture
   (d) homogeneous mixture
   (e) none of the above

3. Which of the following elements is *not* one of the 10 most abundant in Earth's crust, oceans, and atmosphere? (Sec. 3.3)
   (a) aluminum
   (b) iron
   (c) oxygen
   (d) silicon
   (e) silver

4. Refer to the periodic table and predict which of the following elements is an example of a semimetal. (Sec. 3.4)
   (a) Al
   (b) Ca
   (c) Te
   (d) Ti
   (e) Zn

5. Alum, $Al_2(SO_4)_3$, is used in styptic pencils to stop minor bleeding. What is the number of atoms in the chemical formula of alum? (Sec. 3.5)
   (a) 10
   (b) 12
   (c) 12
   (d) 17
   (e) 21

6. Which of the following properties of gasoline is a chemical property? (Sec. 3.6)
   (a) colorless liquid
   (b) burns with air
   (c) density, 0.70 g/mL
   (d) boiling point, 97 °C
   (e) insoluble in water

7. Which of the following is an example of a chemical change? (Sec. 3.7)
   (a) condensation
   (b) crystallization
   (c) oxidation
   (d) sublimation
   (e) none of the above

8. If 2.43 g of magnesium burns in oxygen to produce 4.03 g of magnesium oxide, what is the mass of reacting oxygen gas? (Sec. 3.8)
   (a) 1.60 g
   (b) 2.43 g
   (c) 4.03 g
   (d) 6.46 g
   (e) impossible to predict from the given information

9. What happens to the kinetic energy of gas molecules when the gas is cooled? (Sec. 3.9)
   (a) kinetic energy increases
   (b) kinetic energy decreases
   (c) kinetic energy remains constant
   (d) depends on the gas
   (e) none of the above

10. A nuclear power plant uses radioactive uranium to convert water to steam. The steam drives a turbine that turns a generator to produce electricity. What two forms of energy are represented by the *uranium* and the *steam*? (Sec. 3.10)
   (a) chemical energy and mechanical energy
   (b) chemical energy and heat energy
   (c) electrical energy and heat energy
   (d) nuclear energy and heat energy
   (e) nuclear energy and mechanical energy

Key Concepts

11. Identify the physical state (solid, liquid, or gas) that corresponds to each of the following illustrations:

(a)   (b)   (c)

12. Classify each of the following as an element, compound, homogeneous mixture, or heterogeneous mixture:
(a) iron ore
(b) iron oxide
(c) iron metal
(d) iron alloy

13. Classify the mineral (photo) and molecule (model) of sulfur as an element, compound, homogeneous mixture, or heterogeneous mixture:

14. Examine the model for aspirin and determine the molecular formula. In the model shown, the black sphere = C atom, white = H atom, and red = O atom.

Critical Thinking

15. Is ice floating in water an example of a heterogeneous or a homogeneous mixture?

16. Which of the following compounds has physical and chemical properties similar to cobalt metal: CoO, Co_2O_3, $Co(NO_3)_3$?

17. Using a playground swing as an example, when is the potential energy minimum and the kinetic energy maximum?

18. Using a roller coaster as an example, when is the potential energy maximum and the kinetic energy minimum?

Models of the Atom

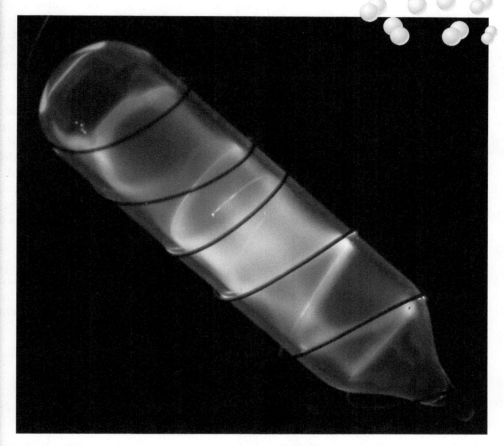

Hydrogen in the Environment Hydrogen is the most common element in the universe, but is less than 1% of Earth's crust. Very little hydrogen exists naturally in Earth's atmosphere as H_2, which is a colorless, odorless gas. Hydrogen emits a purple glow when excited electrically.

"Anyone who says that they can contemplate quantum mechanics
without becoming dizzy has not understood the concept in the least."
Niels Bohr, Danish Physicist (1885–1962)

The concept of an atom was born in Greece about 450 B.C. One of the great issues of the day was whether matter and motion were continuous or discontinuous. Democritus, a Greek philosopher, argued that *matter is discontinuous* and could not be infinitely divided. He believed that at some point a fundamental indivisible particle would emerge. He called this ultimate particle an atom, from the Greek word *atomos*, which means "indivisible."

About 350 B.C., Aristotle—the most influential philosopher of his time—argued that both *matter and motion are continuous*. He believed that matter could be divided an infinite number of times, and that even the smallest particle could be further divided. So powerful was Aristotle's influence that the existence of atoms was not believable, and his point of view prevailed for 21 centuries.

LEARNING OBJECTIVE

▶ To describe the Dalton model of the atom.

4.1 DALTON MODEL OF THE ATOM

In 1803, John Dalton (1766–1844), a modest Quaker schoolteacher, proposed that matter was discontinuous, not continuous as Aristotle had argued over 20 centuries before. But unlike Aristotle, Dalton offered experimental evidence for the particle nature of matter. Although he was not a distinguished scientist, Dalton presented convincing evidence based on the work of the famous French scientists Antoine Lavoisier and Joseph Proust, and the English physicist Robert Boyle.

Dalton proposed that matter consisted of atoms based on the laws of conservation of mass and definite proportion. Citing Proust's experiments in which two elements combine in more than one way, he formulated the law of multiple proportions; for example carbon and oxygen can combine as CO and CO_2.

In the seventeenth century, Robert Boyle, the noted English physicist, had concluded from experiments that a gas was made up of tiny particles. Dalton expanded on Boyle's conclusion and proposed that all matter was composed of particles. In addition to Boyle's experiments, Dalton relied on two other scientific principles, the law of conservation of mass and the law of definite proportion.

In 1789, Antoine Lavoisier established the law of conservation of mass. By carefully weighing substances before and after a chemical reaction, Lavoisier demonstrated that matter was neither created nor destroyed. Although atoms are much too small to weigh directly, this principle allows us to predict the masses of substances involved in a chemical change. In 1799, Joseph Proust established the law of definite proportion (definite composition), which states that a compound always contains the same elements in the same proportion by mass.

Dalton initially presented his evidence for the existence of atoms to the *Literary and Philosophical Society* of Manchester, England. He proposed that an element is composed of tiny, indivisible, indestructible particles. Furthermore, he argued that compounds are simply combinations of two or more atoms of different elements. In 1808, Dalton published the atomic theory in his classic textbook *A New System of Chemical Philosophy.*

CHEMISTRY CONNECTION John Dalton

Q: How was John Dalton able to accept an honorary degree from Oxford University dressed in a scarlet robe when wearing scarlet was forbidden by his Quaker faith?

John Dalton was born the son of a weaver into a devoutly religious family. At the age of 12, he began teaching at a Quaker school and developed an interest in science. He was most interested in meteorology and kept a lifelong daily journal of atmospheric conditions for his hometown of Manchester, England.

By all accounts, Dalton was not an inspiring lecturer, and he was hindered as a researcher by being color-blind. He had only a minimal education and limited finances, but he compensated for this with persistent and meticulous work habits. Dalton's daily study of the weather led him to conclude, like Robert Boyle and Isaac Newton before him, that the air was made up of gas particles. Over time, he began to construct his atomic theory as follows.

According to the law of definite composition, carbon and oxygen always react in the same mass ratio to produce carbon dioxide. Dalton proposed that one atom of carbon combines with two atoms of oxygen to produce a molecule of CO_2, as shown using Dalton's symbolism.

Carbon dioxide, CO_2

◀ **Carbon dioxide, CO_2**

◀ John Dalton
(1766–1844)

Similarly, he proposed that two atoms of hydrogen combine with one atom of oxygen to give a molecule of H_2O.

Water, H_2O

◀ **Water, H_2O**

Methane, CH_4

◀ **Methane, CH_4**

Finally, Dalton reasoned that two atoms of hydrogen in water could substitute for each of the oxygen atoms in carbon dioxide. This would result in a molecule with one carbon atom and four hydrogen atoms, that is, CH_4. At the time, this compound was known as marsh gas, but we now refer to it as methane.

Through experimentation, Dalton indeed found that the combining ratio of carbon to hydrogen in methane was 1 to 4; this agreed perfectly with his prediction. Thus, Dalton had experimental evidence to support the atomic theory.

A: Dalton rationalized that because he was color-blind and saw the ceremonial robe as gray, he was not violating Quaker doctrine.

In a surprisingly short period of time, the atomic theory was generally accepted by the scientific community. The theory can be summarized as follows:

1. An element is composed of tiny, indivisible, indestructible particles called atoms.
2. All atoms of an element are identical and have the same properties.
3. Atoms of different elements combine to form compounds.
4. Compounds contain atoms in small whole number ratios.
5. Atoms can combine in more than one ratio to form different compounds.

As we will learn, Dalton's first two proposals were incorrect, but the atomic theory was nonetheless an important step toward understanding the nature of matter.

4.2 THOMSON MODEL OF THE ATOM

LEARNING OBJECTIVES

▸ To describe the Thomson plum pudding model of the atom.

▸ To state the relative charge on an electron and a proton.

Toward the end of the 1800s, there was disturbing evidence that the atom was divisible after all. Experiments involving the passage of electricity through hydrogen gas led to the discovery of a negatively charged particle called an **electron** (e^-), and a positively charged particle called a **proton** (p^+). The electron was assigned a relative charge of −1, and the proton had an opposite, but equal charge of +1.

In 1903, J. J. Thomson (1856–1940) proposed a subatomic model of the atom. The subatomic model pictured a positively charged atom containing negatively charged electrons. Thomson visualized electrons in homogeneous spheres of positive charge in a way that was analogous to raisins in English plum pudding (Figure 4.1). Thus, the Thomson proposal became popularly known as the *plum pudding model* or *raisin pudding model of the atom.*

Originally, Thomson was only able to determine the relative charge-to-mass ratio of the electron and the proton. However in 1911, after 5 years of tedious observations, the American physicist Robert Millikan (1868–1953) determined the actual charge on the electron. This allowed Thomson to calculate the actual mass of the electron and the proton. Thomson calculated that the mass of the electron is 9.11×10^{-28} g, and that the mass of the proton is 1.67×10^{-24} g.

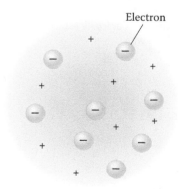

▲ Figure 4.1 **Thomson Model of the Atom** Atoms are pictured as spheres of positive charge. The small negative particles in the sphere represent electrons.

Note J. J. Thomson spent his academic career at Cambridge University and, at the age of 27, became director of the prestigious Cavendish Laboratory. In 1906 he won the Nobel Prize in physics for his work on the electron, and 2 years later he was knighted. Thomson's contribution was far-reaching—seven of his former students and assistants went on to receive Nobel Prizes.

▶ To describe the Rutherford nuclear model of the atom.

▶ To state the relative charge and approximate mass of the electron, proton, and neutron.

4.3 RUTHERFORD MODEL OF THE ATOM

Ernest Rutherford (1871–1937) was digging potatoes on his father's farm in New Zealand when he received the news that he had won a scholarship to Cambridge University. He had actually come in second, but the winner had declined the scholarship to get married. The 24-year-old Rutherford postponed his own wedding plans and immediately set out for England.

At Cambridge, Ernest Rutherford studied subatomic particles and earned his doctorate working for J. J. Thomson. Upon graduation, Rutherford went to McGill University in Canada and began to work in the field of radioactivity, which studies unstable atoms that radiate subatomic particles and energy. After a year he went back to New Zealand, married, and returned to Manchester University in England. There he continued to study radioactivity and coined the terms *alpha ray* and *beta ray* for two types of radiation. He discovered a third type of radiation that was not affected by a magnetic field and gave it the name *gamma ray*. In 1908, Rutherford received the Nobel Prize in chemistry for his work on radioactivity.

In 1906, Rutherford found that alpha rays contained particles identical to those of helium atoms stripped of electrons. He experimented with alpha rays by firing them at thin gold foils. As expected, the particles passed straight through the foil or, on occasion, deflected slightly (Figure 4.2). This observation seemed reasonable because the plum pudding model of the atom pictured homogeneous spheres.

A few years later the true picture of the atom was unveiled. The person who did the experiment was Hans Geiger, Rutherford's assistant and the inventor of the Geiger counter. Here is a description of the experiment in Rutherford's own words:

One day Geiger came to me and said, "Don't you think that young Marsden, whom I am training in radioactive methods, ought to begin a small research?" Now I had thought that too, so I said, "Why not let him see if any alpha particles can be scattered through a large angle?" I may tell you in confidence that I did not believe that they would be, since we knew that the alpha particle was a very fast massive particle, with a great deal of energy. Then I remember two or three days later Geiger coming to me in great excitement and saying, "We have been able to get some of the alpha particles coming backwards." It was quite the most incredible event that has ever happened to me in my life. It was almost as incredible as if you fired a 15-inch shell at a piece of tissue paper and it came back and hit you.

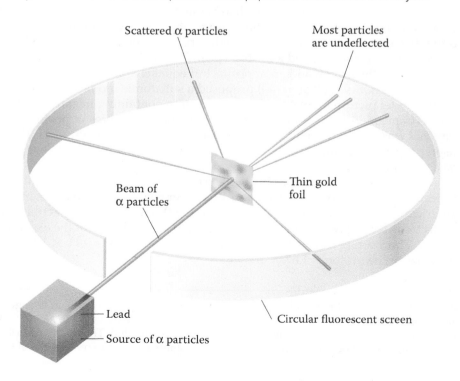

▶ Figure 4.2 **Alpha-Scattering Experiment** The diagram shows the deflection of alpha particles by a thin gold foil. Although the foil was only 0.5 μm thick, a few alpha particles actually rebounded backward.

Rutherford interpreted the alpha-scattering results as follows. He believed that most of the alpha particles passed directly through the foil because an atom is largely empty space with electrons moving about. But in the center of the atom is the **atomic nucleus** containing protons. Rutherford reasoned that, compared to the atom, the nucleus is tiny and has a very high density. The alpha particles that bounced backward recoiled after striking the dense nucleus. The scattering of alpha particles by the atomic nuclei in the gold foil is illustrated in Figure 4.3.

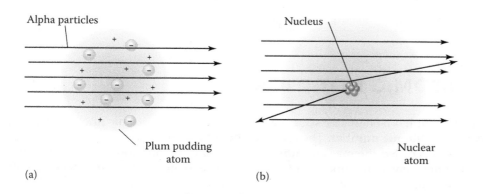

Alpha particles

Plum pudding atom

(a)

Nucleus

Nuclear atom

(b)

◄ **Figure 4.3 Explanation of Alpha-Scattering** (a) Powerful alpha particles should pass through a homogeneous plum pudding gold atom. (b) Because positively charged alpha particles are deflected, Rutherford reasoned correctly that a gold atom has a dense, positively charged nucleus.

In 1911, Rutherford proposed a new model of the atom. He suggested that negatively charged electrons were distributed about a positively charged nucleus. Rutherford was able to estimate the size of the atom and its nucleus. He calculated that an atom has a diameter of about 1×10^{-8} cm, and that the nucleus has a diameter of about 1×10^{-13} cm. The Rutherford model of the atom is illustrated in Figure 4.4.

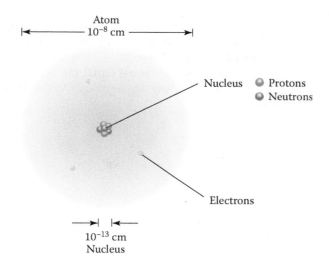

Atom
10^{-8} cm

Nucleus ● Protons
● Neutrons

Electrons

10^{-13} cm
Nucleus

◄ **Figure 4.4 Rutherford Model of the Atom** Most of the mass of an atom is found in the nucleus. Note that the atoms and nuclei are not to scale, as the size of an atom is about 100,000 times larger than the size of the nucleus.

The diameters of atoms and nuclei are extremely small and difficult to comprehend, so consider the following analogy to visualize an atom. The size of an atom compared to the size of its nucleus is similar to a kilometer compared to a centimeter. By analogy, if the atom were as large as the New Orleans Superdome, the nucleus would be the size of a small marble. This analogy clarifies why so few alpha particles were scattered by gold nuclei in the thin foil.

Owing to the heaviness of the nucleus, Rutherford predicted that it contained neutral particles in addition to protons. Twenty years later, one of Rutherford's former students found the elusive neutral particle. In 1932, James Chadwick (1891–1974) discovered the **neutron (n^0)** and 3 years later was awarded the Nobel Prize in physics. We can summarize the data for the electron, proton, and neutron as shown in Table 4.1.

TABLE 4.1 SUBATOMIC PARTICLES

SUBATOMIC PARTICLE	SYMBOL	LOCATION	RELATIVE CHARGE	RELATIVE MASS
electron	e^-	outside nucleus	-1	$1/1836$
proton	p^+	inside nucleus	$+1$	1
neutron	n^0	inside nucleus	0	1

LEARNING OBJECTIVES

▸ To indicate protons, neutrons, and electrons for a given atomic notation.

▸ To indicate the number of neutrons in a given isotope.

4.4 ATOMIC NOTATION

Each element has a characteristic number of protons in its atomic nucleus. This value is called the **atomic number**. The total number of protons and neutrons in the nucleus of an atom is called the **mass number**. A shorthand method for keeping track of protons and neutrons in the nucleus of an atom is called **atomic notation**. By convention, the symbol of the element (Sy) is preceded by a subscript and superscript. The subscript, designated the Z value, represents the atomic number. The superscript, designated the A value, represents the mass number. Thus,

mass number (p^+ and n^0)

$$_{Z}^{A}\text{Sy} \quad — \text{symbol of the element}$$

atomic number (p^+)

As an example, an atom of sodium can be written as $_{11}^{23}\text{Na}$. Here the atomic number (number of protons) is 11, and the mass number (number of protons + neutrons) is 23. From this information, we can determine the number of neutrons. The nucleus of this sodium atom contains 12 neutrons ($A - Z = 23 - 11 = 12$). Because atoms are neutral, the number of negative electrons must equal the number of positive protons. Thus, there are 11 electrons surrounding the nucleus. We can show a simple diagram of the sodium atom as follows:

$$_{11}^{23}\text{Na}$$

12 n^0
11 p^+

11 e^-

Example Exercise 4.1 further illustrates the interpretation of atomic notation to state the composition of an atom.

Example Exercise 4.1 Atomic Notation

Given the atomic notation for the following atoms, draw a diagram showing the arrangement of protons, neutrons, and electrons.

(a) $_{9}^{19}\text{F}$

(b) $_{47}^{109}\text{Ag}$

Solution

We can draw a diagram of an atom by showing protons and neutrons in the nucleus surrounded by electrons.

(a) Because the atomic number is 9 and the mass number is 19, the number of neutrons is 10 (19 − 9). If there are 9 protons, there must be 9 electrons.

$^{19}_{9}\text{F}$

$10\,\text{n}^0$
$9\,\text{p}^+$

$9\,\text{e}^-$

(b) Because the atomic number is 47 and the mass number is 109, the number of neutrons is 62 (109 − 47). If there are 47 protons, there must be 47 electrons.

$^{109}_{47}\text{Ag}$

$62\,\text{n}^0$
$47\,\text{p}^+$

$47\,\text{e}^-$

Practice Exercise

Given the following diagram, indicate the nucleus using atomic notation.

$30\,\text{n}^0$
$25\,\text{p}^+$

$25\,\text{e}^-$

Answer: $^{55}_{25}\text{Mn}$

Concept Exercise

Can atoms of different elements have the same atomic number?

Answer: See Appendix G.

Isotopes

Approximately 20 elements occur naturally with a fixed number of neutrons. For most elements, the number of neutrons in the nucleus varies. Atoms of the same element that have a different number of neutrons in the nucleus are called **isotopes**.

For isotopes, as the number of neutrons varies, so does the mass number. For example, hydrogen occurs naturally as two stable isotopes, protium ($^{1}_{1}\text{H}$) and deuterium ($^{2}_{1}\text{H}$). Protium has only one proton in its nucleus, whereas deuterium has a proton and a neutron. A third isotope of hydrogen, tritium ($^{3}_{1}\text{H}$), is unstable and radioactive. Tritium has one proton and two neutrons in its nucleus. Table 4.2 lists the naturally occurring stable isotopes of the first 10 elements.

TABLE 4.2 NATURALLY OCCURRING STABLE ISOTOPES OF THE FIRST 10 ELEMENTS

ATOMIC NUMBER	MASS NUMBER	ATOMIC NOTATION	ATOMIC NUMBER	MASS NUMBER	ATOMIC NOTATION
1	1	$^{1}_{1}H$	6	13	$^{13}_{6}C$
1	2	$^{2}_{1}H$	7	14	$^{14}_{7}N$
2	3	$^{3}_{2}He$	7	15	$^{15}_{7}N$
2	4	$^{4}_{2}He$	8	16	$^{16}_{8}O$
3	6	$^{6}_{3}Li$	8	17	$^{17}_{8}O$
3	7	$^{7}_{3}Li$	8	18	$^{18}_{8}O$
4	9	$^{9}_{4}Be$	9	19	$^{19}_{9}F$
5	10	$^{10}_{5}B$	10	20	$^{20}_{10}Ne$
5	11	$^{11}_{5}B$	10	21	$^{21}_{10}Ne$
6	12	$^{12}_{6}C$	10	22	$^{22}_{10}Ne$

▶ **Neon Isotopes** The element neon consists of three naturally occurring isotopes: Ne-20, Ne-21, and Ne-22. We can deduce by the atomic mass of neon (20.18 amu) that Ne-20 is the most abundant isotope.

We often refer to an isotope by stating the name of the element followed by its mass number, for example, carbon-12. To write the atomic notation, we must also know the atomic number. In this textbook, the atomic number is found above the symbol of the element in the periodic table. If we refer to the inside front cover of this textbook, we find that the atomic number of C is 6. Thus, we can write the atomic notation for carbon-12 as $^{12}_{6}C$.

Example Exercise 4.2 further illustrates the relationship between atomic notation and the composition of an atomic nucleus.

| Example Exercise 4.2 | Nuclear Composition of Isotopes |

State the number of protons and the number of neutrons in an atom of each of the following isotopes.

(a) $^{37}_{17}Cl$ (b) mercury-202

Solution

The subscript value refers to the atomic number (p^+), and the superscript value refers to the mass number (p^+ and n^0).

(a) Thus, $^{37}_{17}Cl$ has 17 p^+ and 20 n^0 ($37 - 17 = 20$).

(b) In the periodic table, we find that the atomic number of mercury is 80. Thus, the atomic notation, $^{202}_{80}Hg$, indicates 80 p^+ and 122 n^0 ($202 - 80 = 122$).

Practice Exercise

State the number of protons and the number of neutrons in an atom of each of the following isotopes.

(a) $^{120}_{50}Sn$ (b) uranium-238

Answers:

(a) 50 p^+ and 70 n^0 (b) 92 p^+ and 146 n^0

Concept Exercise

Can atoms of different elements have the same mass number?

Answer: See Appendix G.

Note In general, the properties of isotopes of an element are similar. Consider a carbon-12 atom, which has six protons and six neutrons in the nucleus. If the mass number increases by one neutron, we have a carbon-13 atom. Other than a slight change in mass, the properties of carbon-12 and carbon-13 are nearly identical.

On the other hand, when the atomic number of carbon-12 increases by one proton, we have a nitrogen-13 atom. The additional proton changes the properties dramatically. Carbon occurs naturally as coal, diamond, and graphite, whereas nitrogen is a colorless, odorless gas in the atmosphere.

4.5 ATOMIC MASS

We realize, of course, that atoms are much too small to weigh directly on a balance. A carbon atom, for instance, has a mass of only 1.99×10^{-23} g. Instead of weighing atoms, scientists determine the mass of atoms relative to each other. With a special magnetic-field instrument, the mass of an atom can be compared to the mass of a carbon-12 atom. The carbon-12 isotope has been chosen as a reference standard and is assigned a value of exactly 12 atomic mass units. Stated differently, an **atomic mass unit (amu)** is equal to 1/12 the mass of a carbon-12 atom.

LEARNING OBJECTIVES

▶ To explain the concept of relative atomic mass.

▶ To calculate the atomic mass for an element given the mass and abundance of the naturally occurring isotopes.

Simple and Weighted Averages

Before proceeding, let's contrast two kinds of averages. Let's suppose a company manufactures 16-lb and 8-lb shot put balls for Olympic men and women athletes. Of all the shot put balls manufactured, 75% are 16 lb and 25% are 8 lb. What is the average mass of a shot put ball? If we add the two masses together and divide by 2, we obtain the simple average mass. That is,

$$\frac{16 \text{ lb} + 8 \text{ lb}}{2} = 12 \text{ lb}$$

The simple average mass of a shot put ball is 12 lb, but the true average mass must be heavier, and weighted in favor of the higher percentage of 16-lb balls. Since the

▲ **Olympic Shot Put** In the women's Olympic shot put event, female athletes toss an 8 lb steel ball.

percentages are 75% and 25%, we will write the decimal fractions 0.75 and 0.25, and proceed as follows:

$$16\text{-lb balls: } 16 \text{ lb} \times 0.75 = 12 \text{ lb}$$
$$8\text{-lb balls: } 8 \text{ lb} \times 0.25 = \underline{2 \text{ lb}}$$
$$14 \text{ lb}$$

Although the weighted average mass is 14 lb, we should note that no shot put ball weighs 14 lb. An actual shot put ball weighs either 16 lb or 8 lb. A mass of 14 lb represents a theoretical average shot put ball.

Atomic Mass of an Element

The **atomic mass** of an element is the weighted average mass of all naturally occurring isotopes. To calculate the atomic mass, we will use a method similar to the one used in the shot put example. That is, to calculate the weighted average mass of an atom, we must consider the mass as well as the percent abundance of each isotope.

Carbon has two naturally occurring stable isotopes: carbon-12 and carbon-13. We can calculate the atomic mass of carbon given the mass and natural abundance of each isotope.

ISOTOPE	MASS	ABUNDANCE
^{12}C	12.000 amu	98.89%
^{13}C	13.003 amu	1.11%

The natural abundance of each isotope, expressed as a decimal, is 0.9889 and 0.0111. To calculate the true weighted average mass of a carbon atom, we must consider the mass and percentage of each isotope. We proceed as follows:

$$^{12}C: 12.000 \text{ amu} \times 0.9889 = 11.87 \text{ amu}$$
$$^{13}C: 13.003 \text{ amu} \times 0.0111 = \underline{0.144 \text{ amu}}$$
$$12.01 \text{ amu}$$

Even though the atomic mass of carbon is 12.01 amu, we should note that no carbon atom weighs 12.01 amu. An actual carbon atom weighs either 12.000 amu or 13.003 amu. A mass of 12.01 amu represents the mass of a hypothetical average carbon atom. Example Exercise 4.3 further illustrates the calculation of atomic mass from isotopic mass and abundance data.

Example Exercise 4.3 Calculation of Atomic Mass

Silicon is the second most abundant element in Earth's crust. Calculate the atomic mass of silicon given the following data for its three natural isotopes:

ISOTOPE	MASS	ABUNDANCE
^{28}Si	27.977 amu	92.21%
^{29}Si	28.976 amu	4.70%
^{30}Si	29.974 amu	3.09%

Solution

We can find the atomic mass of silicon as follows:

$$^{28}Si: 27.977 \text{ amu} \times 0.9221 = 25.80 \text{ amu}$$
$$^{29}Si: 28.976 \text{ amu} \times 0.0470 = 1.36 \text{ amu}$$
$$^{30}Si: 29.974 \text{ amu} \times 0.0309 = \underline{0.926 \text{ amu}}$$
$$28.09 \text{ amu}$$

The average mass of a silicon atom is 28.09 amu, although we should note that there are no silicon atoms with a mass of 28.09 amu.

Practice Exercise

Calculate the atomic mass of copper given the following data:

ISOTOPE	MASS	ABUNDANCE
^{63}Cu	62.930 amu	69.09%
^{65}Cu	64.928 amu	30.91%

Answer: 63.55 amu

Concept Exercise

A bag of marbles has 75 large marbles with a mass of 2.00 g each, and 25 small marbles with a mass of 1.00 g each. Calculate (a) the simple average mass, and (b) the weighted average mass of the marble collection.

Answer: See Appendix G.

The Periodic Table

We often need to refer to the atomic number and atomic mass of an element. For convenience, this information is listed in the periodic table. In this textbook the atomic number is indicated above the symbol, and the atomic mass is given below the symbol. Figure 4.5 illustrates carbon as it appears in the periodic table.

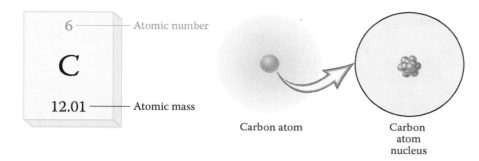

◀ **Figure 4.5 Carbon in the Periodic Table** The atomic number designates the number of protons (6). The atomic mass designates the weighted average mass of the naturally occurring stable isotopes of the element.

When we refer to the periodic table, it is not possible to determine the number of naturally occurring isotopes for a given element. Of the first 83 elements, however, 81 elements have one or more stable isotopes. Only technetium (element 43) and promethium (element 61) are radioactive and unstable. In the periodic table on the inside front cover of this textbook, the mass number of unstable elements is given in parentheses as shown in Figure 4.6.

A value in parentheses below the symbol of an element indicates the mass number of the most stable or best known radioactive isotope. The mass number refers to the total number of protons and neutrons in the unstable nucleus. From the periodic table you can easily distinguish the elements that are stable from those that are unstable and radioactive. Example Exercise 4.4 further illustrates how to use the periodic table as a reference.

▲ **Figure 4.6 Technetium in the Periodic Table** The atomic number designates the number of protons (43). The mass number for this radioactive isotope is 99. Technetium-99 has a total of 43 protons and 56 neutrons in its nucleus.

Example Exercise 4.4 Nuclear Composition from the Periodic Table

Refer to the periodic table on the inside cover of this textbook and determine the atomic number and atomic mass for iron.

Solution

In the periodic table we observe

The atomic number of iron is 26, and the atomic mass is 55.85 amu. From the periodic table information, we should note that it is not possible to determine the number of isotopes for iron or their mass numbers.

Practice Exercise
Refer to the periodic table on the inside cover of this text and determine the atomic number and mass number for the given radioactive isotope of radon gas.

Answers: 86 and (222)

Concept Exercise
Which of the following is *never* a whole number value: atomic number, atomic mass, or mass number?

Answer: See Appendix G.

CHEMISTRY CONNECTION Heavy Water

Q: Do all water molecules have the same mass?

Hydrogen atoms usually have one proton as their nucleus. However, about 1 in 6000 hydrogen atoms has both a proton and a neutron as its nucleus. This isotope of hydrogen is called *deuterium* (D), and is listed in Table 4.2. The mass of deuterium is about twice that of hydrogen. When deuterium atoms replace the hydrogen atoms in water, the resulting compound is referred to as *heavy water*. The systematic name of heavy water is deuterium oxide, and its formula is D_2O.

Heavy water was discovered by the American chemist Harold Urey, who won the Nobel Prize in 1934 for his discovery. Heavy water is colorless, odorless, and tasteless, but it is toxic to humans and animals. The physical and chemical properties of heavy water are similar to those of ordinary light water. The following table lists a few properties of light water versus heavy water.

Heavy water has two important uses in nuclear reactors. When an atomic nucleus splits (i.e., fissions), it releases neutrons. However, these neutrons are moving at a high velocity and must be slowed in order to be captured and cause further nuclear fissions of a radioactive substance such as uranium–235. Heavy water is ideal for slowing down fast neutrons released during the fission process. In addition, heavy water has a higher specific heat than ordinary water, and is used to cool the nuclear reactor and prevent meltdown.

PROPERTIES OF WATER VERSUS HEAVY WATER

PROPERTY	LIGHT WATER, H_2O	HEAVY WATER, D_2O
appearance	colorless, odorless, tasteless liquid	colorless, odorless, tasteless liquid
molecular mass	18.02 amu	20.03 amu
density	1.000 g/mL at 4 °C	1.105 g/mL at 4 °C
freezing point	0.00 °C	3.82 °C
boiling point	100.00 °C	101.42 °C

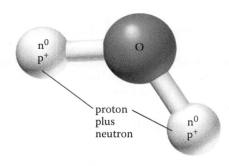

A: Light water, H_2O, has a molecular mass of 18.02 amu, while heavy water, D_2O, is 20.03 amu. Heavy water molecules have a greater mass because deuterium atoms have one more neutron than hydrogen atoms.

LEARNING OBJECTIVE

▶ To state the relationship of wavelength, frequency, and energy of light.

4.6 THE WAVE NATURE OF LIGHT

We can use our imagination to visualize light traveling through space in a fashion similar to an ocean wave. **Wavelength** refers to the distance the light wave travels to complete one cycle. **Frequency** refers to the number of wave cycles completed in each second. The velocity of light is constant, as all wavelengths and frequencies travel at 3.00×10^8 m/s. Figure 4.7 illustrates the wave nature of light.

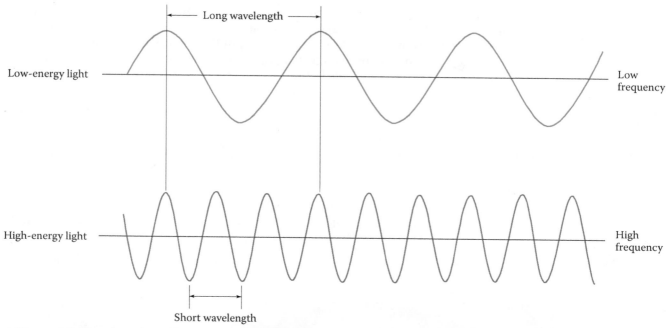

▲ Figure 4.7 **Wavelength and Frequency of Light** Notice that the wavelength is longer for low-energy light than for high-energy light. Also notice that the frequency is greater for high-energy light than for low-energy light.

As the wavelength of light decreases, the frequency of a light wave increases. Conversely, as the wavelength increases, the frequency decreases. As an example, the wavelength decreases from red to violet as the frequency increases. We can visualize a high-frequency light wave moving rapidly up and down while completing many cycles per second. Consequently, high-frequency light is more energetic than low-frequency light, and short-wavelength light is more energetic than long-wavelength light.

Light—A Continuous Spectrum

The term **light** usually refers to radiant energy that is visible. Our eyes can see light in the **visible spectrum** (400–700 nm), but not in the ultraviolet spectrum or the infrared spectrum. The wavelength of ultraviolet radiation is too short to be visible (below 400 nm), and infrared radiation is too long (above 700 nm).

A rainbow is created when sunlight passes through raindrops. Each raindrop acts as a miniature prism and separates sunlight into various bands of color. What we ordinarily observe as white light is actually several colors of light mixed together. When white light passes through a glass prism, it separates into all the colors of the rainbow (Figure 4.8).

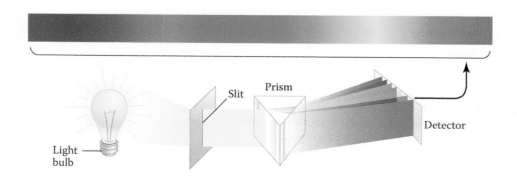

◀ Figure 4.8 **White Light Passing through a Prism** Notice that white light separates into a rainbow of colors when it passes through a glass prism. Similarly, sunlight produces a rainbow when it passes through raindrops that act as miniature prisms.

We also, on occasion, use the term *light* when referring to radiant energy that is not visible. The complete **radiant energy spectrum** is an uninterrupted band, or **continuous spectrum**, of visible and invisible light that ranges from short to long wavelengths. The radiant energy spectrum includes invisible gamma rays, X rays, and microwaves, as well as visible light (Figure 4.9).

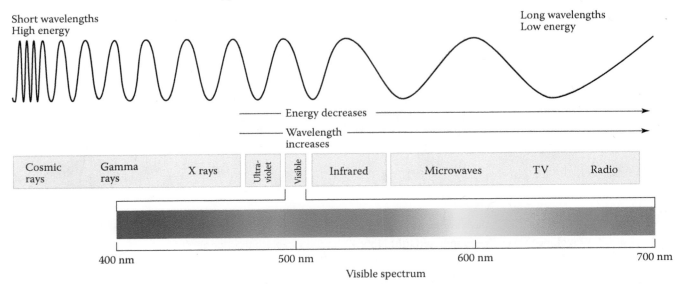

Short wavelengths
High energy

Long wavelengths
Low energy

Energy decreases

Wavelength increases

| Cosmic rays | Gamma rays | X rays | Ultra-violet | Visible | Infrared | Microwaves | TV | Radio |

400 nm   500 nm   600 nm   700 nm

Visible spectrum

▲ Figure 4.9 **The Radiant Energy Spectrum** The complete radiant energy spectrum includes short-wavelength gamma rays through long-wavelength microwaves. Notice that the visible spectrum is only a narrow window in a broad band of radiant energy.

Example Exercise 4.5 illustrates how the wavelength, frequency, and energy of light are related.

Example Exercise 4.5 Properties of Light

Considering blue light and yellow light, which has the

(a) longer wavelength?
(b) higher frequency?
(c) higher energy?

Solution
Referring to Figure 4.9, we notice that the wavelength of yellow light is about 600 nm and that of blue light is about 500 nm. Thus,

(a) *yellow light* has a longer wavelength than blue light.
(b) *blue light* has a higher frequency because it has a shorter wavelength.
(c) *blue light* has a higher energy because it has a higher frequency.

Practice Exercise
Considering infrared light and ultraviolet light, which has the

(a) longer wavelength?   (b) higher frequency?
(c) higher energy?

Answers:

(a) infrared   (b) ultraviolet
(c) ultraviolet

Concept Exercise
The energy of light (increases/decreases) as the wavelength increases. The energy of light (increases/decreases) as the frequency increases.

Answer: See Appendix G.

4.7 THE QUANTUM CONCEPT

LEARNING OBJECTIVE

▶ To explain the quantum concept applied to matter and energy.

In 1900, Max Planck (1858–1947), a German physicist, introduced a revolutionary idea. Planck proposed that the energy radiated by a heated object is not continuous, but rather that the radiation is emitted in small bundles. The idea that energy is composed of discrete units is referred to as the quantum concept.

Although radiant energy has a wave nature, it also has a particle nature, and an individual unit of light energy is referred to as a quantum, or a **photon**. According to the quantum theory, an ordinary light bulb radiates light which has both a wave and particle nature.

We can illustrate the quantum concept with the following analogy. A ball rolling down a ramp loses potential energy continuously. Conversely, a ball rolling down a flight of stairs loses potential energy in discrete units each time it drops from one step to another. In this example, the loss of potential energy is continuous as the ball rolls down the ramp, and the loss is quantized as the ball rolls down the stairs. Figure 4.10 contrasts a continuous change in energy versus a quantized energy change.

◀ Figure 4.10 **Stair Analogy for the Quantum Principle** A ball rolling down a ramp loses potential energy continuously. Conversely, a ball rolling down a flight of stairs loses potential energy in quantized amounts each time it drops from one step to another one.

The following Example Exercise 4.6 further illustrates practical applications of the quantum theory.

Example Exercise 4.6 Quantum Concept

State whether each of the following scientific instruments gives a continuous or a quantized measurement of mass:

(a) triple-beam balance

(b) digital electronic balance

Solution
Refer to Figure PSS.3 if you have not used these balances in the laboratory.

(a) On a triple-beam balance a small metal rider is moved along a beam. Because the metal rider can be moved to any position on the beam, a triple-beam balance gives a *continuous* mass measurement.

(b) On a digital electronic balance the display indicates the mass of an object to a particular decimal place, for example, 5.015 g. Because the last digit in the display must be a whole number, a digital balance gives a *quantized* mass measurement.

Practice Exercise
State whether each of the following musical instruments produces continuous or quantized musical notes:

(a) acoustic guitar   (b) electronic keyboard

Answers:

(a) continuous   (b) quantized

Concept Exercise
Complete the following quantum analogy: a water wave is to a drop of water, as a light wave is to a _____.

Answer: See Appendix G.

▸ To describe the Bohr model of the atom.

▸ To explain the relationship between energy levels in an atom and lines in an emission spectrum.

4.8 BOHR MODEL OF THE ATOM

In 1911, a brilliant young Danish physicist, Niels Bohr (1885–1962), completed his doctorate and left for England to begin postdoctoral work under J. J. Thomson. After a few months, he left Cambridge to join Rutherford at Manchester where the atomic nucleus had been discovered. It took only 2 years for the young Dane to raise our understanding of the atom to yet another level.

In 1913, Bohr speculated that electrons orbit around the atomic nucleus just as planets orbit around the Sun. He further suggested that electron orbits were at a fixed distance from the nucleus and had a definite energy. The electron was said to travel in a fixed-energy orbit referred to as an **energy level**. Moreover, electrons could be found only in specific energy levels and nowhere else. Figure 4.11 illustrates the model of the hydrogen atom proposed by Niels Bohr. This model is referred to as the Bohr model of the atom, or simply, the **Bohr atom**.

Evidence for Energy Levels

The Bohr model was a beautiful mental picture of electrons in atoms. However, no one knew if the model was right or wrong because there was no experimental evidence to support the theory. Coincidentally, about this time, Bohr received an article on the emission of light from hydrogen gas. The article showed that excited hydrogen gas emits separate lines of color, rather than a continuous band of color. The three most prominent lines are violet, blue-green, and red.

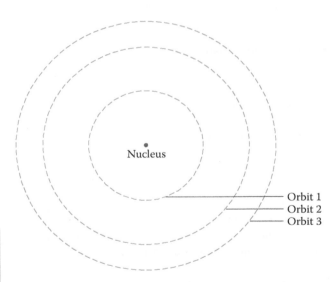

Nucleus

Orbit 1
Orbit 2
Orbit 3

◀ Figure 4.11 **Bohr Model of the Hydrogen Atom** The electron is a specific distance from the nucleus and occupies an orbit of discrete energy. According to the Bohr model, the electron is found only in a given energy level.

▲ **Niels Bohr Stamp** The planetary model of the atom was proposed by Niels Bohr.

If hydrogen gas in a glass tube is subjected to electricity, the excited hydrogen gas releases energy as reddish-purple light. When the reddish-purple light passes through a glass prism, it separates into narrow bands of color. This collection of narrow bands of light is called an **emission line spectrum**, and the individual bands of light are called *spectral lines*. The emission spectrum of hydrogen gas is shown in Figure 4.12.

After examining the emission spectrum of hydrogen, Bohr realized that he had experimental evidence to support his model of the atom. The concept of electron energy levels was supported by the line spectrum of hydrogen. In a gas discharge tube, excited atoms of hydrogen have electrons in a high-energy orbit; for example, the electron may temporarily occupy the second orbit. Because this state is unstable the electron quickly drops from the higher level back to a lower level, that is, from

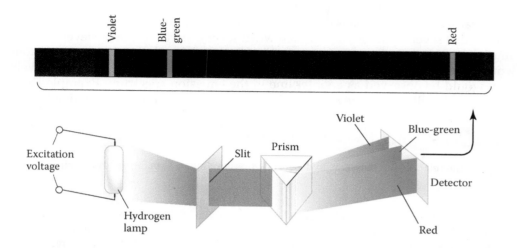

◀ Figure 4.12 **Hydrogen Emission Spectrum** A reddish-purple light is observed when a voltage is applied to a hydrogen lamp. When the reddish-purple light passes through a glass prism, three lines are observed: violet, blue-green, and red.

level 2 to level 1. In the process, the electron loses a discrete amount of energy. This discrete energy loss corresponds to a photon of light energy. The energy of the photon of light equals the amount of energy lost by the electron as it drops from the higher to the lower energy level.

In the hydrogen spectrum, there are three bright lines: red, blue-green, and violet. The red line has the longest wavelength of the three and the lowest energy. Bohr found that the red line corresponds to an excited electron dropping from energy level 3 to 2. The blue-green line is more energetic than the red line and corresponds to an excited electron dropping from energy level 4 to 2. The violet line is the most energetic of the three and is produced when an electron drops from energy level 5 to 2. Figure 4.13 illustrates the correlation between Bohr's electron energy levels and the observed lines in the hydrogen spectrum.

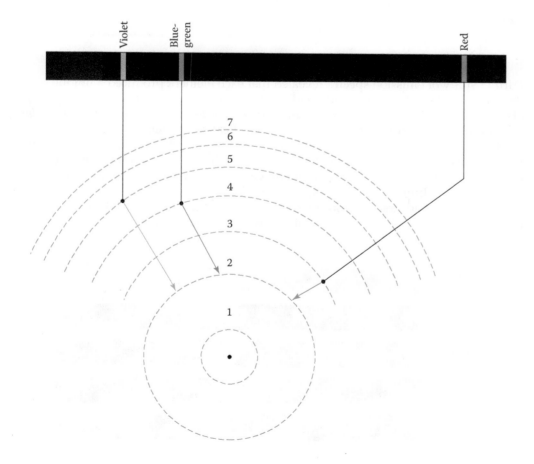

◀ Figure 4.13 **Spectral Lines and Energy Levels in Hydrogen** When an electron drops from energy level **5** to **2**, a violet photon is released. When an electron drops from level **4** to **2**, a blue-green photon is released; from level **3** to **2**, a red photon is released. A visible spectral line corresponds to a large number of identical photons.

Because a single photon is emitted each time an electron drops to a lower level, it follows that several photons are emitted when several electrons change levels. For example, if the electron drops from energy level 5 to 2 in 10 hydrogen atoms, 10 photons would be emitted. Each of the photons would have the same energy, and collectively they would be observed as a violet line in the emission spectrum. Example Exercise 4.7 further illustrates the relationship between energy levels and emission lines.

Example Exercise 4.7   Emission Spectra and Energy Levels

Explain the relationship between an observed emission line in a spectrum and electron energy levels.

Solution
When an electron drops from a higher to a lower energy level, light is emitted. For each electron that drops, a single photon of light energy is emitted. The energy lost by the electron that drops equals the energy of the photon that is emitted. Several photons of light having the same energy are observed as a spectral line.

Practice Exercise
Indicate the number and color of the photons emitted for each of the following electron transitions in hydrogen atoms:

(a) $1 e^-$ dropping from energy level 3 to 2   (b) $10 e^-$ dropping from energy level 3 to 2
(c) $100 e^-$ dropping from energy level 4 to 2   (d) $500 e^-$ dropping from energy level 5 to 2

Answers:

(a) 1 red photon   (b) 10 red photons   (c) 100 blue-green photons   (d) 500 violet photons

Concept Exercise
Which of the following statements are true according to the Bohr model of the atom?

(a) Electrons are attracted to the atomic nucleus.
(b) Electrons have fixed energy as they circle the nucleus.
(c) Electrons lose energy as they drop to an orbit closer to the nucleus.

Answer: See Appendix G.

▲ **Mercury Gas Discharge Tube** The emission lines from mercury vapor illuminates the glass tube with a blue glow.

▶ Figure 4.14 **A Continuous Spectrum versus Line Spectra** A continuous spectrum is produced from an ordinary light bulb. The emission line spectra are produced by excited atoms of elements in the gaseous state.

Emission Spectra as "Atomic Fingerprints"

Further study of emission spectra revealed that each element produced a unique set of spectral lines. This observation indicated that the energy levels must be unique for atoms of each element. Therefore, a line spectrum is sometimes referred to as an *atomic fingerprint*.

Atomic fingerprints are useful in the identification of elements. For instance, in 1868, the atomic fingerprint of a new element was observed in the spectrum from the Sun. This element was named helium, after *helios*, the Greek word for "sun." In 1895, an element was discovered in uranium ore with an atomic fingerprint identical to that observed for helium in the Sun's spectrum. Thus, helium was discovered on Earth 27 years after it had first been observed in the solar spectrum. Figure 4.14 compares a continuous spectrum to the emission line spectra of four elements.

CRITICAL THINKING Neon Lights

Q: Do all "neon" advertising lights contain neon gas?

At the end of the nineteenth century, J. J. Thomson discovered the electron using a gas discharge tube. Thomson constructed his gas discharge tube out of thin glass, placed a metal electrode in each end, and introduced a small amount of gas. When the gas in the tube was electrically excited, he noticed that the tube glowed. He identified the glowing rays as a stream of small negatively charged particles. These particles acquired the name electrons, and Thomson is given credit for their discovery. The glass tubes used by Thomson were similar to cathode-ray tubes, originally used in television sets and computer screens.

In 1913, Niels Bohr explained that exciting gases with electricity caused electrons to be temporarily promoted to higher-energy states within the atom. However, the excited electrons quickly lose energy by emitting light and return to their original state. The light emitted by different gases varies because the energy levels within atoms vary for each element. For example, a gas discharge tube containing hydrogen gas pro-

duces a reddish-purple glow, whereas mercury vapor gives a blue glow.

In 1898, the Scottish chemist William Ramsay discovered the gas neon. Unlike argon, which comprises about 1% of air, neon is much more rare. When neon gas is placed in a narrow glass tube and electrically excited, it produces a reddish-orange light that is very eye-catching. The fact that gas discharge tubes produce an attractive array of colors led naturally to their use as advertising lights. Light from excited neon gas is very intense, and the term *neon light* has become a generic term for all lighted advertising displays.

Obviously, not all lights used in advertising are the same color. That is, "neon lights" can be red, green, blue, and so on. To produce a given color, a gas discharge tube must be filled with a specific gas. For a pink light, helium gas is used, and for a blue light, argon gas can be used. Only when we wish to produce a reddish-orange light is an advertising display actually filled with neon gas.

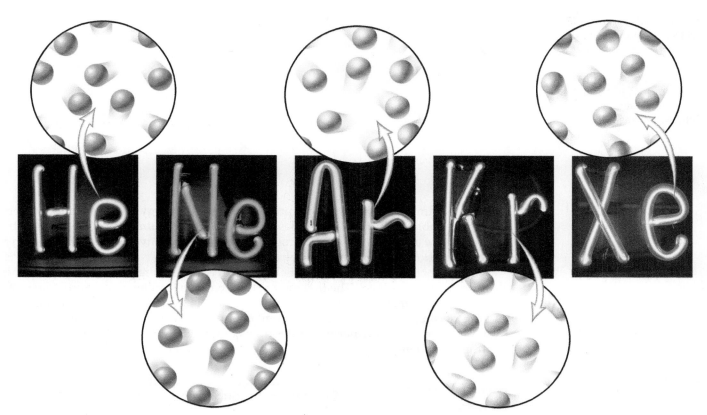

▲ **Light Emission** Notice the color of each light varies depending on the gas contained in the glass tube.

A: Not all "neon lights" contain neon gas; only "neon lights" that have a reddish-orange glow contain neon gas.

▸ To state each sublevel within a given energy level.

▸ To state the number of electrons that can occupy a given sublevel or energy level.

4.9 ENERGY LEVELS AND SUBLEVELS

As we learned in the previous section, in 1913 Niels Bohr proposed a model for the atom that pictured electrons circling around the nucleus in fixed-energy levels. His proposal was supported experimentally by the lines in the emission spectrum of hydrogen. The emission spectra of other elements, however, had far too many lines to interpret. Although Bohr could not explain the spectra of other elements, he did suggest the idea of sublevels within a main energy level. The model that eventually emerged had electrons occupying an **energy sublevel** within a main energy level. These energy sublevels were designated s, p, d, and f—in reference to the *sharp*, *principal*, *diffuse*, and *fundamental* lines, respectively, in the emission spectra of the elements.

The number of sublevels in each level corresponds to the number of the main energy level. That is, the first energy level (1) has one sublevel designated 1s. The second energy level (2) has two sublevels designated 2s and 2p. The third energy level (3) has three sublevels designated 3s, 3p, and 3d. The fourth energy level (4) is composed of 4s, 4p, 4d, and 4f sublevels (Figure 4.15).

▶ Figure 4.15 **A Cross Section of an Atom** The first energy level has one sublevel (1s). The second energy level has two sublevels (2s and 2p). The third energy level has three sublevels (3s, 3p, and 3d). Although the diagram suggests electrons travel in circular orbits, this is a simplification and is not actually the case.

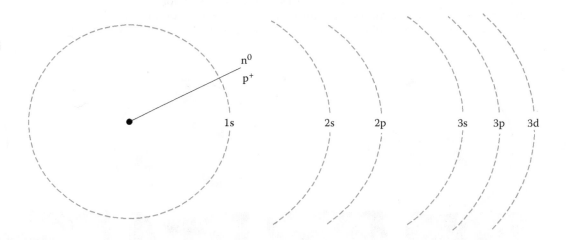

The maximum number of electrons in each of the energy sublevels depends on the type of sublevel. That is, an s sublevel can hold a maximum of 2 electrons. A p sublevel can have a maximum of 6 electrons. A d sublevel can have 10 electrons, and an f sublevel can hold a maximum of 14 electrons.

To find the maximum number of electrons in a main energy level, we add up the electrons in each sublevel. The first energy level has one s sublevel; it can contain only 2 e⁻. The second major energy level has two sublevels, 2s and 2p. The 2s can hold 2 e⁻ and the 2p can hold 6 e⁻. Thus, the second energy level can hold a maximum of 8 e⁻. Example Exercise 4.8 further illustrates how energy levels, sublevels, and number of electrons are related.

Example Exercise 4.8 Energy Levels, Sublevels, and Electrons

What is the maximum number of electrons that can occupy the third energy level?

Solution
The third energy level is split into three sublevels: 3s, 3p, and 3d. The maximum number of electrons that can occupy each sublevel is as follows:

$$s \text{ sublevel} = 2 \text{ e}^-$$
$$p \text{ sublevel} = 6 \text{ e}^-$$
$$d \text{ sublevel} = 10 \text{ e}^-$$

The maximum number of electrons in the third energy level is found by adding the three sublevels together:

$$3s + 3p + 3d = \text{total electrons}$$
$$2\,e^- + 6\,e^- + 10\,e^- = 18\,e^-$$

The third energy level can hold a maximum of 18 electrons. Of course, in elements where the third energy level of an atom is not filled, there are fewer than 18 electrons.

Practice Exercise

What is the maximum number of electrons that can occupy the fourth energy level?

Answers: $32\,e^-$ $(2\,e^- + 6\,e^- + 10\,e^- + 14\,e^-)$

Concept Exercise

What is the theoretical number of sublevels in the tenth energy level?

Answer: See Appendix G.

In summary, electrons are arranged around the nucleus in sublevels that have a specific fixed energy. Electrons farther from the nucleus occupy higher energy levels than those closer to the nucleus. Table 4.3 summarizes how main energy levels, sublevels, and number of electrons are related.

TABLE 4.3 DISTRIBUTION OF ELECTRONS BY ENERGY LEVEL

ENERGY LEVEL	ENERGY SUBLEVEL	ELECTRONS/ SUBLEVEL	ELECTRONS/ ENERGY LEVEL
1	1s	$2\,e^-$	$2\,e^-$
2	2s	$2\,e^-$	
	2p	$6\,e^-$	$8\,e^-$
3	3s	$2\,e^-$	
	3p	$6\,e^-$	
	3d	$10\,e^-$	$18\,e^-$
4	4s	$2\,e^-$	
	4p	$6\,e^-$	
	4d	$10\,e^-$	
	4f	$14\,e^-$	$32\,e^-$

4.10 ELECTRON CONFIGURATION

LEARNING OBJECTIVES

▶ To list the order of sublevels according to increasing energy.

▶ To write the predicted electron configurations for selected elements.

Electrons are arranged about the nucleus in a systematic order. The first electrons fill the energy sublevel closest to the nucleus. Additional electrons fill energy sublevels further and further from the nucleus. In other words, each energy level is filled sublevel by sublevel. The s sublevel is filled before a p sublevel, a p sublevel is filled before a d sublevel, and a d sublevel is filled before an f sublevel.

In general, sublevels are higher in energy as the energy level increases. Therefore, we would expect the order of sublevel filling to be 1s, 2s, 2p, 3s, 3p, 3d, 4s, and so on. This is not quite accurate because there are exceptions. For instance, the 4s sublevel is lower in energy than the 3d sublevel, and the 5s is lower than the 4d sublevel. A partial list of sublevels in order of increasing energy is $1s < 2s < 2p < 3s < 3p < 4s < 3d < 4p < 5s < 4d < 5p < 6s$.

In Chapter 6 we will learn how to predict the order in which sublevels are filled from the position of the element in the periodic table. In fact, the unusual shape of the periodic table reflects the order of sublevels according to increasing energy. For now, you should memorize the order of sublevel filling or refer to Figure 4.16.

▶ Figure 4.16 **Filling Diagram for Energy Sublevels** The order of sublevel filling is arranged according to increasing energy. Electrons first fill the 1s sublevel followed by the 2s, 2p, 3s, 3p, 4s, 3d, 4p, 5s, 4d, 5p, and 6s sublevels.

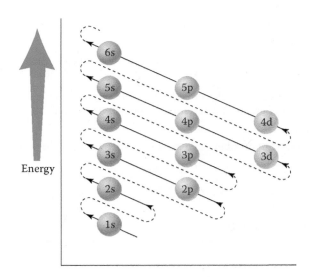

Energy

Example Exercise 4.9 Order of Sublevels

According to increasing energy, what is the next energy sublevel after each of the following sublevels?

(a) 3p   (b) 4d

Solution

If you do not know the order of sublevels, refer to the filling diagram in Figure 4.16.

(a) Although the third energy level has 3s, 3p, and 3d sublevels, the 3d sublevel does not immediately follow the 3p. Instead, the 4s sublevel follows the 3p and precedes the 3d. Thus,

$$3s, 3p, \mathbf{4s}$$

(b) Although the fourth energy level has 4s, 4p, 4d, and 4f sublevels, the 4f sublevel does not immediately follow the 4d. Instead, the 5p sublevel begins accepting electrons after the 4d is filled. Thus,

$$4p, 5s, 4d, \mathbf{5p}$$

Practice Exercise

Which sublevel gains electrons after each of the following sublevels is filled?

(a) 2s   (b) 5p

Answers:

(a) 2p   (b) 6s

Concept Exercise

The energy difference between sublevels (increases/decreases) moving away from the nucleus.

Answer: See Appendix G.

Writing Electron Configurations

The **electron configuration** of an atom is a shorthand statement describing the location of electrons by sublevel. First, the sublevel is written, followed by a superscript indicating the number of electrons. For example, if the 2p sublevel contains two electrons, the standard notation is $2p^2$. Thus,

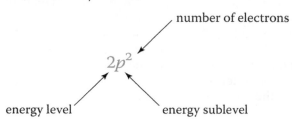

number of electrons

$2p^2$

energy level   energy sublevel

Writing the electron configuration for an atom is a straightforward procedure. First, find the atomic number for the element in the periodic table. The atomic number corresponds to the number of protons in the nucleus, which equals the number of electrons in a neutral atom. Next, write the sublevels according to increasing energy. Each sublevel is filled with electrons in sequence until the total of all the superscripts equals the atomic number of the element.

As an example, let's write the electron configuration for iron. If we refer to the periodic table, we find that the atomic number of iron is 26. Given the atomic number, we know that an iron nucleus must have 26 protons and is surrounded by 26 electrons. The order in which the electron sublevels are arranged according to increasing energy is as follows:

$$1s \; 2s \; 2p \; 3s \; 3p \; 4s \; 3d \; ...$$

The energy sublevels in iron are filled beginning with the $1s$ sublevel and ending when there is a total of 26 electrons. The electron configuration for iron is as follows:

$$\text{Fe:} \quad 1s^2 \, 2s^2 \, 2p^6 \, 3s^2 \, 3p^6 \, 4s^2 \, 3d^6$$

Notice that the sum of the superscripts equals the atomic number of iron (26). Example Exercise 4.10 illustrates the electron configuration for other elements.

Example Exercise 4.10 Electron Configuration

Write the predicted electron configuration for each of the following elements:

(a) F   (b) Sr

Solution

Refer to the periodic table to find the atomic number of an element.

(a) The atomic number of fluorine is 9; therefore, the number of electrons is 9. We can fill sublevels with 9 electrons as follows.

$$\text{F:} \quad 1s^2 \, 2s^2 \, 2p^5$$

(b) The atomic number of strontium is 38; therefore, the number of electrons is 38. We can fill sublevels with 38 electrons as follows:

$$\text{Sr:} \quad 1s^2 \, 2s^2 \, 2p^6 \, 3s^2 \, 3P^6 \, 4s^2 \, 3d^{10} \, 4p^6 \, 5s^2$$

To check your answer, find the total number of electrons by adding up the superscripts. The total is 38 e$^-$; this agrees with the atomic number for Sr.

Practice Exercise

Write the predicted electron configuration for each of the following elements:

(a) argon   (b) cadmium

Answers:

(a) $1s^2 \, 2s^2 \, 2p^6 \, 3s^2 \, 3p^6$ (b) $1s^2 \, 2s^2 \, 2p^6 \, 3s^2 \, 3p^6 \, 4s^2 \, 3d^{10} \, 4p^6 \, 5s^2 \, 4d^{10}$

Concept Exercise

Refer to the periodic table and state whether Cr or Mn has more electrons in the outermost d sublevel.

Answer: See Appendix G.

4.11 QUANTUM MECHANICAL MODEL OF THE ATOM

LEARNING OBJECTIVES

▶ To state the relative size, shape, and energy of s and p orbitals.

▶ To state the number of electrons that can occupy a given orbital.

In the mid-1920s, a new model of the atom began to emerge. A more powerful theory evolved because the behavior of electrons could not be fully explained by the Bohr model of the atom. The German physicist Werner Heisenberg (1901–1976) concluded that it was not possible to accurately determine both the location and energy of an electron. In his **uncertainty principle**, Heisenberg stated that it is impossible to

▲ **Albert Einstein and Niels Bohr** The two famous scientists disagreed on quantum theory, but each provided important insights to further our understanding of the atom.

precisely measure both the location and momentum (or energy) of a small particle simultaneously. In fact, the more accurately the location of an electron in an atom is known, the less precisely its energy can be determined.

In 1932, Heisenberg won the Nobel Prize in physics for his uncertainty principle. Not everyone, however, subscribed to the principle of uncertainty. Some physicists found it unsettling to consider that they might live in a universe ruled by chance. Albert Einstein (1879–1955) was sufficiently troubled by the uncertainty principle that he offered the famous quote: "It seems hard to look into God's cards, but I cannot for a moment believe He plays dice as the current quantum theory alleges He does." Although the uncertainty principle was initially controversial, it was a crucial concept for explaining the new model of the atom.

Gradually, the deeper nature of the atom came into focus. The new model retained the idea of quantized energy levels, but incorporated the concept of uncertainty. The new model that emerged became known as the **quantum mechanical atom**. Recall that in the Bohr model the energy of an electron is defined in terms of a fixed-energy orbit about the nucleus. In the quantum mechanical model the energy of an electron can be described in terms of the probability of it being within a spatial volume surrounding the nucleus. This region of high probability (~95%) for finding an electron of given energy is called an **orbital**.

Sizes and Shapes of *s* and *p* Orbitals

In the quantum mechanical atom, orbitals are arranged about the nucleus according to their size and shape. In general, electrons having higher energy are found in larger orbitals. Similar to the energy levels in the Bohr atom, the energy of orbitals is quantized and assigned a whole number value such as 1, 2, 3, 4, ... As the number increases, the energy and size of an orbital also increases.

We can describe the shapes of orbitals by the letters *s*, *p*, *d*, and *f*. For example, the shape of an *s* orbital is that of a sphere, and the shape of a *p* orbital is that of a dumbbell. We can designate the size and shape of an orbital by combining the number that indicates its energy, and the letter that indicates its shape. For example, the designations 1*s*, 2*p*, and 3*d* indicates three orbitals that differ in size, energy, and shape. All *s* orbitals are spherical, but they are not all the same size. A 3*s* orbital is a larger sphere than a 2*s*, and a 2*s* orbital is larger than a 1*s*. That is, the size and energy of the orbital increase as the energy level increases. Figure 4.17 illustrates the relationship between *s* orbitals about the nucleus.

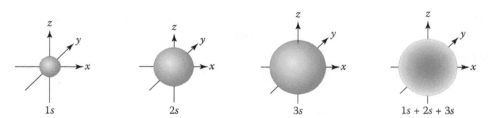

▲ **Figure 4.17 Relative Sizes of s Orbitals** The relative sizes of 1*s*, 2*s*, and 3*s* orbitals are shown. As the main energy level increases, the size and energy of the orbital increases. The nucleus of the atom is located in the center where the three axes intersect. The sketch on the far right illustrates the relationship of the 1*s*, 2*s*, and 3*s* orbitals.

All *p* orbitals have the shape of a dumbbell, but they are not all equal in size or energy. A 3*p* orbital is larger than a 2*p* orbital and is at a higher-energy level. A *p* orbital is said to resemble a dumbbell because it has two lobes. Electrons in a *p* orbital can occupy either of the lobes.

There are three different 2*p* orbitals. Although these three orbitals are identical in size and shape, they differ in their orientation to each other. That is, the three 2*p* orbitals intersect at the nucleus, but they are oriented at right angles to each other.

Figure 4.18 illustrates the relationships between the $2p_x$, $2p_y$, and $2p_z$ orbitals. The p_x orbital is oriented along the x-axis of a three-dimensional system, and the p_y and p_z orbitals are oriented along the y-axis and z-axis, respectively.

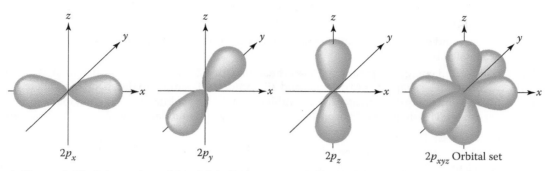

$2p_x$ $\qquad$ $2p_y$ $\qquad$ $2p_z$ $\qquad$ $2p_{xyz}$ Orbital set

▲ **Figure 4.18 Orientation of 2p Orbitals** The size and shape of the three 2p orbitals are identical. The 2p orbitals do not have a fixed orientation, but rather are perpendicular to each other. An electron in a $2p_x$ orbital has the same probability of occupying the $2p_y$ or $2p_z$ orbital.

By analogy, try to visualize a flying insect trapped inside two bottles with the open ends held together. The insect is free to fly about the entire volume of the two bottles. In this analogy, the insect represents an electron, and the two bottles represent the two lobes of a p orbital. Thus, there is a high probability of finding the electron anywhere within the volume of the entire p orbital. Figure 4.19 illustrates this analogy.

So far we have shown the shapes of s and p orbitals. However, there are many other orbitals; for example, in the third energy level there are 3s, 3p, and 3d orbitals, and in the fourth energy level there are 4s, 4p, 4d, and 4f orbitals.

The 3s sublevel contains a single spherical 3s orbital. The 3p sublevel contains three dumbbell-shaped orbitals: $3p_x$, $3p_y$, and $3p_z$. The 3p orbitals are similar in shape, but are larger than 2p orbitals. The 3d sublevel contains five 3d orbitals. Although it is not necessary to know the shapes of d orbitals, the five different 3d orbitals are shown in Figure 4.20.

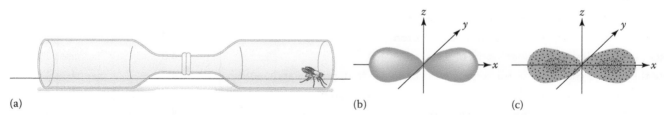

(a) $\qquad$ (b) $\qquad$ (c)

▲ **Figure 4.19 Analogy for a p Orbital** (a) Notice the insect trapped within the bottles held end to end. The insect can be in the left bottle, or the right bottle. (b) Similarly, an electron has a probability of being found anywhere within the two lobes of the p orbital. (c) The concentration of black dots indicates the most probable location of the electrons.

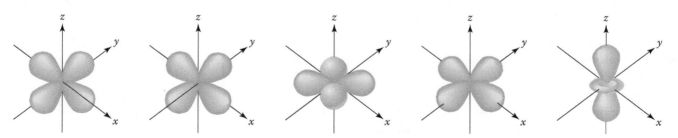

▲ **Figure 4.20 Shapes of 3d Orbitals** The shapes of the five 3d orbitals are not the same. Although four of the 3d orbitals are similar in shape, they have a different orientation to each other.

Example Exercise 4.11 Atomic Orbitals

Describe the relative size, energy, and shape for each of the following orbitals:

(a) 4s versus 3s and 5s   (b) 4p versus 3p and 5p

Solution

The size and energy of an orbital is indicated by the number; the shape of the orbital is designated by the letter.

(a) Size and energy are greater for a 4s orbital than for a 3s orbital, but less than for a 5s orbital. The shape of a 4s orbital—and all s orbitals—is similar to the shape of a sphere.

(b) Size and energy are greater for a 4p orbital than for a 3p orbital, but less than for a 5p orbital. The shape of a 4p orbital—and all p orbitals—is similar to the shape of a dumbbell.

Practice Exercise

Select the orbital in each of the following pairs that fits the description:

(a) the higher-energy orbital: 3p or 4p
(b) the larger size orbital: 4d or 5d

Answers: (a) 4p   (b) 5d

Concept Exercise

Which of the following statements are true according to the quantum mechanical model of the atom?

(a) Orbitals represent quantum energy levels for electrons.
(b) Orbitals represent probability boundaries for electrons.
(c) Orbitals can have different shapes.

Answer: See Appendix G.

Summary

LEARNING OBJECTIVES	SEC	EXERCISES
To describe the Dalton model of the atom.	4.1	Exercises 1–4
To describe the Thomson plum pudding model of the atom.	4.2	Exercises 5–6
To state the relative charge on an electron and a proton.	4.2	Exercises 7–10
To describe the Rutherford nuclear model of the atom.	4.3	Exercises 11–12
To state the relative charge and approximate mass of an electron, proton, and neutron.	4.3	Exercises 13–16
To indicate protons, neutrons, and electrons for a given atomic notation.	4.4	Exercises 17–18
To indicate the number of neutrons in a given isotope.	4.4	Exercises 19–24
To explain the concept of relative atomic mass.	4.5	Exercises 25–32
To calculate the atomic mass of an element given the mass and abundance of the naturally occurring isotopes.	4.5	Exercises 33–36
To state the relationship of wavelength, frequency, and energy of light.	4.6	Exercises 37–44
To explain the quantum concept applied to matter and energy.	4.7	Exercises 45–50
To describe the Bohr model of the atom.	4.8	Exercises 51–52
To explain the relationship between energy levels in an atom and lines in an emission spectrum.	4.8	Exercises 53–64
To state each sublevel within a given energy level.	4.9	Exercises 67–70
To state the number of electrons that can occupy a given sublevel or energy level.	4.9	Exercises 71–72
To list the order of sublevels according to increasing energy.	4.10	Exercises 73–74
To write the predicted electron configurations for selected elements.	4.10	Exercises 75–78
To state the relative size, shape, and energy of s and p orbitals.	4.11	Exercises 79–84
To state the number of electrons that can occupy a given orbital.	4.11	Exercises 85–86

Section 4.1 In 1803, John Dalton proposed that matter consisted of atoms based on the laws of conservation of mass and definite proportion. Citing experiments whereby two elements combine in more than one way, he formulated the law of multiple proportions, that is, CO and CO_2.

Section 4.2 Toward the end of the 1800s, there was evidence that the atom was divisible. When electricity was applied to a gas in a sealed glass tube, negative and positive rays were observed in the tube. Scientists discovered the rays from hydrogen gas were composed of tiny, charged particles they named **electrons** and **protons**.

Section 4.3 In 1911, Ernest Rutherford supervised a classic experiment in which alpha particles were fired at a thin sheet of gold foil. Much to his astonishment, some of the alpha particles bounced backward. He interpreted the results as evidence for a tiny, dense **atomic nucleus** at the center of the atom. The nucleus contains positively charged protons surrounded by negatively charged electrons. Twenty years later, the nucleus was also found to contain a neutral particle called a **neutron**.

Section 4.4 Chemists use a symbolic shorthand called **atomic notation** to designate the composition of a nucleus. Atoms of an element always contain the same number of protons, but the number of neutrons in the nucleus can vary. The number of protons is called the **atomic number** (Z), and the sum of the protons and neutrons is called the **mass number** (A). Atoms with the same atomic number, but a different mass number are called **isotopes**.

Section 4.5 Although the mass of an atom is much too small to measure directly, we can determine its relative mass. Carbon-12 is used as the reference isotope and is assigned a mass of exactly 12 **atomic mass units (amu)**. The masses of all other atoms are related to the mass of carbon-12. To find a representative value for the atomic mass of an element, we average the mass of each isotope. The weighted average mass of all isotopes is termed the **atomic mass** of the element.

Section 4.6 **Light** travels through space as a wave of radiant energy. The crest-to-crest distance between waves is the **wavelength**, and the number of cycles completed in a second is the **frequency**. As the wavelength decreases, the frequency and energy of light increase. The **visible spectrum** extends from 400–700 nm, but the entire **radiant energy spectrum** also includes gamma rays, X-rays, and microwaves. Thus, radiant energy is a **continuous spectrum** of visible and invisible light.

Section 4.7 In 1900, Max Planck introduced the quantum concept. Planck stated that the energy radiated by an object is not continuous, but rather that the radiation is emitted in small bundles. When an object radiates light, it releases a unit of radiant energy called a **photon**.

Section 4.8 In 1913, Niels Bohr suggested that electrons travel in circular orbits about the nucleus. The electron possesses a specific energy and is said to occupy an **energy level**. If an electron changes orbits in the **Bohr atom**, there is a quantum energy change. Bohr argued that an **emission line spectrum** results from electrons dropping from higher energy levels to lower levels. When an electron drops, a photon of light is released having an energy that corresponds to the difference in energy between the two levels.

Section 4.9 A closer examination of emission line spectra from gases revealed **energy sublevels** within main levels. The number of sublevels corresponds to the number of the energy level. For example, the fourth energy level has four sublevels (s, p, d, f). An s sublevel can hold 2 electrons, a p sublevel 6 electrons, a d sublevel 10 electrons, and an f sublevel a maximum of 14 electrons.

Section 4.10 Electrons fill sublevels in order of increasing energy as follows: $1s < 2s < 2p < 3s < 3p < 4s < 3d < 4p < 5s < 4d < 5p < 6s$. Notice that the $4s$ sublevel fills before the $3d$ and the $5s$ sublevel before the $4d$. A description of sublevel filling for an element is given by the **electron configuration**. A superscript following each sublevel indicates the number of electrons in a sublevel; for instance, $1s^2 2s^2 2p^6 3s^1$ is the electron configuration for sodium (atomic number 11).

Section 4.11 In the 1920s our understanding of electrons in atoms became very sophisticated. In 1925 Werner Heisenberg suggested the **uncertainty principle**; that is, it is impossible to simultaneously know both the precise location and the energy of an electron. Instead, the energy of an electron can be known only in terms of its probability of being located somewhere within the atom. This description gave rise to the **quantum mechanical atom**. A location within the atom where there is a high probability of finding an electron having a certain energy is called an **orbital**. An orbital is a region about the nucleus having a given energy, size, shape, and orientation. The shape of an s orbital is spherical, and a p orbital resembles the shape of a dumbbell.

Key Terms *Answers to Key Terms are in Appendix H.*

Select the key term that corresponds to each of the following definitions.

_____ 1. a negatively charged subatomic particle having a tiny mass

_____ 2. a positively charged subatomic particle having an approximate mass of 1 amu

_____ 3. a neutral subatomic particle having an approximate mass of 1 amu

_____ 4. a region in the center of an atom containing protons and neutrons

_____ 5. a value indicating the number of protons in the nucleus of an atom

_____ 6. a value indicating the number of protons and neutrons in the nucleus of an atom

_____ 7. a symbolic method for expressing the composition of an atomic nucleus

_____ 8. atoms of the same element that have a different number of neutrons

_____ 9. a unit of mass exactly equal to 1/12 the mass of a C-12 atom

_____ 10. the average mass of all the naturally occurring isotopes of an element

_____ 11. the distance a light wave travels to complete one cycle

_____ 12. the number of times a light wave completes a cycle in one second

_____ 13. a general term that can refer to either visible or invisible radiant energy

_____ 14. a range of light energy extending from violet to red, that is, approximately 400–700 nm

_____ 15. a range of light energy extending from gamma rays to microwaves

_____ 16. a band of light energy that is uninterrupted

_____ 17. a particle of radiant energy

_____ 18. a model of the atom that describes electrons circling the nucleus in orbits

_____ 19. an orbit of specific energy that electrons occupy as they circle the nucleus

_____ 20. a collection of narrow bands of light produced by atoms of a given element releasing energy

_____ 21. an electron energy level that results from splitting a main energy level

_____ 22. a shorthand description of the arrangement of electrons by sublevels according to increasing energy

_____ 23. the statement that it is impossible to precisely measure the location and energy of a particle at the same time

_____ 24. a sophisticated model of the atom that describes the energy of an electron in terms of its probability of being found in a particular location about the nucleus

_____ 25. a region about the nucleus in which there is a high probability of finding an electron with a given energy

(a) atomic mass (*Sec. 4.5*)

(b) atomic mass unit (amu) (*Sec. 4.5*)

(c) atomic notation (*Sec. 4.4*)

(d) atomic nucleus (*Sec. 4.3*)

(e) atomic number (Z) (*Sec. 4.4*)

(f) Bohr atom (*Sec. 4.8*)

(g) continuous spectrum (*Sec. 4.6*)

(h) electron (e^-) (*Sec. 4.2*)

(i) electron configuration (*Sec. 4.10*)

(j) emission line spectrum (*Sec. 4.8*)

(k) energy level (*Sec. 4.8*)

(l) energy sublevel (*Sec. 4.9*)

(m) frequency (*Sec. 4.6*)

(n) isotope (*Sec. 4.4*)

(o) light (*Sec. 4.6*)

(p) mass number (*A*) (*Sec. 4.4*)

(q) neutron (n^0) (*Sec. 4.3*)

(r) orbital (*Sec. 4.11*)

(s) photon (*Sec. 4.7*)

(t) proton (p^+) (*Sec. 4.2*)

(u) quantum mechanical atom (*Sec. 4.11*)

(v) radiant energy spectrum (*Sec. 4.6*)

(w) uncertainty principle (*Sec. 4.11*)

(x) visible spectrum (*Sec. 4.6*)

(y) wavelength (*Sec. 4.6*)

Exercises *Answers to odd-numbered Exercises are in Appendix I.*

Dalton Model of the Atom (Sec. 4.1)

1. Which of the following of Dalton's proposals proved to be invalid?
   (a) Atoms are indestructible.
   (b) Atoms of the same element are identical.
   (c) Atoms can combine in more than one whole number ratio.

2. Which of the following of Dalton's proposals proved to be invalid?
   (a) Atoms of different elements combine to form compounds.
   (b) Atoms can combine in small whole number ratios.
   (c) Atoms are indivisible.

3. State two experimental laws Dalton used to support the atomic theory.

4. State three scientists whose work Dalton used to support the atomic theory.

Thomson Model of the Atom (Sec. 4.2)

5. What do the raisins represent in the plum pudding model of the atom?

6. What does the pudding represent in the plum pudding model of the atom?

7. What is the simplest negative particle in an atom?

8. What is the simplest positive particle in an atom?

9. What is the relative charge on an electron?

10. What is the relative charge on a proton?

Rutherford Model of the Atom (Sec. 4.3)

11. Where is the location of electrons in an atom?

12. Where is the location of protons and neutrons in an atom?

13. What is the approximate size (in cm) of a nucleus?

14. What is the approximate size (in cm) of an atom?

15. What is the relative charge of an electron and proton?

16. What is the relative mass of an electron and proton?

Atomic Notation (Sec. 4.4)

17. State the number of neutrons in an atom of each of the following isotopes:
   (a) $^{20}_{10}$Ne   (b) $^{40}_{18}$Ar
   (c) $^{80}_{36}$Kr   (d) $^{131}_{54}$Xe

18. State the number of neutrons in an atom of each of the following isotopes:
   (a) $^{23}_{11}$Na   (b) $^{65}_{30}$Zn
   (c) $^{27}_{13}$Al   (d) $^{107}_{47}$Ag

19. State the number of neutrons in an atom of each of the following isotopes:
   (a) hydrogen-1   (b) carbon-13
   (c) cobalt-59   (d) iodine-127

20. State the number of neutrons in an atom of each of the following isotopes:
   (a) hydrogen-2   (b) carbon-14
   (c) cobalt-60   (d) iodine-131

21. Complete the following table and provide the missing information:

Atomic Notation	Atomic Number	Mass Number	Number of Protons	Number of Neutrons	Number of Electrons
$^{11}_{5}$B					
$^{15}_{7}$N					
$^{40}_{20}$Ca					
$^{200}_{80}$Hg					

22. Complete the following table and provide the missing information:

Atomic Notation	Atomic Number	Mass Number	Number of Protons	Number of Neutrons	Number of Electrons
	9			10	
		31	15		
	28			31	
		210	82		

23. Draw a diagram of the arrangement of protons, neutrons, and electrons in an atom of each of the following isotopes:
   (a) $^{7}_{3}$Li   (b) $^{13}_{6}$C
   (c) $^{16}_{8}$O   (d) $^{20}_{10}$Ne

24. Draw a diagram of the arrangement of protons, neutrons, and electrons in an atom of each of the following isotopes:
   (a) ^{31}P   (b) ^{35}Cl
   (c) ^{40}Ar   (d) ^{131}I

Atomic Mass (Sec. 4.5)

25. Distinguish between atomic number and mass number.

26. Distinguish between atomic mass and isotopic mass.

27. What is the assigned mass for the current reference isotope?

28. What is the current atomic mass scale reference isotope?

29. Given that the only naturally occurring isotope of sodium is ^{23}Na, determine its mass from the periodic table.

30. Given that the only naturally occurring isotope of aluminum is ^{27}Al, determine its mass from the periodic table.

31. Given that the only naturally occurring isotope of fluorine is ^{19}F, determine its mass from the periodic table.

32. Given that the only naturally occurring isotope of phosphorus is ^{31}P, determine its mass from the periodic table.

33. Calculate the atomic mass for lithium given the following data for its natural isotopes:
   ^{6}Li   6.015 amu   7.42%
   ^{7}Li   7.016 amu   92.58%

34. Calculate the atomic mass for magnesium given the following data for its natural isotopes:
   ^{24}Mg   23.985 amu   78.70%
   ^{25}Mg   24.986 amu   10.13%
   ^{26}Mg   25.983 amu   11.17%

35. Calculate the atomic mass for iron given the following data for its natural isotopes:
   ^{54}Fe   53.940 amu   5.82%
   ^{56}Fe   55.935 amu   91.66%
   ^{57}Fe   56.935 amu   2.19%
   ^{58}Fe   57.933 amu   0.33%

36. Calculate the atomic mass for zinc given the following data for its natural isotopes:
   ^{64}Zn   63.929 amu   48.89%
   ^{66}Zn   65.926 amu   27.81%
   ^{67}Zn   66.927 amu   4.11%
   ^{68}Zn   67.925 amu   18.57%
   ^{70}Zn   69.925 amu   0.62%

The Wave Nature of Light (Sec. 4.6)

37. Which has the longer wavelength: red light or green light?

38. Which has the shorter wavelength: blue light or violet light?

39. Which has the lower frequency: red light or green light?

40. Which has the higher frequency: blue light or violet light?

41. Which has the lower energy: red light or green light?

42. Which has the higher energy: blue light or violet light?

43. Which wavelength has the lower frequency: 450 nm or 550 nm?

44. Which wavelength has the higher frequency: 550 nm or 650 nm?

The Quantum Concept (Sec. 4.7)

45. What particle represents the quantum nature of light energy?

46. What particle represents the quantum nature of electrical energy?

47. State whether each of the following is continuous or quantized:
   (a) a rainbow
   (b) a line spectrum

48. State whether each of the following is continuous or quantized:
    (a) a spiral staircase
    (b) an elevated ramp
49. State whether each of the following instruments gives a continuous or a quantized measurement of length:
    (a) a metric ruler
    (b) a digital laser
50. State whether each of the following instruments gives a continuous or a quantized measurement of volume:
    (a) 10 mL volumetric pipet
    (b) 10 mL graduated cylinder

Bohr Model of the Atom (Sec. 4.8)

51. Draw the Bohr model of the atom.
52. What is the experimental evidence for electron energy levels in an atom?
53. Which of the following energy level changes for an electron is most energetic: $5 \rightarrow 2$, $4 \rightarrow 2$, or $3 \rightarrow 2$?
54. Which of the following energy level changes for an electron is least energetic: $4 \rightarrow 1$, $3 \rightarrow 1$, or $2 \rightarrow 1$?
55. In a hydrogen atom, what color is the emission line observed when electrons drop from the fourth to the second energy level?
56. In a hydrogen atom, what color is the emission line observed when electrons drop from the fifth to the second energy level?
57. In the emission spectrum from hydrogen gas, what type of energy is released when electrons drop from the fifth to the first energy level?

◀ **Hydrogen Gas Discharge Tube** The emission lines from hydrogen gas illuminate the glass tube with a reddish-purple glow.

58. In the emission spectrum from hydrogen gas, what type of energy is released when electrons drop from the fifth to the fourth energy level?
59. Which of the following lines in the emission spectrum of hydrogen has the least energy: red, blue-green, or violet?
60. Which of the following lines in the emission spectrum of hydrogen has the shortest wavelength: red, blue-green, or violet?
61. How many photons of light are emitted for each of the following?
    (a) 1 e⁻ drops from energy level 3 to 1
    (b) 1 e⁻ drops from energy level 3 to 2
62. How many photons of light are emitted for each of the following?
    (a) 100 e⁻ drop from energy level 3 to 2
    (b) 100 e⁻ drop from energy level 4 to 2

63. What is the color of the spectral line emitted for each of the following electron energy changes in excited hydrogen gas?
    (a) Electrons drop from energy level 2 to 1
    (b) Electrons drop from energy level 3 to 2
    (c) Electrons drop from energy level 4 to 3
64. What is the color of the spectral line emitted for each of the following electron energy changes in excited hydrogen gas?
    (a) Electrons drop from energy level 5 to 1
    (b) Electrons drop from energy level 5 to 2
    (c) Electrons drop from energy level 5 to 4

Energy Levels and Sublevels (Sec. 4.9)

65. What experimental evidence suggests the concept of electrons in energy levels?
66. What experimental evidence suggests main energy levels split into sublevels?
67. State the number of sublevels in each of the following main energy levels:
    (a) 1st   (b) 2nd
    (c) 3rd   (d) 4th
68. Designate all the sublevels within each of the following main energy levels:
    (a) 1st   (b) 2nd
    (c) 3rd   (d) 4th
69. What is the maximum number of electrons in each of the following sublevels?
    (a) 2s   (b) 4p
    (c) 3d   (d) 5f
70. What is the maximum number of electrons in each of the following?
    (a) an s sublevel   (b) a p sublevel
    (c) a d sublevel   (d) an f sublevel
71. What is the maximum number of electrons in the second energy level?
72. What is the maximum number of electrons in the fourth energy level?

Electron Configuration (Sec. 4.10)

73. Draw a filling diagram and predict the sublevel that follows 4s.
74. Draw a filling diagram and predict the sublevel that follows 5s.
75. Write the predicted electron configuration for each of the following elements:
    (a) He   (b) Be
    (c) Co   (d) Cd
76. Write the predicted electron configuration for each of the following elements:
    (a) boron   (b) argon
    (c) manganese   (d) nickel
77. Which element corresponds to each of the following electron configurations?
    (a) $1s^2 2s^1$
    (b) $1s^2 2s^2 2p^6 3s^2 3p^2$
    (c) $1s^2 2s^2 2p^6 3s^2 3p^6 4s^2 3d^2$
    (d) $1s^2 2s^2 2p^6 3s^2 3p^6 4s^2 3d^{10} 4p^6 5s^2$
78. Which element corresponds to each of the following electron configurations?
    (a) $1s^2 2s^2 2p^5$
    (b) $1s^2 2s^2 2p^6 3s^2 3p^6$
    (c) $1s^2 2s^2 2p^6 3s^2 3p^6 4s^2 3d^{10} 4p^6 5s^2 4d^5$
    (d) $1s^2 2s^2 2p^6 3s^2 3p^6 4s^2 3d^{10} 4p^6 5s^2 4d^{10} 5p^5$

Quantum Mechanical Model of the Atom
(Sec. 4.11)

79. Sketch a three-dimensional representation for each of the following orbitals. Label the x-axis, y-axis, and z-axis.
  (a) $1s$ **(b)** $2p_x$
  (c) $3P_Y$ **(d)** $4p_z$

80. Sketch a three-dimensional representation for each of the following orbital sets. Label the x-axis, y-axis, and z-axis.
  (a) $1s, 2s, 2p_x$ **(b)** $3p_x, 3p_Y, 3p_z$

81. Which orbital in each of the following pairs has the higher energy?
  (a) $2s$ or $3s$ **(b)** $2p_x$ or $3p_x$
  (c) $2p_x$ or $2p_y$ **(d)** $4p_y$ or $4p_z$

82. Which orbital in each of the following pairs has the larger size?
  (a) $2s$ or $3s$ **(b)** $2p_x$ or $3p_x$
  (c) $2p_x$ or $2p_y$ **(d)** $4p_y$ or $4p_z$

83. Designate the orbital that fits each of the following descriptions:
  (a) a spherical orbital in the fifth energy level
  (b) a dumbbell-shaped orbital in the fourth energy level

84. Designate the orbital that fits each of the following descriptions:
  (a) a spherical orbital in the sixth energy level
  (b) a dumbbell-shaped orbital in the third energy level

85. State the maximum number of electrons that can occupy each of the following orbitals:
  (a) $1s$ **(b)** $2p$
  (c) $3d$ **(d)** $4f$

86. State the maximum number of electrons that can occupy each of the following sublevels:
  (a) $1s$ **(b)** $2p$
  (c) $3d$ **(d)** $4f$

General Exercises

87. Silver occurs naturally as ^{107}Ag and ^{109}Ag. Given the mass and abundance of silver-109 (108.91 amu and 48.16%), what is the isotopic mass of silver-107?

88. Gallium occurs naturally as ^{69}Ga and ^{71}Ga. Given the mass and abundance of gallium-69 (68.92 amu and 60.10%), what is the isotopic mass of gallium-71?

89. Element 43 is used in medical radiology to locate tumors. Refer to the periodic table and state whether Tc has any stable isotopes.

90. Element 61 was named for the mythological Greek Prometheus who stole fire from the gods. Refer to the periodic table and state whether Pm has any stable isotopes.

91. Indicate the region of the spectrum for each of the following wavelengths of light.
  (a) 280 nm   **(b)** 1200 nm

92. Indicate the region of the spectrum for each of the following wavelengths of light.
  (a) 320 nm   **(b)** 1500 nm

Challenge Exercises

93. Bromine has only two natural isotopes, and they occur in about equal abundance. If ^{79}Br is one of the isotopes, what is the other isotope given the atomic mass of bromine is approximately 80 amu?

94. Silver has only two natural isotopes, and they occur in about equal abundance. If ^{109}Ag is one of the isotopes, what is the other isotope given the atomic mass of silver is approximately 108 amu?

95. Explain why the electron configuration for copper is $1s^2\,2s^2\,2p^6\,3s^2\,3p^6\,4s^1\,3d^{10}$ rather than the predicted $1s^2\,2s^2\,2p^6\,3s^2\,3p^6\,4s^2\,3d^9$.

96. Explain why the electron configuration for silver is $1s^2\,2s^2\,2p^6\,3s^2\,3p^6\,4s^2\,3d^{10}\,4p^6\,5s^1\,4d^{10}$ rather than the predicted $1s^2\,2s^2\,2p^6\,3s^2\,3p^6\,4s^2\,3d^{10}\,4p^6\,5s^2\,4d^9$.

 ## Online Exercises

Research each of the following using an Internet search engine (e.g., Google.com or Yahoo.com) and cite your URL reference.

97. Which element is responsible for the color of rose gold?

98. Which element gives rise to the expression "acid test?"

99. Describe the glow from hydrogen in the plasma state.

100. Describe the color of oxygen in the liquid state.

---

4   Chapter Self-Test   *Answers to Self-Test are in Appendix J.*

1. Which of the following of Dalton's proposals is still valid? (Sec. 4.1)
  (a) An element is composed of tiny particles called atoms.
  (b) Atoms of different elements combine to form compounds.
  (c) Compounds contain atoms in small whole number ratios.
  (d) all of the above
  (e) none of the above

2. What do the raisins represent in the plum pudding model of the atom? (Sec. 4.2)
  (a) electrons
  (b) neutrons
  (c) protons
  (d) nuclei
  (e) none of the above

3. Which subatomic particle has a relative charge of 0 and a mass of 1 amu? (Sec. 4.3)
   (a) alpha
   (b) electron
   (c) neutron
   (d) proton
   (e) none of the above

4. How many neutrons are in the nucleus of an atom of copper-65? (Sec. 4.4)
   (a) 29
   (b) 36
   (c) 65
   (d) 94
   (e) none of the above

5. Element X has two natural isotopes: X-63 (62.940 amu) and X-65 (64.928 amu). Calculate the atomic mass of element X given the abundance of X-63 is 69.17%. (Sec. 4.5)
   (a) 63.55 amu
   (b) 64.00 amu
   (c) 64.32 amu
   (d) 107.85 amu
   (e) 108.46 amu

6. Which of the following colors of light has the highest energy? (Sec. 4.6)
   (a) blue
   (b) green
   (c) red
   (d) violet
   (e) yellow

7. Which of the following is an example of a quantized change in energy? (Sec. 4.7)
   (a) a ball rolling across a playground
   (b) a ball rolling down a ramp
   (c) a ball rolling down a flight of stairs
   (d) all of the above
   (e) none of the above

8. How many photons of light are emitted when the electron in a hydrogen atom drops from energy level 3 to 1? (Sec. 4.8)
   (a) 1
   (b) 2
   (c) 3
   (d) 4
   (e) none of the above

9. What is the maximum number of electrons that can occupy the 3d energy sublevel? (Sec. 4.9)
   (a) 2
   (b) 6
   (c) 8
   (d) 14
   (e) none of the above

10. What is the electron configuration for an atom of manganese? (Sec. 4.10)
    (a) $1s^2 2s^2 2p^6 3s^2 3p^6 3d^5$
    (b) $1s^2 2s^2 2p^6 3s^2 3p^6 4s^2 3d^5$
    (c) $1s^2 2s^2 2p^6 3s^2 3p^6 4s^2 4p^5$
    (d) $1s^2 2s^2 2p^6 3s^2 3p^6 4s^2 4d^5$
    (e) none of the above

11. Which of the following is true for both an orbit and an orbital? (Sec. 4.11)
    (a) An orbit and an orbital always contain two electrons.
    (b) An orbit and an orbital can be described as elliptical.
    (c) An orbit and an orbital represent an electron boundary.
    (d) An orbit and an orbital represent a fixed energy state.
    (e) all of the above

Key Concepts

12. An atomic nucleus can be described by the analogy "like a marble in Dallas Cowboys Stadium." If a marble represents the atomic nucleus, what does the Stadium represent?

▲ **Dallas Cowboys Stadium** By analogy, imagine a marble on the 50-yard line compared to the size of the entire Stadium.

13. The scattering of alpha particles by a thin gold foil has been described by the analogy "like a missile shot through our solar system." If the missile represents an alpha particle, what do the planets in our solar system represent?

14. Complete the following quantum analogy: an *electron* is to electricity, as a _____ is to light.

15. What is the experimental evidence for electrons occupying fixed energy states surrounding the nucleus?

◄ **Neon Gas Discharge Tube** When the reddish-orange light from neon gas passes through a prism, a line spectrum is observed, which is the "atomic fingerprint" for neon.

Critical Thinking

16. Copper has two natural isotopes: Cu-63 and Cu-65. Which isotope is more abundant? (*Hint*: Refer to the periodic table.)

17. Can atoms of different elements have the same number of protons?

18. Can atoms of different elements have the same number of neutrons?

The Periodic Table

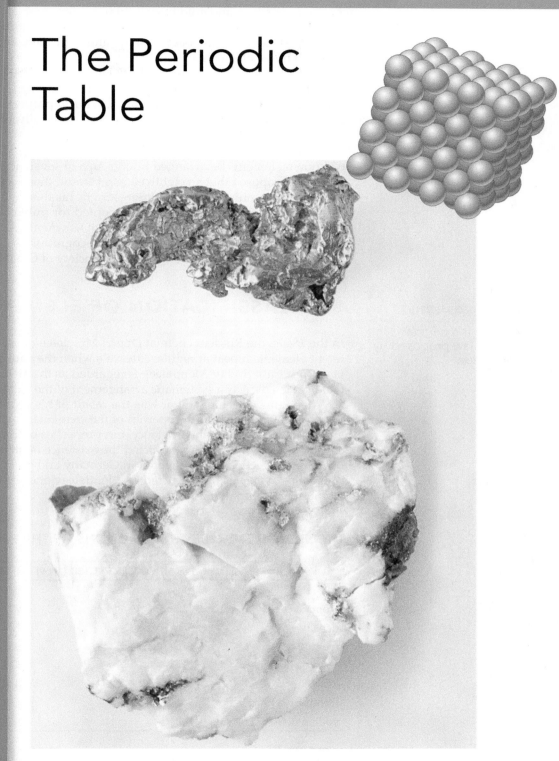

Gold in the Environment A gold nugget (top) is inert to most chemical reactions including reaction with strong acids. Gold is found naturally in Earth's crust, but only in small amounts, about 0.0000005%. Gold ore occurs as native gold in quartz rock (bottom). Seawater contains measurable amounts of gold, but to date all attempts to extract the metal have proven financially unsuccessful.

"It is the function of science to discover the existence of a general reign of order in nature and to find the causes governing this order."
Dmitri Mendeleev, Russian Chemist (1834–1907)

Copper, silver, and gold have been used since prehistoric times. However, not until the 1700s were these metals defined as elements by Robert Boyle (1627–1691). In 1800, 30 elements had been isolated and identified, and by 1870, there were more than 60 known elements.

In 1829, the German chemist J. W. Döbereiner (1780–1849) observed that several elements could be classified into groups of three, or *triads*. All three elements in a triad showed remarkable similarity in their chemical properties. Each triad also revealed an orderly trend in physical properties such as density, melting point, and especially atomic mass.

In 1865, the English chemist J. A. R. Newlands (1837–1898) suggested that the 62 known elements be arranged into groups of seven according to increasing atomic mass. He proposed that an eighth element would then repeat the properties of the first element in the previous group. Interestingly, his theory, called the *law of octaves*, was received with ridicule and was not accepted for publication. Although Newlands's insight into the periodic relationships of the elements was essentially correct, it took 20 years for him to receive professional recognition. In 1887, Newlands graciously accepted the Davy Medal from the Royal Society of Great Britain.

5.1 CLASSIFICATION OF ELEMENTS

LEARNING OBJECTIVE

▶ To apply the original periodic law proposed by Mendeleev.

In the 1860s, the Russian chemist Dmitri Mendeleev proposed that properties of different elements repeat at regular intervals when they are arranged in order of *increasing atomic mass*. Today, Mendeleev is regarded as the architect of the modern periodic table, which depicts a systematic arrangement of the elements.

Mendeleev's achievement was the result of his patient and systematic study of the physical and chemical properties of the elements. Furthermore, he had the insight and courage to predict the existence and properties of three elements before their discovery. In 1869, Mendeleev predicted the existence of an element he called ekasilicon. In 1886, ekasilicon was discovered in Germany and given the name germanium. The properties of ekasilicon predicted by Mendeleev and the observed properties of germanium are compared in Table 5.1.

TABLE 5.1 MENDELEEV'S PREDICTIONS OF THE PROPERTIES FOR EKASILICON (Ek)

PROPERTY	EKASILICON PREDICTED (1869)	GERMANIUM DISCOVERED (1886)
color	gray	gray
atomic mass	72 amu	72.6 amu
density	5.5 g/mL	5.32 g/mL
melting point	very high	937 °C
formula of oxide	EkO_2	GeO_2
density of oxide	4.7 g/mL	4.70 g/mL
formula of chloride	$EkCl_4$	$GeCl_4$
boiling point of chloride	100 °C	86 °C

In 1869, Mendeleev published his original periodic table with the elements arranged in vertical columns. Two years later, he created an updated version showing the elements in horizontal rows. He arranged the elements by increasing atomic mass and began a new row with an element that repeated the properties of a previous element. Figure 5.1 illustrates a portion of Mendeleev's 1871 periodic table of elements.

Group	I	II	III	IV	V	VI	VII	VIII
Formula of Oxide	R_2O	RO	R_2O_3	RO_2	R_2O_5	RO_3	R_2O_7	RO_4
	H							
	Li	Be	B	C	N	O	F	
	Na	Mg	Al	Si	P	S	Cl	
	K	Ca	eka-	Ti	V	Cr	Mn	Fe, Co
	Cu	Zn	eka-	eka-	As	Se	Br	& Ni
	Rb	Sr	Y	Zr	Nb	Mo	—	Ru, Rh
	Ag	Cd	In	Sn	Sb	Te	I	& Pd
	Cs	Ba	Di	Ce	—	—	—	
	—	—	—	—	—	—	—	
	—	—	Er	La	Ta	W	—	Os, Ir
	Au	Hg	Tl	Pb	Bi	—	—	& Pt
	—	—	—	Th	—	U	—	

◀ Figure 5.1 **Mendeleev's Classification of the Elements (1871)** The formula for the oxide of an element is indicated by the notation R_2O, RO, and so on. For example, Group I oxides include Li_2O, Na_2O, and K_2O; and Group II oxides include BeO, MgO, and CaO. In Groups III and IV, Mendeleev indicated the existence of three undiscovered elements, which he named ekaboron, ekaaluminum, and ekasilicon.

CHEMISTRY CONNECTION Dmitri Mendeleev

Q: **Which element in the periodic table is named in honor of Dmitri Mendeleev?**

Dmitri Ivanovich Mendeleev (1834–1907) was born in Siberia, the youngest of 14 to 17 children (records vary). Mendeleev's father was a high school principal, but blindness ended his career when he was quite young. Mendeleev's mother, a woman of remarkable energy and determination, subsequently started a glass factory to support the family. About the time Mendeleev graduated from high school, his father died and his mother's factory burned down. Although destitute, his mother used her influence to get him into college just a few months before her own death.

Mendeleev enrolled at the University of St. Petersburg where he graduated first in his class. Following graduate work in Europe, he returned to St. Petersburg as a professor of chemistry. Mendeleev's consuming interest was finding a common thread that linked the rapidly growing number of elements. In 1869, he published a table that related elements according to increasing atomic mass. He even predicted the existence and properties of three undiscovered elements. In 1875, the predicted element *gallium* was discovered in France (Gallia); in 1879, *scandium* was discovered in Scandinavia; and in 1886, *germanium* was discovered in Germany.

Gradually, scientists recognized the importance of the periodic table, and Mendeleev became the most famous chemist in the world. His professional reputation thrived, and he was invited to major universities throughout Europe and gave lectures in the United States and Canada.

His personal reputation suffered when he divorced his wife and married a young art student. In the eyes of the Russian Orthodox Church he was a bigamist because he did not wait the required 7 years before he remarried. When Czar Alexander II was questioned about Mendeleev's bigamy, he replied, "Yes, Mendeleev has two wives, but I have only one Mendeleev."

In the late nineteenth century, Russia was engulfed in political turmoil. Mendeleev was a liberal and voiced his concern about the rights of students in general and women in

▲ **Dmitri Mendeleev (1834–1907)** A spiral form of the periodic table conveys the concept of chemical evolution. Starting with H, all the elements evolved step by step. Mendeleev's likeness is commemorated in the center of the spiral of elements. Notice that there are 18 rows of elements corresponding to the 18 groups of elements in the periodic table.

particular. His outspoken speech led to his forced resignation from the university in 1890. Fortunately, Mendeleev still had influential friends, and he was named director of the Bureau of Weights and Measures.

In 1906, he missed winning the Nobel Prize by a single vote. Historians speculate that Mendeleev was more deserving of the recognition, but owing to his controversial personality, the prize was awarded instead to Henri Moissan, the French chemist who discovered the element fluorine.

A: Element 101 is named mendelevium, symbol Md, in honor of Mendeleev.

The Noble Gases

The arrangement of the elements expanded significantly with the discovery of the group of similar elements that appear on the far right side of the periodic table. Argon was isolated from air in 1894, and helium, neon, krypton, xenon, and radon were discovered in the ensuing 5 years. Originally, this collection of gaseous elements was referred to as the *inert gases* because they showed no chemical reactivity.

In 1962 a compound containing xenon gas was synthesized at the University of British Columbia. After the first compound was made, several other compounds containing inert gases quickly followed. Although compounds of xenon and krypton have been prepared, the elements argon, neon, and helium have yet to be combined. More recently, the term *noble gas* has been substituted for *inert gas* to convey the unreactive nature of the gases in this group. Similarly, copper, silver, and gold are referred to as noble metals because of their resistance to chemical reaction.

LEARNING OBJECTIVE

▶ To apply the modern periodic law proposed by Moseley.

5.2 THE PERIODIC LAW CONCEPT

In 1869, Mendeleev proposed that elements showed recurring properties according to increasing atomic mass. In 1913, H. G. J. Moseley (1887–1915), a postdoctoral student, bombarded atomic nuclei with high-energy radiation. By studying the X rays that were subsequently emitted, Moseley discovered that the nuclear charge increased by 1 for each element in the periodic table. Thus,

H = 1							He = 2
Li = 3	Be = 4	B = 5	C = 6	N = 7	O = 8	F = 9	Ne = 10
Na = 11	Mg = 12	Al = 13	Si = 14	P = 15	S = 16	Cl = 17	Ar = 18

Moseley correctly concluded that arranging elements according to increasing nuclear charge, rather than atomic mass, more clearly explained their repeating properties. That is, arranging elements according to atomic number better explained the trends found in the periodic table. Elements, therefore, should be arranged according to the number of protons in their nucleus and not their atomic mass. The **periodic law** states that the properties of elements recur in a repeating pattern when arranged according to *increasing atomic number*. As it so happens, with only a few exceptions, these trends are identical.

In 1913, Niels Bohr introduced the concept of electron energy levels and Mendeleev's periodic table soon took on a new shape. The new shape resembled the arrangement used today, as shown in Figure 5.2.

If you closely examine the fourth row in the periodic table, you will notice that the sequence of atomic masses does not increase from Co to Ni, even though Co precedes Ni in the periodic table. But notice that the atomic number of Co (27) is less than the atomic number of Ni (28). It is also true that the properties of cobalt resemble those of the elements in Group 9, and that the properties of Ni are similar to those of the elements in Group 10.

▲ **Figure 5.2** **The Modern Periodic Table of Elements** The atomic numbers increase stepwise throughout the periodic table. Note that atomic masses, with few exceptions, also increase. However, the nuclear charge (that is, the atomic number) more clearly explains the recurring properties of elements.

Example Exercise 5.1 Periodic Law

Find the two elements in the fifth row of the periodic table that violate the original periodic law proposed by Mendeleev.

Solution

Mendeleev proposed that elements be arranged according to increasing atomic mass. Beginning with Rb, each of the elements in the fifth row increases in atomic mass until iodine. Although the atomic numbers of Te (52) and I (53) increase, the atomic masses of Te (127.60) and I (126.90) do not. Experimentally, it is I that has properties similar to F, Cl, and Br; thus, I comes after Te in the periodic table.

Practice Exercise

Find a pair of elements in the periodic table with atomic numbers less than 20 that are an exception to the original periodic law.

Answer: Ar and K

Concept Exercise

The modern periodic law states that elements are arranged according to increasing (atomic mass/atomic number).

Answer: See Appendix G.

5.3 GROUPS AND PERIODS OF ELEMENTS

A vertical column in the periodic table is called a **group** or family of elements, and a horizontal row is called a **period** or series. When we examine the periodic table on the inside front cover of this textbook, we notice there are seven horizontal rows of elements. These periods of elements are numbered 1–7. The first period has only two elements, H and He. The second and third periods each have eight elements, Li through Ne, and Na through Ar. The fourth and fifth periods have 18 elements, K through Kr and Rb through Xe.

When Mendeleev constructed his original periodic table, he did not know where to place hydrogen as its properties were unlike any group of elements. Because hydrogen is a gas, it has physical properties similar to nonmetals. On the

LEARNING OBJECTIVES

▶ To classify the elements according to their groups (families) and periods (series) in the periodic table.

▶ To designate a group of elements in the periodic table using both the American convention (IA–VIIIA) and the IUPAC convention (1–18).

other hand, hydrogen reacts by losing an electron—and losing electrons is a chemical property of metals. Today, H appears at the top of the far left column in most periodic tables.

There are 18 vertical columns in the periodic table. In the past, American chemists have used a Roman numeral followed by the letter A or B to designate a group of elements, for example IA, IIA, IIB. In the periodic table, you will notice that Group IA contains the elements Li to Fr, Group IIA has the elements Be to Ra, and Group IIB has the elements Zn, Cd, Hg.

Since the 1920s, a controversy has existed over the numbering of the groups in the periodic table. Recently, the International Union of Pure and Applied Chemistry (IUPAC) resolved the dispute by proposing to number the groups using the numerals 1 to 18. For example, IUPAC recommends that Group IA be designated Group 1, Group IIB be designated Group 12, and Group VIIIA be designated Group 18. Currently, chemists are in the process of adopting the IUPAC convention. Hence, the periodic tables in this textbook will list both conventions, for example, IA/1, IIB/12, and VIIIA/18.

In the periodic table, groups of elements can also be referred to by their family names. The family name for Group IA/1 is **alkali metals**. The elements in Group IIA/2 are called **alkaline earth metals**. The elements in Group VIIA/17 are called **halogens**. Group VIIIA/18 elements are all gases that are usually unreactive under normal conditions; they are called **noble gases**.

Representative Elements and Transition Elements

Groups of elements are classified as either representative elements or transition elements. **Representative elements** (also called *main-group elements*) are found in the A groups, on the left and right sides of the periodic table. As a rule, the chemical behavior of representative elements is predictable. For example, magnesium always reacts with oxygen to produce MgO.

Transition elements are found in the B groups in the middle of the periodic table. The chemical behavior of transition elements is not as predictable as that of representative elements. For instance, in the presence of limited oxygen, iron reacts to form FeO; if excess oxygen gas is available, the product is Fe_2O_3.

Inner transition elements are found beneath the main portion of the periodic table. These two series are placed below the main portion to avoid an unduly wide periodic table. The first series of elements, Ce through Lu, lie between La and Hf in the periodic table and are considered part of Period 6. This series is called the **lanthanide series** because it follows lanthanum. The elements Ce through Lu have similar properties, and they occur together in nature along with Sc, Y, and La. The natural abundance of these elements in Earth's crust is less than 0.005%, and they are collectively referred to as **rare earth elements**.

The second series of inner transition elements, Th through Lr, is called the **actinide series** because it follows element 89, actinium. The actinide series is considered part of Period 7. All the elements in this series are radioactive; in fact, except for trace amounts, none of the elements past uranium is naturally occurring. Element 93 and beyond are created in particle accelerators called "atom smashers." The isotopes of these elements have very short lifetimes, often less than a millisecond. The elements following uranium, Np through element 118, are called **transuranium elements**. The periodic table shown in Figure 5.3 summarizes the names of the important groups and periods.

> **Example Exercise 5.2** Groups and Periods of Elements

Select the symbol of the element that fits each of the following descriptions:

(a) the alkali metal in the fourth period
(b) the halogen in the third period
(c) the rare earth with the lowest atomic mass
(d) the metal in Group VIIB/7 and Period 4

Solution

Referring to the periodic table in Figure 5.3, we have

(a) K

(b) Cl

(c) Sc

(d) Mn

Practice Exercise

Select the symbol of the element that fits each of the following descriptions:

(a) the alkaline earth metal in the sixth period

(b) the noble gas in the third period

(c) the actinide with the highest atomic mass

(d) the semimetal in Group IIIA/13

Answers:

(a) Ba

(b) Ar

(c) Lr

(d) B

Concept Exercise

What is the group number for each of the following families of elements?

(a) alkali metals   (b) alkaline earth metals

(c) halogens   (d) noble gases

Answer: See Appendix G.

▲ Figure 5.3 **Names of Groups and Periods** The common names of groups and periods are shown for selected families and series.

CRITICAL THINKING | IUPAC Group Numbers

Q: Which two groups of transition elements in the periodic table have the same designation according to both the American convention and European convention?

Recently, the designation of groups of elements in the periodic table has been a topic of interest. In the 1970s a lingering controversy surfaced that was addressed by IUPAC. Previously, in the United States, elements on the left side and right side of the periodic table had been designated A groups. The elements in the middle of the periodic table were labeled B groups. This so-called American convention is shown next.

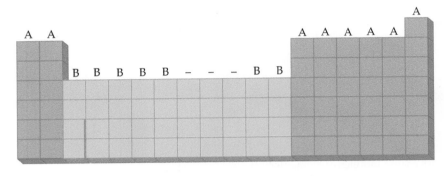

◀ **Periodic Table of Elements—American Convention** Representative elements are placed in A groups and transition elements are in B groups.

In Europe, elements on the left side of the periodic table had been previously designated A groups, and those on the right side had been labeled B groups. The so-called European convention is shown in the following illustration.

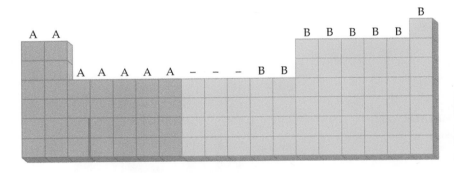

◀ **Periodic Table of Elements—European Convention** The elements on the left are A groups, and the elements on the right are B groups.

After much discussion in 1985 IUPAC proposed that groups of elements be designated by the numerals 1–18. Currently, IUPAC recommends that groups of elements be numbered as shown in the following periodic table.

◀ **Periodic Table of Elements—IUPAC Convention** Groups of elements are indicated by the sequential numerals 1–18.

One of the reasons for the IUPAC recommendation is that the last digit in the group number corresponds to the Roman numeral in both the American and European conventions. For example, in group 13, the number 3 corresponds to the Roman numeral III in both the American (IIIA) and European (IIIB) versions.

A: Groups IB and IIB have the same designation in both the American and European versions of the periodic table. These two groups are labeled 11 and 12 using IUPAC convention.

5.4 PERIODIC TRENDS

We can visualize atoms as spheres and express their size in terms of atomic radius. The atomic radius is the distance from the nucleus to the outermost electrons. As this distance is very small, we will express the atomic radius in units of nanometers.

In the periodic table there are two general trends in atomic size. First, as we move through a group of elements from bottom to top, the radii of the atoms decrease. We can explain the decrease in radius because there are fewer energy levels of electrons surrounding the nucleus. As the number of energy levels decreases, the distance from the nucleus to the outermost electrons decreases. Therefore, the trend in *atomic radius decreases up a group.*

Second, as we move left to right within a period of elements, the radii of the atoms decrease. The explanation for this decrease is as follows: The atomic number increases from left to right, and therefore, the number of protons increases. As the number of protons in the nucleus increases across a period, the positive nuclear charge increases. This has the effect of pulling the negative electrons closer to the nucleus and reducing the size of the atom. Thus, the *atomic radius decreases across a period* from left to right.

Figure 5.4 illustrates trends in the size of atomic radii for a portion of the periodic table. Transition elements and inner transition elements have been omitted as there are numerous exceptions to the general trends. Moreover, the atomic radii of transition elements in a given sublevel are reasonably similar in size.

▸ To describe the trend in metallic character within a group or period.

▸ To describe the trend in atomic size within a group or period.

◂ Figure 5.4 **Atomic Radii of Selected Representative Elements** The values for atomic radii are given in nanometers (nm). Some references list atomic radii in picometers (pm); for example, the atomic radius of Li is 152 pm.

The periodic table shows a horizontal trend in metallic character of the elements. First, recall that metals are on the left side of the periodic table and nonmetals are on the right side. The most reactive metals are on the far left side, and the most reactive nonmetals are on the far right side of the table. Thus, as we move from left to right, *metallic character decreases across a period.*

The periodic table also shows a vertical trend in metallic character of the elements. A metal reacts by losing its outermost valence electrons. As we move up a group, the atomic radius is smaller and the outermost electrons are closer to the nucleus. When the negatively charged electrons and the positively charged nucleus are closer together, it is more difficult for an atom to lose an electron. Therefore, *metallic character decreases up a group.* Figure 5.5 illustrates the general trends in the periodic table for atomic radius and metallic character.

▲ **Figure 5.5 General Trends in Atomic Radii and Metallic Character** The general trend for the atomic radius is to decrease both up a group and across a period from left to right. The metallic character trend in the periodic table is similar.

Example Exercise 5.3 Periodic Table Predictions

Based on the general trends in the periodic table, predict which element in each of the following pairs has the smaller atomic radius:

(a) Na or K   (b) P or N   (c) Ca or Ni   (d) Si or S

Solution

The general trend in atomic radii decreases up a group and across a period from left to right. Referring to the periodic table,

(a) Na is above K in Group IA/1; the atomic radius of Na is smaller.
(b) N is above P in Group VA/15; the atomic radius of N is smaller.
(c) Ni is to the right of Ca in Period 4; the atomic radius of Ni is smaller.
(d) S is to the right of Si in Period 3; the atomic radius of S is smaller.

Practice Exercise

Based on the general trends in the periodic table, predict which element in each of the following pairs has the most metallic character:

(a) Sn or Pb   (b) Ag or Sr   (c) Al or B   (d) Br or As

Answers:

(a) Pb   (b) Sr   (c) Al   (d) As

Concept Exercise

Which period represents the smallest atomic radius? Which group represents the most metallic character?

Answer: See Appendix G.

5.5 PROPERTIES OF ELEMENTS

Mendeleev designed the periodic table so that elements with similar properties were placed in the same group. He was then able to predict yet undiscovered elements from the gaps in his periodic table. He successfully predicted the properties of ekasilicon (i.e., germanium), for example, after noticing a trend in properties such as color, density, melting point, and atomic mass.

▶ To predict a physical property for an element given the values of other elements in the same group.

▶ To predict a chemical formula for a compound given the formulas of other compounds containing an element in the same group.

Predicting Physical Properties

Today, chemists have access to information regarding properties of elements cataloged in reference books such as the *Handbook of Chemistry and Physics*. However, we can use the same procedure that Mendeleev used to estimate the numerical value for a physical property. For example, if we know the density of two elements in the same group, we can make a reasonable estimate of the density for another element in the same group. Table 5.2 lists selected physical properties of alkali metals, which appear in Group IA/1 in the periodic table.

TABLE 5.2 PHYSICAL PROPERTIES OF ALKALI METALS

ELEMENT	ATOMIC RADIUS (nm)	DENSITY (g/mL at 20 °C)	MELTING POINT (°C)	ATOMIC MASS (amu)
Li	0.152	0.53	180.5	6.94
Na	0.186	0.97	97.8	22.99
K	0.227	0.86	63.3	39.10
Rb	0.248	1.53	38.9	85.47
Cs	0.266	1.87	28.4	132.91

*Note the density of K is slightly less than that of Na. Small irregularities in group trends are not unusual.

Notice that the properties of the radioactive element francium, Fr, are not included with those of the other alkali metals in Table 5.2. We can, however, make some reasonable predictions about its physical properties based on the trends shown by the other elements. Because Fr is below Cs in Group IA/1, we can predict that its atomic radius is greater than 0.266 nm, its density is greater than 1.87 g/mL, its melting point is less than 28.4 °C, and its atomic mass is greater than 132.91 amu.

Example Exercise 5.4 Predicting Physical Properties

Predict the missing value (?) for each physical property listed below. The (a) atomic radius, (b) density, and (c) melting point are given for two of three alkaline earth metals in Group IIA/2.

ELEMENT	ATOMIC RADIUS	DENSITY AT 20 °C	MELTING POINT
Ca	0.197 nm	1.54 g/mL	(?) °C
Sr	0.215 nm	(?) g/mL	769 °C
Ba	(?) nm	3.65 g/mL	725 °C

Solution

We can estimate a value for the physical property of an element by observing the trend in values for other elements within the same group.

(a) To determine the atomic radius value for Ba, we first find the increase from Ca to Sr; that is, 0.215 nm − 0.197 nm = 0.018 nm. We then add the difference (0.018 nm) to the atomic radius of Sr and obtain 0.215 nm + 0.018 nm = 0.233 nm. We assumed that the atomic radius increased the same amount from Sr to Ba as it did from Ca to Ba. (The *Handbook of Chemistry and Physics* value is *0.217 nm*.)

(b) Notice that Sr lies between Ca and Ba in Group IIA/2. Thus, we can estimate that the density of Sr lies midway between Ca and Ba. To find the density of Sr, we calculate the average value for Ca and Ba; that is, $(1.54 \text{ g/mL} + 3.65 \text{ g/mL})/2 = 2.60 \text{ g/mL}$. (The literature value is *2.63 g/mL*.)

(c) From the general trend, we can predict that the melting point of Ca is greater than that of Sr. To determine the value, let's find the increase in melting point from Ba to Sr. It is $769\,°C - 725\,°C = 44\,°C$. Now we add $44\,°C$ to the value of Sr: $769\,°C + 44\,°C = 813\,°C$. Therefore, we predict the melting point of Ca as $813\,°C$. (The literature value is *839 °C*.)

Practice Exercise

Predict the missing value (?) for each physical property listed below. The (a) atomic radius, (b) density, and (c) melting point are given for two of the metals in Group VIII/10.

ELEMENT	ATOMIC RADIUS	DENSITY AT 20 °C	MELTING POINT
Ni	0.125 nm	8.91 g/cm^3	(?) °C
Pd	0.138 nm	(?) g/cm^3	1554 °C
Pt	(?) nm	21.5 g/cm^3	1772 °C

Answers: (a) 0.151 nm (b) 15.2 g/cm^3 (c) 1336 °C

Concept Exercise

Given the atomic radius (0.186 nm), density (0.97 g/mL), and melting point ($98\,°C$) for sodium, estimate the corresponding values of lithium.

Answer: See Appendix G.

Predicting Chemical Properties

In Chapter 7 we will study chemical reactions systematically. However, it is possible to predict the products of chemical reactions by understanding the organization of elements in the periodic table. For example, if we know that magnesium and oxygen react to give magnesium oxide (MgO), we can predict that the other Group IIA/2 elements react in a similar fashion. That is, calcium, strontium, and barium should react with oxygen to give similar oxides (CaO, SrO, and BaO), and they do. There are exceptions to the general rule, but the principle of using the periodic table is helpful to our understanding of chemical properties.

▲ **Gallium Metal** Gallium has chemical properties similar to aluminum. However, gallium has a much lower melting point (30 °C), and will melt in the hand.

Example Exercise 5.5 Predicting Chemical Properties

Metallic sodium reacts with chlorine gas to give sodium chloride, NaCl. Predict the products formed when (a) lithium and (b) potassium react with chlorine gas.

Solution

Because Li and K are in the same group as Na (Group IA/1), we can predict that the products are similar to NaCl. Thus,

(a) lithium metal should react with chlorine gas to give LiCl.

(b) potassium metal should react with chlorine gas to give KCl.

Practice Exercise

The chemical formulas for the oxides of potassium, calcium, gallium, and germanium are, respectively, K_2O, CaO, Ga_2O_3, and GeO_2. Refer to the periodic table and predict the chemical formula for each of the following compounds:

(a) rubidium oxide (b) strontium oxide
(c) indium oxide (d) lead oxide

Answers: (a) Rb_2O (b) SrO (c) In_2O_3 (d) PbO_2

Concept Exercise

Predict which of the following metals has chemical properties most similar to zinc: Fe, Cu, or Cd.

Answer: See Appendix G.

5.6 BLOCKS OF ELEMENTS

LEARNING OBJECTIVES

▶ To predict the highest energy sublevel for an element given its position in the periodic table.

▶ To predict the electron configuration for an element given its position in the periodic table.

In Section 4.9 we learned that the order of electron energy sublevels according to increasing energy is $1s < 2s < 2p < 3s < 3p < 4s < 3d < 4p < 5s < 4d < 5p < 6s$. In this section, we will see that the unusual shape of the periodic table is the result of the ordering of energy sublevels. That is, the order of energy sublevels follows the systematic arrangement of elements by groups.

Elements in Groups IA/1 and IIA/2 fill s sublevels. The s sublevels are to the left in the periodic table and are collectively called the *s block* of elements. Elements in Groups IIIA/13 through VIIIA/18 fill p sublevels, and are referred to as the *p block* of elements. Transition elements in Groups IIIB/3 through IIB/12 fill d sublevels, and likewise make up the *d block* of elements. Finally, the inner transition elements (Ce–Lu and Th–Lr) fill f sublevels, and comprise the *f block* of elements. Figure 5.6 illustrates the s, p, d, and f block elements in the periodic table.

PERIODIC TABLE OF THE ELEMENTS

Representative s-block elements

Transition d-block elements

Representative p-block elements

Inner Transition f-block elements

▲ Figure 5.6 **Blocks of Elements in the Periodic Table** The relationship between energy sublevels and the s, p, d, and f blocks of elements in the periodic table are shown.

In Chapter 4 we had to memorize that the $3d$ energy sublevel comes after the $4s$ energy sublevel. Now, we can simply refer to the periodic table and see that s block elements precede each d sublevel. Also, recall that the number of sublevels corresponds to the number of the main energy level. For example, in the third main level, there are three sublevels ($3s$, $3p$, and $3d$). In the fourth main level, there are four sublevels ($4s$, $4p$, $4d$, and $4f$).

We can see in Figure 5.6 that members of the lanthanide and actinide series are f block elements. The lanthanides are filling the $4f$ energy sublevel, and the actinides are filling the $5f$ sublevel.

Example Exercise 5.6 Energy Sublevels and the Periodic Table

State the highest energy sublevel in each of the following elements:

(a) H (b) S (c) Ni (d) U

Solution

Refer to the periodic table and determine the energy sublevel based on the period and block of the elements.

(a) Hydrogen has only one electron; thus, H is filling a $1s$ sublevel.

(b) Sulfur is in the third period and is a p block element; S is filling a $3p$ sublevel.

(c) Nickel is in the first series of d block elements; Ni is filling a $3d$ sublevel.

(d) Uranium is in the second series of f block elements; U is filling a $5f$ sublevel.

Practice Exercise

State the energy sublevel being filled in each of the following series of elements:

(a) Cs – Ba (b) Y – Cd (c) In – Xe (d) Ce – Lu

Answers: (a) $6s$ (b) $4d$ (c) $5p$ (d) $4f$

Concept Exercise

Refer to the periodic table and state the highest energy sublevel in a silver atom.

Answer: See Appendix G.

Electron Configuration of Elements

In Section 4.10, we learned to write the **electron configuration** for an element after memorizing the order of sublevel filling. Now that we understand the relationship of sublevels in the periodic table, we can write electron configurations by referring to blocks of elements and counting the number of electrons in each block.

The electron configuration for Na (atomic number 11) is $1s^2 2s^2 2p^6 3s^1$. As a short-hand method, we can abbreviate the electron configuration by indicating the inner-most electrons with the symbol of the preceding noble gas. The preceding noble gas with an atomic number less than 11 is neon (atomic number 10). The symbol for neon is placed in brackets, [Ne], followed by the outermost electrons. That is, the electron configuration for Na can be written as $[Ne]3s^1$.

Example Exercise 5.7 Electron Configuration and the Periodic Table

Refer to a periodic table and write the predicted electron configuration for each of the following elements by counting the number of electrons in each block:

(a) P (b) Co

Solution

Now that you understand blocks of elements in the periodic table, you can predict the order of sublevels according to increasing energy.

(a) Phosphorus is the third element in the $3p$ sublevel. The electron configuration for P is
$1s^2 2s^2 2p^6 3s^2 3p^3$, or $[Ne] 3s^2 3p^3$.

(b) Cobalt is the seventh element in the $3d$ sublevel. The electron configuration for Co is
$1s^2 2s^2 2p^6 3s^2 3p^6 4s^2 3d^7$ or $[Ar] 4s^2 3d^7$.

Practice Exercise

Refer to a periodic table and write the predicted electron configuration for each of the following elements.

(a) Zn (b) Se

Answers:

(a) $1s^2 2s^2 2p^6 3s^2 3p^6 4s^2 3d^{10}$ or $[Ar] 4s^2 3d^{10}$

(b) $1s^2 2s^2 2p^6 3s^2 3p^6 4s^2 3d^{10} 4p^4$ or $[Ar] 4s^2 3d^{10} 4p^4$

Concept Exercise

Refer to the periodic table and predict the number of 5*d* electrons in a Pt atom.

Answer: See Appendix G.

Note There are a few exceptions in the predicted electron configurations for some of the elements. That is, some elements have actual electron configurations that vary from their predicted arrangements. On occasion, electrons in a lower energy sublevel jump to an unfilled sublevel of slightly higher energy. Some of these exceptions are easy to explain, whereas others are not. For our purposes, we will disregard these exceptions and write electron configurations based on the general predictions for the order of sublevel filling.

5.7 VALENCE ELECTRONS

LEARNING OBJECTIVE

▶ To predict the number of valence electrons for any representative element.

When an atom undergoes a chemical reaction, only the outermost electrons are involved. These electrons are farthest from the nucleus, and more available to react with another atom. These outermost electrons are called **valence electrons**. Valence electrons form chemical bonds between atoms and are responsible for the chemical behavior of the element. For our purposes, we will ignore transition elements and consider only the representative elements. In these cases, the number of valence electrons is equal to the total number of electrons in the outermost *s* and *p* sublevels.

We can predict the number of valence electrons by noting the group number in the periodic table. Using the Roman numeral convention, we see that the group number is identical to the total number of valence electrons. That is, elements in Group IA have one valence electron, and elements in Group IIA have two valence electrons. Group IIIA elements have two electrons from an *s* sublevel plus one electron from a *p* sublevel, for a total of three valence electrons. Group IVA elements have four valence electrons, Group VA elements have five valence electrons, and so on.

With the IUPAC designations for group numbers, the last digit (for example, the "8" in 18) indicates the number of valence electrons. Group 13 elements have three valence electrons, Group 14 elements have four valence electrons, Group 15 elements have five valence electrons, and so on. Note that the *s* and *p* sublevels can have a maximum of two and six electrons, respectively. Thus, the maximum number of valence electrons (*s* sublevel + *p* sublevel) is equal to $8\,e^-\,(2\,e^- + 6\,e^-)$.

Lithium is in Group IA/1, and so a lithium atom has only one valence electron. Oxygen is in Group VIA/16 and has six valence electrons. The following example further illustrates the relationship between group number and number of valence electrons:

Example Exercise 5.8 Valence Electrons and the Periodic Table

Refer to the periodic table and predict the number of valence electrons for an atom of each of the following representative elements:

(a) Na
(b) Al
(c) S
(d) Xe

Solution

Find the element in the periodic table, note the group number, and indicate the number of valence electrons.

(a) Sodium is in Group IA/1, and so Na has 1 valence electron.
(b) Aluminum is in Group IIIA/13, and so Al has 3 valence electrons.
(c) Sulfur is in Group VIA/16, and so S has 6 valence electrons.
(d) Xenon is in Group VIIIA/18, and so Xe has 8 valence electrons.

Practice Exercise

Refer to the periodic table and state the number of valence electrons for any element in each of the following groups:

(a) Group IIA
(b) Group VA
(c) Group 14
(d) Group 17

Answers:

(a) 2   (b) 5
(c) 4   (d) 7

Concept Exercise

Why are predictions for the number of valence electrons only for representative elements?

Answer: See Appendix G.

Note We can quickly predict the number of valence electrons for any main-group element by referring to its group number in the periodic table. However, the transition elements are filling d sublevels, not an s or p sublevel, which complicates the discussion. Therefore, we will not predict the number of valence electrons for a transition element.

LEARNING OBJECTIVE

▶ To draw the electron dot formula for any representative element.

▲ Figure 5.7 **Electron Dot Formulas** The electron dot formula for an atom of an element uses the symbol for the element to represent the core electrons. Dots represent valence electrons, which are arranged clockwise around the symbol.

5.8 ELECTRON DOT FORMULAS

We said previously that only valence electrons are involved when an element undergoes a chemical reaction. That's because valence electrons are farthest from the nucleus and are the most accessible. To keep track of valence electrons, chemists have devised a notation called the **electron dot formula**. Electron dot formulas are also referred to as *Lewis structures* in honor of G. N. Lewis (1875–1946), a famous American chemist who conceived the notion of valence electrons.

An electron dot formula shows the symbol of an element surrounded by its valence electrons. The symbol of the element represents the **core electrons** in an atom. That is, the symbol represents the inner electrons, which are not available for bonding. Dots are placed around the symbol to represent the valence electrons. Figure 5.7 illustrates the general symbol for an electron dot formula.

In practice, we will use the following guidelines for drawing electron dot formulas:

Guidelines for Drawing Electron Dot Formulas of Atoms

1. Write the symbol of the element to represent the core electrons.
2. We then draw a maximum of two dots on each side of the symbol. A dot represents 1 valence electron, and the maximum number is 8 electrons (s sublevel $+ p$ sublevel $= 2\,e^- + 6\,e^- = 8\,e^-$).
3. Determine the number of valence electrons from the group number of the element in the periodic table. Draw one dot around the symbol for each valence electron.

Although there is no absolute rule for placing dots, the first dot is usually placed to the right of the symbol, the second dot beneath the symbol, the third dot to the left of the symbol, and the fourth dot above the symbol. The fifth dot pairs with the first dot. The sixth, seventh, and eighth dots pair with the second, third, and fourth dots, respectively, moving clockwise around the symbol.

As an example, consider the element phosphorus. Phosphorus is in Group VA/15 and, therefore, has five valence electrons. We can draw the electron dot formula for phosphorus as follows. First, write the symbol for phosphorus, then add five dots, one at a time, as follows:

$$\text{P} \quad > \quad \text{P}\cdot \quad > \quad \text{P}\cdot \quad > \quad \cdot\text{P}\cdot \quad > \quad \cdot\text{P}\cdot \quad > \quad \cdot\text{P}\colon$$

$$\text{core} \quad + \quad 1\,e^- \quad + \quad 2\,e^- \quad + \quad 3\,e^- \quad + \quad 4\,e^- \quad + \quad 5\,e^-$$

Keep in mind that the placement of dots is not intended to show the actual positions of valence electrons. In point of fact, electrons are in constant motion, moving about the nucleus. Electron dot formulas are intended only to help us keep track of valence electrons. The following example exercise further illustrates electron dot formulas.

Example Exercise 5.9 Electron Dot Formulas

Draw the electron dot formula for each of the following elements:

(a) Si   (b) Xe

Solution

Let's find the group number of the element in the periodic table and note the number of valence electrons. We write the symbol of the element and place the same number of dots around the symbol as there are valence electrons. In these examples, Si has 4 valence electrons and Xe has 8. The electron dot formulas are as follows:

(a) $\cdot\text{Si}\cdot$ (b) $\colon\ddot{\text{Xe}}\cdot$

Practice Exercise

Draw the electron dot formula for each of the following elements:

(a) K   (b) I

Answers:

(a) K $\cdot$ (b) $\colon\ddot{\text{I}}\colon$

Concept Exercise

Propose two ways of drawing the electron dot formula for Mg.

Answer: See Appendix G.

5.9 IONIZATION ENERGY

Although electrons can be removed from all elements, metals lose electrons more easily than nonmetals. In fact, metals undergo chemical reactions by losing one or more valence electrons. Since electrons are negatively charged, metals become positively charged after losing an electron. Any atom bearing a charge is called an **ion**.

Energy is always required to remove an electron from an atom. By definition, the amount of energy necessary to remove an electron from a neutral atom in the gaseous state is called the **ionization energy**, or ionization potential. We can illustrate ionization of a sodium atom as follows:

$$\text{Na} \quad \xrightarrow{\text{ionization energy}} \quad \text{Na}^+ + e^-$$

Figure 5.8 shows the relative energy required to remove a single electron from an atom of elements 1–86.

Notice in Figure 5.8 that the elements having the highest ionization energy belong to the same group—the noble gases. One reason this group shows little tendency to undergo reaction is the difficulty with which an electron is removed. We can also reason that noble gases have high ionization energies because their valence shells are completely filled, and so they do not need to gain or lose electrons to become stable.

LEARNING OBJECTIVES

▶ To state the general trends of ionization energy in the periodic table.

▶ To state the group with the highest and the lowest ionization energy.

▶ To predict the element in a pair having the higher ionization energy.

▶ **Figure 5.8 Ionization Energy** The diagram shows the energy required to remove a single electron from a neutral atom of an element in the gaseous state. Note the alkali metals have the lowest ionization energy, and the noble gases have the highest ionization energy.

On the other hand, notice that the elements having the lowest ionization energy are alkali metals. Because they are in the same group, all alkali metals have a similar electron configuration. That is, they all have one electron in an s sublevel. If we remove an electron from an alkali metal, the resulting ion will have the same number of electrons as the preceding noble gas. For example, a lithium ion has 2 electrons (the same as He), a sodium ion has 10 electrons (the same as Ne), and a potassium ion has 18 electrons (the same as Ar). When an alkali metal loses an electron, it achieves a noble gas electron configuration, which is exceedingly stable.

There are general trends in the periodic table regarding ionization energy. Within a group of elements, the energy required to remove an electron increases as the atomic radius decreases. As we proceed up a group, the atomic radius decreases since the valence electrons are closer to the nucleus and are more tightly held. Thus, the ionization energy *increases up a group of elements*. As we move from left to right in the periodic table, the nuclear charge becomes greater. The energy required to remove an electron, therefore, increases. In general, the ionization energy *increases from left to right across a period of elements*.

Example Exercise 5.10   Ionization Energy and the Periodic Table

Based on the general trends in the periodic table, predict which element in each of the following pairs has the higher ionization energy:

(a) Li or Na   (b) O or F

Solution

Let's refer to a periodic table and apply the general trends in ionization energy, which increases up a group and across a period.

(a) Li is above Na in Group IA/1, and so Li has the higher ionization energy.

(b) F is right of O in Period 2, and so F has the higher ionization energy.

Practice Exercise

Based on the general trends in the periodic table, predict which element in each of the following pairs has the higher ionization energy:

(a) Na or Mg   (b) O or S

Answers: (a) Mg (b) O

Concept Exercise

Which group in the periodic table has the highest ionization energy? Which group has the lowest ionization energy?

Answer: See Appendix G.

Note The amount of energy involved when a neutral atom gains an electron is called *electron affinity*. Metals show a weak tendency to gain an electron and have a low electron affinity. Nonmetals have a strong tendency to gain electrons and have a high electron affinity. The nonmetals closest to the noble gases have the highest electron affinity, so we can predict the electron affinity for F is greater than for O; and Cl is greater than S.

5.10 IONIC CHARGES

LEARNING OBJECTIVES

In general, when metals and nonmetals react, metals tend to lose electrons and nonmetals tend to gain electrons. More specifically, metals lose electrons from their valence shell, and nonmetals add electrons to their valence shell. Recall that an atom that bears a charge as a result of gaining or losing electrons is called an *ion*. Thus, metals become positive ions, and nonmetals become negative ions; in other words, they acquire an **ionic charge**.

The positive ionic charge on a metal ion is related to its number of valence electrons. Metals in Group IA/1 give up one valence electron to produce a positive ionic charge of 1+. Elements in Group IIA/2 give up their two valence electrons to produce a positive ionic charge of 2+. Metals in Group IIIA/13 usually lose three electrons and have an ionic charge of 3+. Group IVA/14 metals can lose four electrons, producing a charge of 4+.

The negative charge on a nonmetal ion is also governed by its number of valence electrons. Nonmetals in Group VIIA/17 have seven valence electrons and tend to add one electron to assume a noble gas configuration with eight valence electrons. After gaining one electron, the nonmetal has a negative ionic charge of 1−. Elements in Group VIA/16 gain two valence electrons, which produces an ionic charge of 2−. Nonmetals in Group VA/15 add three valence electrons, which give an ionic charge of 3−.

Figure 5.9 shows several common elements and their ionic charges as predicted by the position of the element in the periodic table.

▶ To predict the ionic charge for any representative element.

▶ To write the predicted electron configuration for selected ions.

▲ Figure 5.9 **Periodic Table of Selected Ions** Notice that metals have a positive ionic charge equal to their group number. Nonmetals have a negative ionic charge equal to 8 minus their A group number in the periodic table. Both metals and nonmetals attempt to assume a stable noble gas electron configuration.

Lithium is in Group IA/1, and so a lithium ion has an ionic charge of 1+. The lithium ion is written Li^+, with the 1 (in 1+) understood. Oxygen is in Group VIA/16, has an ionic charge of 2−, and is shown as O^{2-}. The following examples further illustrate the relationship between group number and ionic charge.

Example Exercise 5.11   Ionic Charge and the Periodic Table

Predict the ionic charge for each of the following ions based on the group number of the element in the periodic table:

(a) Al ion

(b) S ion

Solution

We refer to the periodic table to find the group number of the element.

(a) Aluminum is in Group IIIA/13. The metal atom loses 3 e^-, and so the ionic charge is 3+, that is, Al^{3+}.

(b) Sulfur is in Group VIA/16. The nonmetal atom gains 2 e^-, and so the ionic charge is 2−, that is, S^{2-}.

Practice Exercise

Predict the ionic charge for each of the following ions based on the group number of the element in the periodic table:

(a) Mg ion

(b) Br ion

Answers:

(a) Mg^{2+}

(b) Br^-

Concept Exercise

Predict the common ionic charge for Group IA/1 elements, for Group IIA/2 elements, and for Group VIIA/17 elements.

Answer: See Appendix G.

In Section 5.9 we learned that Group IA/1 elements form ions by losing one electron. We showed that each Group IA/1 ion has an electron configuration identical to that of the previous noble gas element. Similarly, Group VIIA/17 elements gain one electron to assume an electron configuration identical to that of the next noble gas element.

For example, a sodium ion (Na^+) and a fluoride ion (F^-) each have 10 electrons, as does a neutral neon atom. Although their properties are not related, their electron configurations are identical. By definition, two or more ions having the same number of electrons are said to be **isoelectronic**. The sodium ion, the fluoride ion, and the neon atom are said to be members of an isoelectronic series.

Example Exercise 5.12   Predicting Isoelectronic Ions

Refer to the periodic table and predict which of the following ions are isoelectronic with the noble gas argon:

(a) K^+

(b) Br^-

(c) Ca^{2+}

(d) O^{2-}

Solution

We refer to the periodic table to find the atomic number of the element.

(a) K^+ has 18 electrons (19 − 1); it is isoelectronic with argon (18 e^-).

(b) Br^- has 36 electrons (35 + 1); it is isoelectronic with krypton (36 e^-).

(c) Ca^{2+} has 18 electrons (20 − 2); it is isoelectronic with argon (18 e^-).

(d) O^{2-} has 10 electrons (8 + 2); it is isoelectronic with neon (10 e^-).

Practice Exercise

Refer to the periodic table and predict which of the following ions are isoelectronic with the noble gas xenon:

(a) Cs^+

(b) Cl^-

(c) La^{3+}

(d) Se^{2-}

Answers:

(a) Cs^+ is isoelectronic with xenon

(b) Cl^- is isoelectronic with argon

(c) La^{3+} are isoelectronic with xenon

(d) Se^{2-} is isoelectronic with krypton

Concept Exercise

Predict the next ion in the isoelectronic series: Se^{2-}, Br^-, Kr, Rb^+, Sr^{2+}.

Answer: See Appendix G.

Electron Configuration of Ions

In Section 5.6 we learned how to predict the electron configuration of an element from the blocks of elements in the periodic table. Now we will learn how to write the electron configuration of an ion. First we find the element in the periodic table, and then we write out the electron configuration as we did in Section 5.6.

When writing the electron configuration for positive ions, we remove the number of electrons that corresponds to the positive charge on the ion. For example, the electron configuration for a sodium atom is $1s^2 2s^2 2p^6 3s^1$. Sodium ion is Na^+, so it loses one electron. That is,

$$\begin{array}{ccc} \text{Na atom} & \text{loses 1 e}^- & Na^+ \\ 1s^2 2s^2 2p^6 3s^1 & \longrightarrow & 1s^2 2s^2 2^6 \end{array}$$

We should note that transition metals lose two electrons from the highest s sublevel first before losing electrons from their outer d sublevel. In the fourth-period elements, for example, $4s$ electrons are lost before $3d$ electrons. The electron configuration for a manganese(II) ion is $1s^2 2s^2 2p^6 3s^2 3p^6 3d^5$. Note that manganese forms a Mn^{2+} ion by losing two electrons from the $4s$ sublevel rather than the $3d$ sublevel. That is,

$$\begin{array}{ccc} \text{Mn atom} & \text{loses 2 e}^- & Mn^{2+} \\ 1s^2 2s^2 2p^6 3s^2 3p^6 4s^2 3d^5 & \longrightarrow & 1s^2 2s^2 2p^6 3s^2 3p^6 3d^5 \end{array}$$

As shown in Section 5.6, electron configurations can be simplified by using a noble gas symbol to represent the core electrons. This method of showing electron configuration is called **core notation**. In the preceding example with a Mn atom, we can write the electron configuration as $[Ar] 4s^2 3d^5$ using core notation. For Mn^{2+}, we can write the electron configuration as $[Ar] 3d^5$.

When writing the electron configuration for negative nonmetal ions, we must add the number of electrons that corresponds to the negative charge on the ion. For example, the electron configuration for chlorine is $[Ne] 3s^2 3p^5$. Since chloride ion is Cl^-, it gains one electron. That is,

$$\begin{array}{ccc} \text{Cl atom} & \text{gains 1 e}^- & Cl^- \\ [Ne] 3s^2 3p^5 & \longrightarrow & [Ne] 3s^2 3p^6 \end{array}$$

We can write the electron configuration of Cl^- as [Ar]. The following example exercise further illustrates how to write the electron configuration of ions.

Example Exercise 5.13 Electron Configuration of Ions

Refer to the periodic table and write the predicted electron configuration for each of the following ions using core notation:

(a) Fe^{3+} (b) Se^{2-}

Solution

We refer to the periodic table to recall the blocks of elements so that we can write the electron configuration for the element.

(a) The electron configuration for an Fe atom is $[Ar] 4s^2 3d^6$. The core electron configuration for an Fe^{3+} ion is $[Ar] 3d^5$.

(b) The electron configuration for a Se atom is $[Ar] 4s^2 3d^{10} 4p^4$. The electron configuration for a Se^{2-} ion is $[Ar] 4s^2 3d^{10} 4p^6$ or simply [Kr].

Practice Exercise

Refer to the periodic table and write the predicted electron configuration for each of the following ions using core notation:

(a) Cd^{2+}

(b) P^{3-}

Answers:

(a) $[Kr]\, 4d^{10}$

(b) $[Ne]\, 3s^2\, 3p^6$, or $[Ar]$

Concept Exercise

What is the electron configuration for radon gas using core notation?

Answer: See Appendix G.

CHEMISTRY CONNECTION   Evolution of Chemical Elements

Q: All the chemical elements may be derived from which single element?

Although biologists are keenly interested in the "origin of species," chemists are equally curious about the origin of elements. The scientific community is not in total agreement, but in general, scientists believe that the chemical elements evolved from the simplest element hydrogen. This theory that the chemical elements evolved from hydrogen was first hypothesized in the nineteenth century, and coincided with Darwin's *On the Origin of Species* published in 1859, which set forth the principle of biological evolution.

The universe is calculated to be about 14 billion years old beginning with an event referred to as the "Big Bang." The Big Bang signaled the creation of our universe and was characterized by inconceivably high temperatures. Subsequently, the universe cooled rapidly and subatomic particles including protons, neutrons, and electrons began to form. There is evidence for both hydrogen and helium being formed in the Big Bang, but we also know that helium is currently being formed by our Sun through the process of nuclear fusion. That is, two hydrogen nuclei ($_1$H) fuse together to form one helium nucleus ($_2$He). It is reasonable to speculate that heavier nuclei can form through further nuclear fusion by a process termed *nucleosynthesis*.

There are a number of mechanisms that have been put forth to explain the creation of elements heavier than helium. For example, the fusion of hydrogen and helium can produce lithium ($_3$Li), which in turn can yield beryllium ($_4$Be), and eventually carbon ($_6$C). There is also evidence for the direct fusion of three helium nuclei ($_2$He) to give carbon ($_6$C). Although the study of chemical elements is clearly within the scope of chemists, the ultimate answer(s) to the evolution of the elements may come from astrophysics, the branch of astronomy that studies the physical nature of stars and other planetary bodies. Astrophysicists apply the laws of physics and chemistry to interpret astronomical observations.

◀ **Milky Way Galaxy** Gravity acting on debris from the Big Bang produced regions of high density including galaxies having numerous stars. Some of these stars simply burned out, whereas others reached high core temperatures capable of nucleosynthesis of heavier elements. Eventually, these stars collapsed and exploded creating supernovas and sending chemical elements throughout the universe.

A: Hydrogen was first formed from the Big Bang and, directly or indirectly, gave rise to the evolution of heavier chemical elements.

Summary

LEARNING OBJECTIVES

	SEC	EXERCISES
To apply the original periodic law proposed by Mendeleev.	5.1	Exercises 1–4
To apply the modern periodic law proposed by Moseley.	5.2	Exercises 5–8
To classify the elements according to their groups (families) and periods (series) in the periodic table.	5.3	Exercises 9–20
To designate a group of elements in the periodic table using both the American convention (IA–VIIIA) and the IUPAC convention (1–18).	5.3	Exercises 21–28
To describe the trend in metallic character within a group or period.	5.4	Exercises 29–30, 33–34
To describe the trend in atomic size within a group or period.	5.4	Exercises 31–32, 35–36
To predict a physical property for an element given the values of other elements in the same group.	5.5	Exercises 37–40
To predict a chemical formula for a compound given the formulas of other compounds containing an element in the same group.	5.5	Exercises 41–46
To predict the highest energy sublevel for an element given its position in the periodic table.	5.6	Exercises 47–54
To predict the electron configuration for an element given its position in the periodic table.	5.6	Exercises 55–56
To predict the number of valence electrons for any representative element.	5.7	Exercises 57–60
To draw the electron dot formula for any representative element.	5.8	Exercises 61–62
To state the general trends of ionization energy in the periodic table.	5.9	Exercises 63–64
To state the group with the highest and the lowest ionization energy.	5.9	Exercises 65–66
To predict the element in a pair having the higher ionization energy.	5.9	Exercises 67–70
To predict the ionic charge for any representative element.	5.10	Exercises 71–76
To write the predicted electron configuration for selected ions.	5.10	Exercises 77–80

Section 5.1 In 1869, Dmitri Mendeleev explained the recurring properties of more than 60 elements by arranging them according to increasing atomic mass. In 1871, Mendeleev published a revised periodic table of elements, which even included undiscovered elements and their predicted properties.

Section 5.2 In 1913, H. G. J. Moseley showed that the positive charge on the nucleus of each element in the periodic table increases progressively. As a result, the **periodic law** was rewritten, and it is now stated that physical and chemical properties repeat periodically when the elements are arranged in order of increasing atomic number.

Section 5.3 The periodic table is organized by vertical columns called **groups** and horizontal rows called **periods**. The main-group elements in Groups 1, 2, and 13–18 are referred to as **representative elements**, and the elements in Groups 3–12 are called **transition elements**. The elements in Groups 1, 2, 17, and 18 are referred to as the **alkali metals**, **alkaline earth metals**, **halogens**, and **noble gases**, respectively. The elements following lanthanum (Ce–Lu) are referred to as **lanthanides** and the elements following actinium (Th–Lr) are called **actinides**. Collectively, lanthanides and actinides are

known as **inner transition elements**. The elements Sc, Y, La, and Ce–Lu are referred to as **rare earth elements**. The elements beyond uranium are called **transuranium elements**.

Section 5.4 The periodic table is divided into metals on the left side and nonmetals on the right. Semimetals have intermediate properties and are found between the metals and the nonmetals. The atomic radius decreases up a group and from left to right. The metallic character also decreases up a group and from left to right.

Section 5.5 The trends in the periodic table enable us to predict physical and chemical properties. If we are given the atomic radius and oxide formula of two elements in a group, we can make a reasonable prediction for the atomic radius and oxide formula of another element in the same group.

Section 5.6 The elements in the periodic table are arranged by sublevels according to increasing energy. We can easily predict the energy sublevel containing the outermost electrons by referring to the periodic table. We can write the **electron configuration** by noting the sublevels in the s, p, d, and f blocks of elements.

Section 5.7 We can use the periodic table to quickly predict the number of electrons in the outermost s and p sublevels of an element, that is, the number of **valence electrons**. The number of valence electrons corresponds to the group number in the periodic table. For example, a Group IA/1 element has 1 valence electron, and a Group VIIA/17 element has 7 valence electrons.

Section 5.8 We can diagram an atom by letting the symbol of the element represent the **core electrons** and drawing dots to represent the valence electrons. This diagram is referred to as the **electron dot formula** of the element.

Section 5.9 When an element loses or gains electrons, the resulting positively or negatively charged atoms are called **ions**. The amount of energy required to remove an electron from an atom is called the **ionization energy**. Since each noble gas has its valence shell filled, its ionization energy is extremely high. Conversely, each alkali metal has a low ionization energy

because it has to lose only one valence electron to acquire a noble gas electron structure. Ionization energy increases up a group and from left to right in the periodic table.

Section 5.10 We can predict the **ionic charge** for a representative element from its group number. Metals lose valence electrons and nonmetals gain electrons to obtain a noble gas structure. For example, potassium is in Group IA/1 and loses 1 valence electron to form K^+. Sulfur is in Group VIA/16, has 6 valence electrons, and gains 2 electrons to form S^{2-}. The resulting K^+ and S^{2-} ions each have 18 electrons and are said to be **isoelectronic**. To write the electron configuration for an ion, we add or subtract electrons corresponding to the ionic charge. For the magnesium ion, Mg^{2+}, we subtract 2 electrons, and for the fluoride ion, F^-, we add 1 electron. Since Mg^{2+} and F^- each have 10 electrons, they are isoelectronic, and we can write their electron configurations as $1s^2\,2s^2\,2p^6$ or simply in **core notation** as [Ne].

Key Terms *Answers to Key Terms are in Appendix H.*

Select the key term that corresponds to each of the following definitions.

_____ 1. the properties of elements recur in a repeating pattern when arranged by increasing atomic number

_____ 2. a vertical column of elements in the periodic table

_____ 3. a horizontal row of elements in the periodic table

_____ 4. the Group IA/1 elements, excluding hydrogen

_____ 5. the Group IIA/2 elements

_____ 6. the Group VIIA/17 elements

_____ 7. the relatively unreactive Group VIIIA/18 elements

_____ 8. the Group A (1, 2, and 13–18) elements in the periodic table

_____ 9. the Group B (3–12) elements in the periodic table

_____ 10. the elements with atomic numbers 58–71

_____ 11. the elements with atomic numbers 90–103

_____ 12. the elements in the lanthanide and actinide series

_____ 13. the elements with atomic numbers 21, 39, 57, and 58–71

_____ 14. the elements beyond atomic number 92

_____ 15. a shorthand description of the arrangement of electrons by sublevels according to increasing energy

_____ 16. the inner electrons in an atom which are not available for bonding

_____ 17. the electrons that occupy the outermost s and p sublevels of an atom

_____ 18. the chemical symbol of an element surrounded by a dot representing each valence electron

_____ 19. an atom that bears a charge as a result of gaining or losing valence electrons

_____ 20. the amount of energy necessary to remove an electron from an atom

_____ 21. refers to the positive charge on a metal atom that has lost electrons or to the negative charge on a nonmetal atom that has gained electrons

_____ 22. refers to ions having the same electron configuration; for example, Mg^{2+} and O^{2-} each have 10 electrons

_____ 23. a method of writing an electron configuration in which core electrons are represented by a noble gas symbol in brackets followed by the valence electrons, for example, $[Ne]3s^2$

(a) actinide series (*Sec. 5.3*)
(b) alkali metals (*Sec. 5.3*)
(c) alkaline earth metals (*Sec. 5.3*)
(d) core electrons (*Sec. 5.8*)
(e) core notation (*Sec. 5.10*)
(f) electron configuration (*Sec. 5.6*)
(g) electron dot formula (*Sec. 5.8*)
(h) group (*Sec. 5.3*)
(i) halogens (*Sec. 5.3*)
(j) inner transition elements (*Sec. 5.3*)
(k) ion (*Sec. 5.9*)
(l) ionic charge (*Sec. 5.10*)
(m) ionization energy (*Sec. 5.9*)
(n) isoelectronic (*Sec. 5.10*)
(o) lanthanide series (*Sec. 5.3*)
(p) noble gases (*Sec. 5.3*)
(q) period (*Sec. 5.3*)
(r) periodic law (*Sec. 5.2*)
(s) rare earth elements (*Sec. 5.3*)
(t) representative elements (*Sec. 5.3*)
(u) transition elements (*Sec. 5.3*)
(v) transuranium elements (*Sec. 5.3*)
(w) valence electrons (*Sec. 5.7*)

Exercises *Answers to odd-numbered Exercises are in Appendix I.*

Classification of Elements (Sec. 5.1)

1. Why did Mendeleev not include helium in his periodic table of 1871?
2. Why did Mendeleev not include krypton in his periodic table of 1871?
3. Why did Mendeleev not include radium in his periodic table of 1871?
4. Why did Mendeleev not include plutonium in his periodic table of 1871?

0,30€ CIENCIA QUÍMICA

España

Correos

TABLA PERIÓDICA DE ELEMENTOS DE MENDELÉIEV

DISEÑO: J. GARCÍA MARTÍNEZ   R RCM-FNMT 2007

▲ In 2007 Spain issued a periodic table postage stamp commemorating the 100th anniversary of Mendeleev's death. The tiny white squares indicate the position of elements predicted by Mendeleev before their actual discovery.

The Periodic Law Concept (Sec. 5.2)

5. Before Moseley's discovery in 1913, the periodic law stated that physical and chemical properties tend to repeat periodically when elements are arranged according to what trend?
6. After Moseley's discovery in 1913, the periodic law stated that physical and chemical properties tend to repeat periodically when elements are arranged according to what trend?
7. Which two elements in the fourth period violate the original periodic law as stated by Mendeleev?
8. Which two elements in the fifth period violate the original periodic law as stated by Mendeleev?

Groups and Periods of Elements (Sec. 5.3)

9. Vertical columns in the periodic table are referred to by what two terms?
10. Horizontal rows in the periodic table are referred to by what two terms?
11. What is the term for the elements that belong to Groups IA–VIIIA (Groups 1, 2, and 13–18)?
12. What is the term for the elements that belong to Groups IIIB–IIB (Groups 3–12)?
13. What is the term for the elements in the series that follows element 57?
14. What is the term for the elements in the series that follows element 89?
15. What is the term for the two series of elements that include Ce–Lu and Th–Lr?

16. Which three elements are rare earth elements, but not lanthanides?
17. What is the term for the elements on the left side of the periodic table?
18. What is the term for the elements on the right side of the periodic table?
19. Which radioactive elements are semimetals because their appearance resembles that of metals?
20. Which nonradioactive elements are semimetals because their appearance resembles that of metals?
21. Identify the group number corresponding to each of the following families of elements:
    (a) alkali metals   (b) alkaline earth metals
    (c) halogens   (d) noble gases
22. Identify the group number corresponding to each of the following families of elements:
    (a) boron group   (b) oxygen group
    (c) nickel group   (d) copper group
23. According to IUPAC, what is the designation for each of the following groups indicated by the American convention?
    (a) Group IA   (b) Group IIIA
    (c) Group VA   (d) Group VIIA
    (e) Group IB   (f) Group IIIB
    (g) Group VB   (h) Group VIIB
24. According to the American convention using Roman numerals, what is the group number designation for each of the following?
    (a) Group 2   (b) Group 4
    (c) Group 6   (d) Group 8
    (e) Group 11   (f) Group 12
    (g) Group 16   (h) Group 18
25. Refer to the periodic table and select the symbol of the element that fits each of the following descriptions:
    (a) the Group VA/15 semimetal in the fifth period
    (b) the sixth-period representative element with properties similar to Sr
    (c) the fifth-period transition element with properties similar to Ti
    (d) the lighter-than-air noble gas used in blimps and party balloons
26. Refer to the periodic table and select the symbol of the element that fits each of the following descriptions:
    (a) the Group IVA/14 semimetal in the fourth period
    (b) the third-period alkali metal
    (c) the halogen that is normally a solid and not radioactive
    (d) the lanthanide that is not naturally occurring
27. Refer to the periodic table and select the symbol of the element that fits each of the following descriptions:
    (a) the third-period alkaline earth metal
    (b) the halogen that exists as a reddish-brown liquid at normal conditions
    (c) the rare earth element whose atomic number is greatest
    (d) the actinide with properties similar to Ce

28. Refer to the periodic table and select the symbol of the element that fits each of the following descriptions:
  (a) the fourth-period representative element with properties similar to O
  (b) the sixth-period transition element with properties similar to Ni
  (c) the rare earth element whose atomic mass is lowest
  (d) the radioactive noble gas

Periodic Trends (Sec. 5.4)

29. According to the general trend, metallic character for a period of elements (increases/decreases) proceeding from left to right in the periodic table.

30. According to the general trend, metallic character (increases/decreases) proceeding up a group of elements in the periodic table.

31. According to the general trend, the atomic radius for a period of elements (increases/decreases) proceeding from left to right in the periodic table.

32. According to the general trend, the atomic radius (increases/decreases) proceeding up a group of elements in the periodic table.

33. According to general trends in the periodic table, predict which element in each of the following pairs has greater metallic character:
  (a) B or Al   **(b)** Na or K
  (c) Mg or Ba   **(d)** H or Fe

34. According to general trends in the periodic table, predict which element in each of the following pairs has greater metallic character:
  (a) K or Ca
  (b) Mg or Al
  (c) Fe or Cu
  (d) S or Ar

35. According to general trends in the periodic table, predict which element in each of the following pairs has the larger atomic radius:
  (a) Li or Na
  (b) N or P
  (c) Mg or Ca
  (d) Ar or Kr

36. According to general trends in the periodic table, predict which element in each of the following pairs has the larger atomic radius:
  (a) Rb or Sr
  (b) As or Se
  (c) Pb or Bi
  (d) I or Xe

Properties of Elements (Sec. 5.5)

37. Predict the missing value (?) for each property listed below. The atomic radius, density, and melting point are given for elements in Group IA/1.

Element	Atomic Radius	Density at 20 °C	Melting Point
K	(?) nm	0.86 g/mL	63.3 °C
Rb	0.248 nm	(?) g/mL	38.9 °C
Cs	0.266 nm	1.90 g/mL	(?) °C

38. Predict the missing value (?) for each property listed below. The atomic radius, density, and melting point are given for elements in Group VIB/6.

Element	Atomic Radius	Density at 20 °C	Melting Point
Cr	0.125 nm	7.14 g/mL	(?) °C
Mo	(?) nm	10.28 g/mL	2617 °C
W	0.137 nm	(?) g/mL	3410 °C

39. Predict the missing value (?) for each property listed below. The atomic radius, density, and boiling point are given for elements in Group VIIA/17.

Element	Atomic Radius	Density at 20 °C	Boiling Point
Cl	(?) nm	1.56 g/mL	−34.6 °C
Br	0.115 nm	(?) g/mL	58.8 °C
I	0.133 nm	4.97 g/mL	(?) °C

40. Predict the missing value (?) for each property listed below. The atomic radius, density, and boiling point are given for elements in Group VIIIA/18.

Element	Atomic Radius	Density at STP	Boiling Point
Ar	0.180 nm	1.78 g/L	(?) °C
Kr	(?) nm	3.74 g/L	−152 °C
Xe	0.210 nm	(?) g/L	−107 °C

41. The formulas for the chlorides of potassium, calcium, boron, and germanium are, respectively, KCl, $CaCl_2$, BCl_3, and $GeCl_4$. Using the periodic table, predict the chemical formulas for each of the following similar compounds:
  (a) potassium fluoride   **(b)** calcium fluoride
  (c) boron bromide   **(d)** germanium iodide

42. The formulas for the oxides of sodium, magnesium, aluminum, and silicon are, respectively, Na_2O, MgO, Al_2O_3, and SiO_2. Using the periodic table, predict the chemical formulas for each of the following similar compounds:
  (a) lithium oxide   **(b)** barium oxide
  (c) gallium oxide   **(d)** tin oxide

43. The chemical formula for barium chloride is $BaCl_2$. Predict the formulas for each of the following similar compounds:
  (a) calcium fluoride   **(b)** calcium chloride
  (c) calcium bromide   **(d)** calcium iodide

44. The chemical formula for zinc oxide is ZnO. Predict the formulas for each of the following similar compounds:
  (a) cadmium oxide   **(b)** cadmium sulfide
  (c) cadmium selenide   **(d)** cadmium telluride

45. Depending upon reaction conditions, nitrogen and oxygen can produce either N_2O_3 and N_2O_5. Predict two formulas for each of the following compounds:
  (a) arsenic oxide   **(b)** antimony oxide

46. Depending upon reaction conditions, phosphorus and sulfur can produce either P_2S_3 and P_2S_5. Predict two formulas for each of the following compounds:
  (a) arsenic sulfide   **(b)** antimony sulfide

Blocks of Elements (Sec. 5.6)

47. What type of energy sublevel is being filled by the elements in Groups IA/1 and IIA/2?

48. What type of energy sublevel is being filled by the elements in Groups IIIA/13 through VIIIA/18?

49. What type of energy sublevel is being filled by the transition elements?

50. What type of energy sublevel is being filled by the inner transition elements?

51. Which energy sublevel is being filled by the lanthanide series?

52. Which energy sublevel is being filled by the actinide series?

53. Refer to the periodic table and state the highest energy sublevel for each of the following elements:
   (a) H   (b) Na
   (c) Sm   (d) Br
   (e) Sr   (f) C
   (g) Sn   (h) Cs

54. Refer to the periodic table and state the highest energy sublevel for each of the following elements:
   (a) He   (b) K
   (c) U   (d) Pd
   (e) Be   (f) Co
   (g) Si   (h) Pt

55. Refer to the periodic table and write the predicted electron configuration for each of the following elements:
   (a) Li   (b) F
   (c) Mg   (d) P
   (e) Ca   (f) Mn
   (g) Ga   (h) Rb

56. Refer to the periodic table and write the predicted electron configuration for each of the following elements:
   (a) B   (b) Ti
   (c) Na   (d) O
   (e) Ge   (f) Ba
   (g) Pd   (h) Kr

Valence Electrons (Sec. 5.7)

57. State the number of valence electrons in each of the following groups as predicted from the periodic table:
   (a) Group IA/1   (b) Group IIIA/13
   (c) Group VA/15   (d) Group VIIA/17

58. State the number of valence electrons in each of the following groups as predicted from the periodic table:
   (a) Group IIA/2   (b) Group IVA/14
   (c) Group VIA/16   (d) Group VIIIA/18

59. State the number of valence electrons for each of the following elements:
   (a) H   (b) B
   (c) N   (d) F
   (e) Ca   (f) Si
   (g) O   (h) Ar

60. State the number of valence electrons for each of the following elements:
   (a) He   (b) Pb
   (c) Se   (d) Ne
   (e) Cs   (f) Ga
   (g) Sb   (h) Br

Electron Dot Formulas (Sec. 5.8)

61. Draw the electron dot formula for each of the following elements:
   (a) H   (b) B
   (c) N   (d) F
   (e) Ca   (f) Si
   (g) O   (h) Ar

62. Draw the electron dot formula for each of the following elements:
   (a) He   (b) Pb
   (c) Se   (d) Ne
   (e) Cs   (f) Ga
   (g) Sb   (h) Br

Ionization Energy (Sec. 5.9)

63. According to the general trend, the ionization energy for a group of elements (increases/decreases) proceeding up a group in the periodic table.

64. According to the general trend, the ionization energy for a period of elements (increases/decreases) proceeding from left to right in the periodic table.

65. Which group of elements has the lowest ionization energy?

66. Which group of elements has the highest ionization energy?

67. Refer to the periodic table and predict which element in each of the following pairs has the higher ionization energy:
   (a) Mg or Ca   (b) S or Se
   (c) Sn or Pb   (d) N or P

68. Refer to the periodic table and predict which element in each of the following pairs has the higher ionization energy:
   (a) Ga or Ge   (b) Si or P
   (c) Br or Cl   (d) As or Sb

69. Refer to the periodic table and predict which element in each of the following pairs has the lower ionization energy:
   (a) Rb or Cs   (b) He or Ar
   (c) B or Al   (d) F or I

70. Refer to the periodic table and predict which element in each of the following pairs has the lower ionization energy:
   (a) Mg or Si   (b) Pb or Bi
   (c) Ca or Ga   (d) P or Cl

Ionic Charges (Sec. 5.10)

71. State the predicted ionic charge of metal ions in each of the following groups of elements:
   (a) Group IA/1   (b) Group IIA/2
   (c) Group IIIA/13   (d) Group IVA/14

72. State the predicted ionic charge of nonmetal ions in each of the following groups of elements:
   (a) Group IVA/14   (b) Group VA/15
   (c) Group VIA/16   (d) Group VIIA/17

73. Write the ionic charge for each of the following ions as predicted from the group number in the periodic table:
   (a) Cs ion   (b) Ga ion
   (c) O ion   (d) I ion

74. Write the ionic charge for each of the following ions as predicted from the group number in the periodic table:
   (a) Be ion   (b) Sn ion
   (c) P ion   (d) S ion

75. Refer to the periodic table and predict which of the following ions are isoelectronic with the noble gas argon:
(a) Al^{3+} (b) Ca^{2+}
(c) S^{2-} (d) N^{3-}

76. Refer to the periodic table and predict which of the following ions are isoelectronic with the noble gas krypton:
(a) K^+ (b) Sr^{2+}
(c) Cl^- (d) Se^{2-}

77. Refer to the periodic table and write the predicted electron configuration for each of the following positive ions using core notation:
(a) Mg^{2+} (b) K^+
(c) Fe^{2+} (d) Zr^{2+}

78. Refer to the periodic table and write the predicted electron configuration for each of the following positive ions using core notation:
(a) Ti^{2+} (b) Zn^{2+}
(c) Y^{3+} (d) Cs^+

79. Refer to the periodic table and write the predicted electron configuration for each of the following negative ions using core notation:
(a) F^- (b) S^{2-}
(c) N^{3-} (d) I^{3-}

80. Refer to the periodic table and write the predicted electron configuration for each of the following negative ions using core notation:
(a) Br^- (b) Te^{2-}
(c) As^{3-} (d) O^{2-}

General Exercises

81. Use the American convention to designate the group number corresponding to each of the following groups listed by the European convention:
(a) Group IA
(b) Group IB
(c) Group IIIA
(d) Group IIIB

82. Use the IUPAC convention to designate the group number corresponding to each of the following groups listed by the European convention:
(a) Group IIA
(b) Group IIB
(c) Group IVA
(d) Group IVB

83. Predict the atomic radius, density, and melting point for radioactive francium.

Element	Atomic Radius	Density at 20 °C	Melting Point
Rb	0.248 nm	1.53 g/mL	38.9 °C
Cs	0.266 nm	1.87 g/mL	28.4 °C
Fr	(?) nm	(?) g/mL	(?) °C

84. Predict the atomic radius, density, and melting point for radioactive radium.

Element	Atomic Radius	Density at 20 °C	Melting Point
Sr	0.215 nm	2.63 g/mL	769 °C
Ba	0.217 nm	3.65 g/mL	725 °C
Ra	(?) nm	(?) g/mL	(?) °C

85. Refer to the periodic table and write the predicted electron configuration for each of the following elements using core notation:
(a) Sr   (b) Ru
(c) Sb   (d) Cs

86. Refer to the periodic table and write the predicted electron configuration for each of the following elements using core notation:
(a) W   (b) Bi
(c) Ra   (d) Ac

87. Explain why the ionization energy for hydrogen is much higher than that of other Group IA/1 elements.

88. Predict two ionic charges for hydrogen. Write the formulas of the two ions and explain the ionic charges.

Challenge Exercises

89. Examine Figure 5.1 and determine the name of the element that Mendeleev predicted before its discovery and called ekaboron.

90. Examine Figure 5.1 and determine the name of the element that Mendeleev predicted before its discovery and called ekaaluminum.

91. Explain why the ionization energy for the alkali metals is less than the ionization energy for the alkaline earth metals.

92. Explain why the ionization energy for aluminum, contrary to the general trend, is less than the ionization energy for magnesium.

 ## Online Exercises

Research each of the following using an Internet search engine (e.g., Google.com or Yahoo.com) and cite your URL reference.

93. What name was given to Element 104 by Russian physicists after their discovery in 1964?

94. What name was given to Element 104 by American physicists after their discovery in 1969?

95. Which element gives rise to the term amalgam in dental fillings?

96. Medical diagnosis of the large intestine is performed by X-ray after a barium enema. Why is insoluble barium sulfate used for the procedure rather than a soluble barium compound?

5 Chapter Self-Test

Answers to Self-Test are in Appendix J.

1. Which of the following scientists contributed to the development of the periodic table of elements? (Sec. 5.1)
   (a) J. W. Döbereiner   (b) Dmitri Mendeleev
   (c) H. G. J. Moseley   (d) J. A. R. Newlands
   (e) all of the above

2. The modern periodic law states that the properties of the elements repeat when the periodic table is arranged according to which of the following? (Sec. 5.2)
   (a) increasing atomic number
   (b) increasing mass number
   (c) increasing atomic mass
   (d) increasing isotopic mass
   (e) none of the above

3. Which of the following is a third-period alkali metal? (Sec. 5.3)
   (a) Ca   (b) K
   (c) Mg   (d) Na
   (e) Sr

4. Which of the following elements has the most metallic character? (Sec. 5.4)
   (a) Li   (b) Na
   (c) Be   (d) Mg
   (e) Al

5. Calculate the predicted atomic radius for selenium, Se, given the atomic radius of sulfur, S, (0.104 nm) and tellurium, Te, (0.143 nm). (Sec. 5.5)
   (a) 0.039 nm   (b) 0.062 nm
   (c) 0.124 nm   (d) 0.163 nm
   (e) 0.182 nm

6. Which energy sublevel is being filled by the elements Sc to Zn? (Sec. 5.6)
   (a) $3d$ (b) $4s$
   (c) $4p$ (d) $4d$
   (e) $4f$

7. Predict the number of valence electrons for a Group VIIA/17 element. (Sec. 5.7)
   (a) 1   (b) 2
   (c) 3   (d) 7
   (e) 17

8. What is the electron dot formula for an atom of neon? (Sec. 5.9)
   (a) Ne·   (b) ·Ne·
   (c) ·Ṅe·   (d) :Ṅe:
   (e) :N̈e:

9. Which of the following elements has the highest ionization energy? (Sec. 5.9)
   (a) H   (b) He
   (c) Ne   (d) Cl
   (e) F

10. Which of the following groups has a predictable ionic charge of three negative? (Sec. 5.10)
    (a) Group IIIA/13
    (b) Group IIIB/3
    (c) Group VA/15
    (d) Group VB/5
    (e) Group VIIIA/18

Key Concepts

11. State the trends in the periodic table for decreasing metallic character.

12. State the trends in the periodic table for decreasing atomic radii.

13. State the trends in the periodic table for increasing ionization energy.

14. Given the chemical formulas for Al_2O_3, SiO_2, and P_2O_5, predict the formula for arsenic oxide, $As_?O_?$.

Critical Thinking

15. Can ions of different elements have the same number of electrons?

16. Can ions of different elements have the same number of protons?

17. Can ions of different elements have the same number of neutrons?

18. The following photograph shows a watchglass containing antimony, sulfur, and antimony sulfide. Based on typical characteristics of semimetals and nonmetals, identify the (a) yellow, (b) gray, and (c) orange substances.

Language of Chemistry

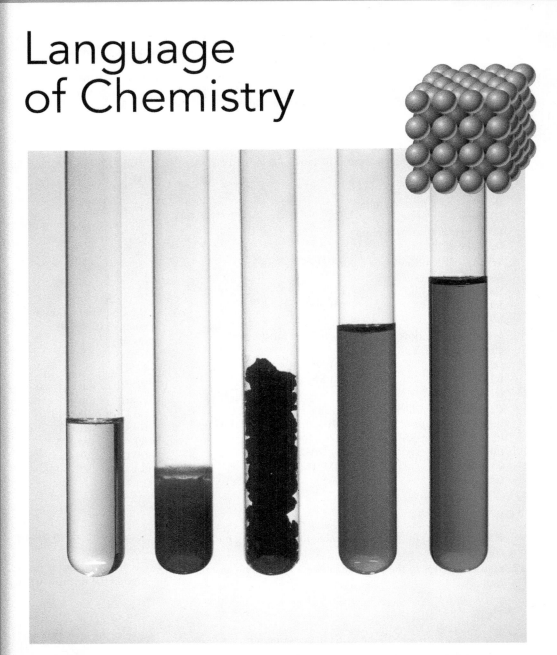

Manganese in the Environment Manganese metal is more reactive than zinc, but less reactive than aluminum. Manganese metal (center) is found naturally in the environment, and constitutes about 0.1% of Earth's crust. Manganese solutions (shown) exhibit a range of colors.

"Science is organized knowledge. Wisdom is organized life."
Immanuel Kant, German Philosopher (1724–1804)

During the Middle Ages, alchemists identified many substances that they named in a haphazard fashion. There were only a few dozen substances, so this did not pose a great problem. Toward the end of the 1700s, however, they had identified more than 10,000 substances, and the number of compounds was growing rapidly. Chemists then faced the staggering task of providing names for all these substances. The problem of assigning names was eventually solved by using a set of systematic rules.

The French chemist Antoine Lavoisier developed the first systematic method of naming substances. He proposed that chemical names refer to the composition of the compound and be derived from Latin or Greek. In 1787, Lavoisier, with the aid of others, published *Methods of Chemical Nomenclature*. The naming system he proposed was so clear and logical that it was universally accepted in a short time. In fact, it was so simple and insightful that it became the basis for our current system of naming.

6.1 CLASSIFICATION OF COMPOUNDS

In 1921, the International Union of Pure and Applied Chemistry (IUPAC) formed the Commission on the Nomenclature of Inorganic Chemistry. In 1938, the IUPAC Committee on the Reform of Inorganic Nomenclature met in Berlin. Two years later it released a comprehensive set of rules. Although the rules have been expanded and revised, the 1940 rules remain as the official international system for naming chemical compounds. These rules are referred to as **IUPAC nomenclature**.

Classifying Inorganic Compounds

An **inorganic compound** does not contain the element carbon. However, carbon dioxide (CO_2), and compounds containing carbonate (CO_3^{2-}) or hydrogen carbonate (HCO_3^-) are exceptions and are considered inorganic. According to the 1940 IUPAC rules, inorganic compounds can be placed in one of several categories. Five common classes are binary ionic, ternary ionic, binary molecular, binary acid, and ternary oxyacid.

A **binary ionic compound** contains two elements, a metal and a nonmetal. Examples of binary ionic compounds are KCl and $AlCl_3$. A **ternary ionic compound** contains three elements with at least one metal and one nonmetal. Examples of ternary ionic compounds are KNO_3 and $Al(NO_3)_3$. A **binary molecular compound** contains two elements that are both nonmetals. Water, H_2O, is a common example, as is ammonia, NH_3.

An **aqueous solution** is produced when a compound dissolves in water. Aqueous solutions are indicated by the symbol (aq). A **binary acid** is an aqueous solution of a compound containing hydrogen and one other nonmetal. Formulas of acids begin with H, and examples of binary acids are $HCl(aq)$ and $H_2S(aq)$.

A **ternary oxyacid** is an aqueous solution of a compound containing hydrogen, a nonmetal, and oxygen. Examples of ternary oxyacids are $HNO_3(aq)$ and $H_2SO_4(aq)$. Figure 6.1 illustrates the relationships among the five types of compounds we will classify according to IUPAC rules.

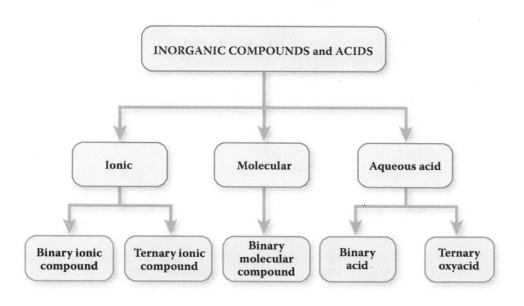

◂ **Figure 6.1 Classification of Inorganic Compounds and Acids** According to IUPAC nomenclature, inorganic compounds and acids are divided into five categories: binary ionic, ternary ionic, binary molecular, binary acid, and ternary oxyacid.

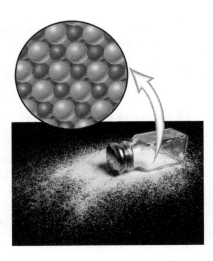

◄ **Table Salt** Sodium chloride, NaCl, is an example of a binary ionic compound composed of metal and nonmetal ions.

The following example exercise illustrates the classification of different types of compounds and aqueous acids.

Example Exercise 6.1 Classifying Compounds and Acids

Classify each of the following as a binary ionic compound, ternary ionic compound, binary molecular compound, binary acid, or ternary oxyacid:

(a) calcium oxide, CaO
(b) sulfur dioxide, SO_2
(c) silver chromate, Ag_2CrO_4
(d) hydrofluoric acid, $HF(aq)$
(e) carbonic acid, $H_2CO_3(aq)$

Solution
We can refer to the periodic table and classify each compound or solution as follows:

(a) CaO contains two elements, a metal and nonmetal. Thus, CaO is a *binary ionic compound*.
(b) SO_2 contains two elements, both nonmetals. Thus, SO_2 is a *binary molecular compound*.
(c) Ag_2CrO_4 contains three elements, two metals and a nonmetal. Thus, Ag_2CrO_4 is a *ternary ionic compound*.
(d) $HF(aq)$ is a compound of hydrogen and a nonmetal dissolved in water. Thus, $HF(aq)$ is a *binary acid*.
(e) $H_2CO_3(aq)$ is a compound containing three elements, including hydrogen and oxygen, dissolved in water. Thus, $H_2CO_3(aq)$ is a *ternary oxyacid*.

Practice Exercise
Classify each of the following as a binary ionic compound, ternary ionic compound, binary molecular compound, binary acid, or ternary oxyacid:

(a) carbon disulfide, CS_2
(b) lithium dichromate, $Li_2Cr_2O_7$
(c) magnesium iodide, MgI_2
(d) nitric acid, $HNO_3(aq)$
(e) hydrochloric acid, $HCl(aq)$

Answers:
(a) binary molecular compound
(b) ternary ionic compound
(c) binary ionic compound
(d) ternary oxyacid
(e) binary acid

Concept Exercise
How do you distinguish a binary molecular compound from a binary acid?

Answer: See Appendix G.

Classifying Ions

According to IUPAC nomenclature, ions are named systematically, depending on the category in which they are placed. A positive ion is referred to as a **cation**, and a negative ion is referred to as an **anion**. A single atom of a metal with a positive charge, or a single atom of a nonmetal with a negative charge, is called a **monoatomic ion**. A group of atoms bound together and having an overall positive or negative charge is called a **polyatomic ion**. Figure 6.2 illustrates the classification of and relationship of these ions.

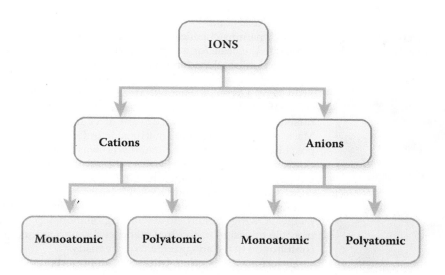

◀ **Figure 6.2 Classification of Ions** According to the IUPAC nomenclature, ions are divided into four categories: monoatomic cations, polyatomic cations, monoatomic anions, and polyatomic anions.

The following example exercise illustrates the classification of different types of ions:

Example Exercise 6.2 Classifying Cations and Anions

Classify each of the following ions as a monoatomic cation, monoatomic anion, polyatomic cation, or polyatomic anion:

(a) barium ion, Ba^{2+}
(b) chloride ion, Cl^-
(c) ammonium ion, NH_4^+
(d) carbonate ion, CO_3^{2-}

Solution
We can classify each ion as follows:

(a) Ba^{2+} is a single atom with a positive charge. Thus, Ba^{2+} is a *monoatomic cation*.
(b) Cl^- is a single atom with a negative charge. Thus, Cl^- is a *monoatomic anion*.
(c) NH_4^+ has five atoms and a positive charge. Thus, NH_4^+ is a *polyatomic cation*.
(d) carbonate ion, CO_3^{2-} has four atoms and a negative charge. Thus, carbonate ion, CO_3^{2-} is a *polyatomic anion*.

Practice Exercise
Classify each of the following ions as a monoatomic cation, monoatomic anion, polyatomic cation, or polyatomic anion:

(a) hydronium ion, H_3O^+
(b) sulfide ion, S^{2-}
(c) permanganate ion, MnO_4^-
(d) stannous ion, Sn^{2+}

Answers:

(a) polyatomic cation
(b) monoatomic anion
(c) polyatomic anion
(d) monoatomic cation

Concept Exercise
What is the distinction between Hg^{2+} and Hg_2^{2+}?

Answer: See Appendix G.

$(NH_4)_2CO_3$

▲ **Ammonium Carbonate, $(NH_4)_2CO_3$** Ammonium carbonate decomposes in air to give ammonia, NH_3, and carbon dioxide, CO_2; it is used in smelling salts and is found in baking powder.

Antoine and Marie Lavoisier

Q: Who provided invaluable laboratory assistance to Lavoisier, translated the experimental results into other languages, and helped spread the enormous body of work throughout Europe and America?

Antoine Lavoisier (1743–1794) was born into an affluent French family and received an excellent education. He initially became a lawyer like his father, but later turned to science. Lavoisier was a gifted experimenter and is generally considered the founder of modern chemistry. He established a magnificent laboratory that attracted scientists from around the world.

In 1787, Lavoisier published a book entitled *Methods of Chemical Nomenclature*. The book designated systematic principles for naming chemical substances and was so logical that it became the basis for our present rules of nomenclature. In 1789, he published the landmark textbook *Elementary Treatise on Chemistry*, which offered the first modern view of chemistry.

In 1771, Lavoisier married Marie-Anne Pierrette Paulze (1758–1836). Marie was only 13 years old and she had been raised and educated in a convent after her mother died. Marie's father arranged the marriage in order to thwart a proposal by an influential nobleman who was more than three times her age. Despite her youth, she proved invaluable to Lavoisier's work and joined him in the laboratory. Marie recorded the experimental work through her drawings and notes, and translated the results from French into other languages. Owing to their close working relationship, it is impossible to assign individual credit and separate their joint contribution to the advancement of chemistry.

Unfortunately, Marie's father was an important official in a firm that collected taxes. Although Lavoisier did not collect taxes, he received royalties from the same firm. When the French Revolution broke out, revolutionaries threw tax collectors into jail. Lavoisier was first barred from his laboratory and then arrested. After a farce trial, he was sentenced to the guillotine, along with his father-in-law and other tax collectors.

On May 8, 1794, Lavoisier was executed and buried in an unmarked grave. The French court declared that France had no need for scientists, but the famous mathematician Lagrange lamented, "Only a moment was required to strike off his head, and a hundred years may not be enough to produce another like it again." Within two years, the French people regretted their hasty decision and began unveiling statues of Lavoisier.

◀ **Antoine Lavoisier** Antoine Lavoisier is shown with Marie in their laboratory.

A: Lavoisier's multilingual wife, Marie-Anne, is recognized for keeping laboratory records and translating scientific papers into other languages.

LEARNING OBJECTIVES

▶ To write systematic names and formulas for common monoatomic ions.

▶ To predict the ionic charge for ions of representative elements.

6.2 MONOATOMIC IONS

Metal atoms can lose valence electrons and become positively charged cations; examples include Na^+, Ca^{2+}, and Al^{3+}. Conversely, nonmetal atoms can gain valence electrons and become negatively charged anions; examples include, Cl^-, S^{2-}, and P^{3-}.

Naming Metal Ions

According to IUPAC nomenclature rules, cations are named for the parent metal followed by the word *ion*. For example, Na^+ is named sodium ion, Mg^{2+} is named magnesium ion, and Al^{3+} is named aluminum ion.

Main-group metals usually form one cation; tin and lead are exceptions. Transition metals, however, often form more than one cation. Iron, for example, can form Fe^{2+} and Fe^{3+}. To name a metal cation having more than one ionic charge, it is necessary to specify the charge. IUPAC recommends that the cation be named for the parent metal followed by its charge specified by Roman numerals in parentheses. Thus, Fe^{2+} is named iron(II) ion, and Fe^{3+} is named iron(III) ion. Similarly, Cu^+ is named copper(I) ion and Cu^{2+} is named copper(II) ion. This method of naming transition metal cations is called the **Stock system**. We should note that the names of Ag^+, Zn^{2+}, and Cd^{2+} are transition metal exceptions and do not require Roman numerals.

In addition to the Stock system, IUPAC allows, but discourages, an older method for naming metal cations having two common ionic charges. It is called the **Latin system** or the suffix system. This system takes the Latin name of the metal and then adds the suffix –*ous* or –*ic*. The lower of the two ionic charges receives the –*ous* suffix, and the higher charge receives the –*ic* suffix. For example, the Latin name for iron is *ferrum*. To name an iron ion, we take the stem *ferr*– and add the suffix –*ous* or –*ic*. Thus, Fe^{2+} is named ferrous ion, and Fe^{3+} is named ferric ion. The Latin name for copper is *cuprum*. Similarly, we add the suffix –*ous* or –*ic* to the stem *cupr*–. Thus, we have Cu^+ for cuprous ion, and Cu^{2+} for cupric ion.

The formula for the mercury(I) ion is an exception. When mercury loses an electron, the resulting ion, Hg^+, becomes more stable by combining with another Hg^+ ion. Thus, the mercury(I) ion is written Hg_2^{2+}. The Latin name for mercury, *hydrargyrum*, is difficult to pronounce, and so IUPAC recommends adding the suffix to the English name. Thus, Hg_2^{2+} is named mercurous ion, and Hg^{2+} is named mercuric ion. Table 6.1 lists the systematic names for common cations.

TABLE 6.1 COMMON MONOATOMIC CATIONS

CATION	STOCK SYSTEM	LATIN SYSTEM
Al^{3+}	aluminum ion	
Ba^{2+}	barium ion	
Cd^{2+}	cadmium ion	
Ca^{2+}	calcium ion	
Co^{2+}	cobalt(II) ion	cobaltous ion
Co^{3+}	cobalt(III) ion	cobaltic ion
Cu^+	copper(I) ion	cuprous ion
Cu^{2+}	copper(II) ion	cupric ion
Cr^{3+}	chromium(III) ion	
H^+	hydrogen ion	
Fe^{2+}	iron(II) ion	ferrous ion
Fe^{3+}	iron(III) ion	ferric ion
Pb^{2+}	lead(II) ion	plumbous ion
Pb^{4+}	lead(IV) ion	plumbic ion
Li^+	lithium ion	
Mg^{2+}	magnesium ion	
Mn^{2+}	manganese(II) ion	
Hg_2^{2+}	mercury(I) ion*	mercurous ion
Hg^{2+}	mercury(II) ion	mercuric ion
Ni^{2+}	nickel(II) ion	
K^+	potassium ion	
Ag^+	silver ion	
Na^+	sodium ion	
Sr^{2+}	strontium ion	
Sn^{2+}	tin(II) ion	stannous ion
Sn^{4+}	tin(IV) ion	stannic ion
Zn^{2+}	zinc ion	

*Note that the mercury(I) ion is diatomic and is written Hg_2^{2+}.

Naming Nonmetal Ions

As we now know, nonmetal atoms can gain valence electrons and become negatively charged ions called anions. According to IUPAC rules, nonmetal ions are named by using the *nonmetal stem* plus the suffix *–ide*. Examples of nonmetal ions are Cl^-, chloride ion; S^{2-}, sulfide ion; and P^{3-}, phosphide ion. Table 6.2 lists the systematic names for common anions.

TABLE 6.2 COMMON MONOATOMIC ANIONS

ANION	IUPAC NAME	ANION	IUPAC NAME
Br^-	bromide ion	N^{3-}	nitride ion
Cl^-	chloride ion	O^{2-}	oxide ion
F^-	fluoride ion	P^{3-}	phosphide ion
I^-	iodide ion	S^{2-}	sulfide ion

Predicting Formulas of Monoatomic Cations

We can use the periodic table to help learn the names and formulas of the ions and predict their charge based on the group number of the element. Recall that Group IA/1 metals always form 1+ ions. Thus, we have Li^+, Na^+, and K^+. Also recall that the Group IIA/2 elements always form 2+ ions. Thus, we have Mg^{2+}, Ca^{2+}, Sr^{2+}, and Ba^{2+}. Similarly, we can predict that aluminum in Group IIIA/13 forms a 3+ ion, that is, Al^{3+}.

Not all metal ions are predictable from the periodic table. Tin and lead in Group IVA/14 can each form two ions: Sn^{2+} or Sn^{4+} and Pb^{2+} or Pb^{4+}. Therefore, you will have to memorize the formulas for these ions.

With few exceptions all transition elements have two *s* electrons as well as a variable number of *d* electrons. In general, a transition metal loses its two *s* electrons to form an ion with a 2+ charge, for example, Ni^{2+}. Many transition metals form additional ions having charges that are unpredictable. You will have to memorize the names of these ions. Figure 6.3 shows the relationship of ionic charge to the position of the element in the periodic table.

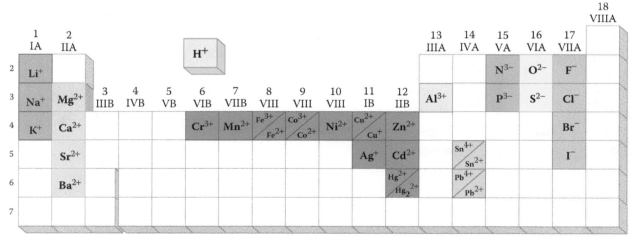

▲ Figure 6.3 **Periodic Table of Selected Ions** Note the correlation of ionic charge and group number. Although transition elements can exhibit more than one ionic charge, nearly all these metals exhibit a charge of 2+.

Although we should memorize the names and formulas of ions, the periodic table is a valuable resource for verifying ionic charges. The following example exercise illustrates the names and formulas of monoatomic cations:

Example Exercise 6.3 Names and Formulas of Monoatomic Cations

Provide the formula for the following monoatomic cations:

(a) barium ion
(b) cobalt(II) ion

Solution

We can use the periodic table to predict the charge on a cation.

(a) Barium is found in Group IIA/2 and can lose two valence electrons. We predict the formula of the ion is Ba^{2+}.

(b) Cobalt is a transition metal and can lose two or more valence electrons. The Roman numeral (II) indicates the loss of two electrons, and so the formula of the ion is Co^{2+}.

Practice Exercise

Supply a systematic name for the following monoatomic cations:

(a) Al^{3+} (b) Co^{3+}

Answers:

(a) aluminum ion   (b) cobalt(III) ion or cobaltic ion

Concept Exercise

How does the Stock system specify a variable charge on a cation?

Answer: See Appendix G.

Predicting Formulas of Monoatomic Anions

Nonmetals gain electrons to form negative ions in a predictable fashion. The halogens in Group VIIA/17 need only one electron to become isoelectronic with a noble gas. Thus, the halogens have a 1– charge and the formulas F^-, Cl^-, Br^-, and I^-. The elements in Group VIA/16 gain two electrons to become isoelectronic with a noble gas. These elements have a 2– charge and the formulas O^{2-}, S^{2-}, and Se^{2-}. Nitrogen and phosphorus are in Group VA/15 and gain three electrons. These elements have a 3– charge and the formulas N^{3-}, and P^{3-}.

Example Exercise 6.4 Names and Formulas of Monoatomic Anions

Provide the formula for each of the following monoatomic anions:

(a) fluoride ion
(b) oxide ion

Solution

Recall that nonmetals gain electrons so as to acquire a noble gas electron configuration.

(a) Fluorine is found in Group VIIA/17 and can gain one electron to become isoelectronic with neon. We predict the formula for the fluoride ion is F^-.

(b) Oxygen is found in Group VIA/16 and can gain two electrons to become isoelectronic with neon. We predict the formula for the oxide ion is O^{2-}.

Practice Exercise

Supply a systematic name for each of the following monoatomic anions:

(a) Br^- (b) N^{3-}

Answers:

(a) bromide ion   (b) nitride ion

Concept Exercise

Which one of the following is a monoatomic anion: iodide, iodate, or iodite?

Answer: See Appendix G.

▶ To write systematic names and formulas for common polyatomic ions.

6.3 POLYATOMIC IONS

Polyatomic anions generally contain one or more elements combined with oxygen. Such an anion is referred to as an **oxyanion**, a term that reflects its composition. Most oxyanions have names ending in the suffix *–ate*. Examples include the nitrate ion, NO_3^-, and the sulfate ion, SO_4^{2-}.

A few oxyanions have names ending in the suffix *–ite*. Examples include the nitrite ion, NO_2^-, and the sulfite ion, SO_3^{2-}. Notice that in each case the formula for ions with the suffix *–ite* has one less oxygen than that for ions with the suffix *–ate*.

This suffix pattern can provide clues when naming some polyatomic ions. Given the formula for the chlorate ion, ClO_3^-, we can predict the formula for the chlorite ion. Since the suffix *–ate* has changed to the suffix *–ite*, the formula has one less oxygen. Therefore, the formula for the chlorite ion is ClO_2^-. The general relationship between the suffixes *–ate* and *–ite* allows us to simplify our task of memorizing formulas of ions.

There are two important polyatomic ions that have the suffix *–ide*. The cyanide ion, CN^-, and the hydroxide ion, OH^-, are exceptions, and their names should be memorized. In addition to these two polyatomic anions, there is the ammonium cation, NH_4^+, whose formula is derived from that for ammonia gas, NH_3. Table 6.3 lists the common polyatomic ions whose formulas should be memorized.

TABLE 6.3 COMMON POLYATOMIC IONS

CATION		IUPAC NAME	
NH_4^+		ammonium ion	

ANION	IUPAC NAME	ANION	IUPAC NAME
$C_2H_3O_2^-$	acetate ion	OH^-	hydroxide ion*
CO_3^{2-}	carbonate ion	ClO^-	hypochlorite ion
ClO_3^-	chlorate ion	NO_3^-	nitrate ion
ClO_2^-	chlorite ion	NO_2^-	nitrite ion
CrO_4^{2-}	chromate ion	ClO_4^-	perchlorate ion
CN^-	cyanide ion*	MnO_4^-	permanganate ion
$Cr_2O_7^{2-}$	dichromate ion	PO_4^{3-}	phosphate ion
HCO_3^-	hydrogen carbonate ion	SO_4^{2-}	sulfate ion
HSO_4^-	hydrogen sulfate ion	SO_3^{2-}	sulfite ion

*Note that the suffix *–ide* is an exception to the general *–ate* and *–ite* rule.

The following example exercise illustrates how general principles can be used to assist you in memorizing the names and formulas of polyatomic ions:

Example Exercise 6.5 Names and Formulas of Polyatomic Ions

Provide a systematic name for each of the following polyatomic oxyanions:
(a) CO_3^{2-} (b) CrO_4^{2-} (c) ClO_2^- (d) HSO_4^-

Solution
We can make reasonable predictions for the names of many polyatomic ions. This makes the task of memorization much easier.

(a) CO_3^{2-} contains carbon, and we predict the name has the suffix *–ate*. Thus, we predict CO_3^{2-} is named the *carbonate ion*.

(b) CrO_4^{2-} contains chromium, and we predict the name has the suffix *–ate*. Thus, we predict CrO_4^{2-} is named the *chromate ion*.

(c) ClO_2^- is related to ClO_3^-, which is named the chlorate ion. Because ClO_2^- has one less oxygen atom, the suffix changes to *–ite*. Thus, we predict ClO_2^- is named the *chlorite ion*.

(d) HSO_4^- is related to the sulfate ion, SO_4^{2-}. With the addition of hydrogen, the name becomes the *hydrogen sulfate ion*.

Practice Exercise

Provide the formula for each of the following polyatomic oxyanions:

(a) acetate ion   (b) dichromate ion

(c) perchlorate ion   (d) hydrogen carbonate ion

Answers:

(a) $C_2H_3O_2^-$ (b) $Cr_2O_7^{2-}$ (c) ClO_4^- (d) HCO_3^-

Concept Exercise

How does systematic naming distinguish between a monoatomic anion and a polyatomic anion?

Answer: See Appendix G.

Note You may find it useful to make flashcards to help you memorize ions. Write the name of the ion on one side of a card and the formula of the ion on the other side. Your task will be easier if you recall the following:

1. There is one common polyatomic cation, NH_4^+.
2. Most oxyanions have the suffix *–ate*.
3. The suffix *–ate* changes to the suffix *–ite* for an oxyanion with one less oxygen atom; for example, nitrate, NO_3^-, changes to nitrite, NO_2^-.
4. There are two common polyatomic anions that are exceptions: OH^- and CN^- each have the suffix *–ide*.

6.4 WRITING CHEMICAL FORMULAS

LEARNING OBJECTIVE

▶ To write chemical formulas for ionic compounds composed of monoatomic ions and polyatomic ions.

An ionic compound is composed of positive and negative ions. A **formula unit** is the simplest representative particle in an ionic compound. Because a formula unit is neutral, the total positive charge must equal the total negative charge in both the formula unit and the ionic compound. That is, the total positive charge from the metal ions must be the same as the total negative charge from the nonmetal ions.

Ordinary sodium chloride contains the ions Na^+ and Cl^-. The positive and negative ions have equal but opposite charges, so the formula for the compound is NaCl. Calcium chloride contains the ions Ca^{2+} and Cl^-. Since the charges are not the same, it is necessary to have two Cl^- ions for each Ca^{2+} ion; therefore, the formula is $CaCl_2$. Aluminum chloride contains the ions Al^{3+} and Cl^-, and it is necessary to have three Cl^- ions for each Al^{3+} ion. The formula for the compound is $AlCl_3$.

The following example exercise provides additional illustrations of how to write formulas for ionic compounds:

Example Exercise 6.6 Writing Formulas of Binary Ionic Compounds

Write the chemical formula for the following binary compounds given their constituent ions:

(a) copper(I) oxide, Cu^+ and O^{2-}
(b) cadmium oxide, Cd^{2+} and O^{2-}
(c) cobalt(III) oxide, Co^{3+} and O^{2-}

Solution

(a) The copper(I) ion has a charge of 1+, and the oxide ion has a charge of 2–. Thus, two positive ions are required for each negative ion in a neutral formula unit. The formula of copper(I) oxide is written Cu_2O.

(b) Because the cadmium ion and oxide ion each have a charge of 2, the ratio is 1:1, that is, Cd_1O_1. It is not necessary to write the subscript 1, and so the formula of cadmium oxide is simply CdO.

(c) This example is more difficult. The cobalt(III) ion has a charge of 3+ and the oxide ion has a charge of 2–. Because the lowest common multiple is 6, two 3+ ions are required to cancel the charge of three 2– ions. The ratio is 2:3, and the formula of cobalt(III) oxide is written Co_2O_3.

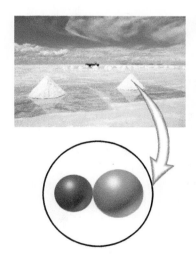

NaCl

▲ **Salt, NaCl** Table salt is an example of a binary ionic compound composed of sodium ions and chloride ions.

Practice Exercise

Write the chemical formula for the following binary compounds given their constituent ions:

(a) iron(II) sulfide, Fe^{2+} and S^{2-}

(b) mercury(I) fluoride, Hg_2^{2+} and F^-

(c) lead(IV) oxide, Pb^{4+} and O^{2-}

Answers:

(a) FeS

(b) Hg_2F_2

(c) PbO_2

Concept Exercise

What is the formula for a metal oxide if the charge on the metal (M) is 3+?

Answer: See Appendix G.

Note You can quickly verify that the chemical formula is written correctly by crossing over the charge on each ion. Consider aluminum oxide, which contains Al^{3+} and O^{2-}. The 3+ charge on the aluminum ion becomes the subscript 3 for the oxygen, and the 2− charge on the oxide ion becomes the subscript 2 for the aluminum ion. That is,

$$Al^{3+} \quad O^{2-} = Al_2O_3$$

Formula Units Containing Polyatomic Ions

As mentioned earlier, formula units are the simplest particles representing an ionic compound, and the total positive charge is equal to the total negative charge. Previously, we learned to write neutral formula units for binary ionic compounds. Similarly, in a formula unit containing K^+ and SO_4^{2-}, two K^+ ions are required to balance the charge for each SO_4^{2-}. Thus, a neutral formula unit is written K_2SO_4.

Magnesium sulfate contains Mg^{2+} and SO_4^{2-}. Because the magnitude of the charge is the same on each ion, the ratio of positive ion to negative ion is 1:1. The formula unit is written $MgSO_4$.

Ammonium sulfate is a nitrogen-supplying component in fertilizer and contains NH_4^+ and SO_4^{2-} ions. Because the negative charge is greater for SO_4^{2-}, two NH_4^+ ions are necessary to give a neutral formula unit. To avoid misunderstanding, parentheses are placed around the NH_4^+ ion. The correct formula is written $(NH_4)_2SO_4$. The following example exercise provides additional illustrations of how to write formulas for ionic compounds:

Example Exercise 6.7 Writing Formulas of Ternary Ionic Compounds

Write the chemical formula for each of the following ternary compounds given their constituent ions:

(a) calcium carbonate, Ca^{2+} and CO_3^{2-}

(b) calcium hydroxide, Ca^{2+} and OH^-

(c) calcium phosphate, Ca^{2+} and PO_4^{3-}

Solution

(a) Because the positive and negative ions each have a charge of 2, one positive ion and one negative ion are required to produce a neutral formula unit, and the formula is $CaCO_3$. Calcium carbonate occurs naturally as ordinary chalk.

(b) The positive ion has a charge of 2+, and the negative ion has a charge of 1−. Therefore, one positive ion and two negative ions are required to produce a neutral formula unit. Because OH^- is a polyatomic ion, parentheses are required, and the formula is written $Ca(OH)_2$. Calcium hydroxide is known as "slaked lime" and is sometimes used to mark the boundaries of an athletic field.

(c) The positive ion has a charge of 2+, and the negative ion has a charge of 3−. The lowest common multiple of the charges is 6. Three positive ions are required for every two negative ions to produce a neutral formula unit. A calcium phosphate formula unit is written $Ca_3(PO_4)_2$. Calcium phosphate is found in tooth enamel.

$CaCO_3$

▲ **Chalk** White chalk is traditionally composed of calcium carbonate, $CaCO_3$; pastel chalk is composed of calcium sulfate, $CaSO_4$.

Practice Exercise

Write the chemical formula for each of the following ternary compounds given their constituent ions:

(a) copper(II) permanganate, Cu^{2+} and MnO_4^-
(b) iron(III) carbonate, Fe^{3+} and CO_3^{2-}
(c) potassium dichromate, K^+ and $Cr_2O_7^{2-}$

Answers:

(a) $Cu(MnO_4)_2$ (b) $Fe_2(CO_3)_3$ (c) $K_2Cr_2O_7$

Concept Exercise

What is the formula for a metal carbonate if the charge on the metal (M) is 3+?

Answer: See Appendix G.

Note As before, we can verify that the formula is correct by simply crossing over the charge on each ion. Consider calcium phosphate, which contains Ca^{2+} and PO_4^{3-}. The 2+ charge on the calcium ion becomes the subscript 2 for the phosphate ion. Phosphate is a polyatomic ion, so we must use parentheses, that is, (PO_4). Conversely, the 3– charge on the phosphate ion becomes the subscript 3 for the calcium ion.

$$Ca^{2+} \, PO_4^{3-} = Ca_3(PO_4)_2$$

CRITICAL THINKING   **Nutritional Potassium**

Q: How can potassium be an essential mineral in the human diet when it reacts explosively in water?

The human body requires many minerals such as calcium, sodium, and potassium, as well as trace amounts of iron, zinc, and selenium. Minerals perform numerous functions in the body, such as building strong bones, transmitting nerve impulses, making hormones, and maintaining a regular heartbeat.

One role of potassium is to maintain normal amounts of water in body tissues and avoid excessive water retention. Potassium is also important for building muscle and metabolizing proteins and carbohydrates. Although there is no recommended daily allowance (RDA) for potassium, the National Library of Medicine suggests about 2 grams of potassium a day.

The best dietary sources of potassium include fish (especially cod and sardines), meat, peas, tomatoes, potatoes, leafy green vegetables, citrus fruits, bananas, melons, dried fruit, nuts, and chocolate. People with high blood pressure are often put on a diet low in sodium, and a "salt substitute" high in potassium.

Pregnant women and people with chronic diseases are at risk to develop potassium deficiency. Depleted potassium levels may also be caused by vomiting, diarrhea, or use of diuretic or cortisone medications. Symptoms of potassium deficiency include fatigue, slow reflexes, muscle weakness, and dry skin. If potassium levels are depleted quickly, a person can experience heart problems. If potassium levels are not replenished quickly, a person can suffer heart failure and death.

▲ **Potassium in Water** Potassium metal reacts explosively in water as shown; potassium chloride, KCl, simply dissolves in water.

Conversely, ingesting extreme amounts of potassium or other minerals can be unhealthy. In some cases, an excess mineral can make it difficult for the body to absorb other minerals and vitamins. The best remedy to avoid vitamin and mineral deficiencies is a balanced diet that includes a wide variety of fruits, green vegetables, protein sources, whole grains, and dairy products daily.

A: Nutritionists state the need for potassium in the diet. To be more precise, humans require potassium salt (not potassium metal) in their diet. In fact, individuals on low-salt diets may use a "salt substitute" containing KCl, in lieu of table salt, NaCl.

▶ To write systematic names and formulas for binary ionic compounds.

▶ To predict the chemical formulas for binary ionic compounds.

6.5 BINARY IONIC COMPOUNDS

Positively charged metal ions and negatively charged nonmetal ions compose neutral binary ionic compounds. The oppositely charged cation and anion are attracted to each other and create compounds in which the overall charge is zero. That is, an ionic compound has an overall charge of zero even though it contains charged ions.

Binary Compounds Containing a Transition Metal

Some binary ionic compounds contain transition metal ions–which have a variable ionic charge, for instance, Fe^{2+} and Fe^{3+}. To name such a compound correctly, we first have to determine the ionic charge of the metal cation. The following example exercise illustrates the determination of ionic charge:

Fe_2O_3

▲ **Hematite, Fe₂O₃** Hematite is a mineral found in nature that contains iron.

Example Exercise 6.8 Determining Ionic Charge in a Compound

Determine the ionic charge for iron in the mineral hematite, Fe_2O_3.

Solution
The charge on an oxide ion is 2−, and there are three oxide ions. The total negative charge must be equal to six negative:

$$O^{2-} + O^{2-} + O^{2-} = 6 \text{ negative}$$

Because all compounds are electrically neutral, the total positive charge must equal the total negative charge: 6 negative = 6 positive. Thus, the two iron ions have a total charge of six positive:

$$Fe^{x+} + Fe^{x+} = 6 \text{ positive}$$
$$Fe^{x+} = 3 \text{ positive}$$

The iron ion is therefore Fe^{3+}. The name of Fe_2O_3 is iron(III) oxide according to the Stock system. It is named ferric oxide according to the Latin system.

Practice Exercise
Determine the ionic charge for each transition metal in the following compounds:

(a) Cu_3P (b) CoN

Answers:

(a) Cu^+ (b) Co^{3+}

Concept Exercise
What is the ionic charge on a metal (M), given the formula of the oxide, MO_2?

Answer: See Appendix G.

HgS

▲ **Cinnabar, HgS** Cinnabar is a mineral found in nature that contains mercury.

Naming Binary Ionic Compounds

When writing a chemical formula, the positive cation is always written before the negative anion. Therefore, in naming binary ionic compounds, the metal cation is named first followed by the nonmetal anion. We learned in Section 6.2 that monoatomic anions end with the suffix *–ide*. For example, MgO is composed of the magnesium ion and the oxide ion and is named magnesium oxide.

The mineral cinnabar, HgS, is composed of the mercury ion and the sulfide ion. Mercury has two possible ions, Hg_2^{2+} and Hg^{2+}. Because the ionic charge on a sulfide ion is 2−, the mercury ion is Hg^{2+}. Thus, we can name HgS mercury(II) sulfide according to the Stock system. Alternatively, we can name HgS mercuric sulfide according to the Latin system.

Example Exercise 6.9 Names of Binary Ionic Compounds

Supply a systematic name for each of the following binary ionic compounds:

(a) ZnO (b) SnF_2

Solution

We can name an ionic compound by designating the two ions.

(a) ZnO contains the zinc ion and the oxide ion; ZnO is named zinc oxide.
(b) SnF_2 contains the tin(II) ion and the fluoride ion. Thus, SnF_2 is named tin(II) fluoride. The Latin system name is stannous fluoride, which is an active ingredient in a popular toothpaste.

Practice Exercise

Supply a systematic name for each of the following binary ionic compounds:

(a) Mn_3P_2 (b) Fe_2S_3

Answers:

(a) manganese(II) phosphide (b) iron(III) sulfide or ferric sulfide

Concept Exercise

Which of the following is a binary ionic compound: sodium chloride, sodium chlorate, or sodium chlorite?

Answer: See Appendix G.

Example Exercise 6.10 Formulas of Binary Ionic Compounds

Provide the formula for each of the following binary ionic compounds:

(a) lithium fluoride (b) lead(II) sulfide

Solution

We write the formula for a binary ionic compound by combining ions so that the total positive charge equals the total negative charge.

(a) Lithium fluoride is composed of Li^+ and F^-; thus, the formula of the compound is written LiF.
(b) Lead(II) sulfide is composed of Pb^{2+} and S^{2-}; thus, the formula of the compound is written PbS.

Practice Exercise

Provide the formula for the following binary ionic compounds:

(a) copper(II) iodide (b) mercury(II) oxide

Answers:

(a) CuI_2 (b) HgO

Concept Exercise

Which of the following is a binary ionic compound: LiCl, $LiClO_3$, or $LiClO_2$?

Answer: See Appendix G.

PbS

▲ **Galena, PbS** Galena is a mineral found in nature that contains lead.

Predicting Formulas of Binary Ionic Compounds

We have learned the value of the periodic table in mastering the formulas of ions. Now we are going to use the periodic table to predict the chemical formulas of binary ionic compounds.

We can predict the formulas of compounds based on the formula of a similar compound. Let's begin with alkali metal chlorides. Sodium is in Group IA/1. The formula of sodium chloride is NaCl. All alkali metal chlorides, in fact, have a similar chemical formula. For the alkali metal family, the chloride compounds have the following formulas: LiCl, NaCl, and KCl.

We can predict the formulas for alkaline earth metal chlorides in a similar manner. Barium is in Group IIA/2, and the formula for barium chloride is $BaCl_2$. Therefore, the formulas for the other alkaline earth metal chlorides are $MgCl_2$, $CaCl_2$, and $SrCl_2$.

Example Exercise 6.11 Predicting Formulas of Binary Ionic Compounds

Predict the chemical formula for each of the following binary compounds given the formula of aluminum oxide, Al_2O_3:

(a) gallium oxide   (b) aluminum sulfide

Solution

To predict the chemical formula, we compare the elements that are different in the similar compounds.

(a) The elements Ga and Al are both in Group IIIA/3, and so the formula is Ga_2O_3.
(b) The elements S and O are both in Group VIA/16, and so the formula is Al_2S_3.

Practice Exercise

Predict the chemical formula for each of the following binary compounds given the formula of magnesium chloride, $MgCl_2$:

(a) radium chloride   (b) magnesium fluoride

Answers:

(a) $RaCl_2$ (b) MgF_2

Concept Exercise

Predict the formula for potassium iodide, given the formula of sodium fluoride, NaF.

Answer: See Appendix G.

LEARNING OBJECTIVES

▸ To write systematic names and formulas for ternary ionic compounds.

▸ To predict the chemical formulas for ternary ionic compounds.

6.6 TERNARY IONIC COMPOUNDS

Compounds containing a metal and two other elements are classified as ternary ionic compounds. Typically, ternary ionic compounds have a monoatomic metal cation and a polyatomic oxyanion, for example, $NaNO_3$.

Like all ionic compounds, the cation is written first in the formula. The names of ternary ionic compounds usually have the suffix *–ate* or *–ite*. For example, $KClO_3$ is potassium chlorate, and $KClO_2$ is potassium chlorite.

Ternary Compounds Containing a Transition Metal

Some ternary compounds contain transition metal ions that have a variable ionic charge, for instance, Fe^{2+} and Fe^{3+}. To name such a compound correctly, we first have to determine the ionic charge of the transition metal cation.

Example Exercise 6.12 Determining Ionic Charge in a Compound

Determine the ionic charge for iron in $Fe_3(PO_4)_2$.

Solution

The charge on a phosphate ion is 3− and there are two phosphate ions. Therefore, the total negative charge must be equal to six negative:

$$PO_4^{3-} + PO_4^{3-} = 6 \text{ negative}$$

Because all compounds are electrically neutral, the total positive charge must equal the total negative charge: 6 negative = 6 positive. Thus, the three iron ions have a total charge of six positive.

$$Fe^{x+} + Fe^{x+} + Fe^{x+} = 6 \text{ positive}$$

$$Fe^{x+} = 2 \text{ positive}$$

The iron ion is therefore Fe^{2+}. The name of $Fe_3(PO_4)_2$ is iron(II) phosphate according to the Stock system. It is named ferrous phosphate according to the Latin system.

Practice Exercise

Determine the ionic charge for the metal cation in each of the following compounds:

(a) $Hg(OH)_2$ (b) $Co(ClO_3)_3$

Answers:

(a) Hg^{2+} (b) Co^{3+}

Concept Exercise

What is the ionic charge on a metal (M), given the formula of the carbonate, MCO_3?

Answer: See Appendix G.

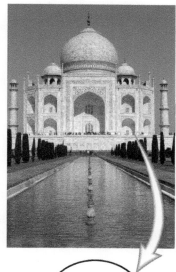

Naming Ternary Ionic Compounds

Like all ionic compounds, ternary ionic compounds are named by designating the cation followed by the anion. The mineral marble, $CaCO_3$, is composed of the calcium ion and the carbonate ion and is named calcium carbonate. $Ca(NO_3)_2$ is composed of the calcium ion and two nitrate ions and is named calcium nitrate.

    The compound $CuSO_4$ is composed of a copper ion and a sulfate ion. Copper, however, has two possible ions, Cu^+ and Cu^{2+}. Because the sulfate charge is $2-$, the charge on copper must be $2+$ because ionic compounds are neutral. The copper ion is Cu^{2+}, so the name of the compound is copper(II) sulfate, or cupric sulfate.

$CaCO_3$

▲ **Marble, CaCO₃** Marble, $CaCO_3$, is a mineral found in nature that was used to construct the Taj Mahal in India.

Example Exercise 6.13   Names of Ternary Ionic Compounds

Supply a systematic name for the following ternary ionic compounds:

(a) $KMnO_4$ (b) $Hg(NO_3)_2$

Solution

We can name an ionic compound by designating the two ions.

(a) $KMnO_4$ is composed of the potassium ion and the permanganate ion. Thus, the compound is named potassium permanganate.

(b) $Hg(NO_3)_2$ contains the mercury(II) ion and the nitrate ion. Therefore, it is named mercury(II) nitrate, or mercuric nitrate.

Practice Exercise

Supply a systematic name for each of the following ternary ionic compounds.

(a) $BaCrO_4$ (b) $Cu(NO_2)_2$

Answers:

(a) barium chromate   (b) copper(II) nitrite or cupric nitrite

Concept Exercise

Which of the following is a ternary ionic compound: potassium nitride, potassium nitrate, or potassium nitrite?

Example Exercise 6.14   Formulas of Ternary Ionic Compounds

Provide the formula for each of the following ternary ionic compounds:

(a) nickel(II) acetate   (b) iron(III) sulfate

Solution

We can write the formula by combining the cation and polyatomic anion into a neutral formula unit.

(a) Nickel(II) acetate is composed of Ni^{2+} and $C_2H_3O_2^-$. The formula of the compound is written $Ni(C_2H_3O_2)_2$.

(b) Iron(III) sulfate contains Fe^{3+} and SO_4^{2-}; the formula is written $Fe_2(SO_4)_3$.

Practice Exercise

Provide the formula for each of the following ternary ionic compounds.

(a) mercury(I) nitrite   (b) tin(IV) permanganate

Answers:

(a) $Hg_2(NO_2)_2$ (b) $Sn(MnO_4)_4$

Concept Exercise

Which of the following is a ternary ionic compound: LiCl, LiClO, or $LiClO_2$?

Answer: See Appendix G.

Predicting Formulas of Ternary Ionic Compounds

The periodic table can be used to predict the formulas of ternary ionic compounds. For example, if we know that the formula of potassium nitrate is KNO_3, we can predict the formulas of sodium nitrate and lithium nitrate. Because Li, Na, and K are all in Group IA/1, we can predict that the compounds have similar chemical formulas, that is, $LiNO_3$, $NaNO_3$, and KNO_3. The following example exercise illustrates how to predict formulas of ternary ionic compounds.

Example Exercise 6.15   Predicting Formulas of Ternary Ionic Compounds

Predict the chemical formula for each of the following ternary ionic compounds given the formula of calcium carbonate, $CaCO_3$:

(a) radium carbonate   (b) calcium silicate

Solution

To predict the formula, we compare the elements that are different in the similar compounds.

(a) The elements Ra and Ca are both in Group IIA/2. Thus, the formula for radium carbonate is $RaCO_3$.

(b) The elements Si and C are both in Group IVA/14. Therefore, the formula for calcium silicate is $CaSiO_3$.

Practice Exercise

Predict the chemical formula for each of the following ternary compounds given the formula of potassium chlorate, $KClO_3$:

(a) lithium chlorate   (b) potassium bromate

Answers:

(a) $LiClO_3$ (b) $KBrO_3$

Concept Exercise

Predict the formula for strontium sulfate, given the formula of calcium sulfate, $CaSO_4$.

Answer: See Appendix G.

LEARNING OBJECTIVE

▶ To write systematic names and formulas for binary molecular compounds.

6.7 BINARY MOLECULAR COMPOUNDS

Recall that a binary molecular compound is composed of two nonmetal elements. The simplest representative particle in a binary molecular compound is a **molecule**. In general, the more nonmetallic element is written second in the chemical formula. IUPAC prescribes the following order for writing the elements in a compound: C, P, N, H, S, I, Br, Cl, O, F. Notice that hydrogen is in the middle of the series. Thus, the binary compounds of hydrogen are written as follows: CH_4, PH_3, NH_3, H_2S, HI, HBr, HCl, H_2O, and HF.

Naming Binary Molecular Compounds

In the naming of binary molecular compounds, IUPAC specifies that the first element in the compound be named followed by the second element bearing the suffix *–ide*. Thus, binary ionic and binary molecular compounds both end in the suffix *–ide*. It also specifies that the number of atoms of each element be indicated by Greek prefixes. The Greek prefixes in Table 6.4 indicate the number of atoms of each element that correspond to the subscripts in the chemical formula.

TABLE 6.4 GREEK PREFIXES FOR BINARY MOLECULAR COMPOUNDS

ATOMS	PREFIX	ATOMS	PREFIX
1	*mono–*	6	*hexa–*
2	*di–*	7	*hepta–*
3	*tri–*	8	*octa–*
4	*tetra–*	9	*nona–**
5	*penta–*	10	*deca–*

*Although the Latin prefix *nona–* is commonly used, IUPAC prefers the Greek prefix *ennea–*.

According to the official IUPAC recommendations, the prefix *mono–* is always omitted unless its presence is necessary to avoid confusion. The only common exceptions are CO and NO. The name of CO includes the prefix *mono–* in front of oxygen and is written carbon monoxide. Similarly, NO is named nitrogen monoxide.

Let's consider the binary molecular compound P_4S_3. This compound is found on match tips and ignites in air when struck on a rough surface (Figure 6.4). The ratio is four phosphorus atoms to three sulfur atoms, so the Greek prefixes are *tetra–* and *tri–*, respectively. Thus, the name of P_4S_3 is tetraphosphorus trisulfide. A different compound, P_4S_7, has the same elements but is named tetraphosphorus heptasulfide.

Example Exercise 6.16 Names of Binary Molecular Compounds

Give the IUPAC systematic name for each of the following binary molecular compounds:

(a) IF_6 (b) Br_3O_8

Solution

We name binary molecular compounds by attaching the suffix *–ide* to the second nonmetal and indicate the atomic ratios by Greek prefixes.

(a) IF_6 is first named iodine fluoride. After supplying the Greek prefixes for the atomic ratios, we have *iodine hexafluoride*.
(b) Br_3O_8 is first named bromine oxide. After supplying the Greek prefixes for the atomic ratios, we have *tribromine octaoxide*.

Practice Exercise

Give the IUPAC systematic name for each of the following binary molecular compounds:

(a) Cl_2O_5 (b) P_4S_{10}

Answers:

(a) dichlorine pentaoxide (b) tetraphosphorus decasulfide

Concept Exercise

Which of the following is named using Greek prefixes to specify the number of atoms of each element: Fe_2O_3 or P_2O_3?

Answer: See Appendix G.

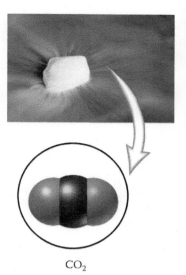

▲ **Carbon Dioxide, CO_2**
Dry Ice is an example of a binary molecular compound.

P_4S_3

▲ Figure 6.4 **Chemistry of Matches** The substances P_4S_3 and $KClO_3$ are present on the tip of a match. When the match is struck on a rough surface, the two chemicals ignite and produce a flame. The products from the reaction are P_2O_5, KCl, and SO_2, the last of which is responsible for the characteristic sulfur smell.

Example Exercise 6.17 Formulas of Binary Molecular Compounds

Provide the formula for each of the following binary molecular compounds:

(a) diphosphorus pentasulfide   (b) tetraiodine nonaoxide

Solution

To write the formula, we give the symbol for each element followed by a subscript indicating the number of atoms.

(a) Diphosphorus pentasulfide is composed of two phosphorus atoms and five sulfur atoms. The formula of the compound is written P_2S_5.

(b) Tetraiodine nonaoxide is composed of four iodine atoms and nine oxygen atoms. The formula of the compound is written I_4O_9.

Practice Exercise

Provide the formula for each of the following binary molecular compounds:

(a) diphosphorus tetraiodide   (b) sulfur hexafluoride

Answers:

(a) P_2I_4 (b) SF_6

Concept Exercise

Which of the following is a binary molecular compound: magnesium oxide or nitrogen oxide?

Answer: See Appendix G.

Note For ease of pronunciation, double vowels are sometimes avoided in naming compounds with Greek prefixes. For example, if the Greek prefix ends in "a" or "o" and the nonmetal is oxygen, two pronunciations are common. That is, the name may be pronounced tetraoxide or tetroxide, pentaoxide or pentoxide, etc. However, according to the official IUPAC recommendations, vowels are not to be dropped and tetraoxide is preferred. The one exception is monoxide, not monooxide.

▶ To write systematic names and formulas for binary acids.

HF

▲ **Hydrofluoric Acid, HF**

6.8 BINARY ACIDS

A binary acid is an aqueous solution of a compound containing hydrogen and a nonmetal. The chemical formulas of acids always begin with H, for example, HCl(*aq*). A binary acid is produced by dissolving a binary molecular compound, such as HCl, in water. The resulting aqueous solution, HCl(*aq*), is a binary acid.

Binary acids are systematically named by using the prefix *hydro–* before the nonmetal stem and adding the suffix *–ic acid*. As an example, consider the acid used to treat swimming pools and sold in supermarkets under the common name muriatic acid. Muriatic acid is aqueous hydrogen chloride, that is, HCl(*aq*). The IUPAC name for muriatic acid is formed as follows: hydro + chlor + ic acid. The systematic name for HCl(*aq*) is hydrochloric acid.

Example Exercise 6.18 Names of Binary Acids

Give the IUPAC systematic name for HF(*aq*), a binary acid.

Solution

Binary acids are named as *hydro–* plus nonmetal stem plus *–ic acid*. Because HF(*aq*) contains the nonmetal fluorine, we construct the systematic name as follows: hydro + fluor + ic acid gives *hydrofluoric acid.*

Practice Exercise

Give the IUPAC systematic name for H_2S(*aq*).

Answer: hydrosulfuric acid

Concept Exercise

Which of the following acids is named using a *hydro–* prefix: HBr(*aq*), HBrO$_2$(*aq*), HBrO$_3$(*aq*)?

Answer: See Appendix G.

Note Be careful not to confuse the names of a binary acid and a binary molecular compound. A binary acid is a compound of hydrogen and a nonmetal dissolved in water. For example, HCl(*aq*) is a binary acid and is named hydrochloric acid. On the other hand, HCl(*g*) is a gaseous binary molecular compound and is named hydrogen chloride.

CRITICAL THINKING   IUPAC Nomenclature

Q: What is the official systematic name for stomach acid?

Alchemists, the forerunners of modern chemists, are usually associated with attempts to convert lead to gold. They did, however, produce a rich vocabulary describing chemical substances. Unfortunately, their names for substances did not offer a clue to the chemical composition.

In the eighteenth century, Antoine Lavoisier, the founder of modern chemistry, provided the first published naming system that indicated the chemical composition of substances. In the nineteenth century, the great Swedish chemist J. J. Berzelius adopted Lavoisier's ideas and extended the system into the Germanic languages, which in turn were translated into English.

In 1892, a conference held in Geneva, Switzerland, laid the foundation for an internationally accepted system of nomenclature for organic compounds. Subsequently, the International Union of Pure and Applied Chemistry (IUPAC) was formed.

In 1921, IUPAC addressed the issue of systematic nomenclature for *inorganic compounds*. Almost 20 years elapsed before IUPAC issued a systematic set of rules. Interestingly, these so-called 1940 IUPAC rules were consistent with the methods proposed in Lavoisier's text 150 years earlier. The official recommendations suggest that there is more than one acceptable system of nomenclature. For example, CuSO$_4$ can be named copper(II) sulfate according to the preferred Stock system of nomenclature or cupric sulfate according to the Latin system.

Although common names persist, IUPAC disapproves the use of common names and discourages the use of names that

▲ Muriatic Acid, HCl

do not indicate the chemical composition. Examples of common names include "baking soda" or "sodium bicarbonate" for sodium hydrogen carbonate, NaHCO$_3$. Hydrochloric acid, HCl(*aq*), is commonly referred to as "stomach acid" or "swimming pool acid," and is sold in the supermarket under the common name "muriatic acid."

A: Stomach acid is aqueous HCl, and its systematic name is hydrochloric acid.

6.9 TERNARY OXYACIDS

LEARNING OBJECTIVE

▶ To write systematic names and formulas for ternary oxyacids.

A ternary oxyacid is an aqueous solution of a compound containing hydrogen and an oxyanion. Most ternary oxyacids are named by attaching the suffix *–ic acid* to the *nonmetal stem* of the oxyanion. For example, the name of HNO$_3$(*aq*) is systematically formed as follows: *nonmetal stem* plus *ic acid*. The name of HNO$_3$(*aq*) is nitr + ic acid, or *nitric acid.*

Some ternary oxyacids are named by attaching the suffix *–ous acid* to the *nonmetal stem* of the oxyanion. For example, the name of HNO$_2$(*aq*) is systematically formed as follows: *nonmetal stem* + *ous acid*. The name of HNO$_2$(*aq*) is nitr + ous acid, or *nitrous acid.*

H_2SO_4

▲ **Sulfuric Acid, H_2SO_4**
Aqueous sulfuric acid, $H_2SO_4(aq)$, is found in automobile batteries; hence, it is commonly termed *battery acid*.

A ternary oxyacid with the suffix *–ic acid* contains an oxyanion ending in *–ate*. Thus, the name of a compound containing the oxyanion will bear the suffix *–ate*. Consider sulfuric acid, $H_2SO_4(aq)$, which contains the sulfate oxyanion, SO_4^{2-}. The name of the compound Na_2SO_4 is sodium sulfate.

Similarly, a ternary oxyacid with the suffix *–ous acid* contains an oxyanion ending in *–ite*. Consider sulfurous acid, $H_2SO_3(aq)$, which contains the sulfite oxyanion, SO_3^{2-}. The name of the compound Na_2SO_3 is sodium sulfite. We can illustrate the ternary oxyacid relationship to its compounds as shown in Table 6.5.

TABLE 6.5 TERNARY OXYACIDS AND RELATED COMPOUNDS

TERNARY	OXYACID	TERNARY	COMPOUND
HClO	**Hypo**chlor**ous** acid	NaClO	sodium **hypo**chlor**ite**
HClO$_2$	Chlor**ous** acid	NaClO$_2$	sodium chlor**ite**
HClO$_3$	Chlor**ic** acid	NaClO$_3$	sodium chlor**ate**
HClO$_4$	**Per**chlor**ic** acid	NaClO$_4$	sodium **per**chlor**ate**

Now that we have provided an overview of ternary oxyacids, let's try the following example exercise that illustrates systematic naming:

Example Exercise 6.19 Names of Ternary Oxyacids

Give the IUPAC systematic name for $H_3PO_4(aq)$, a ternary oxyacid.

Solution
Ternary oxyacids are named as *–ic acids* or *–ous acids*. Because $H_3PO_4(aq)$ contains the phosphate oxyanion, it is an *–ic acid*. We construct the systematic name as follows: phosphor + ic acid gives *phosphoric acid*.

Practice Exercise
Give the IUPAC systematic name for $H_3PO_3(aq)$, a ternary oxyacid.

Answer: phosphorous acid

Concept Exercise
Which of the following acids is named *nonmetal stem* plus *–ic acid:* $HBr(aq)$, $HBrO_2(aq)$, $HBrO_3(aq)$?

Answer: See Appendix G.

Summary

LEARNING OBJECTIVES

LEARNING OBJECTIVES	SEC	EXERCISES
To classify a compound as a binary ionic, a ternary ionic, or a binary molecular compound.	6.1	Exercises 1–2
To classify an acid as a binary acid or a ternary oxyacid.	6.1	Exercises 1–2
To classify an ion as a monoatomic cation, a monoatomic anion, a polyatomic cation, or a polyatomic anion.	6.1	Exercises 3–4
To write systematic names and formulas for common monoatomic ions.	6.2	Exercises 5–14
To predict the ionic charge for ions of representative elements.	6.2	Exercises 5–14
To write systematic names and formulas for common polyatomic ions.	6.3	Exercises 15–18
To write chemical formulas for ionic compounds composed of monoatomic ions and polyatomic ions.	6.4	Exercises 19–24
To write systematic names and formulas for binary ionic compounds.	6.5	Exercises 25–30
To predict the chemical formulas for binary ionic compounds.	6.5	Exercises 31–34
To write systematic names and formulas for ternary ionic compounds.	6.6	Exercises 35–40
To predict the chemical formulas for ternary ionic compounds.	6.6	Exercises 41–44
To write systematic names and formulas for binary molecular compounds.	6.7	Exercises 45–48
To write systematic names and formulas for binary acids.	6.8	Exercises 49–50
To write systematic names and formulas for ternary oxyacids.	6.9	Exercises 51–56

Section 6.1 **Inorganic compounds** do not contain carbon and are named according to a systematic set of rules referred to as **IUPAC nomenclature**. The IUPAC rules classify substances as belonging to one of five categories: **binary ionic**, **ternary ionic**, **binary molecular**, **binary acid**, or **ternary oxyacid**. A substance dissolved in water is referred to as an **aqueous solution**. Ionic compounds are composed of positive **cations** and negative **anions**. A **monoatomic ion** is a single atom having a charge, whereas a **polyatomic ion** is a group of two or more atoms bearing a charge.

Section 6.2 The names of monoatomic cations are derived from a metal, for example, the sodium ion, Na^+. Cations having two possible ionic charges require further identification. The ionic charge may be indicated using either the Stock system or the Latin system. The **Stock system** indicates the charge on the metal with Roman numerals in parentheses. The **Latin system** adds the suffix *–ous* or *–ic* to the Latin name of the element. Thus, Cu^{2+} is named copper(II) ion according to the Stock system, and cupric ion using the Latin system.

The names of monoatomic anions are derived from a nonmetal. A monoatomic anion is named using the nonmetal stem and adding the suffix *–ide*. Examples of nonmetal ions include the chloride ion, Cl^-, and the oxide ion, O^{2-}.

Section 6.3 A polyatomic anion that contains one or more elements combined with oxygen is called an **oxyanion**. The names of most polyatomic oxyanions have the suffix *–ate*, for example, the nitrate ion, NO_3^-. A few oxyanions have

the suffix *–ite*, for example, the nitrite ion, NO_2^-. The nitrite ion has one less oxygen atom than the nitrate ion. Oxyanions having one less oxygen atom end with the suffix *–ite*, such as the sulfite ion, SO_3^{2-}, with one less oxygen than the sulfate ion, SO_4^{2-}.

Section 6.4 The simplest representative particle in an ionic compound is called a **formula unit**. The net charge for a formula unit is zero. That is, the total positive charge for the cations in the compound must be the same as the total negative charge for the anions.

Section 6.5 Binary ionic compounds have names ending with the suffix *–ide*. For example, NaCl is named sodium chloride, $CaBr_2$ is named calcium bromide, and AlF_3 is named aluminum fluoride.

Section 6.6 Ternary ionic compounds have names ending with the suffix *–ate* or *–ite*. For example, $CaSO_4$ is named calcium sulfate, and $CaSO_3$ is named calcium sulfite. A ternary compound containing CN^- or OH^- is an exception and each ends with the suffix *–ide*. For example, NaOH is named sodium hydroxide, and KCN is named potassium cyanide.

Section 6.7 Binary molecular compounds contain two nonmetals, and the simplest representative particle is called a **molecule**. Binary molecular compounds are named using a Greek prefix and the suffix *–ide*; for example, SO_2 and SO_3 are named sulfur dioxide and sulfur trioxide, respectively.

Section 6.8 A binary acid is an aqueous solution of a hydrogen containing compound. Binary acids are named *hydro + nonmetal stem + –ic acid*. For example, hydrogen chloride dissolved in water, HCl(*aq*), is named hydrochloric acid.

Section 6.9 Ternary oxyacids are usually named *nonmetal stem + –ic acid*. For example, an aqueous solution of $HNO_3(aq)$ is named nitric acid. A few ternary oxyacids are named *nonmetal stem + –ous acid*. An aqueous solution of $HNO_2(aq)$ is named nitrous acid.

NOMENCLATURE ORGANIZER

TOPIC	PROCEDURE	EXAMPLE
Classification of Compounds Sec. 6.1	When a formula has two elements, a metal and a nonmetal, it is a **binary ionic compound**. When a formula has three elements and at least one metal, it is a **ternary ionic compound**. When a formula has two nonmetal elements, it is a **binary molecular compound**. When a formula has H and a nonmetal in an aqueous solution, it is a **binary acid**. When a formula has H, a nonmetal, and oxygen in an aqueous solution, it is a **ternary oxyacid**.	binary ionic compound, KCl ternary ionic compound, $KClO_3$ binary molecular compound, HCl binary acid, HCl(*aq*) ternary oxyacid, $HClO_3(aq)$
Monoatomic Ions Sec. 6.2	Representative metal ions are named for the element. Transition metal ions are named using (1) the **Stock system**, or (2) the **Latin system**. Nonmetals are named for the element plus the **suffix –ide**.	K^+, potassium ion Fe^{2+}, iron(II) ion or ferrous ion Cl^-, chloride ion
Polyatomic Ions Sec. 6.3	Polyatomic oxyanions are named with (1) the **suffix –ate**, or (2) the **suffix –ite** when there is one less oxygen atom in the oxyanion. There are two common polyatomic anion exceptions that have the **suffix –ide**.	ClO_3^-, chlorate ion ClO_2^-, chlorite ion OH^-, hydroxide ion CN^-, cyanide ion
Writing Chemical Formulas Sec. 6.4	In writing formulas of ionic compounds, the ratio of cations and anions must provide a total positive charge equal to the total negative charge so that the compound is electrically neutral.	Fe^{2+} and O^{2-} = FeO Fe^{3+} and O^{2-} = Fe_2O_3 Fe^{2+} and ClO_3^- = $Fe(ClO_3)_2$ Fe^{3+} and ClO_3^- = $Fe(ClO_3)_3$
Binary Ionic Compounds Sec. 6.5	Binary ionic compounds end in the **suffix –ide**. The metal cation is named first followed by the name of the anion.	KCl, potassium chloride $FeCl_2$ iron(II) chloride, or ferrous chloride
Ternary Ionic Compounds Sec. 6.6	Ternary ionic compounds end in the **suffix –ate** or the **suffix –ite**. The metal cation is named first followed by the name of the oxyanion.	$KClO_3$, potassium chlorate $KClO_2$, potassium chlorite
Binary Molecular Compounds Sec. 6.7	Binary molecular compounds end in the **suffix –ide**. The number of nonmetal atoms is indicated by a Greek prefix.	CO, carbon monoxide CO_2, carbon dioxide
Binary Acids Sec. 6.8	Binary acids are named hydro- plus nonmetal stem plus **–ic acid**.	HCl(*aq*), hydrochloric acid
Ternary Oxyacids Sec. 6.9	Ternary oxyacids are named with (1) a **nonmetal stem** plus **–ic acid**, or (2) a **nonmetal stem** plus **–ous acid**.	$HClO_3(aq)$, chloric acid $HClO_2(aq)$, chlorous acid

Key Terms *Answers to Key Terms are in Appendix H.*

Select the key term that corresponds to each of the following definitions.

_____ **1.** the international system of rules for naming chemical compounds

_____ **2.** a compound that does not contain the element carbon

_____ **3.** a compound that contains one metal and one nonmetal

_____ **4.** a compound that contains three elements, including at least one metal

_____ **5.** a compound that contains two nonmetals

_____ **6.** a substance dissolved in water

_____ **7.** an aqueous compound that contains hydrogen and a nonmetal

_____ **8.** an aqueous compound that contains hydrogen, a nonmetal, and oxygen

_____ **9.** any positively charged ion

_____ **10.** any negatively charged ion

_____ **11.** a single atom that has a positive or negative charge

_____ **12.** a group of atoms bound together and having an overall positive or negative charge

_____ **13.** a system for naming ionic compounds that designates the charge on a cation with Roman numerals

_____ **14.** a system for naming ionic compounds that designates the charge on a cation with an *–ic* or *–ous* suffix

_____ **15.** a polyatomic anion that contains one or more elements combined with oxygen, for example, CO_3^{2-}

_____ **16.** the simplest representative particle in a compound composed of ions

_____ **17.** the simplest representative particle in a compound composed of nonmetal atoms

(a) anion (*Sec. 6.1*)

(b) aqueous solution (*Sec. 6.1*)

(c) binary acid (*Sec. 6.1*)

(d) binary ionic compound (*Sec. 6.1*)

(e) binary molecular compound (*Sec. 6.1*)

(f) cation (*Sec. 6.1*)

(g) formula unit (*Sec. 6.4*)

(h) inorganic compound (*Sec. 6.1*)

(i) IUPAC nomenclature (*Sec. 6.1*)

(j) Latin system (*Sec. 6.2*)

(k) molecule (*Sec. 6.7*)

(l) monoatomic ion (*Sec. 6.1*)

(m) oxyanion (*Sec. 6.3*)

(n) polyatomic ion (*Sec. 6.1*)

(o) Stock system (*Sec. 6.2*)

(p) ternary ionic compound (*Sec. 6.1*)

(q) ternary oxyacid (*Sec. 6.1*)

Exercises *Answers to odd-numbered Exercises are in Appendix I.*

Classification of Compounds (Sec. 6.1)

1. Classify each of the following as a binary ionic compound, ternary ionic compound, binary molecular compound, binary acid, or ternary oxyacid:
   (a) water, H_2O
   (b) table salt, NaCl
   (c) limestone, $CaCO_3$
   (d) stomach acid, $HCl(aq)$

2. Classify each of the following as a binary ionic compound, ternary ionic compound, binary molecular compound, binary acid, or ternary oxyacid:
   (a) ammonia, NH_3
   (b) rust, Fe_2O_3
   (c) barite, $BaSO_4$
   (d) battery acid, $H_2SO_4(aq)$

3. Classify each of the following as a monoatomic cation, monoatomic anion, polyatomic cation, or polyatomic anion:
   (a) hydronium ion, H_3O^+
   (b) aluminum ion, Al^{3+}
   (c) chloride ion, Cl^-
   (d) chlorate ion, ClO_3^-

4. Classify each of the following as a monoatomic cation, monoatomic anion, polyatomic cation, or polyatomic anion:
   (a) ammonium ion, NH_4^+
   (b) strontium ion, Sr^{2+}
   (c) sulfide ion, S^{2-}
   (d) sulfate ion, SO_4^{2-}

Monoatomic Ions (Sec. 6.2)

5. Supply the Stock system name for each of the following monoatomic cations:
   (a) Ca^{2+}
   (b) Cd^{2+}
   (c) Co^{2+}
   (d) Cu^{2+}

6. Supply the Stock system name for each of the following monoatomic cations:
   (a) Ba^{2+}
   (b) Zn^{2+}
   (c) Co^{3+}
   (d) Cu^+

7. Provide the formula for each of the following monoatomic cations:
   (a) potassium ion
   (b) barium ion
   (c) iron(II) ion
   (d) tin(II) ion

8. Provide the formula for each of the following monoatomic cations:
   (a) lithium ion
   (b) silver ion
   (c) iron(III) ion
   (d) tin(IV) ion

9. Supply the Latin system name for each of the following monoatomic cations:
   (a) Cu^{2+}
   (b) Fe^{2+}
   (c) Sn^{2+}
   (d) Pb^{2+}

10. Supply the Latin system name for each of the following monoatomic cations:
    (a) Cu^+
    (b) Fe^{3+}
    (c) Sn^{4+}
    (d) Pb^{4+}

11. Provide the formula for each of the following monoatomic cations:
    (a) cobaltous ion
    (b) cobaltic ion

12. Provide the formula for each of the following monoatomic cations:
    (a) mercurous ion **(b)** mercuric ion

13. Supply a systematic name for each of the following monoatomic anions:
    (a) F^- **(b)** Cl^-
    (c) Br^- **(d)** I^-

14. Supply a systematic name for each of the following monoatomic anions:
    (a) O^{2-} **(b)** S^{2-}
    (c) N^{3-} **(d)** P^{3-}

Polyatomic Ions (Sec. 6.3)

15. Supply a systematic name for each of the following oxyanions:
    (a) NO_3^- **(b)** NO_2^-
    (c) ClO_3^- **(d)** ClO_2^-

16. Supply a systematic name for each of the following oxyanions:
    (a) CO_3^{2-} **(b)** HCO_3^-
    (c) SO_4^{2-} **(d)** HSO_4^-

17. Provide the formula for each of the following polyatomic ions:
    (a) chromate ion **(b)** dichromate ion
    (c) hydroxide ion **(d)** cyanide ion

NaOH

◀ **Sodium Hydroxide, NaOH** Sodium hydroxide, NaOH, is used in oven cleaner and drain cleaner. Because it is strongly caustic and contains sodium, it is commonly referred to as "caustic soda."

18. Provide the formula for each of the following polyatomic ions:
    (a) chlorate ion **(b)** perchlorate ion
    (c) permanganate ion **(d)** acetate ion

Writing Chemical Formulas (Sec. 6.4)

19. Write the chemical formula for the following binary compounds given their constituent ions:
    (a) aluminum bromide, Al^{3+} and Br^-
    (b) cadmium sulfide, Cd^{2+} and S^{2-}
    (c) manganese(II) phosphide, Mn^{2+} and P^{3-}
    (d) lead(IV) fluoride, Pb^{4+} and F^-

20. Write the chemical formula for the following binary compounds given their constituent ions:
    (a) lithium chloride, Li^+ and Cl^-
    (b) silver oxide, Ag^+ and O^{2-}

(c) chromium(III) iodide, Cr^{3+} and I^-
(d) tin(II) nitride, Sn^{2+} and N^{3-}

21. Write the chemical formula for the following ternary compounds given their constituent ions:
    (a) potassium nitrate, K^+ and NO_3^-
    (b) ammonium dichromate, NH_4^+ and $Cr_2O_7^{2-}$
    (c) aluminum sulfite, Al^{3+} and SO_3^{2-}
    (d) chromium(III) hypochlorite, Cr^{3+} and ClO^-

22. Write the chemical formula for the following ternary compounds given their constituent ions:
    (a) iron(III) hydrogen carbonate, Fe^{3+} and HCO_3^-
    (b) cuprous carbonate, Cu^+ and CO_3^{2-}
    (c) mercury(II) cyanide, Hg^{2+} and CN^-
    (d) stannic acetate, Sn^{4+} and $C_2H_3O_2^-$

23. Write the chemical formula for the following ternary compounds given their constituent ions:
    (a) strontium nitrite, Sr^{2+} and NO_2^-
    (b) zinc permanganate, Zn^{2+} and MnO_4^-
    (c) calcium chromate, Ca^{2+} and CrO_4^{2-}
    (d) chromium(III) perchlorate, Cr^{3+} and ClO_4^-

24. Write the chemical formula for the following ternary compounds given their constituent ions:
    (a) lead(IV) sulfate, Pb^{4+} and SO_4^{2-}
    (b) stannous chlorite, Sn^{2+} and ClO_2^-
    (c) cobalt(II) hydroxide, Co^{2+} and OH^-
    (d) mercurous phosphate, Hg_2^{2+} and PO_4^{3-}

Binary Ionic Compounds (Sec. 6.5)

25. Supply a systematic name for each of the following binary ionic compounds:
    (a) MgO **(b)** ZnO
    (c) CdO **(d)** BaO

26. Supply a systematic name for each of the following binary ionic compounds:
    (a) LiBr **(b)** SrI_2
    (c) Na_3N **(d)** AlF_3

27. Supply a Stock system name for each of the following binary ionic compounds:
    (a) CoO **(b)** FeO
    (c) HgO **(d)** SnO

28. Supply a Stock system name for each of the following binary ionic compounds:
    (a) $MnCl_2$ **(b)** NiF_2
    (c) $SnBr_2$ **(d)** CrP

29. Provide the formula for each of the following binary ionic compounds:
    (a) copper(I) oxide **(b)** iron(III) nitride
    (c) mercury(II) chloride **(d)** lead(IV) sulfide

◀ **Cuprite** Cuprite, copper(I) oxide, is a mineral found in nature that contains copper.

30. Provide the formula for each of the following binary ionic compounds:
    (a) cuprous sulfide
    (b) ferrous phosphide
    (c) mercuric iodide
    (d) plumbic oxide

31. Predict the chemical formula for each of the following binary ionic compounds given the formula of sodium chloride, NaCl:
    (a) rubidium chloride
    (b) sodium bromide

32. Predict the chemical formula for each of the following binary ionic compounds given the formula of calcium oxide, CaO:
    (a) beryllium oxide
    (b) calcium selenide

33. Predict the chemical formula for each of the following binary ionic compounds given the formula of aluminum nitride, AlN:
    (a) gallium nitride
    (b) aluminum arsenide

34. Predict the chemical formula for each of the following binary ionic compounds given the formula of titanium oxide, TiO_2:
    (a) zirconium oxide
    (b) titanium sulfide

Ternary Ionic Compounds (Sec. 6.6)

35. Supply a systematic name for each of the following ternary ionic compounds:
    (a) $LiMnO_4$
    (b) $Sr(ClO_2)_2$
    (c) $BaCO_3$
    (d) $(NH_4)_2Cr_2O_7$

36. Supply a systematic name for each of the following ternary ionic compounds:
    (a) $KClO_3$
    (b) $Mg(NO_3)_2$
    (c) Ag_2SO_4
    (d) $Al_2(CrO_4)_3$

37. Supply a Stock system name for each of the following ternary ionic compounds:
    (a) $CuSO_4$
    (b) $FeCrO_4$
    (c) $Hg(NO_2)_2$
    (d) $Pb(C_2H_3O_2)_2$

38. Supply a Latin system name for each of the following ternary ionic compounds:
    (a) Cu_2SO_4
    (b) $Fe_2(CrO_4)_3$
    (c) $Hg_2(NO_2)_2$
    (d) $Pb(C_2H_3O_2)_4$

39. Provide the formula for each of the following ternary ionic compounds:
    (a) manganese(II) acetate
    (b) copper(II) chlorite
    (c) tin(II) phosphate
    (d) iron(III) hypochlorite

40. Provide the formula for each of the following ternary ionic compounds:
    (a) cuprous chlorite
    (b) plumbic sulfite
    (c) mercuric chlorate
    (d) ferrous chromate

41. Predict the chemical formula for each of the following ternary ionic compounds given the formula of sodium sulfate, Na_2SO_4:
    (a) francium sulfate
    (b) sodium sulfite

42. Predict the chemical formula for each of the following ternary ionic compounds given the formula of scandium nitrate, $Sc(NO_3)_3$:
    (a) lanthanum nitrate
    (b) scandium nitrite

43. Predict the chemical formula for each of the following ternary ionic compounds given the formula of barium chlorate, $Ba(ClO_3)_2$:
    (a) radium chlorate
    (b) barium bromate

44. Predict the chemical formula for each of the following ternary ionic compounds given the formula of iron(III) sulfate, $Fe_2(SO_4)_3$:
    (a) cobalt(III) sulfate
    (b) iron(III) selenate

Binary Molecular Compounds (Sec. 6.7)

45. Give a systematic name for each of the following binary molecular compounds:
    (a) BrF
    (b) CF_4
    (c) I_2O_4
    (d) Cl_2O_3

46. Give a systematic name for each of the following binary molecular compounds:
    (a) BrCl
    (b) SF_6
    (c) I_4O_9
    (d) Cl_2O_7

47. Provide the formula for each of the following binary molecular compounds:
    (a) dinitrogen pentaoxide
    (b) carbon tetrachloride
    (c) iodine monobromide
    (d) dihydrogen sulfide

48. Provide the formula for each of the following binary molecular compounds:
    (a) chlorine dioxide
    (b) sulfur tetrafluoride
    (c) iodine monochloride
    (d) nitrogen monoxide

Binary Acids (Sec. 6.8)

49. Give the IUPAC systematic name for each of the following binary acids:
    (a) HBr(aq)
    (b) HI(aq)

50. Provide the formula for each of the following binary acids:
    (a) hydrosulfuric acid
    (b) hydroselenic acid

Ternary Oxyacids (Sec. 6.9)

51. Give the IUPAC systematic name for each of the following ternary oxyacids:
    (a) $HClO_2$(aq)
    (b) H_3PO_4(aq)

52. Give the IUPAC systematic name for each of the following ternary oxyacids:
    (a) $HClO_4$(aq)
    (b) H_2SO_3(aq)

53. Provide the formula for each of the following ternary oxyacids:
    (a) acetic acid
    (b) nitric acid

54. Provide the formula for each of the following ternary oxyacids:
    (a) carbonic acid
    (b) nitrous acid

55. Predict the chemical formula for each of the following ternary oxyacids given the formula of hypochlorous acid, HClO(aq):
    (a) hypoiodous acid
    (b) hypobromous acid

56. Predict the chemical formula for each of the following ternary oxyacids given the formula of phosphoric acid, H_3PO_4(aq):
    (a) arsenic acid
    (b) phosphorous acid

General Exercises

57. State the ionic charge for each of the following substances:
    (a) iron metal atoms
    (b) ferrous ions
    (c) iron(III) ions
    (d) iron compounds

58. State the ionic charge for each of the following substances:
    (a) chlorine gas molecules
    (b) chloride ions
    (c) hypochlorite ion
    (d) chlorine compounds

59. Predict which of the following polyatomic anions has an ionic charge of 2−. (*Hint:* The total number of valence electrons must be an even number.)
    (a) periodate ion, $IO_4^{?-}$
    (b) silicate ion, $SiO_3^{?-}$

60. Predict which of the following polyatomic anions has an ionic charge of 1–. (*Hint:* The total number of valence electrons must be an even number.)
    (a) thiocyanate ion, $SCN^{?-}$ (b) thiosulfate ion, $S_2O_3^{?-}$

61. Complete the following table by combining cations and anions into chemical formulas. Give the Stock system name for each of the compounds.

IONS	chloride ion	sulfide ion	phosphide ion
copper(I) ion	CuCl copper(I) chloride		
cobalt(III) ion			
lead(IV) ion			

62. Complete the following table by combining cations and anions into chemical formulas. Give the Stock system name for each of the compounds.

IONS	fluoride ion	oxide ion	nitride ion
copper(II) ion	CuF_2 copper(II) fluoride		
cobalt(II) ion			
lead(II) ion			

63. Complete the following table by combining cations and oxyanions into chemical formulas. Give the Latin name for each of the compounds.

IONS	hydroxide ion	sulfate ion	phosphate ion
mercurous ion	$Hg_2(OH)_2$ mercurous hydroxide		
ferrous ion			
stannous ion			

64. Complete the following table by combining cations and oxyanions into chemical formulas. Give the Latin system name for each of the compounds.

IONS	cyanide ion	sulfite ion	permanganate ion
mercuric ion	$Hg(CN)_2$ mercuric cyanide		
ferric ion			
stannic ion			

65. State the suffix in the name for each of the following:
    (a) Na_2S (b) $H_2S(aq)$

66. State the suffix in the name for each of the following:
    (a) NaI   (b) $HI(aq)$

67. State the suffix in the name for each of the following:
    (a) Na_2SO_3 (b) $H_2SO_3(aq)$

68. State the suffix in the name for each of the following:
    (a) $NaIO_2$ (b) $HIO_2(aq)$

69. State the suffix in the name for each of the following:
    (a) Na_2SO_4 (b) $H_2SO_4(aq)$

70. State the suffix in the name for each of the following:
    (a) $NaIO_3$ (b) $HIO_3(aq)$

71. Write the chemical formula for each of the following household chemicals:
    (a) dihydrogen oxide (common liquid)
    (b) sodium hypochlorite (bleach)
    (c) sodium hydroxide (caustic soda)
    (d) sodium bicarbonate (baking soda)

72. Write the chemical formula for each of the following household chemicals:
    (a) acetic acid (vinegar solution)
    (b) aqueous nitrogen trihydride (ammonia solution)
    (c) aqueous magnesium hydroxide (milk of magnesia)
    (d) aqueous sodium hydrogen sulfate (porcelain cleaner)

73. Give the name for each of the following compounds containing a semimetal. (*Hint:* Name the formula as a binary molecular compound.)
    (a) BF_3 (b) $SiCl_4$
    (c) As_2O_5 (d) Sb_2O_3

74. Write the formula for each of the following compounds containing a semimetal.
    (a) boron tribromide   (b) trisilicon tetranitride
    (c) diarsenic trioxide   (d) diantimony pentaoxide

75. The compound titanium oxide occurs in the mineral rutile. Use the periodic table to predict the formula for titanium oxide, given the formula of zirconium oxide, ZrO_2.

◀ **Rutile** Rutile is a mineral found in nature that contains titanium.

76. The compound zirconium silicate occurs in cubic zirconia. Use the periodic table to predict the formula for zirconium silicate, given the formula of titanium silicate, $TiSiO_4$.

Challenge Exercises

77. The element actinium is unstable and radioactive. Use the periodic table to predict the formula for actinium chloride, given the formula of lanthanum chloride, $LaCl_3$.

78. The element lawrencium is unstable and radioactive. Use the periodic table to predict the chemical formula for lawrencium chloride, given the formula of lutetium chloride, $LuCl_3$.

Online Exercises

http://www

Research each of the following using an Internet search engine (e.g., Google.com or Yahoo.com) and cite your URL reference.

79. Eating fish from water containing high concentrations of mercury can lead to severe medical problems. Which species of fish contain the highest concentration of mercury?

80. Manganese is essential in the human diet, yet inhaling manganese dust can lead to severe medical problems. What is the role of manganese in metabolism and which organs in the human body store manganese?

6 Chapter Self-Test

Answers to Self-Test are in Appendix J.

1. Gaseous HCl is classified as which of the following? (Sec. 6.1)
   (a) binary ionic
   (b) ternary ionic
   (c) binary molecular
   (d) binary acid
   (e) ternary oxyacid

2. What is the Stock system name for Hg^{2+}? (Sec. 6.2)
   (a) mercury(I) ion
   (b) mercury(II) ion
   (c) mercuric ion
   (d) mercurous ion
   (e) none of the above

3. What is the chemical formula for the hypochlorite ion? (Sec. 6.3)
   (a) ClO^-
   (b) ClO_2^-
   (c) ClO_3^-
   (d) ClO_4^-
   (e) none of the above

4. What is the chemical formula for the ternary compound composed of Cr^{3+} and OH^- ions? (Sec. 6.4)
   (a) CrOH
   (b) $CrOH_3$
   (c) $Cr(OH)_3$
   (d) Cr_3OH
   (e) none of the above

5. What is the Latin system name for $CuCl_2$? (Sec. 6.5)
   (a) cuprous chloride
   (b) cupric chloride
   (c) copper(I) chloride
   (d) copper(II) chloride
   (e) none of the above

6. What is the Stock system name for $CuSO_4$? (Sec. 6.6)
   (a) cuprous sulfate
   (b) cupric sulfite
   (c) copper(I) sulfate
   (d) copper(II) sulfate
   (e) none of the above

7. What is the systematic name for gaseous H_2S? (Sec. 6.7)
   (a) hydrogen sulfide
   (b) hydrosulfuric acid
   (c) sulfurous acid
   (d) sulfuric acid
   (e) none of the above

8. What is the systematic name for aqueous H_2S? (Sec. 6.8)
   (a) hydrogen sulfide
   (b) hydrosulfuric acid
   (c) sulfurous acid
   (d) sulfuric acid
   (e) none of the above

9. What is the systematic name for aqueous H_2SO_4? (Sec. 6.9)
   (a) hydrogen sulfide
   (b) hydrosulfuric acid
   (c) sulfurous acid
   (d) sulfuric acid
   (e) none of the above

Key Concepts

10. Classify each of the following as binary ionic, ternary ionic, binary molecular, binary acid, or ternary oxyacid: NaCl, HCl, HCl(*aq*), $NaClO_3$, $HClO_3$(*aq*).

11. Which of the following compounds is named using the suffix *–ide*: NaCl, $NaClO_2$, $NaClO_3$?

12. Which of the following compounds is named using the suffix *–ate*: NaCl, $NaClO_2$, $NaClO_3$?

13. Which of the following compounds is named using the suffix *–ite*: NaCl, $NaClO_2$, $NaClO_3$?

14. Which of the following acids is named *hydro + nonmetal stem + –ic acid*: HCl(*aq*), $HClO_3$(*aq*), $HClO_2$(*aq*)?

15. Which of the following acids is named *nonmetal stem + –ic acid*: HCl(*aq*), $HClO_3$(*aq*), $HClO_2$(*aq*)?

16. Which of the following acids is named *nonmetal stem + –ous acid*: HCl(*aq*), $HClO_3$(*aq*), $HClO_2$(*aq*)?

HCl

◀ **Hydrochloric Acid, HCl**
Aqueous hydrochloric acid, HCl, is found in swimming pools and is produced in the stomach to aid digestion; hence, it is commonly referred to as "stomach acid."

Critical Thinking

17. Examine the periodic table and propose an explanation why copper ions can have a charge of either 1+ or 2+.

18. Examine the periodic table and propose an explanation why iron ions can have a charge of either 2+ or 3+.

Chemical Reactions

Potassium in the Environment Potassium metal is stored in mineral oil (shown left). Potassium is too reactive to be found naturally in the environment, and reacts violently with water (shown right). The reaction with water produces potassium hydroxide that turns an indicator pink.

"Science is built of facts the way a house is built of bricks; but an accumulation of facts is no more science than a pile of bricks is a house."
Henri Poincare, French Physicist (1854–1912)

Every day substances are constantly being altered in some way. These alterations can be classified as a physical or a chemical change. In a *physical change,* the chemical composition of the substance remains constant. For instance, when we melt ice or boil water, we cause a physical change. The chemical composition of the ice and the water, H_2O, is the same before and after the change.

In a *chemical change,* the chemical composition of the substance does not remain constant. For example, when we drop an antacid tablet into a glass of water, we produce a chemical change. The chemical composition of the antacid tablet is not the same before and after the change. The evidence for the formation of a new substance is the gas bubbles that are released in the glass of water.

We may observe a *chemical reaction* when a substance undergoes a chemical change and forms a new substance. When we form a new substance, we usually observe one of the following: a change in color, an odor or bubbles indicating the liberation of a gas, or light or heat from the release of energy. For instance, we can mix flour, yeast, and water and put the mixture into an oven, and in a short time we can smell the odor of bread baking. A chemical reaction has occurred in which the flour, yeast, and water have combined to produce a new substance, evidenced by a change in color and smell.

CHEMISTRY CONNECTION Fireworks

Q: What element is responsible for the red-orange color in the fireworks display?

Have you ever watched a Fourth of July fireworks display and wondered how the colors were produced? The color of fireworks is produced by the chemicals in a rocket shell, which is fitted with a fuse and fired into the air. When the fuse burns, gunpowder ignites and sets off an explosion that shoots chemicals throughout the sky. If the rocket shell is packed with a sodium compound, an orange-yellow color is observed. If the shell is packed with a barium compound, a yellow-green color is observed.

◀ **Fourth of July Fireworks**

Interestingly, the colors of fireworks and the colors of neon signs are based on the same principle. In a fireworks display an element is energized by heat, whereas in a "neon light" an element is energized by electricity. In either case, electrons are first excited and then immediately lose energy by emitting light. The observed color corresponds to the wavelength of the light emitted. For example, if the emitted light has a wavelength near 650 nm, it is observed as red. If the light has a wavelength near 450 nm, it appears blue.

Chemists can identify an element by the characteristic color of its flame test. In the laboratory, a flame test is performed by placing a small amount of chemical on the tip of a wire and holding the wire in a hot flame. For example, sodium gives an orange-yellow flame test, and barium a yellow-green flame test. Flame-test colors are identical to fireworks colors containing the same element. The red-orange flame-test color of calcium is illustrated.

However, not all chemicals produce a colored display. You may recall having seen fireworks that simply produce a shower of white sparks. Powdered aluminum or magnesium metals are used to produce this effect. The following table lists the chemicals used to produce various colors in fireworks:

CHEMICAL	FIREWORKS COLOR
Na compounds	orange-yellow
Ba compounds	yellow-green
Ca compounds	red-orange
Sr compounds	bright red
Li compounds	scarlet-red
Cu compounds	blue-green
Al or Mg metals	white sparks

◀ **Calcium Flame Test**
The flame test for calcium is red-orange.

A: The red-orange color suggests that the element is calcium.

7.1 EVIDENCE FOR CHEMICAL REACTIONS

LEARNING OBJECTIVE

▶ To state four observations that are evidence for a chemical reaction.

If we combine substances, the resulting change can be physical or chemical. We can distinguish between a physical and a chemical change by observing the change. Each of the following indicates a chemical change; that is, a **chemical reaction** has taken place.

1. **A gas is produced.** We can observe a gas in a number of ways; for example, we may see bubbles in a solution. When we add an Alka-Seltzer tablet to water, it begins to fizz. The fizzing is evidence for a chemical reaction and the release of carbon dioxide gas, which is produced by the reaction of citric acid and baking soda in the tablet.

2. **An insoluble solid is produced in a solution.** A substance dissolves in water to give an **aqueous solution**. If we add two aqueous solutions together, we may observe solid particles in the solution. This insoluble solid is called a **precipitate**. The formation of a precipitate is evidence for a reaction.

3. **A permanent color change is observed.** Many chemical reactions involve a permanent change in color. For example, adding aqueous ammonia to a copper(II) sulfate solution changes the color from light blue to deep blue. To observe an acid reacting with a base, we use an indicator, a substance that changes color. The indicator enables us to indirectly follow a reaction that would otherwise not be visible.

4. **An energy change is observed.** In chemical reactions there is always a change in energy. A reaction that releases heat is said to be an **exothermic reaction**; conversely, a reaction that absorbs heat is said to be an **endothermic reaction**. For example, when an emergency flare is ignited, heat and light are observed. Heat and light are two forms of energy indicating that an exothermic chemical reaction has taken place.

In summary, each of the above four criteria—the production of a gas, the formation of a precipitate, a change in color, or a change in energy—is a signal that a chemical reaction has occurred. This is shown in Figure 7.1. A chemical reaction, however, may have occurred even though no change is obvious. In some reactions, for example, acid–base reactions, the energy change may be too subtle to notice and an external indicator may be necessary.

▶ Figure 7.1 **Evidence for a Chemical Reaction** Each of these images is evidence for a chemical reaction: (a) the gas bubbles released from magnesium metal in acid; (b) the heat and light released from potassium metal in water; and (c) the color change and the precipitate produced by two aqueous solutions.

(a) (b) (c)

Example Exercise 7.1 Evidence for a Reaction

Which of the following is experimental evidence for a chemical reaction?

(a) Pouring vinegar on baking soda gives foamy bubbles.
(b) Mixing two solutions produces insoluble particles.
(c) Mixing two colorless solutions gives a yellow solution.
(d) Mixing two solutions produces a temperature increase.

Solution
We can analyze each of these observations based on the criteria for a chemical reaction.

(a) The bubbles produced indicate a chemical reaction is occurring.
(b) The insoluble particles formed indicate a chemical reaction.
(c) The yellow color produced indicates a chemical reaction.
(d) The temperature increase indicates heat energy is being released from a chemical reaction.

Practice Exercise

What are four observations that a chemical reaction has occurred?

Answers:

(a) a gas is released   (b) a precipitate is produced

(c) a permanent color change is observed   (d) an energy change is noted

Concept Exercise

What four observations are evidence for a chemical reaction?

Answer: See Appendix G.

7.2 WRITING CHEMICAL EQUATIONS

In this chapter we will use formulas and symbols to describe a chemical reaction; that is, we will write a **chemical equation**. Consider the following description of a chemical reaction: substance A and substance B undergo a chemical change that produces substances C and D. We can state this description in symbols as follows:

$$A + B \rightarrow C + D$$

In this general chemical equation, A and B are called the **reactants**, and C and D are called the **products**.

We can provide more information about the reaction if we specify the physical state of each substance, that is, solid, liquid, or gas. The physical state is indicated by the abbreviation (s), (l), or (g). By convention, we indicate an aqueous solution by the symbol (aq) and a precipitate by the symbol (s). For example, an aqueous solution of A reacts with a gaseous substance B to yield a precipitate C and an aqueous solution D. This statement can be written as follows:

$$A(aq) + B(g) \rightarrow C(s) + D(aq)$$

A **catalyst** is a substance that speeds up a reaction without being consumed or permanently altered. For example, the catalytic converter in an automobile contains a metallic catalyst that speeds up the conversion of unburned fuel to carbon dioxide and water. The presence of a catalyst is indicated by placing its formula above the arrow. Table 7.1 lists the symbols that are used to describe chemical reactions.

Let's interpret the symbols in the following chemical equation for the reaction of acetic acid and baking soda.

$$HC_2H_3O_2(aq) + NaHCO_3(s) \rightarrow NaC_2H_3O_2(aq) + H_2O(l) + CO_2(g)$$

The formulas and symbols are read as follows: aqueous acetic acid is added to solid sodium hydrogen carbonate, which produces aqueous sodium acetate, water, and carbon dioxide gas.

LEARNING OBJECTIVES

▶ To identify seven elements that occur naturally as diatomic molecules: H_2, N_2, O_2, F_2, Cl_2, Br_2, I_2.

▶ To write a chemical equation from the description of a chemical reaction.

TABLE 7.1 CHEMICAL EQUATION SYMBOLS

SYMBOL	INTERPRETATION OF CHEMICAL EQUATION SYMBOL
$\rightarrow$	produces, yields, gives (separates reactants from products)
$+$	reacts with, added to, plus (separates two or more reactants or products)
$\xrightarrow{\Delta}$	heat is a catalyst for the reaction
$\xrightarrow{Fe}$	iron is a catalyst for the reaction
NR	no reaction
(s)	solid substance or precipitate
(l)	liquid substance
(g)	gaseous substance
(aq)	aqueous solution

Naturally Occurring Diatomic Molecules

H_2, N_2, O_2, F_2, Cl_2, Br_2, and I_2

Chemical reactions often involve hydrogen, nitrogen, or oxygen gases. These non-metals occur naturally as **diatomic molecules**, that is, H_2, N_2, and O_2. Moreover, the halogens also occur naturally as diatomic molecules and are therefore written as F_2, Cl_2, Br_2, and I_2. If one of these elements appears in a chemical equation, it is written as a diatomic molecule.

The following example exercise further illustrates how to write a chemical equation from the description of a chemical reaction.

Example Exercise 7.2 Writing Chemical Equations

Write a chemical equation for each of the following chemical reactions:

(a) Mercury liquid and fluorine gas react to give solid mercury(II) fluoride.
(b) Zinc metal reacts with sulfuric acid to give aqueous zinc sulfate and hydrogen gas.

Solution
To write the chemical equation, we must provide formulas and symbols for each substance. We can describe each of the preceding chemical reactions as follows:

(a) $Hg(l) + F_2(g) \rightarrow HgF_2(s)$
(b) $Zn(s) + H_2SO_4(aq) \rightarrow ZnSO_4(aq) + H_2(g)$

Practice Exercise
Write a chemical equation for each of the following chemical reactions:

(a) Aqueous solutions of sodium iodide and silver nitrate yield silver iodide precipitate and aqueous sodium nitrate.
(b) Acetic acid reacts with aqueous potassium hydroxide to give aqueous potassium acetate plus water.

Answers:

(a) $NaI(aq) + AgNO_3(aq) \rightarrow AgI(s) + NaNO_3(aq)$
(b) $HC_2H_3O_2(aq) + KOH(aq) \rightarrow KC_2H_3O_2(aq) + H_2O(l)$

Concept Exercise
Which seven nonmetals occur naturally as diatomic molecules?

Answer: See Appendix G.

LEARNING OBJECTIVE

▶ To write balanced chemical equations.

7.3 BALANCING CHEMICAL EQUATIONS

In the previous section we translated the description of a chemical reaction into a chemical equation. In each case, the number of atoms of each element was equal in the reactants and products. Because the number of atoms of each element is the same on each side of the arrow, the chemical reaction is said to be a balanced chemical equation.

More often, the number of atoms of each element in the reactants and products is not the same. Therefore, it is necessary to balance the number of atoms of each element on each side of the chemical reaction. We balance a chemical reaction by placing a whole number **coefficient** in front of each substance. It is important to note that a co-efficient multiplies all subscripts in the chemical formula that follows. That is, 3 H_2O indicates six hydrogen atoms and three oxygen atoms.

Let's consider the reaction of hydrogen gas with chlorine gas to give hydrogen chloride, a gas with a sharp odor. We can write the chemical reaction as follows:

$$H_2(g) + Cl_2(g) \longrightarrow HCl(g)$$

Notice that the **subscript** for H_2 and Cl_2 is 2, but that only one H atom and one Cl atom appear in the product. Thus, the equation is not balanced. To balance the number of H atoms on both sides of the equation, we place the coefficient 2 in front of the HCl. This gives us

$$H_2(g) + Cl_2(g) \longrightarrow 2\,HCl(g)$$

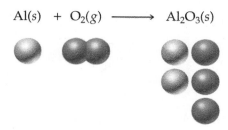

After adding the reaction coefficient 2, we have two molecules of HCl. That is, we have two H atoms and two Cl atoms on each side of the equation. The equation is now balanced.

Let's try a more difficult example. Aluminum metal is heated with oxygen gas to give solid aluminum oxide. The formula for aluminum oxide is Al_2O_3. The chemical equation is

$$Al(s) + O_2(g) \longrightarrow Al_2O_3(s)$$

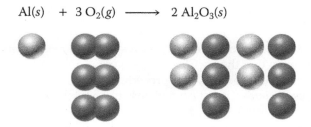

Notice that two O atoms appear in the reactants but that three O atoms appear in the product. This reaction is not balanced. To balance the numbers of O atoms, we will use the lowest common multiple of 2 and 3; the number is 6. We place the coefficient 3 in front of the O_2 to give six oxygen atoms in the reactants and the coefficient 2 in front of Al_2O_3 to give six oxygen atoms in the products. That gives us

$$Al(s) + 3\,O_2(g) \longrightarrow 2\,Al_2O_3(s)$$

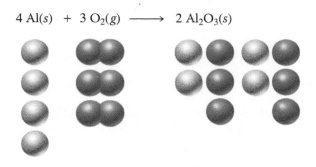

The numbers of Al atoms, however, are not balanced. On the reactant side we have one Al atom. On the product side, we have two units of Al_2O_3, for a total of four Al atoms. We can place the coefficient 4 in front of the reacting Al metal. This gives a balanced chemical equation:

$$4\,Al(s) + 3\,O_2(g) \longrightarrow 2\,Al_2O_3(s)$$

This method of placing coefficients by systematically analyzing each side of an equation is called *balancing by inspection*. Although there is no formal prescription for balancing an equation by inspection, we can list some general guidelines.

General Guidelines for Balancing a Chemical Equation

1. Before placing a coefficient in an equation, verify the formula of each substance for correct subscripts. Note that subscripts of formulas are never changed to balance an equation. In fact, if an equation is difficult to balance, it is usually because of an incorrect subscript in the formula.

2. Balance each element in the equation by placing a coefficient in front of each substance. Coefficients of 1 are assumed and do not appear in the balanced chemical equation.

   (a) Begin balancing the equation starting with the most complex formula.

   (b) Balance polyatomic ions as a single unit. However, if a polyatomic ion breaks down, you must balance each atom separately.

   (c) The coefficients in an equation must be whole numbers. Occasionally, it is helpful to use a fractional coefficient to balance an element in a diatomic molecule; for example,

$$H_2(g) + \tfrac{1}{2}O_2(g) \longrightarrow H_2O(l)$$

If a fraction is used, such as 1/2, we must then multiply the equation by 2 to obtain whole number coefficients. Thus, the balanced equation is

$$2\,H_2(g) + O_2(g) \longrightarrow 2\,H_2O(l)$$

3. After balancing the equation, check ($\sqrt{}$) each symbol of every element (or polyatomic ion) to verify that the coefficients are correct. Proceed back and forth between reactants and products. The procedure for verification is to multiply the coefficient times the subscript of each element; the totals should be the same on both sides of the equation.

Finally, check the coefficients to make sure they represent the smallest whole number ratio. It may be possible to obtain a smaller set of coefficients. Although the following equation is balanced,

$$2\,N_2(g) + 6\,H_2(g) \rightarrow 4\,NH_3(g)$$

you must reduce the coefficients by a factor of 2 to obtain the correct balanced equation:

$$N_2(g) + 3\,H_2(g) \rightarrow 2\,NH_3(g)$$

▲ **Insoluble Lead(II) Iodide**
Lead(II) iodide, PbI_2, forms a yellow precipitate in an aqueous solution.

We can write an equation for the formation of the yellow precipitate shown in Figure 7.1c. In the reaction, aqueous solutions of lead(II) nitrate and potassium iodide produce a yellow precipitate of lead(II) iodide and an aqueous solution of potassium nitrate. We can write a chemical equation for the reaction as follows:

$$Pb(NO_3)_2(aq) + KI(aq) \rightarrow PbI_2(s) + KNO_3(aq)$$

Let's begin balancing with $Pb(NO_3)_2$ because it is the most complex formula. Notice that one Pb atom appears on each side of the equation. However, there are two

NO_3^- ions on the reactant side and only one NO_3^- ion on the product side. We can balance the NO_3^- polyatomic ion by placing a 2 in front of KNO_3. Thus,

$$Pb(NO_3)_2(aq) + KI(aq) \rightarrow PbI_2(s) + 2\,KNO_3(aq)$$

We now have two K on the right side of the equation and only one K on the left. Thus, we need the coefficient 2 in front of KI:

$$Pb(NO_3)_2(aq) + 2\,KI(aq) \rightarrow PbI_2(s) + 2\,KNO_3(aq)$$

Notice the coefficient 2 in front of KI gives two I, which is equal to the two I in PbI_2. As a final inspection, let's check off each element and polyatomic ion to verify that we indeed have a balanced equation:

$$\overset{\checkmark\ \ \checkmark}{Pb(NO_3)_2}(aq) + 2\,\overset{\checkmark\checkmark}{KI}(aq) \rightarrow \overset{\checkmark\ \checkmark}{PbI_2}(s) + 2\,\overset{\checkmark\ \ \checkmark}{KNO_3}(aq)$$

The following example exercises further illustrate the general guidelines for balancing a chemical equation:

Example Exercise 7.3 Balancing Chemical Equations

Aqueous solutions of calcium nitrate and sodium carbonate react to give a white precipitate of calcium carbonate and aqueous sodium nitrate. Write a balanced chemical equation given

$$Ca(NO_3)_2(aq) + Na_2CO_3(aq) \rightarrow CaCO_3(s) + NaNO_3(aq)$$

Solution
We see that $Ca(NO_3)_2$ has two NO_3^- ions in the formula. There is only one NO_3^- ion on the right side, so we insert the coefficient 2 as follows:

$$Ca(NO_3)_2(aq) + Na_2CO_3(aq) \rightarrow CaCO_3(s) + 2NaNO_3(aq)$$

The coefficient 2 in front of $NaNO_3$ generates two Na on the right side, and we have two Na on the left side. Notice we have one CO_3 on each side, and one Ca on each side. Finally, we can check off each element and polyatomic ion to verify that the chemical equation is balanced.

$$\overset{\checkmark\ \ \checkmark}{Ca(NO_3)_2}(aq) + \overset{\checkmark\ \ \checkmark}{Na_2CO_3}(aq) \rightarrow \overset{\checkmark\ \ \checkmark}{CaCO_3}(s) + 2\,\overset{\checkmark\ \ \checkmark}{NaNO_3}(aq)$$

Practice Exercise
Aqueous solutions of aluminum sulfate and barium nitrate react to yield a white precipitate of barium sulfate and aqueous aluminum nitrate. Write a balanced chemical equation given

$$Al_2(SO_4)_3(aq) + Ba(NO_3)_2(aq) \rightarrow BaSO_4(s) + Al(NO_3)_3(aq)$$

Answer: $\overset{\checkmark\ \ \checkmark}{Al_2(SO_4)_3}(aq) + 3\,\overset{\checkmark\ \ \checkmark}{Ba(NO_3)_2}(aq) \rightarrow 3\,\overset{\checkmark\ \ \checkmark}{BaSO_4}(s) + 2\,\overset{\checkmark\ \ \checkmark}{Al(NO_3)_3}(aq)$

Concept Exercise
Do you change a subscript in a chemical formula to balance an equation?

Answer: See Appendix G.

▲ **Insoluble Calcium Carbonate** Chalk, calcium carbonate, $CaCO_3$, is insoluble in an aqueous solution.

Example Exercise 7.4 Balancing Chemical Equations

Sulfuric acid reacts with aqueous sodium hydroxide to give aqueous sodium sulfate and water. Write a balanced chemical equation given

$$H_2SO_4(aq) + NaOH(aq) \rightarrow Na_2SO_4(aq) + H_2O(l)$$

Solution
Let's start with Na_2SO_4, which contains the same number of atoms as H_2SO_4. There is one SO_4 on each side of the equation, and so SO_4 is balanced. However, there are two Na on the right side of the equation and one Na on the left. We must place the coefficient 2 in front of NaOH.

$$H_2SO_4(aq) + 2\,NaOH(aq) \rightarrow Na_2SO_4(aq) + HOH(l)$$

To balance this reaction more easily, we can write the formula for water as HOH. Notice that we now have two OH on the left side of the equation, and one OH on the right side. By placing a 2 in front of the HOH, we can balance the OH. The two H on the right side are balanced by the two H in H_2SO_4. Finally, we check off each atom and polyatomic ion to verify that we have a balanced chemical equation.

$$H_2SO_4(aq) + 2\,NaOH(aq) \rightarrow Na_2SO_4(aq) + 2\,HOH(l)$$

Practice Exercise

Nitric acid reacts with aqueous barium hydroxide to give aqueous barium nitrate and water. Write a balanced chemical equation given

$$HNO_3(aq) + Ba(OH)_2(aq) \rightarrow Ba(NO_3)_2(aq) + HOH(l)$$

Answer: $2\,HNO_3(aq) + Ba(OH)_2(aq) \rightarrow Ba(NO_3)_2(aq) + 2\,HOH(l)$

Concept Exercise

Why write water as HOH for the product of a neutralization reaction?

Answer: See Appendix G.

Note Balancing an equation is a straightforward task. Start with the most complex formula and balance systematically, back and forth, between reactants and products. If you encounter difficulty in the final step, it is usually because the original equation had an incorrect subscript in a chemical formula.

7.4 CLASSIFYING CHEMICAL REACTIONS

LEARNING OBJECTIVE

▶ To classify a chemical reaction as one of the following types: combination, decomposition, single-replacement, double-replacement, or neutralization.

Because there are millions of chemical reactions, how can we attempt to master such a large topic? The answer lies in the same way that we learned previously to master chemical formulas. We can *classify chemical reactions* and put them in categories.

In this chapter, we will begin with five simple types of reactions: combination, decomposition, single-replacement, double-replacement, and neutralization. We can briefly describe these five types as follows:

1. A **combination reaction** involves simpler substances being combined into a more complex compound. It is also referred to as a *synthesis reaction*. In the general case, substance A combines with substance Z to produce compound AZ. The chemical equation is

$$A + Z \rightarrow AZ$$

2. In a **decomposition reaction** a single compound is broken down into two or more simpler substances. In this case, heat is usually applied to decompose the compound. In the general case, compound AZ decomposes into substances A and Z. The chemical equation is

$$AZ \xrightarrow{\Delta} A + Z$$

3. In a **single-replacement reaction** a more reactive element displaces another element from a compound or aqueous solution. The substance that is displaced shows less tendency to undergo reaction; that is, it is less active. In one case, metal A replaces metal B in BZ to give AZ and B. The chemical equation is

$$A + BZ \rightarrow AZ + B$$

4. In a **double-replacement reaction** two compounds exchange anions. Compound AX reacts with compound BZ to yield the products AZ and BX. The general form of the reaction is

$$AX + BZ \rightarrow AZ + BX$$

5. An acid and a base react with each other in a **neutralization reaction**. Acid HX reacts with base BOH to give the compound BX and water. We can write the general form of the reaction as

$$HX + BOH \rightarrow BX + HOH$$

When we examine a neutralization reaction, we see that it is actually a special type of double-replacement reaction. An acid and a base simply switch anions. Notice that we wrote water as HOH rather than H_2O. Using the formula HOH shows the double-replacement nature of the neutralization reaction and makes it easier to balance the equation.

Example Exercise 7.5 Classifying Chemical Reactions

Classify each of the following reactions as combination, decomposition, single-replacement, double-replacement, or neutralization.

(a) Copper metal heated with oxygen gas produces solid copper(II) oxide.

$$2\,Cu(s) + O_2(g) \xrightarrow{\Delta} 2\,CuO(s)$$

(b) Heating powdered iron(III) carbonate produces solid iron(III) oxide and carbon dioxide gas.

$$Fe_2(CO_3)_3(s) \xrightarrow{\Delta} Fe_2O_3(s) + 3\,CO_2(g)$$

(c) Aluminum metal reacts with aqueous manganese(II) sulfate to give aqueous aluminum sulfate and manganese metal.

$$2\,Al(s) + 3\,MnSO_4(aq) \rightarrow Al_2(SO_4)_3(aq) + 3\,Mn(s)$$

(d) Aqueous sodium chromate reacts with aqueous barium chloride to give insoluble barium chromate and aqueous sodium chloride.

$$Na_2CrO_4(aq) + BaCl_2(aq) \rightarrow BaCrO_4(s) + 2\,NaCl(aq)$$

(e) Nitric acid reacts with aqueous potassium hydroxide to give aqueous potassium nitrate and water.

$$HNO_3(aq) + KOH(aq) \rightarrow KNO_3(aq) + H_2O(l)$$

Solution

We can classify the type of each reaction as follows:

(a) The two elements Cu and O_2 synthesize a single compound; this is an example of a *combination* reaction.

(b) The compound $Fe_2(CO_3)_3$ is heated and breaks down into a simpler compound and a gas; this is an example of a *decomposition* reaction.

(c) The metal Al displaces the metal Mn from aqueous $MnSO_4$; this is an example of a *single-replacement* reaction.

(d) The two compounds Na_2CrO_4 and $BaCl_2$ exchange anions; this is an example of a *double-replacement* reaction.

(e) The acid HNO_3 reacts with the base KOH to form KNO_3 and water; this is an example of a *neutralization* reaction.

Practice Exercise

Classify the following reactions as combination, decomposition, single-replacement, double-replacement, or neutralization:

(a) $Zn(s) + CuSO_4(aq) \rightarrow ZnSO_4(aq) + Cu(s)$
(b) $2\,Sr(s) + O_2(g) \rightarrow 2\,SrO(s)$
(c) $Cd(HCO_3)_2(s) \rightarrow CdCO_3(s) + H_2O(g) + CO_2(g)$
(d) $HC_2H_3O_2(aq) + NaOH(aq) \rightarrow NaC_2H_3O_2(aq) + H_2O(l)$
(e) $AgNO_3(aq) + KCl(aq) \rightarrow AgCl(s) + KNO_3(aq)$

Answers:

(a) single-replacement   (b) combination
(c) decomposition   (d) neutralization
(e) double-replacement

Concept Exercise

How can a decomposition reaction be easily distinguished from other types of chemical reactions?

Answer: See Appendix G.

▸ To write a balanced chemical equation for the reaction of a metal and oxygen gas.

▸ To write a balanced chemical equation for the reaction of a nonmetal and oxygen gas.

▸ To write a balanced chemical equation for the reaction of a metal and a nonmetal.

7.5 COMBINATION REACTIONS

There are many examples of combination reactions. For instance, heating a metal in air can cause the metal to combine with oxygen and form a compound. In this section, we will study three important kinds of combination reactions.

Metal and Oxygen Gas

In one kind of combination reaction, a metal and oxygen gas react to give a metal oxide. In the following example, magnesium metal and oxygen gas combine to give magnesium oxide:

$$\text{metal} + \text{oxygen gas} \rightarrow \text{metal oxide}$$

$$2\,Mg(s) + O_2(g) \xrightarrow{\Delta} 2\,MgO(s)$$

A metal and oxygen react to give a metal oxide compound. We can usually predict the formulas of metal oxides containing a main-group metal. On the other hand, we cannot predict the formulas of most metal oxides containing a transition metal. For transition metal oxides, the ionic charge of the metal must be given to write the chemical formula of the metal oxide.

The following example exercise further illustrates how to write balanced equations for a combination reaction of a metal and oxygen gas:

▲ **Igniting Magnesium Metal**
A strip of magnesium metal reacts with oxygen in air to give white smoke, MgO, and a bright white light.

> **Example Exercise 7.6** Combination Reaction of a Metal and Oxygen Gas

Write a balanced chemical equation for each of the following combination reactions:

(a) Zinc metal is heated with oxygen gas in air to yield solid zinc oxide.

(b) Chromium metal is heated with oxygen gas to give solid chromium(III) oxide.

Solution

A metal and oxygen react to produce a metal oxide.

(a) Zinc is a metal with a predictable charge, that is, Zn^{2+}. The formula of zinc oxide is ZnO. The balanced equation for the reaction is

$$2\,Zn(s) + O_2(g) \xrightarrow{\Delta} 2\,ZnO(s)$$

(b) Chromium is a metal with a variable charge. From the name chromium(III) oxide, we know the ion is Cr^{3+}. The formula of the oxide is, therefore, Cr_2O_3, and the balanced equation for the reaction is

$$4\,Cr(s) + 3\,O_2(g) \xrightarrow{\Delta} 2\,Cr_2O_3(s)$$

Practice Exercise

Write a balanced chemical equation for each of the following combination reactions:

(a) Lead metal is heated with oxygen in air to yield solid lead(IV) oxide.

(b) Cobalt metal is heated with oxygen gas to give solid cobalt(III) oxide.

Answers:

(a) $Pb(s) + O_2(g) \xrightarrow{\Delta} PbO_2(s)$ (b) $4\,Co(s) + 3\,O_2(g) \xrightarrow{\Delta} 2\,Co_2O_3(s)$

Concept Exercise

What is the product from heating a metal and oxygen gas?

Answer: See Appendix G.

Nonmetal and Oxygen Gas

In this kind of combination reaction, a nonmetal and oxygen gas react to give a nonmetal oxide. In the following example, yellow sulfur powder and oxygen gas combine to give sulfur dioxide gas.

nonmetal + oxygen gas → nonmetal oxide

$$S(s) + O_2(g) \xrightarrow{\Delta} SO_2(g)$$

Nonmetal oxides demonstrate multiple combining capacities, for example, CO and CO_2. In general, the formula of a nonmetal oxide product is unpredictable and varies with temperature and pressure. For example, nitrogen and oxygen gases can combine to give all of the following: NO, NO_2, N_2O, N_2O_3, N_2O_4, and N_2O_5. Therefore, to complete and balance an equation of a nonmetal and oxygen gas, we must be given the name or formula of the nonmetal oxide.

The following example exercise further illustrates how to write balanced equations for a combination reaction of a nonmetal and oxygen gas:

▲ **Igniting Sulfur Powder** A small portion of yellow sulfur burns with the oxygen in air to give an intense blue flame and sulfur dioxide gas, SO_2, which has a sharp odor.

Example Exercise 7.7 Combination Reaction of a Nonmetal and Oxygen Gas

Write a balanced chemical equation for each of the following combination reactions:

(a) Carbon is heated with oxygen gas to produce carbon dioxide gas.

(b) Phosphorus and oxygen gas react to give solid diphosphorus pentaoxide.

Solution

A nonmetal and oxygen combine to produce a nonmetal oxide.

(a) The formula of the nonmetal oxide is unpredictable. We are given that the product is carbon dioxide and not carbon monoxide. The balanced equation for the reaction is

$$C(s) + O_2(g) \xrightarrow{\Delta} CO_2(g)$$

(b) The formula for the oxide of phosphorus is not predictable, but we have the name of the nonmetal oxide product. The formula for diphosphorus pentaoxide is P_2O_5. The balanced equation is

$$4\,P(s) + 5\,O_2(g) \longrightarrow 2\,P_2O_5(s)$$

Practice Exercise

Write a balanced chemical equation for each of the following combination reactions:

(a) Nitrogen gas is heated with oxygen to give dinitrogen trioxide gas.

(b) Chlorine gas is heated with oxygen to give dichlorine monoxide gas.

Answers:

(a) $2\,N_2(g) + 3\,O_2(g) \xrightarrow{\Delta} 2\,N_2O_3(g)$

(b) $2\,Cl_2(g) + O_2(g) \xrightarrow{\Delta} 2\,Cl_2O(g)$

Concept Exercise

What is the product from heating a nonmetal and oxygen gas?

Answer: See Appendix G.

▲ **Igniting Sodium and Chlorine** Sodium metal reacts strongly with chlorine gas to give a bright yellow light and sodium chloride, NaCl, powder.

Metal and Nonmetal

In this kind of combination reaction, a metal and a nonmetal react to give an ionic compound. In the following example, silvery sodium metal and yellow chlorine gas combine to give solid sodium chloride:

$$\text{metal} + \text{nonmetal} \rightarrow \text{ionic compound}$$

$$2\,Na(s) \quad + \quad Cl_2(g) \quad \xrightarrow{\Delta} \quad 2\,NaCl(s)$$

When a metal and a nonmetal react, they produce a binary ionic compound. If the compound contains a main-group metal, the formula is usually predictable. If the compound contains a transition metal, the formula is not predictable.

The following example exercise further illustrates how to write a balanced equation for a combination reaction of a metal and a nonmetal:

Example Exercise 7.8 Combination Reaction of a Metal and a Nonmetal

Write a balanced chemical equation for each of the following combination reactions:

(a) Aluminum metal is heated with sulfur powder to yield solid aluminum sulfide.
(b) Chromium metal is heated with iodine crystals to give solid chromium(III) iodide.

Solution
A metal and a nonmetal react to produce a binary ionic compound.

(a) The formula of the product is predictable. Aluminum combines with sulfur to give aluminum sulfide, Al_2S_3. The balanced equation for the reaction is

$$2\,Al(s) + 3\,S(s) \xrightarrow{\Delta} Al_2S_3(s)$$

(b) Chromium is a transition metal, and so we cannot predict the formula for the product. We are given the name of the compound, chromium(III) iodide, and so the formula is CrI_3. The equation is

$$2\,Cr(s) + 3\,I_2(s) \xrightarrow{\Delta} 2\,CrI_3(s)$$

Practice Exercise
Write a balanced chemical equation for each of the following combination reactions:

(a) Calcium metal is heated with fluorine gas to yield solid calcium fluoride.
(b) Manganese metal reacts with bromine vapor to give crystalline manganese(IV) bromide.

Answers:

(a) $Ca(s) + F_2(g) \xrightarrow{\Delta} CaF_2(s)$ (b) $Mn(s) + 2\,Br_2(g) \rightarrow MnBr_4(s)$

Concept Exercise
What is the product from heating a metal and nonmetal?

Answer: See Appendix G.

LEARNING OBJECTIVES

▶ To write a balanced equation for the decomposition of a metal hydrogen carbonate.

▶ To write a balanced equation for the decomposition of a metal carbonate.

▶ To write a balanced equation for the decomposition of a compound that releases oxygen gas.

7.6 DECOMPOSITION REACTIONS

There are many examples of decomposition reactions. For instance, heating a compound may cause it to decompose into two or more simpler substances. In this section, we will study three important kinds of decomposition reactions.

Metal Hydrogen Carbonates

A metal hydrogen carbonate undergoes a decomposition reaction when it is heated. For example, you may be aware that baking soda is a natural fire extinguisher. That is, heat from a fire decomposes baking soda (sodium hydrogen carbonate) and releases carbon dioxide gas. Because carbon dioxide is more dense than air, it can smother a fire by excluding oxygen from the flame.

The decomposition of a metal hydrogen carbonate yields a metal carbonate, water, and carbon dioxide. In the following example, sodium hydrogen carbonate is decomposed by heating to give sodium carbonate, water, and carbon dioxide:

metal hydrogen carbonate $\xrightarrow{\Delta}$ **metal carbonate + water + carbon dioxide**

$$2\,NaHCO_3(s) \xrightarrow{\Delta} Na_2CO_3(s) + H_2O(g) + CO_2(g)$$

During the decomposition reaction of a metal hydrogen carbonate, the ionic charge of the metal does not change. Therefore, the formula of the metal carbonate is predictable. Even transition metal hydrogen carbonates are predictable. If nickel(II) hydrogen carbonate decomposes, one of the products is nickel(II) carbonate. That is,

$$Ni(HCO_3)_2(s) \xrightarrow{\Delta} NiCO_3(s) + H_2O(g) + CO_2(g)$$

The following example exercise further illustrates how to write balanced equations for a decomposition reaction of a metal hydrogen carbonate:

Example Exercise 7.9 Decomposition Reaction of a Hydrogen Carbonate

Write a balanced chemical equation for each of the following decomposition reactions:

(a) Lithium hydrogen carbonate decomposes on heating.
(b) Lead(II) hydrogen carbonate decomposes on heating.

Solution
A metal hydrogen carbonate decomposes with heat to give a metal carbonate, water, and carbon dioxide gas.

(a) All the formulas are predictable, including that of the product, Li_2CO_3. The balanced equation for the reaction is

$$2\,LiHCO_3(s) \xrightarrow{\Delta} Li_2CO_3(s) + H_2O(g) + CO_2(g)$$

(b) Although the ionic charge of lead is variable, we are given that lead(II) hydrogen carbonate is the reactant. Therefore, the product is lead(II) carbonate, $PbCO_3$. The balanced equation for the reaction is

$$Pb(HCO_3)_2(s) \xrightarrow{\Delta} PbCO_3(s) + H_2O(g) + CO_2(g)$$

Practice Exercise
Write a balanced chemical equation for each of the following decomposition reactions:

(a) Barium hydrogen carbonate is decomposed with heat.
(b) Copper(I) hydrogen carbonate is decomposed with heat.

Answers:
(a) $Ba(HCO_3)_2(s) \xrightarrow{\Delta} BaCO_3(s) + H_2O(g) + CO_2(g)$
(b) $2\,CuHCO_3(s) \xrightarrow{\Delta} Cu_2CO_3(s) + H_2O(g) + CO_2(g)$

Concept Exercise
What is the product from heating a metal hydrogen carbonate?

Answer: See Appendix G.

Metal Carbonates

After a metal hydrogen carbonate decomposes into a metal carbonate, the metal carbonate can further decompose with prolonged heating. The carbonate can decompose into a metal oxide while releasing carbon dioxide gas.

In the following example, calcium carbonate is decomposed by heating to give calcium oxide and carbon dioxide:

metal carbonate $\xrightarrow{\Delta}$ **metal oxide + carbon dioxide**

$$CaCO_3(s) \xrightarrow{\Delta} CaO(s) + CO_2(g)$$

The ionic charge of the metal does not change during the decomposition reaction of a metal carbonate. Therefore, we can predict the formula for the metal oxide product from the decomposition of a metal carbonate. If nickel(II) carbonate is decomposed, one of the products is nickel(II) oxide. That is,

$$NiCO_3 \overset{\Delta}{\rightarrow} NiO(s) + CO_2(g)$$

The following example exercise further illustrates how to write balanced equations for a decomposition reaction of a metal carbonate:

Example Exercise 7.10   Decomposition Reaction of a Carbonate

Write a balanced chemical equation for each of the following decomposition reactions:

(a) Magnesium carbonate decomposes on heating.
(b) Copper(I) carbonate decomposes on heating.

Solution
A metal carbonate decomposes with heat to a metal oxide and carbon dioxide gas.

(a) All the formulas are predictable including that of the metal oxide, MgO. The balanced equation for the reaction is

$$MgCO_3(s) \overset{\Delta}{\rightarrow} MgO(s) + CO_2(g)$$

(b) The ionic charge of copper can be either 1+ or 2+. Because the reactant is copper(I) carbonate, the product is copper(I) oxide, that is, Cu_2O. Thus, the balanced equation for the reaction is

$$Cu_2CO_3(s) \overset{\Delta}{\rightarrow} Cu_2O(s) + CO_2(g)$$

Practice Exercise
Write a balanced chemical equation for each of the following decomposition reactions:

(a) Aluminum carbonate is decomposed on heating.
(b) Iron(II) carbonate is decomposed on heating.

Answers:
(a) $Al_2(CO_3)_3(s) \overset{\Delta}{\rightarrow} Al_2O_3(s) + 3\,CO_2(g)$
(b) $FeCO_3(s) \overset{\Delta}{\rightarrow} FeO(s) + CO_2(g)$

Concept Exercise
What is the product from heating a metal carbonate?

Answer: See Appendix G.

Miscellaneous Oxygen-Containing Compounds

We can often decompose an oxygen-containing ionic compound, which releases oxygen gas. However, we cannot always predict the products. In this kind of decomposition reaction, we must be given the formulas of the products.

In the following example, orange mercury(II) oxide powder is decomposed by heating to give droplets of shiny liquid mercury and oxygen gas:

$$\textbf{oxygen-containing compound} \overset{\Delta}{\rightarrow} \textbf{substance} + \textbf{oxygen gas}$$

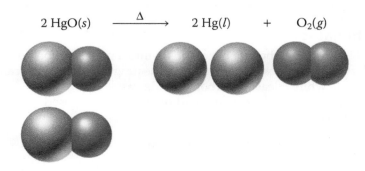

$$2\,HgO(s) \xrightarrow{\Delta} 2\,Hg(l) + O_2(g)$$

▲ **Decomposing Mercury(II) Oxide** A small portion of orange HgO powder decomposes with heat to give oxygen gas, O_2, and beads of silvery metallic mercury.

The following example exercise illustrates how to write balanced equations for miscellaneous decomposition reactions:

Example Exercise 7.11 Decomposition Reaction Producing Oxygen Gas

Write a balanced chemical equation for each of the following decomposition reactions:

(a) Solid potassium chlorate decomposes upon heating to give solid potassium chloride and oxygen gas.

(b) Solid sodium nitrate decomposes upon heating to give solid sodium nitrite and oxygen gas.

Solution

There is no general format for these reactions; however, we are given the names of the reactants and products.

(a) We can write the reaction for the decomposition of potassium chlorate and balance the chemical equation as follows:

$$2\,KClO_3(s) \xrightarrow{\Delta} 2\,KCl(s) + 3\,O_2(g)$$

(b) We can write the reaction for the decomposition of sodium nitrate and balance the chemical equation as follows:

$$2\,NaNO_3(s) \xrightarrow{\Delta} 2\,NaNO_2(s) + O_2(g)$$

Practice Exercise

Write a balanced chemical equation for each of the following decomposition reactions:

(a) Solid lead(IV) oxide decomposes upon heating to give solid lead(II) oxide and oxygen gas.

(b) Aqueous hydrogen peroxide, H_2O_2, decomposes upon heating to give water and oxygen gas.

Answers:

(a) $2\,PbO_2(s) \xrightarrow{\Delta} 2\,PbO(s) + O_2(g)$

(b) $2\,H_2O_2(aq) \xrightarrow{\Delta} 2\,H_2O(l) + O_2(g)$

Concept Exercise

What is the usual product from heating an oxygen-containing compound?

Answer: See Appendix G.

7.7 THE ACTIVITY SERIES CONCEPT

When a metal undergoes a single replacement reaction, it displaces another metal from a compound or aqueous solution. The metal that displaces the other metal does so because it has a greater tendency to undergo a reaction; in other words, it is more active. If metal A is more active than metal B, metal A will displace metal B from compound BZ. We can show the reaction as

$$A + BZ \longrightarrow AZ + B$$

The activity of a metal is a measure of its ability to compete in a single replacement reaction. In an **activity series** (or electromotive series), a sequence of metals is arranged according to their ability to undergo reaction. Metals that are most reactive appear first in the activity series. Metals that are least reactive appear last in the series. The relative activity of several metals is listed in the margin.

We can see that lithium precedes potassium in the series, which in turn precedes barium, and so on. Although hydrogen (H) is not a metal, it is included in the series as a reference. Metals that precede (H) in the series react with an aqueous acid; metals that follow (H) in the series do not react with acids. Notice that the metals Cu, Ag, Hg, and Au do not react with acids.

LEARNING OBJECTIVES

▶ To predict whether a metal reacts with an aqueous salt solution.

▶ To predict whether a metal reacts with an aqueous acid.

▶ To predict whether a metal reacts with water at 25 °C.

Activity Series for Metals
Li > K > Ba > Sr > Ca >
Na > Mg > Al > Mn >
Zn > Fe > Cd > Co >
Ni > Sn > Pb > (H) >
Cu > Ag > Hg > Au

Consider the reaction of iron metal in an aqueous solution of copper(II) sulfate:

$$Fe(s) + CuSO_4(aq) \quad \rightarrow \quad FeSO_4(aq) + Cu(s)$$

◀ **Iron in a Copper Solution**
An iron nail reacts in an aqueous blue $CuSO_4$ solution to give a reddish-brown deposit of Cu metal on the nail.

Iron precedes copper in the series, and so Fe displaces Cu from the aqueous solution. If we perform the reaction in the laboratory, a reddish-brown copper deposit appears on the iron metal. It is this type of experiment that establishes the order of metals in the activity series; that is, Fe >>> Cu.

Conversely, there is no reaction if we place copper metal in an aqueous solution of iron(II) sulfate. That is, Cu cannot displace Fe from the solution because copper follows iron in the activity series. Thus, if we put copper wire into a solution of iron(II) sulfate, we observe

$$Cu(s) + FeSO_4(aq) \quad \rightarrow \quad NR$$

Now let's consider the reaction of iron wire with sulfuric acid. The reaction releases gas bubbles in the solution, and the equation is

$$Fe(s) + H_2SO_4(aq) \quad \rightarrow \quad FeSO_4(aq) + H_2(g)$$

Iron precedes (H) in the activity series, and so Fe displaces H_2 gas from a sulfuric acid solution. When we observe the reaction, we see tiny bubbles of hydrogen gas on the iron wire. Now consider the reaction of copper metal and sulfuric acid:

$$Cu(s) + H_2SO_4(aq) \quad \rightarrow \quad NR$$

Copper is after (H) in the activity series, so Cu cannot displace H_2 gas from sulfuric acid. When we observe the copper wire in sulfuric acid, there is no evidence for reaction.

Active Metals

List of Active Metals
Li > K > Ba > Sr >
Ca > Na

There are a few metals that are so reactive they react directly with water at room temperature. These metals are called the **active metals** and include most of the metals in Groups IA/1 and IIA/2. Specifically, Li, Na, K, Rb, Cs, Ca, Sr, and Ba react with water. The most common active metals are listed in the margin.

Consider an experiment in which sodium metal is dropped into water. Sodium is an active metal and reacts with water according to the following equation:

$$2\,Na(s) + 2\,H_2O(l) \quad \rightarrow \quad 2\,NaOH(aq) + H_2(g)$$

The following example exercise further illustrates how to predict the reactivity of metals with aqueous solutions, acids, and water:

Example Exercise 7.12 — Predictions Based on the Activity Series

Predict whether or not a reaction occurs for each of the following:

(a) Aluminum foil is added to an iron(II) sulfate solution.
(b) Iron wire is added to an aluminum sulfate solution.
(c) Manganese metal is added to acetic acid.
(d) Magnesium metal is added to water.

Solution
We refer to the activity series for the reactivity of each of the metals.

(a) Aluminum precedes iron in the activity series: Al > Fe. Thus, a reaction occurs, and Al displaces Fe from the solution.
(b) Conversely, iron follows aluminum in the activity series: Al > Fe. Thus, there is *no reaction*.
(c) Manganese precedes hydrogen in the activity series: Mn > (H). Thus, a reaction occurs, and Mn produces H_2 gas that bubbles from the solution.
(d) Magnesium is not an active metal. Therefore, magnesium does not react with water, and there is *no reaction*.

Practice Exercise
Predict whether or not a reaction occurs for each of the following:

(a) A gold ring is dropped into sulfuric acid.
(b) A zinc granule is dropped into hydrochloric acid.
(c) A cadmium foil is put into a lead(II) nitrate solution.
(d) A chromium strip is put into water.

Answers:
(a) There is *no reaction* because Au follows (H) in the activity series.
(b) There is a reaction because Zn precedes (H) in the activity series.
(c) There is a reaction because Cd precedes Pb in the activity series.
(d) There is *no reaction* because Cr is not an active metal.

Concept Exercise
Which of the following metals reacts with aqueous silver nitrate: Zn, Cu, Au?

Answer: See Appendix G.

▲ **Gold in Acid** A gold ring gives no reaction in an aqueous sulfuric acid, H_2SO_4, solution.

Note In this introduction to the concept of an activity series, we have considered only the activity of metals. In addition, the ability of nonmetals to undergo a reaction also gives rise to an activity series. For example, the halogens demonstrate the following activity series: F > Cl > Br > I. Consider the reaction

$$Cl_2(g) + 2\,NaBr(aq) \quad \rightarrow \quad 2\,NaCl(aq) + Br_2(l)$$

A reaction occurs because Cl precedes Br in the activity series; thus, the more active Cl displaces the less active Br from the solution. Conversely, Cl follows F in the series. Therefore, Cl is less reactive than F and cannot displace it from the solution. Thus,

$$Cl_2(g) + NaF(aq) \quad \rightarrow \quad NR$$

▶ To write a balanced chemical equation for the reaction of a metal in an aqueous solution.

▶ To write a balanced chemical equation for the reaction of a metal in an aqueous acid.

▶ To write a balanced chemical equation for the reaction of an active metal in water.

▲ **Copper in a Silver Solution**
A copper wire reacts in a colorless $AgNO_3$ solution to give white crystals of Ag and a light-blue aqueous solution.

7.8 SINGLE-REPLACEMENT REACTIONS

There are many examples of single-replacement reactions in which a more active metal displaces a less active metal from a solution. In general, the activity of a metal follows the metallic character trend in the periodic table. To determine the relative reactivity of a specific metal, we refer to the activity series.

Metal and Aqueous Salt Solution

One kind of single-replacement reaction involves a metal reacting with an ionic compound (salt) in aqueous solution. The general equation for the reaction is

$$\text{metal}_1(s) + \text{salt}_1(aq) \rightarrow \text{metal}_2(s) + \text{salt}_2(aq)$$

Consider the reaction of metallic copper wire in an aqueous solution of silver nitrate. The balanced equation for the reaction is

$$Cu(s) + 2\,AgNO_3(aq) \rightarrow 2\,Ag(s) + Cu(NO_3)_2(aq)$$

If we refer to the activity series, we note that copper is the more active metal. That is, copper lies above silver in the series. Therefore, Cu metal can displace Ag metal from an aqueous solution.

Now let's consider the reaction of metallic silver wire in an aqueous solution of copper nitrate. Because Ag metal is less active than Cu metal, we can predict that there is no reaction. That is,

$$Ag(s) + Cu(NO_3)_2(aq) \rightarrow NR$$

Metal and Aqueous Acid Solution

Another kind of single-replacement reaction is that of a metal with an aqueous acid. A metal and an aqueous acid react to produce hydrogen gas and an aqueous solution of an ionic compound (salt). The general equation for the reaction is

$$\text{metal}(s) + \text{acid}(aq) \rightarrow \text{salt}(aq) + \text{hydrogen}(g)$$

Consider the reaction of iron metal and sulfuric acid. First, refer to the activity series to check the position of iron. Iron is above hydrogen in the series. Therefore, iron displaces hydrogen gas from the acid. If we assume that the reaction produces iron(II) sulfate, we can write the balanced chemical equation.

$$Fe(s) + H_2SO_4(aq) \longrightarrow FeSO_4(aq) + H_2(g)$$

Active Metal and Water

In this type of single-replacement reaction, an active metal and water react to give a metal hydroxide and hydrogen gas. The general equation for the reaction is

$$\text{metal}(s) + \text{water}(l) \rightarrow \text{metal hydroxide}(aq) + \text{hydrogen}(g)$$

Consider the reaction of calcium metal in water to give calcium hydroxide and hydrogen gas. The balanced equation for the reaction is

$$Ca(s) + 2\,H_2O(l) \longrightarrow Ca(OH)_2(aq) + H_2(g)$$

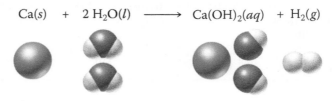

The following example exercise further illustrates how to write balanced chemical equations for the three types of single-replacement reactions:

Example Exercise 7.13   Single-Replacement Reactions

Write a balanced chemical equation for each of the following single-replacement reactions:

(a) Nickel metal is placed in a tin(II) sulfate solution.
(b) Cobalt metal is put in a cadmium nitrate solution.
(c) Manganese chips are added to sulfuric acid.
(d) A chunk of potassium is dropped into water.

Solution
First, we will refer to the activity series for the relative positions of each of the metals. Then we will write the equations.

(a) Nickel is above tin in the activity series: Ni > Sn. Therefore, a reaction occurs and Ni displaces Sn from the solution.

$$Ni(s) + SnSO_4(aq) \longrightarrow NiSO_4(aq) + Sn(s)$$

(b) Cobalt is below cadmium in the series: Cd > Co. Therefore, there is no reaction.

$$Co(s) + Cd(NO_3)_2(aq) \longrightarrow NR$$

(c) Manganese is above hydrogen in the series: Mn > (H). Therefore, a reaction occurs, and Mn releases H_2 gas bubbles from the solution.

$$Mn(s) + H_2SO_4(aq) \longrightarrow MnSO_4(aq) + H_2(g)$$

(d) Potassium is a Group IA/1 active metal. Therefore, a reaction occurs, and K releases H_2 gas from the solution.

$$2\,K(s) + 2\,H_2O(l) \longrightarrow 2\,KOH(aq) + H_2(g)$$

Practice Exercise
Write a balanced chemical equation for each of the following single-replacement reactions:

(a) Nickel metal is placed in a silver nitrate solution.
(b) Gold metal is placed in a silver nitrate solution.
(c) A chunk of cadmium metal is dropped into hydrochloric acid.
(d) A small piece of strontium metal is dropped into water.

Answers:

(a) $Ni(s) + 2\,AgNO_3(aq) \longrightarrow 2\,Ag(s) + Ni(NO_3)_2(aq)$
(b) $Au(s) + AgNO_3(aq) \longrightarrow NR$
(c) $Cd(s) + 2\,HCl(aq) \longrightarrow CdCl_2(aq) + H_2(g)$
(d) $Sr(s) + 2\,H_2O(l) \longrightarrow Sr(OH)_2(aq) + H_2(g)$

Concept Exercise
Which of the following metals reacts with an aqueous acid: Zn, Cu, Au?

Answer See Appendix G.

▲ **Calcium in Water** A piece of calcium metal in water reacts to give bubbles of hydrogen gas.

Note In a single-replacement reaction, it may not be possible to predict the ionic charge of the resulting metal cation. For example, when copper metal reacts with silver nitrate solution, the resulting compound may contain either Cu^+ or Cu^{2+}.

7.9 SOLUBILITY RULES

In a double-replacement reaction, which we will discuss in Section 7.10, two aqueous solutions may react to form a compound that is not soluble, that is, a precipitate. When we observe that a precipitate is produced in a solution, we have evidence for a chemical reaction.

LEARNING OBJECTIVE

▶ To predict whether an ionic compound dissolves in water given the general rules for solubility.

▲ **Insoluble Silver Chloride**
Aqueous solutions of silver nitrate and sodium chloride react to give white, insoluble AgCl.

It is important to be able to identify an insoluble compound in an aqueous solution. In Table 7.2, there are general rules for predicting the solubility of ionic compounds in water. However, there are exceptions to the general rules, and a few of these exceptions are indicated; for example, Na_2CO_3 is soluble in water (Rule 6).

TABLE 7.2 SOLUBILITY RULES FOR IONIC COMPOUNDS

Ionic compounds containing the following ions are generally *soluble* in water:
1. alkali metal ions and the ammonium ion, Li^+, Na^+, K^+, NH_4^+
2. acetate ion, $C_2H_3O_2^-$
3. nitrate ion, NO_3^-
4. halide ions ($X = Cl^-$, Br^-, I^-) (AgX, Hg_2X_2, and PbX_2 are exceptions and *insoluble*)
5. sulfate ion, an SO_4^{2-} ($SrSO_4$, $BaSO_4$, and $PbSO_4$ are exceptions and *insoluble*)

Ionic compounds containing the following ions are generally *insoluble* in water:*
6. carbonate ion, CO_3^{2-} (see Rule 1 exceptions, which are *soluble*)
7. chromate ion, CrO_4^{2-} (see Rule 1 exceptions, which are *soluble*)
8. phosphate ion, PO_4^{3-} (see Rule 1 exceptions, which are *soluble*)
9. sulfide ion, S^{2-} (CaS, SrS, BaS, and Rule 1 exceptions are *soluble*)
10. hydroxide ion, OH^- [$Ca(OH)_2$, $Sr(OH)_2$, $Ba(OH)_2$, and Rule 1 exceptions are *soluble*]

*These compounds are actually slightly soluble, or very slightly soluble, in water.

Now let's apply the solubility rules to selected compounds and determine whether or not the compound is soluble in water.

Example Exercise 7.14   Applying Solubility Rules

State whether each of the following compounds is soluble or insoluble in water:

(a) sodium sulfate, Na_2SO_4
(b) aluminum nitrate, $Al(NO_3)_3$
(c) barium sulfate, $BaSO_4$
(d) lead(II) chromate, $PbCrO_4$
(e) ammonium sulfide, $(NH_4)_2S$

Solution
We refer to the solubility rules in Table 7.2.

(a) Sodium sulfate contains the alkali metal ion Na^+. According to Rule 1, Na_2SO_4 is *soluble*.
(b) Aluminum nitrate contains the nitrate ion NO_3^-. According to Rule 3, $Al(NO_3)_3$ is *soluble*.
(c) Barium sulfate contains the sulfate ion SO_4^{2-}. According to the Rule 5 exception, $BaSO_4$ is *insoluble*.
(d) Lead(II) chromate contains the chromate ion CrO_4^{2-}. According to Rule 7, $PbCrO_4$ is *insoluble*.
(e) Ammonium sulfide contains the ammonium ion NH_4^+. According to Rule 1, $(NH_4)_2S$ is *soluble*.

Practice Exercise
State whether each of the following compounds is soluble or insoluble in water:

(a) lead(II) acetate, $Pb(C_2H_3O_2)_2$ (b) mercury(II) bromide, $HgBr_2$
(c) magnesium carbonate, $MgCO_3$ (d) zinc phosphate, $Zn_3(PO_4)_2$
(e) calcium hydroxide, $Ca(OH)_2$

Answers:

(a) soluble (Rule 2)   (b) soluble (Rule 4)
(c) insoluble (Rule 6)   (d) insoluble (Rule 8)
(e) soluble (Rule 10 exception)

Concept Exercise
Which of the following compounds is soluble in water: $Pb(NO_3)_2$, $PbCl_2$, $PbCO_3$?

Answer: See Appendix G.

7.10 DOUBLE-REPLACEMENT REACTIONS

LEARNING OBJECTIVE

▸ To write a balanced chemical equation for the reaction of two salts in aqueous solution.

In a double-replacement precipitation reaction, two ionic compounds in an aqueous solution switch anions and produce an insoluble substance. The general form of the reaction is

$$AX + BZ \rightarrow AZ + BX$$

In the reaction of AX and BZ, we can assume that either AZ or BX is an insoluble precipitate. If both AZ and BX are soluble, there is no precipitate, and hence there is no chemical reaction. Consider the double-replacement reaction of two salts in aqueous solution:

$$salt_1(aq) + salt_2(aq) \rightarrow salt_3(s) + salt_4(aq)$$

As an example, when we add an aqueous solution of silver nitrate to an aqueous solution of sodium carbonate, we observe a white precipitate. In this reaction, the two compounds switch anions to give insoluble silver carbonate and sodium nitrate. We can write the balanced chemical equation as follows:

$$2\,AgNO_3(aq) + Na_2CO_3(aq) \rightarrow Ag_2CO_3(s) + 2\,NaNO_3(aq)$$

By referring to solubility Rule 6, we find that most compounds containing the carbonate ion, CO_3^{2-}, are insoluble. Because silver carbonate is insoluble, it is written as $Ag_2CO_3(s)$ in the above equation. The (s) indicates that Ag_2CO_3 is an insoluble precipitate. The following example exercise further illustrates how to write balanced equations for double-replacement reactions:

▲ **Insoluble Silver Carbonate**
Aqueous solutions of silver nitrate and sodium carbonate react to give an insoluble precipitate of Ag_2CO_3.

Example Exercise 7.15 Double-Replacement Reactions

Write a balanced chemical equation for each of the following double-replacement reactions.
(a) Aqueous barium chloride is added to a potassium chromate solution.
(b) Aqueous strontium acetate is added to a lithium hydroxide solution.

Solution
For double-replacement reactions, we switch anions for the two compounds and check the solubility rules for an insoluble compound.

(a) Barium chloride and potassium chromate give barium chromate and potassium chloride. According to solubility Rule 7, we find that barium chromate is insoluble. The balanced equation is

$$BaCl_2(aq) + K_2CrO_4(aq) \rightarrow BaCrO_4(s) + 2\,KCl(aq)$$

(b) Strontium acetate and lithium hydroxide react as follows:

$$Sr(C_2H_3O_2)_2(aq) + 2\,LiOH(aq) \rightarrow Sr(OH)_2(aq) + 2\,LiC_2H_3O_2(aq)$$

However, the solubility rules indicate that $Sr(OH)_2$ and $LiC_2H_3O_2$ are soluble. Therefore, the equation is written

$$Sr(C_2H_3O_2)_2(aq) + LiOH(aq) \rightarrow NR$$

Practice Exercise
Write a balanced chemical equation for each of the following double-replacement reactions:
(a) Aqueous zinc sulfate is added to a sodium carbonate solution.
(b) Aqueous manganese(II) nitrate is added to a potassium hydroxide solution.

Answers:
(a) $ZnSO_4(aq) + Na_2CO_3(aq) \rightarrow ZnCO_3(s) + Na_2SO_4(aq)$
(b) $Mn(NO_3)_2(aq) + 2\,KOH(aq) \rightarrow Mn(OH)_2(s) + 2\,KNO_3(aq)$

Concept Exercise
Identify the insoluble product from the reaction of silver nitrate and sodium chloride.

Answer: See Appendix G.

▶ To write a balanced chemical equation for the reaction of an acid and a base.

7.11 NEUTRALIZATION REACTIONS

In a neutralization reaction, an acid and a base react to produce an aqueous ionic compound and water. An **acid** is a substance that releases hydrogen ions, H^+, in water; a **base** is a substance that releases hydroxide ions, OH^-, in water. The resulting ionic compound is called a **salt** and is composed of the cation from the base and the anion from the acid. The general form of the reaction is

$$HX + BOH \rightarrow BX + HOH$$

A neutralization reaction is a special case of a double-replacement reaction. Notice that we have written water as HOH to emphasize the switching of ions. You will also discover that writing water as HOH is helpful in balancing equations for neutralization reactions. In a neutralization reaction, an acid and a base react to produce a salt and water:

$$\textbf{acid}(aq) + \textbf{base}(aq) \rightarrow \textbf{salt}(aq) + \textbf{water}(l)$$

As an example, when we add hydrochloric acid to sodium hydroxide solution, we obtain sodium chloride and water. We can write the balanced chemical equation as follows:

$$HCl(aq) + NaOH(aq) \rightarrow NaCl(aq) + HOH(l)$$

Other than a slight warming, there is no evidence of reaction. To provide evidence for this neutralization reaction, we can add a drop of the acid–base indicator phenolphthalein to the HCl. Phenolphthalein is colorless in acid and pink in base. Initially, the HCl acid solution is colorless; however, as we add NaOH base, we see flashes of color and eventually the solution turns pink. With an acid–base indicator we can observe a color change, which is evidence for a chemical reaction.

The following example exercise provides additional practice in writing balanced equations for neutralization reactions:

▲ **Phenolphthalein Acid–Base Indicator** In an acid–base neutralization reaction, the phenolphthalein indicator signals a change. If we have acid in a flask and add base, the indicator changes from colorless to pink.

Example Exercise 7.16 Neutralization Reactions

Write a balanced chemical equation for each of the following neutralization reactions:
(a) Nitric acid neutralizes an ammonium hydroxide solution.
(b) Sulfuric acid neutralizes a potassium hydroxide solution.

Solution
A neutralization reaction produces a salt and water.
(a) Nitric acid and ammonium hydroxide produce ammonium nitrate and water. The balanced equation is

$$HNO_3(aq) + NH_4OH(aq) \rightarrow NH_4NO_3(aq) + HOH(l)$$

(b) Sulfuric acid and potassium hydroxide produce potassium sulfate and water. The balanced equation is

$$H_2SO_4(aq) + 2\,KOH(aq) \rightarrow K_2SO_4(aq) + 2\,HOH(l)$$

Practice Exercise
Write a balanced chemical equation for each of the following neutralization reactions:
(a) Chloric acid neutralizes a strontium hydroxide solution.
(b) Phosphoric acid neutralizes a sodium hydroxide solution.

Answers:
(a) $2\,HClO_3(aq) + Sr(OH)_2(aq) \rightarrow Sr(ClO_3)_2(aq) + 2\,HOH(l)$
(b) $H_3PO_4(aq) + 3\,NaOH \rightarrow Na_3PO_4(aq) + 3\,HOH(l)$

Concept Exercise
Identify the salt product from the reaction of hydrochloric acid and sodium hydroxide.

Answer: See Appendix G.

CRITICAL THINKING Household Chemicals

Q: Is it possible that mixing two common household chemicals can produce a deadly gas?

Salt and sugar are two familiar chemicals on your kitchen table. Vinegar, another kitchen chemical, is a solution of acetic acid. Citrus fruit contains citric acid and is responsible for the sour taste of lemons and limes. Aspirin contains acetylsalicylic acid, which can irritate the lining of the stomach if taken in excess.

Hydrochloric acid, used to acidify swimming pools and clean concrete, is sold in the supermarket as muriatic acid. Sulfuric acid, found in automobile batteries, is a dangerous chemical that should be handled with great caution.

Perhaps the most dangerous chemical in the home is caustic soda, NaOH, which is sold as drain cleaner and as oven cleaner. If it contacts your skin, it gives a slippery sensation and causes redness and irritation. If taken internally, caustic soda could be fatal, especially to an infant. Household ammonia is also potentially dangerous and should not be used with bleach. Together, these two chemicals produce a poisonous gas.

▲ **Common Household Chemicals**

COMMON HOUSEHOLD CHEMICALS

NAME	FORMULA	PRODUCT/USE	SAFETY
Acids			
acetic acid	$HC_2H_3O_2(aq)$	vinegar	
carbonic acid	$H_2CO_3(aq)$	carbonated drinks	
hydrochloric acid	$HCl(aq)$	swimming pools	avoid contact*
sulfuric acid	$H_2SO_4(aq)$	battery acid	avoid contact*†
Bases			
ammonia	$NH_3(aq)$	window cleaner	
sodium hydrogen carbonate	$NaHCO_3(s)$	baking soda, antacid	
magnesium hydroxide	$Mg(OH)_2(aq)$	milk of magnesia	
sodium hydroxide	$NaOH(aq)$	drain and oven cleaner	avoid contact*†
Miscellaneous			
aluminum hydroxide	$Al(OH)_3(s)$	antacid tablets	
dry ice	$CO_2(s)$	keep items cold	avoid contact
Epsom salts	$MgSO_4 \cdot 7H_2O(s)$	salt bath, laxative	
sodium hypochlorite	$NaClO(aq)$	bleach	avoid contact*
Organic			
ethylene glycol	$C_2H_4(OH)_2(l)$	antifreeze	avoid ingestion†
isopropyl alcohol	$CH_3CHOHCH_3(l)$	rubbing alcohol	avoid ingestion†
naphthalene	$C_{10}H_8(s)$	moth repellent	avoid ingestion†
trichloroethane	$C_2H_3Cl_3(l)$	spot remover	avoid ingestion†

*In the event of contact, flush with water.
†In the event of ingestion, seek medical attention immediately

A: Caution must be exercised when using any chemicals; for example, household ammonia and ordinary bleach, when mixed, release a poisonous gas.

Summary

LEARNING OBJECTIVES	SEC	EXERCISES
To state four observations that are evidence for a chemical reaction.	7.1	Exercises 1–6
To identify seven elements that occur naturally as diatomic molecules: H_2, N_2, O_2, F_2, Cl_2, Br_2, I_2.	7.2	Exercises 7–8
To write a chemical equation from the description of a chemical reaction.	7.2	Exercises 7–16
To write balanced chemical equations.	7.3	Exercises 17–20
To classify a chemical reaction as one of the following types: combination, decomposition, single-replacement, double-replacement, or neutralization	7.4	Exercises 21–24
To write a balanced equation for the reaction of a metal and oxygen gas.	7.5	Exercises 25–26
To write a balanced equation for the reaction of a nonmetal and oxygen gas.	7.5	Exercises 27–28
To write a balanced equation for the reaction of a metal and a nonmetal.	7.5	Exercises 29–36
To write a balanced equation for the decomposition of a metal hydrogen carbonate.	7.6	Exercises 37, 38, and 41
To write a balanced equation for the decomposition of a metal carbonate.	7.6	Exercises 39, 40, and 42
To write a balanced equation for the decomposition of a compound that releases oxygen gas.	7.6	Exercises 43–46
To predict whether a metal reacts with an aqueous salt solution.	7.7	Exercises 47–48
To predict whether a metal reacts with an aqueous acid.	7.7	Exercises 49–50
To predict whether a metal reacts with water at 25 °C.	7.7	Exercises 51–52
To write a balanced equation for the reaction of a metal in an aqueous solution.	7.8	Exercises 53–56, and 61–62
To write a balanced equation for the reaction of a metal in an aqueous acid.	7.8	Exercises 57–58, and 63–64
To write a balanced equation for the reaction of an active metal in water.	7.8	Exercises 59–60, and 65–66
To predict whether an ionic compound dissolves in water given the general rules for solubility.	7.9	Exercises 67–70
To write a balanced equation for the reaction of two salts in an aqueous solution.	7.10	Exercises 71–74
To write a balanced equation for the reaction of an acid and a base.	7.11	Exercises 75–78

Section 7.1 In this chapter we learned that the evidence for a **chemical reaction** is any of the following: a gas is detected, a **precipitate** is formed in an **aqueous solution**, or a color change or energy change is observed. An **exothermic reaction** releases heat energy, and an **endothermic reaction** absorbs heat energy.

Section 7.2 A **reactant** substance undergoes a chemical change to become a **product**. A **catalyst** is a substance that speeds up a reaction without being permanently altered. A **chemical equation** describes a reaction using formulas and symbols. Seven nonmetal elements occur naturally as **diatomic molecules**, and their formulas are written as H_2, N_2, O_2, F_2, Cl_2, Br_2, and I_2.

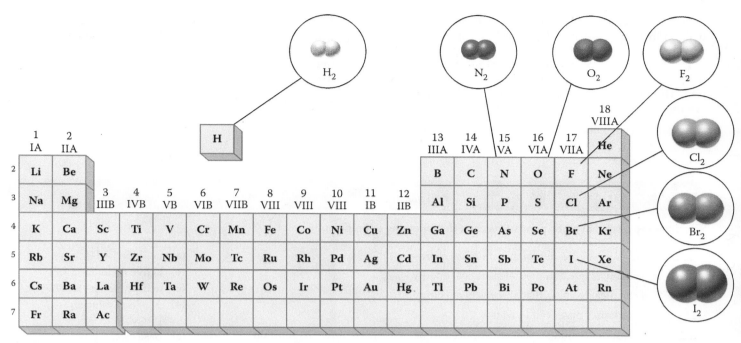

▲ **Diatomic Molecules** Seven elements occur naturally as diatomic molecules: H_2, N_2, O_2, F_2, and Cl_2 are gases; bromine, Br_2, occurs as a liquid; and iodine, I_2, as solid crystals.

Section 7.3 To balance a chemical equation, **coefficients** are systematically placed in front of each substance until there is the same number of atoms or ions of each element on both sides of the equation. If the reaction coefficient is 1, it is omitted. Similarly, if a formula **subscript** is 1, such as oxygen in H_2O, it is omitted.

Section 7.4 Although there are thousands of chemical reactions, most can be classified as one of the following: combination, decomposition, single replacement, double replacement, or neutralization. Table 7.3 lists these five basic types.

TABLE 7.3 TYPES OF CHEMICAL REACTIONS

REACTION TYPE	GENERAL FORMAT
Combination reaction	A + Z → AZ
Decomposition reaction	AZ → A + Z
Single-replacement reaction	A + BZ → AZ + B
Double-replacement reaction	AX + BZ → AZ + BX
Neutralization reaction	HX + BOH → BX + HOH

Section 7.5 We have examined three kinds of combination reactions: a metal and oxygen, a nonmetal and oxygen, and a metal and a nonmetal. Often, we can predict the products from the reaction. Nonmetals, however, combine with oxygen gas to give a variety of oxides, and the product is not predictable. In summary,

1. **metal + oxygen**(g) → **metal oxide**
2. **nonmetal + oxygen**(g) → **nonmetal oxide**
3. **metal + nonmetal** → **ionic compound**

Section 7.6 We have examined three kinds of decomposition reactions. In the first type, a metal hydrogen carbonate is decomposed by heating to give a metal carbonate product. In the second, a metal carbonate is decomposed to a metal oxide. Most oxygen-containing polyatomic ions, such as chlorate and nitrate, decompose to give oxygen gas. In summary,

1. **metal hydrogen carbonate** $\xrightarrow{\Delta}$ **metal carbonate + water + carbon dioxide** (g)
2. **metal carbonate** $\xrightarrow{\Delta}$ **metal oxide + carbon dioxide** (g)
3. **oxygen-containing compound** $\xrightarrow{\Delta}$ **substance + oxygen** (g)

Section 7.7 The **activity series** lists the relative ability of a metal to undergo reaction. A metal higher in the series always displaces a metal lower in the series. Metals that are more active than (H) displace hydrogen gas from an acid solution. **Active metals** include Li, Na, K, Ba, Sr, and Ca; each of these metals displaces hydrogen gas from water.

Section 7.8 We have examined three kinds of single-replacement reactions: a metal and aqueous solution, a metal and a dilute acid, and an active metal and water. In summary,

1. **metal$_1$ + salt$_1$**(aq) → **metal$_2$ + salt$_2$**(aq)
2. **metal + acid**(aq) → **salt**(aq) + **hydrogen**(g)
3. **metal + water** → **metal hydroxide**(aq) + **hydrogen**(g)

Section 7.9 An insoluble substance does not dissolve completely in water although it may dissolve slightly. To determine whether a substance is soluble or insoluble, we will simply refer to the solubility rules in Table 7.2.

Section 7.10 In a double-replacement precipitation reaction, two ionic compounds (salts) react in an aqueous solution. The two compounds react by switching anions and forming an insoluble substance, salt$_3$(s). In general,

$$\textbf{salt}_1(aq) + \textbf{salt}_2(aq) \rightarrow \textbf{salt}_3(s) + \textbf{salt}_4(aq)$$

Section 7.11 In a neutralization reaction an **acid** and a **base** react to yield a **salt** and water. A neutralization reaction is a special type of double-replacement reaction. Writing the formula for water as HOH is helpful when balancing neutralization reactions:

$$\textbf{acid}(aq) + \textbf{base}(aq) \rightarrow \textbf{salt}(aq) + \textbf{water}(l)$$

Key Terms   *Answers to Key Terms are in Appendix H.*

Select the key term that corresponds to each of the following definitions.

_____ **1.** the process of undergoing a chemical change

_____ **2.** a chemical reaction that releases heat energy

_____ **3.** a chemical reaction that absorbs heat energy

_____ **4.** a substance dissolved in water

_____ **5.** an insoluble solid substance produced from a reaction in aqueous solution

_____ **6.** a representation using formulas and symbols to describe a chemical change

_____ **7.** a substance undergoing a chemical reaction

_____ **8.** a substance resulting from a chemical reaction

_____ **9.** a substance that speeds up a reaction without being permanently changed

_____ **10.** a particle composed of two nonmetal atoms

_____ **11.** a digit in front of a chemical formula that helps to balance a chemical equation

_____ **12.** a digit in a chemical formula that represents the number of atoms or ions appearing in the substance

_____ **13.** a type of reaction in which two substances produce a single compound

_____ **14.** a type of reaction in which a single compound produces two or more substances

_____ **15.** a type of reaction in which a more active metal displaces a less active metal from a solution

_____ **16.** a type of reaction in which two cations in different compounds exchange anions

_____ **17.** a type of reaction in which an acid and a base produce a salt and water

_____ **18.** a relative order of metals arranged by their ability to undergo a reaction

_____ **19.** a metal that reacts with water at room temperature

_____ **20.** a substance that releases hydrogen ions in water

_____ **21.** a substance that releases hydroxide ions in water

_____ **22.** an ionic compound produced by an acid–base reaction

(a) acid (*Sec. 7.11*)
(b) active metal (*Sec. 7.7*)
(c) activity series (*Sec. 7.7*)
(d) aqueous solution (*aq*) (*Sec. 7.1*)
(e) base (*Sec. 7.11*)
(f) catalyst (*Sec. 7.2*)
(g) chemical equation (*Sec. 7.2*)
(h) chemical reaction (*Sec. 7.1*)
(i) coefficient (*Sec. 7.3*)
(j) combination reaction (*Sec. 7.4*)
(k) decomposition reaction (*Sec. 7.4*)
(l) diatomic molecule (*Sec. 7.2*)
(m) double-replacement reaction (*Sec. 7.4*)
(n) endothermic reaction (*Sec. 7.1*)
(o) exothermic reaction (*Sec. 7.1*)
(p) neutralization reaction (*Sec. 7.4*)
(q) precipitate (*Sec. 7.1*)
(r) product (*Sec. 7.2*)
(s) reactant (*Sec. 7.2*)
(t) salt (*Sec. 7.11*)
(u) single-replacement reaction (*Sec. 7.4*)
(v) subscript (*Sec. 7.3*)

Exercises   *Answers to odd-numbered Exercises are in Appendix I.*

Evidence for Chemical Reactions (Sec. 7.1)

1. Which of the following is evidence for a chemical reaction?
   (a) Heating copper in air produces a black solid.
   (b) Heating copper in a vacuum gives a red-brown film.

2. Which of the following is evidence for a chemical reaction?
   (a) Heating baking soda releases water vapor.
   (b) Heating violet iodine crystals gives a purple gas.

3. Which of the following is evidence for a chemical reaction?
   (a) Mixing two aqueous solutions produces a precipitate.
   (b) Mixing two colorless solutions gives a blue solution.

4. Which of the following is evidence for a chemical reaction?
   (a) Mixing two aqueous solutions produces gas bubbles.
   (b) Mixing two solutions produces an insoluble solid.

5. Which of the following is evidence for a chemical reaction?
   (a) Dropping sodium metal into water gives a yellow flame.
   (b) Dropping iron metal into acid produces gas bubbles.

6. Which of the following is evidence for a chemical reaction?
   (a) Dropping potassium metal into water gives a violet flame.
   (b) Dropping zinc metal into acid produces gas bubbles.

Writing Chemical Equations (Sec. 7.2)

7. Write a chemical equation for magnesium metal combining with bromine liquid to give magnesium bromide solid.

8. Write a chemical equation for iron metal combining with chlorine gas to give yellow ferrous chloride solid.

◀ **Iron in Chlorine Gas** Iron wool reacts in chlorine gas to give sparks and a yellow-brown $FeCl_3$ residue.

9. Write a chemical equation for solid zinc hydrogen carbonate decomposing to yield solid zinc carbonate, water, and carbon dioxide gas.

10. Write a chemical equation for solid cadmium hydrogen carbonate decomposing to yield solid cadmium carbonate, water, and carbon dioxide gas.

11. Write a chemical equation for the reaction of cadmium metal with aqueous cobalt(II) nitrate to produce aqueous cadmium nitrate and cobalt metal.

12. Write a chemical equation for the reaction of manganese metal with aqueous nickel(II) nitrate to produce aqueous manganese(II) nitrate and nickel metal.

13. Write a chemical equation for the reaction of aqueous solutions of lithium iodide and silver nitrate to give silver iodide precipitate and aqueous lithium nitrate.

14. Write a chemical equation for the reaction of aqueous solutions of potassium chromate and calcium sulfate to give calcium chromate precipitate and aqueous potassium sulfate.

15. Write a chemical equation for the reaction of nitric acid with aqueous ammonium hydroxide to give aqueous ammonium nitrate plus water.

16. Write a chemical equation for the neutralization of acetic acid with aqueous sodium hydroxide to give aqueous sodium acetate plus water.

Balancing Chemical Equations (Sec. 7.3)

17. Balance each of the following chemical equations by inspection:
   (a) $H_2(g) + N_2(g) \rightarrow NH_3(g)$
   (b) $Al_2(CO_3)_3(s) \rightarrow Al_2O_3(s) + CO_2(g)$
   (c) $Sr(s) + H_2O(l) \rightarrow Sr(OH)_2(aq) + H_2(g)$
   (d) $K_2SO_4(aq) + Ba(OH)_2(aq) \rightarrow BaSO_4(s) + KOH(aq)$
   (e) $H_3PO_4(aq) + Mn(OH)_2(s) \rightarrow Mn_3(PO_4)_2(s) + H_2O(l)$

18. Balance each of the following chemical equations by inspection:
   (a) $Co(s) + O_2(g) \rightarrow Co_2O_3(s)$
   (b) $LiClO_3(s) \rightarrow LiCl(s) + O_2(g)$
   (c) $Cu(s) + AgC_2H_3O_2(aq) \rightarrow Cu(C_2H_3O_2)_2(aq) + Ag(s)$
   (d) $Pb(NO_3)_2(aq) + LiCl(aq) \rightarrow PbCl_2(s) + LiNO_3(aq)$
   (e) $H_2SO_4(aq) + Al(OH)_3(aq) \rightarrow Al_2(SO_4)_3(aq) + H_2O(l)$

19. Balance each of the following chemical equations by inspection:
   (a) $H_2CO_3(aq) + NH_4OH(aq) \rightarrow (NH_4)_2CO_3(aq) + H_2O(l)$
   (b) $Hg_2(NO_3)_2(aq) + NaBr(aq) \rightarrow Hg_2Br_2(s) + NaNO_3(aq)$
   (c) $Mg(s) + HC_2H_3O_2(aq) \rightarrow Mg(C_2H_3O_2)_2(aq) + H_2(g)$
   (d) $LiNO_3(s) \rightarrow LiNO_2(s) + O_2(g)$
   (e) $Pb(s) + O_2(g) \rightarrow PbO(s)$

20. Balance each of the following chemical equations by inspection:
   (a) $HClO_4(aq) + Ba(OH)_2(s) \rightarrow Ba(ClO_4)_2(s) + H_2O(l)$
   (b) $Co(NO_3)_2(aq) + H_2S(g) \rightarrow CoS(s) + HNO_3(aq)$
   (c) $Fe(s) + Cd(NO_3)_2(aq) \rightarrow Fe(NO_3)_3(aq) + Cd(s)$
   (d) $Fe_2(CO_3)_3(s) \rightarrow Fe_2O_3(s) + CO_2(g)$
   (e) $Sn(s) + P(s) \rightarrow Sn_3P_2(s)$

Classifying Chemical Reactions (Sec. 7.4)

21. Classify each reaction in Exercise 17 as one of the following: combination, decomposition, single replacement, double replacement, or neutralization.

22. Classify each reaction in Exercise 18 as one of the following: combination, decomposition, single replacement, double replacement, or neutralization.

23. Classify each reaction in Exercise 19 as one of the following: combination, decomposition, single replacement, double replacement, or neutralization.

24. Classify each reaction in Exercise 20 as one of the following: combination, decomposition, single replacement, double replacement, or neutralization.

Combination Reactions (Sec. 7.5)

25. Write a balanced equation for each of the following combination reactions:
   (a) Nickel metal is heated with oxygen gas to produce nickel(II) oxide.
   (b) Iron wool is heated with oxygen gas to produce gray iron(III) oxide.

◀ **Iron in Oxygen Gas** Iron wool reacts in oxygen gas to give bright white light and a gray Fe_2O_3 residue.

26. Write a balanced equation for each of the following combination reactions:
    (a) Tin metal is heated with oxygen gas to yield tin(IV) oxide.
    (b) Lead metal is heated with oxygen gas to yield lead(II) oxide.

27. Write a balanced equation for each of the following combination reactions:
    (a) Carbon is heated with oxygen to give carbon monoxide gas.
    (b) Phosphorus is heated with oxygen to give solid diphosphorus pentaoxide.

28. Write a balanced equation for each of the following combination reactions:
    (a) Nitrogen is heated with oxygen to form dinitrogen pentaoxide gas.
    (b) Chlorine is heated with oxygen to form dichlorine trioxide gas.

29. Write a balanced equation for each of the following combination reactions:
    (a) Copper is heated with chlorine gas to produce solid copper(I) chloride.
    (b) Cobalt is heated with sulfur powder to produce solid cobalt(II) sulfide.

30. Write a balanced equation for each of the following combination reactions:
    (a) Iron is heated with fluorine gas to yield iron(III) fluoride.
    (b) Lead is heated with phosphorus powder to yield lead(IV) phosphide.

31. Write a balanced equation for each of the following combination reactions:
    (a) Chromium is heated with oxygen to give chromium(III) oxide.
    (b) Chromium is heated with nitrogen to give chromium(III) nitride.

32. Write a balanced equation for each of the following combination reactions:
    (a) Sulfur is heated with oxygen to form sulfur dioxide gas.
    (b) Sulfur is heated with oxygen and Pt catalyst to form sulfur trioxide gas.

33. Complete and balance each of the following combination reactions:
    (a) $Li + O_2 \rightarrow$ (b) $Ca + O_2 \rightarrow$

34. Complete and balance each of the following combination reactions:
    (a) $Sr + O_2 \rightarrow$ (b) $Al + O_2 \rightarrow$

35. Complete and balance each of the following combination reactions:
    (a) $Na + I_2 \rightarrow$ (b) $Ba + N_2 \rightarrow$

36. Complete and balance each of the following combination reactions:
    (a) $Zn + P \rightarrow$ (b) $Al + S \rightarrow$

Decomposition Reactions (Sec. 7.6)

37. Write a balanced equation for each of the following decomposition reactions:
    (a) Potassium hydrogen carbonate decomposes by heating to give solid potassium carbonate, water, and carbon dioxide gas.
    (b) Strontium hydrogen carbonate decomposes by heating to give solid strontium carbonate, water, and carbon dioxide gas.

38. Write a balanced equation for each of the following decomposition reactions:
    (a) Silver hydrogen carbonate decomposes by heating to give solid silver carbonate, water, and carbon dioxide gas.
    (b) Nickel(II) hydrogen carbonate decomposes by heating to give nickel(II) carbonate, water, and carbon dioxide gas.

39. Write a balanced equation for each of the following decomposition reactions:
    (a) Cobalt(III) carbonate decomposes with heat to give solid cobalt(III) oxide, and carbon dioxide gas.
    (b) Tin(IV) carbonate decomposes with heat to give solid tin(IV) oxide, and carbon dioxide gas.

40. Write a balanced equation for each of the following decomposition reactions:
    (a) Chromium(III) carbonate decomposes with heat to give solid chromium(III) oxide and carbon dioxide gas.
    (b) Lead(IV) carbonate decomposes with heat to give solid lead(IV) oxide and carbon dioxide gas.

41. Complete and balance each of the following decomposition reactions:
    (a) $AgHCO_3(s) \rightarrow$ (b) $Zn(HCO_3)_2(s) \rightarrow$

42. Complete and balance each of the following decomposition reactions:
    (a) $Li_2CO_3(s) \rightarrow$ (b) $CdCO_3(s) \rightarrow$

43. Write a balanced equation for each of the following decomposition reactions:
    (a) Calcium nitrate decomposes on heating to give solid calcium nitrite and oxygen gas.
    (b) Silver sulfate decomposes on heating to give solid silver sulfite and oxygen gas.

44. Write a balanced equation for each of each of the following decomposition reactions:
    (a) Stannous chlorate decomposes on heating to give solid stannous chloride and oxygen gas.
    (b) Plumbic oxide decomposes on heating to give solid plumbous oxide and oxygen gas.

45. Balance each of the following decomposition reactions:
    (a) $NaClO_3(s) \rightarrow NaCl(s) + O_2(g)$
    (b) $Ca(NO_3)_2(s) \rightarrow Ca(NO_2)_2(s) + O_2(g)$

46. Balance each of the following decomposition reactions:
    (a) $AlPO_4(s) \rightarrow AlPO_3(s) + O_2(g)$
    (b) $SnSO_4(s) \rightarrow SnSO_3(s) + O_2(g)$

The Activity Series Concept (Sec. 7.7)

(Refer to the activity series in Section 7.7, or refer to Appendix C, to answer the following questions.)

47. Predict which of the following metals reacts with aqueous copper(II) nitrate.
    (a) Ag   (b) Sn   (c) Co   (d) Mn

48. Predict which of the following metals reacts with aqueous cadmium(II) nitrate.
    (a) Hg   (b) Pb   (c) Ni   (d) Cr

49. Predict which of the following metals reacts with sulfuric acid.
    (a) Ag   (b) Sn   (c) Co   (d) Mn

50. Predict which of the following metals reacts with hydrochloric acid.
    (a) Hg   (b) Pb   (c) Ni   (d) Cr

51. Predict which of the following metals reacts with water at room temperature:
    (a) Li   (b) Mg   (c) Ca   (d) Al

52. Predict which of the following metals reacts with water at room temperature:
(a) Ba   (b) **Mn**   (c) Sn   (d) K

Single-Replacement Reactions (Sec. 7.8)

53. Write a balanced equation for each of the following single-replacement reactions:
(a) Copper wire is placed in an aluminum nitrate solution.
(b) Aluminum wire is placed in a copper(II) nitrate solution.

54. Write a balanced equation for each of the following single-replacement reactions:
(a) Silver wire is put into a cadmium nitrate solution.
(b) Cadmium wire is put into a silver nitrate solution.

55. Write a balanced equation for each of the following single-replacement reactions:
(a) Nickel metal is put into a lead(II) acetate solution.
(b) Lead metal is put into a nickel(II) acetate solution.

56. Write a balanced equation for each of the following single-replacement reactions:
(a) Iron is added to a mercury(II) sulfate solution.
(b) Mercury is added to a iron(II) sulfate solution.

57. Write a balanced equation for each of the following single-replacement reactions:
(a) Magnesium metal is added to nitric acid.
(b) Manganese metal is added to hydrochloric acid.

58. Write a balanced equation for each of the following single-replacement reactions:
(a) Zinc granules are placed in carbonic acid.
(b) Cadmium metal is added to acetic acid.

59. Write a balanced equation for each of the following single-replacement reactions:
(a) A soft, gray piece of lithium is added to water.
(b) A small piece of barium is added to water.

60. Write a balanced equation for each of the following single-replacement reactions:
(a) A gray chunk of cesium is added to water.
(b) A piece of radioactive radium is added to water.

61. Complete and balance each of the following single-replacement reactions:
(a) $Zn(s) + Pb(NO_3)_2(aq) \rightarrow$
(b) $Cd(s) + Fe(NO_3)_2(aq) \rightarrow$

62. Complete and balance each of the following single-replacement reactions:
(a) $Mg(s) + NiSO_4(aq) \rightarrow$
(b) $Al(s) + SnSO_4(aq) \rightarrow$

63. Complete and balance each of the following single-replacement reactions:
(a) $Zn(s) + HNO_3(aq) \rightarrow$
(b) $Cd(s) + HNO_3(aq) \rightarrow$

64. Complete and balance each of the following single-replacement reactions:
(a) $Mg(s) + H_2SO_4(aq) \rightarrow$
(b) $Al(s) + H_2SO_4(aq) \rightarrow$

65. Complete and balance each of the following single-replacement reactions:
(a) $K(s) + H_2O(l) \rightarrow$
(b) $Ba(s) + H_2O(l) \rightarrow$

◀ Zinc in a Lead Solution
Zinc metal reacts in an aqueous $Pb(NO_3)_2$ solution to give a gray deposit of spongy Pb metal.

◀ Magnesium in Acid
Magnesium metal reacts in aqueous sulfuric acid, H_2SO_4, to give bubbles of hydrogen gas.

66. Complete and balance each of the following single-replacement reactions:
(a) $Mg(s) + H_2O(l) \rightarrow$
(b) $Ca(s) + H_2O(l) \rightarrow$

Solubility Rules (Sec. 7.9)

(Refer to the solubility rules in Table 7.2, or Appendix D, to answer the following questions.)

67. Predict which of the following compounds are soluble in water:
(a) aluminum nitrate, $Al(NO_3)_3$
(b) sodium sulfate, Na_2SO_4
(c) cobalt(II) hydroxide, $Co(OH)_2$
(d) iron(III) phosphate, $FePO_4$

68. Predict which of the following compounds are soluble in water:
(a) ammonium sulfide, $(NH_4)_2S$
(b) zinc carbonate, $ZnCO_3$
(c) tin(II) chromate, $SnCrO_4$
(d) lead(II) acetate, $Pb(C_2H_3O_2)_2$

69. Predict which of the following compounds are insoluble in water:
(a) mercury(I) chloride, Hg_2Cl_2
(b) mercury(II) chloride, $HgCl_2$
(c) silver bromide, $AgBr$
(d) lead(II) iodide, PbI_2

70. Predict which of the following compounds are insoluble in water:
(a) strontium carbonate, $SrCO_3$
(b) calcium hydroxide, $Ca(OH)_2$
(c) nickel(II) sulfide, NiS
(d) mercury(II) bromide, $HgBr_2$

Double-Replacement Reactions (Sec. 7.10)

71. Write a balanced chemical equation for each of the following double-replacement reactions:
(a) Aqueous solutions of tin(II) chloride and potassium sulfide react to give a tin(II) sulfide precipitate and aqueous potassium chloride.
(b) Aqueous solutions of cobalt(II) nitrate and sodium chromate react to give a cobalt(II) chromate precipitate and aqueous sodium nitrate.

72. Write a balanced chemical equation for each of the following double-replacement reactions:
(a) Aqueous solutions of chromium(III) iodide and sodium hydroxide react to give a chromium(III) hydroxide precipitate and aqueous sodium iodide.
(b) Aqueous solutions of nickel(II) sulfate and mercury(I) nitrate react to give a mercury(I) sulfate precipitate and aqueous nickel(II) nitrate.

73. Complete and balance each of the following double-replacement reactions:
(a) $AgC_2H_3O_2(aq) + SrI_2(aq) \rightarrow$
(b) $FeSO_4(aq) + Ca(OH)_2(aq) \rightarrow$

74. Complete and balance each of the following double-replacement reactions:
(a) $MgSO_4(aq) + BaCl_2(aq) \rightarrow$
(b) $AlBr_3(aq) + Na_2CO_3(aq) \rightarrow$

Neutralization Reactions (Sec. 7.11)

75. Write a balanced equation for each of the following neutralization reactions:
(a) Lithium hydroxide solution is added to carbonic acid.
(b) Calcium hydroxide solution is added to nitric acid.

76. Write a balanced equation for each of the following neutralization reactions:
(a) Potassium hydroxide solution is added to phosphoric acid.
(b) Strontium hydroxide solution is added to acetic acid.

77. Complete and balance each of the following neutralization reactions:
(a) $HNO_3(aq) + Ba(OH)_2(aq) \rightarrow$
(b) $H_2SO_4(aq) + NaOH(aq) \rightarrow$

78. Complete and balance each of the following neutralization reactions:
(a) $HNO_2(aq) + Ba(OH)_2(aq) \rightarrow$
(b) $H_2SO_3(aq) + NaOH(aq) \rightarrow$

General Exercises

79. If a chemical equation is impossible to balance, what is most likely the problem?

80. If the sum of the coefficients of reactants is equal to 5, is the sum of the coefficients of products equal to 5?

81. Balance each of the following chemical equations by inspection:
(a) $Fe(s) + H_2O(g) \rightarrow Fe_3O_4(s) + H_2(g)$
(b) $FeS(s) + O_2(g) \rightarrow Fe_2O_3(s) + SO_2(g)$

82. Balance each of the following chemical equations by inspection:
(a) $FeO(l) + Al(l) \rightarrow Al_2O_3(l) + Fe(l)$
(b) $MnO_2(l) + Al(l) \rightarrow Al_2O_3(l) + Mn(l)$

83. Balance each of the following chemical equations by inspection:
(a) $F_2(g) + NaBr(aq) \rightarrow Br_2(l) + NaF(aq)$
(b) $Sb_2S_3(s) + HCl(aq) \rightarrow SbCl_3(aq) + H_2S(g)$

84. Balance each of the following chemical equations by inspection:
(a) $PCl_5(s) + H_2O(l) \rightarrow H_3PO_4(aq) + HCl(aq)$
(b) $TiCl_4(s) + H_2O(g) \rightarrow TiO_2(s) + HCl(g)$

85. Balance each of the following combustion reactions by inspection:
(a) $CH_4(g) + O_2(g) \rightarrow CO_2(g) + H_2O(g)$
(b) $C_3H_8(g) + O_2(g) \rightarrow CO_2(g) + H_2O(g)$

86. Balance each of the following combustion reactions by inspection:
(a) $CH_4O(l) + O_2(g) \rightarrow CO_2(g) + H_2O(g)$
(b) $C_3H_8O(l) + O_2(g) \rightarrow CO_2(g) + H_2O(g)$

Challenge Exercises

87. Iron is prepared industrially by passing carbon monoxide gas through molten iron ore, Fe_2O_3, in a blast furnace at 1500 °C. Assuming the only products are molten iron and carbon dioxide gas, write a balanced chemical equation for the manufacture of iron.

88. Chlorine is prepared industrially by heating hydrogen chloride gas with oxygen gas. Assuming the only products are water and chlorine gas, write a balanced chemical equation for the manufacture of chlorine.

Online Exercises

Research each of the following using an Internet search engine (e.g., Google.com or Yahoo.com) and cite your URL reference.

89. The Ostwald process is an industrial method for manufacturing nitric acid. Write three balanced equations for the Ostwald process, starting by heating ammonia and oxygen gases.

90. The Contact process is the industrial method for manufacturing sulfuric acid. Write three balanced equations for the Contact process, starting with burning sulfur powder in oxygen gas.

7 Chapter Self-Test   *Answers to Self-Test are in Appendix J.*

1. Which of the following is evidence for a chemical reaction? (Sec. 7.1)
   (a) a gas is released
   (b) a precipitate is formed
   (c) a permanent color change
   (d) all of the above
   (e) none of the above

2. Which of the following represents an element in its natural state? (Sec. 7.2)
   (a) F_2
   (b) Cl_2
   (c) Br_2
   (d) I_2
   (e) all of the above

3. What is the coefficient of hydrogen gas after balancing the following equation? (Sec. 7.3)

   $$\_N_2(g) + \_H_2(g) \rightarrow \_NH_3(g)$$

   (a) 1
   (b) 2
   (c) 3
   (d) 4
   (e) none of the above

4. Which type of chemical reaction is illustrated in question 3? (Sec. 7.4)
   (a) combination reaction
   (b) decomposition reaction
   (c) single-replacement reaction
   (d) double-replacement reaction
   (e) neutralization reaction

5. Predict the product from the following reaction: (Sec. 7.5)

   $$Mg(s) + O_2 \xrightarrow{\Delta}$$

   (a) MgO
   (b) Mg_2O
   (c) MgO_2
   (d) Mg_2O_3
   (e) Mg_3O_2

6. Predict the products from the following reaction: (Sec. 7.6)

   $$LiHCO_3(s) \xrightarrow{\Delta}$$

   (a) Li, H_2, and CO_2
   (b) Li, H_2O, and CO_2
   (c) Li_2CO_3, H_2, and CO_2
   (d) Li_2CO_3, H_2O, and CO_2
   (e) Li_2CO_3 and H_2O

7. Which of the following metals reacts with sulfuric acid? (Sec. 7.7)
   (a) Ag
   (b) Cu
   (c) Fe
   (d) all of the above
   (e) none of the above

8. What are the products from the following reaction? (Sec. 7.8)

   $$Mg(s) + H_2SO_4(aq) \rightarrow$$

   (a) MgO and H_2SO_3
   (b) MgO and H_2S
   (c) $MgSO_4$ and H_2
   (d) $MgSO_4$ and H_2O
   (e) no reaction

9. Which of the following compounds is *insoluble* in water? (Sec. 7.9)
   (a) $(NH_4)_2CO_3$
   (b) $BaSO_4$
   (c) K_2CrO_4
   (d) Na_2S
   (e) $Sr(OH)_2$

10. What are the products from the following reaction? (Sec. 7.10)

    $$Fe(NO_3)_3(aq) + Na_3PO_4(aq) \rightarrow$$

    (a) FeP and $NaNO_3$
    (b) $FePO_3$ and $NaNO_2$
    (c) $FePO_3$ and $NaNO_3$
    (d) $FePO_4$ and $NaNO_2$
    (e) $FePO_4$ and $NaNO_3$

11. What are the predicted products from the following neutralization reaction? (Sec. 7.11)

    $$H_2SO_4(aq) + NH_4OH(aq) \rightarrow$$

    (a) NH_4SO_3 and H_2O
    (b) NH_4SO_4 and O_2
    (c) $(NH_4)_2SO_4$ and O_2
    (d) $(NH_4)_2SO_4$ and H_2O
    (e) no reaction

Key Concepts

12. Write a balanced equation for the combination of iron metal with oxygen gas to give solid iron(III) oxide.

13. Write a balanced equation for the decomposition of solid calcium hydrogen carbonate with heat to give calcium carbonate powder, steam, and carbon dioxide gas.

14. Write a balanced equation for the reaction of zinc metal with aqueous nickel(II) nitrate to produce aqueous zinc nitrate and nickel metal.

15. Write a balanced equation for the neutralization of nitric acid with aqueous ammonium hydroxide to give aqueous ammonium nitrate and water.

16. Write a balanced equation for the combustion of ethanol, C_2H_5OH, with oxygen to give carbon dioxide and water.

Critical Thinking

17. Write a balanced equation for the reaction of hydrochloric acid dripping into a test tube containing baking soda, as shown in the illustration.

18. Write a balanced equation for the reaction of potassium iodide solution poured into a beaker containing lead(II) nitrate solution, as shown in the illustration.

8

The Mole Concept

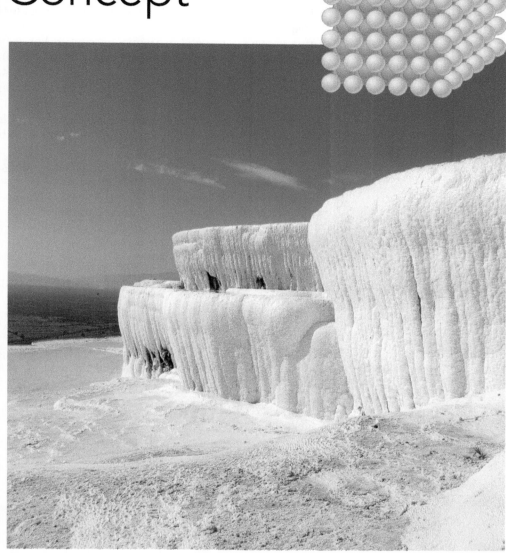

Calcium in the Environment Calcium is more reactive than magnesium, but less reactive than sodium and other alkali metals. Calcium metal is too reactive to be found naturally in the environment, but calcium carbonate is found naturally in limestone (shown).

".Chance favors the prepared mind."
Louis Pasteur, French Chemist (1822–1895)

Is it possible to keep track of atoms by counting them? The answer is "yes," although we cannot count them directly. Atoms are much too small to count individually, so we count them in groups. We count atoms in the same way we count eggs by the dozen (12), pencils by the gross (144), and sheets of paper by the ream (500). Because atoms are so tiny, we must consider a very large group of atoms.

When considering a very large number, it may be difficult to comprehend its magnitude. In this chapter, we will encounter an extremely large number— 602,000,000,000,000,000,000,000 (6.02×10^{23}). This number refers to a group of atoms and is called *Avogadro's number*. To appreciate the enormity of this number, consider the following analogy. If you had Avogadro's number of marbles, the volume of the group of marbles would be the size of the Moon.

8.1 AVOGADRO'S NUMBER

LEARNING OBJECTIVES

▶ To state the value of Avogadro's number: 6.02×10^{23}.

▶ To state the mass of Avogadro's number of atoms for any element by referring to the periodic table.

To count the number of atoms in a sample, consider the following experiment. Let's weigh enough atoms so that the mass in grams has the same numerical value as the atomic mass expressed in atomic mass units. For example, let's weigh enough carbon atoms to equal a mass of 12.01 g (atomic mass = 12.01 amu).

But how many atoms are in 12.01 g of carbon? Because atoms are so tiny, the number of carbon atoms in 12.01 g must be extremely large. Experiments have shown that there are 6.02×10^{23} carbon atoms in 12.01 g. This very large number is referred to as **Avogadro's number** (symbol N) in honor of the Italian scientist Amedeo Avogadro (1776–1856). Avogadro's number is sometimes referred to as the "chemist's dozen."

To count Avogadro's number of atoms we only have to know the atomic mass of the element. Because one carbon atom has a mass of 12.01 amu, then 6.02×10^{23} carbon atoms have a mass of 12.01 g. The following example exercise further illustrates how to count Avogadro's number of atoms.

CHEMISTRY CONNECTION   Analogies for Avogadro's Number

Q: **If the Moon were composed of a collection of small marbles, how many marbles correspond to the size of the Moon?**

Length Analogy: If 6.02×10^{23} hydrogen atoms were laid side by side, the total length would be long enough to encircle Earth about a million times.

Mass Analogy: The mass of 6.02×10^{23} Olympic shotput balls would be about equal to the mass of Earth.

hydrogen atoms

Volume Analogy: The volume occupied by 6.02×10^{23} softballs would be about the size of Earth.

Earth

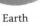

6.02×10^{23}

A: It would require 6.02×10^{23} ordinary small marbles to equal the size of the Moon.

Example Exercise 8.1 Atomic Mass and Avogadro's Number

Refer to the atomic masses in the periodic table inside the front cover of this textbook. State the mass of Avogadro's number of atoms for each of the following elements:

(a) copper
(b) mercury
(c) sulfur
(d) helium

Solution

The atomic mass of each element is listed below the symbol of the element in the periodic table: Cu = 63.55 amu, Hg = 200.59 amu, S = 32.07 amu, and He = 4.00 amu. The mass of Avogadro's number of atoms is the atomic mass expressed in grams. Therefore, 6.02×10^{23} atoms of

(a) Cu = 63.55 g
(b) Hg = 200.59 g
(c) S = 32.07 g
(d) He = 4.00 g

Practice Exercise

Refer to the periodic table and state the mass for each of the following:

(a) 1 atom of Au   (b) 6.02×10^{23} atoms of Au

Answers:

(a) 196.97 amu   (b) 196.97 g

Concept Exercise

What is the mass of an average platinum atom? What is the mass of Avogadro's number of Pt atoms?

Answer: See Appendix G.

8.2 MOLE CALCULATIONS I

The **mole** (symbol **mol**) is a unit of measure for an amount of a chemical substance. We define a mole as the amount of substance that contains Avogadro's number of particles, that is, 6.02×10^{23} particles. The individual particles may be atoms, molecules, formula units, or any other particles. Thus,

1 mol = Avogadro's number (N) = 6.02×10^{23} atoms, molecules, or formula units

The mole relationship allows us to convert between the number of particles and the mass of substance. Now we are ready to try some mole calculations. Remember to apply the following three steps in the unit analysis method of problem solving.

LEARNING OBJECTIVE

▶ To relate the moles of a substance to the number of particles.

Applying the Unit Analysis Method

Step 1: Write down the unit asked for in the answer.
Step 2: Write down the given value related to the answer.
Step 3: Apply unit factor(s) to convert the unit in the given value to the unit in the answer. To illustrate,

given value (Step 2)	*unit factor(s)* × (Step 3)	*unit in answer* = (Step 1)

We can perform calculations that relate number of moles and number of particles. For instance, we can determine how many molecules of chlorine are in 0.250 mol of the yellow gas. By applying the unit analysis method of problem solving, we have

$$0.250 \text{ mol } Cl_2 \times \frac{6.02 \times 10^{23} \text{ molecules } Cl_2}{1 \text{ mol } Cl_2} = 1.51 \times 10^{23} \text{ molecules } Cl_2$$

The following example exercises will help to reinforce the unit analysis method of problem solving for calculations involving the mole concept:

Example Exercise 8.2 Mole Calculations I

Calculate the number of sodium atoms in 0.120 mol Na.

Strategy Plan

Step 1: What unit is asked for in the answer?	Step 1:	atoms Na
Step 2: What given value is related to the answer?	Step 2:	0.120 mol Na
Step 3: What unit factor(s) should we apply? Since 1 mol Na = 6.02×10^{23} atoms Na, the two unit factors are 1 mol Na/6.02×10^{23} atoms Na, and its reciprocal 6.02×10^{23} atoms Na/1 mol Na.	Step 3:	$\dfrac{1 \text{ mol Na}}{6.02 \times 10^{23} \text{ atoms Na}}$ or $\dfrac{6.02 \times 10^{23} \text{ atoms Na}}{1 \text{ mol Na}}$

Unit Analysis Map

given value	unit factor	unit in answer
0.120 mol Na	$\times \dfrac{6.02 \times 10^{23} \text{ atoms Na}}{1 \text{ mol Na}}$	= ? atoms Na

Solution

We apply the unit factor 6.02×10^{23} atoms Na/1 mol Na to cancel moles Na (mol Na), which appears in the denominator.

$$0.120 \text{ mol Na} \times \frac{6.02 \times 10^{23} \text{ atoms Na}}{1 \text{ mol Na}} = 7.22 \times 10^{22} \text{ atoms Na}$$

The answer is rounded to three digits because the given value and unit factor each have three significant digits.

Practice Exercise

Calculate the number of molecules in 0.0763 mol of chlorine gas, Cl_2.

Answer: 4.59×10^{22} molecules Cl_2

Concept Exercise

What is the number of atoms in 1.00 mol of a metallic element?

Answer: See Appendix G.

We can also perform the reverse procedure and determine the number of moles of substance given the number of particles. For instance, we can calculate the number of moles of violet iodine crystals corresponding to 2.50×10^{23} molecules of I_2. Applying the unit analysis method of problem solving, we have

$$2.50 \times 10^{23} \text{ molecules } I_2 \times \frac{1 \text{ mol } I_2}{6.02 \times 10^{23} \text{ molecules } I_2} = 0.415 \text{ mol } I_2$$

◄ **The Mole Concept—Avogadro's Number** The photograph shows a mole of oxygen, a mole of water, and a mole of table salt. The balloon contains 6.02×10^{23} molecules of O_2 gas, the graduated cylinder holds 6.02×10^{23} molecules of H_2O, and the watchglass has 6.02×10^{23} formula units of NaCl.

Example Exercise 8.3 Mole Calculations I

Calculate the number of moles of potassium in 1.25×10^{21} atoms K.

Strategy Plan

Step 1: What unit is asked for in the answer?	**Step 1:**	mol K
Step 2: What given value is related to the answer?	**Step 2:**	1.25×10^{21} atoms K
Step 3: What unit factor(s) should we apply? Because 1 mol K = 6.02×10^{23} atoms K, the two unit factors are 1 mol K/6.02×10^{23} atoms K, and its reciprocal 6.02×10^{23} atoms K/1 mol K.	**Step 3:**	$\dfrac{1 \text{ mol K}}{6.02 \times 10^{23} \text{ atoms K}}$ or $\dfrac{6.02 \times 10^{23} \text{ atoms K}}{1 \text{ mol K}}$

Unit Analysis Map

given value	*unit factor*	*unit in answer*
1.25×10^{21} atoms K	$\times \dfrac{1 \text{ mol K}}{6.02 \times 10^{23} \text{ atoms K}}$	$= \quad ? \text{ mol K}$

Solution

We apply the unit factor 1 mol K/6.02 × 10²³ atoms K to cancel atoms K (atoms K), which appears in the denominator.

$$1.25 \times 10^{21} \text{ atoms K} \times \frac{1 \text{ mol K}}{6.02 \times 10^{23} \text{ atoms K}} = 2.08 \times 10^{-3} \text{ mol K}$$

The answer is rounded to three digits because the given value and unit factor each have three significant digits.

Practice Exercise

Calculate the number of moles of iodine in 5.34×10^{25} molecules of I_2.

Answer: 88.7 mol I_2

Concept Exercise

What is the number of molecules in 1.00 mol of a diatomic nonmetal?

Answer: See Appendix G.

▶ To calculate the molar mass of a substance given its chemical formula.

8.3 MOLAR MASS

A mole is an amount of substance that indicates the number of particles in a sample. That is, 1 mol of an element contains 6.02×10^{23} atoms. Since the atomic mass of carbon is 12.01 amu, we know that 1 mol of carbon has a mass of 12.01 g. In fact, the atomic mass of any substance expressed in grams corresponds to 1 mol of the substance. In our discussion, we will refer to the atomic mass of a substance expressed in grams as the **molar mass** (symbol **MM**).

The molar mass of an element is equal to its atomic mass expressed in grams. By referring to the periodic table, we find that the atomic mass of iron is 55.85 amu. Thus, the molar mass of iron is 55.85 g/mol. Naturally occurring oxygen is O_2, so the molar mass of oxygen gas is equal to two times 16.00 g, or 32.00 g/mol.

We can calculate the molar mass of a compound by adding the molar masses of each element. For example, we can find the molar mass of iron(III) oxide, Fe_2O_3, by summing the masses as follows:

$$Fe_2O_3: 2(55.85 \text{ g/mol Fe}) + 3(16.00 \text{ g/mol O}) = 159.70 \text{ g/mol}$$

$$Fe_2O_3: 111.70 \text{ g/mol Fe} + 48.00 \text{ g/mol O} = 159.70 \text{ g/mol}$$

The calculated molar mass of Fe_2O_3 is 159.70 g/mol. Notice that we used 16.00 g as the molar mass of oxygen. Even though the element occurs naturally as molecules of oxygen, it is atoms of oxygen that are combined in compounds. The following example exercise further illustrates the calculation of molar mass:

Example Exercise 8.4 Molar Mass Calculations

Calculate the molar mass for each of the following substances:

(a) silver metal, Ag
(b) ammonia gas, NH_3
(c) magnesium nitrate, $Mg(NO_3)_2$

Solution

We begin by finding the atomic mass of each element in the periodic table. The molar mass equals the sum of the atomic masses expressed in g/mol.

(a) The atomic mass of Ag is 107.87 amu, and the molar mass of silver equals 107.87 g/mol.
(b) The sum of the atomic masses for NH_3 is 14.01 g + 3(1.01) amu = 17.04 amu. The molar mass of ammonia equals 17.04 g/mol.
(c) The sum of the atomic masses for $Mg(NO_3)_2$ is
    24.31 g + 2(14.01 + 16.00 + 16.00 + 16.00) amu = 148.33 amu. The molar mass of magnesium nitrate equals 148.33 g/mol.

Practice Exercise

Calculate the molar mass for each of the following substances:

(a) manganese metal, Mn

(b) sulfur hexafluoride, SF_6

(c) strontium acetate, $Sr(C_2H_3O_2)_2$

Answers:

(a) 54.94 g/mol

(b) 146.07 g/mol

(c) 205.72 g/mol

Concept Exercise

The molecular mass of water is 18.02 amu. What is the mass of Avogadro's number of water molecules?

Answer: See Appendix G.

▲ **The Mole Concept—Molar Mass** The photograph shows a mole of water, sulfur, table sugar, mercury, and copper (clockwise). The molar masses are as follows: 18.02 g/mol H_2O, 32.07 g/mol S, 342.34 g/mol $C_{11}H_{22}O_{11}$, 200.59 g/mol Hg, and 63.55 g/mol Cu.

▶ To relate the mass of a substance to the number of particles.

8.4 MOLE CALCULATIONS II

The mole is the central unit in chemistry. It is an amount of a substance and relates the number of particles to the mass of the substance, that is,

$$6.02 \times 10^{23} \text{ particles} = 1 \text{ mol} = \text{molar mass of substance}$$

We can perform calculations that relate mass to the number of particles. For instance, we can find the mass of 2.55×10^{23} atoms of lead. By applying the unit analysis method of problem solving, we first find the number of moles:

$$2.55 \times 10^{23} \text{ atoms Pb} \times \frac{1 \text{ mol Pb}}{6.02 \times 10^{23} \text{ atoms Pb}} = 0.424 \text{ mol Pb}$$

To calculate the mass of lead, we multiply the number of moles of lead by its molar mass. From the periodic table we find that the molar mass of Pb is 207.2 g/mol:

$$0.424 \text{ mol Pb} \times \frac{207.2 \text{ g Pb}}{1 \text{ mol Pb}} = 87.8 \text{ g Pb}$$

The following example exercises reinforce mole calculations involving Avogadro's number and molar mass.

Example Exercise 8.5 Mole Calculations II

What is the mass in grams of 2.01×10^{22} atoms of sulfur?

Strategy Plan

Step 1: What unit is asked for in the answer?

Step 1: | g S

Step 2: What given value is related to the answer?

Step 2: | 2.01×10^{22} atoms S

Step 3: What unit factor(s) should we apply? By definition, 1 mol S = 6.02×10^{23} atoms S, and the molar mass from the periodic table is 32.07 g S = 1 mol S; the two pairs of unit factors are shown in Step 3.

Step 3:

$\dfrac{1 \text{ mol S}}{6.02 \times 10^{23} \text{ atoms S}}$ or $\dfrac{6.02 \times 10^{23} \text{ atoms S}}{1 \text{ mol S}}$

$\dfrac{1 \text{ mol S}}{32.07 \text{ g S}}$ or $\dfrac{32.07 \text{ g S}}{1 \text{ mol S}}$

Unit Analysis Map

given value		**unit factor 1**		**unit factor 2**		**unit in answer**
2.01×10^{22} atoms S	$\times$	$\dfrac{1 \text{ mol S}}{6.02 \times 10^{23} \text{ atoms S}}$	$\times$	$\dfrac{32.07 \text{ g S}}{1 \text{ mol S}}$	=	? g S

Solution

We apply the unit factor 1 mol S/6.02×10^{23} atoms S to cancel atoms S (atoms S), and 32.07 g S/1 mol S to cancel mol S (mol S):

$$2.01 \times 10^{22} \text{ atoms S} \times \frac{1 \text{ mol S}}{6.02 \times 10^{23} \text{ atoms S}} \times \frac{32.07 \text{ g S}}{1 \text{ mol S}} = 1.07 \text{ g S}$$

Practice Exercise

What is the mass of 7.75×10^{22} formula units of lead(II) sulfide, PbS?

Answer: 30.8 g PbS

Concept Exercise

What is the mass of Avogadro's number of sulfur molecules, S_8?

Answer: See Appendix G.

Example Exercise 8.6 Mole Calculations II

How many O_2 molecules are present in 0.470 g of oxygen gas?

Strategy Plan

Step 1: What unit is asked for in the answer?

Step 1: molecules O_2

Step 2: What given value is related to the answer?

Step 2: 0.470 g O_2

Step 3: What unit factor(s) should we apply? The molar mass from the periodic table is 32.00 g O_2 = 1 mol O_2, and by definition, 1 mol O_2 = 6.02×10^{23} molecules O_2. Thus, the two pairs of unit factors are shown in Step 3.

Step 3:

$$\frac{1 \text{ mol } O_2}{32.00 \text{ g } O_2} \quad or \quad \frac{32.00 \text{ g } O_2}{1 \text{ mol } O_2}$$

$$\frac{1 \text{ mol } O_2}{6.02 \times 10^{23} \text{ molecules } O_2} \quad or \quad \frac{6.02 \times 10^{23} \text{ molecules } O_2}{1 \text{ mol } O_2}$$

Unit Analysis Map

given value		*unit factor 1*		*unit factor 2*		*unit in answer*
0.470 g O_2	$\times$	$\dfrac{1 \text{ mol } O_2}{32.00 \text{ g } O_2}$	$\times$	$\dfrac{6.02 \times 10^{23} \text{ molecules } O_2}{1 \text{ mol } O_2}$		= ? molecules O_2

Solution

We apply the unit factor 1 mol O_2/32.00 g O_2 to cancel g O_2 (g O_2), and 6.02×10^{23} molecules O_2/1 mol O_2 to cancel moles O_2 (mol O_2). Thus,

$$0.470 \text{ g } O_2 \times \frac{1 \text{ mol } O_2}{32.00 \text{ g } O_2} \times \frac{6.02 \times 10^{23} \text{ molecules } O_2}{1 \text{ mol } O_2} = 8.84 \times 10^{21} \text{ molecules } O_2$$

Practice Exercise

How many molecules are found in 0.175 g of fluorine gas, F_2?

Answer: 4.06×10^{21} formula units LiF

Concept Exercise

What is the mass of Avogadro's number of ozone, O_3, molecules?

Answer: See Appendix G.

Mass of an Atom or Molecule

Now, let's try a different type of problem. What is the mass of a single molecule of water, given that the molar mass of water is 18.02 g/mol? This problem requires a ratio of units in the answer, that is, g/molecule:

$$\text{given value} \times \frac{\text{unit}}{\text{factor}} = \frac{\text{g}}{\text{molecule}}$$

To arrive at an answer having compound units, we start with a ratio of two units. Because the molar mass of water is 18.02 g/mol, we can write

$$\frac{18.02 \text{ g}}{1 \text{ mol } H_2O} \times \frac{\text{unit}}{\text{factor}} = \frac{\text{g}}{\text{molecule}}$$

▲ Water molecule—H_2O

Avogadro's number provides the unit factor $1 \text{ mol } H_2O/6.02 \times 10^{23}$ molecules. We can apply the unit factor and cancel units as follows:

$$\frac{18.02 \text{ g}}{1 \text{ mol } H_2O} \times \frac{1 \text{ mol } H_2O}{6.02 \times 10^{23} \text{ molecules}} = 2.99 \times 10^{-23} \text{ g/molecule}$$

The following example exercise further illustrates how to apply the mole concept to determine the mass of an individual atom or molecule.

Example Exercise 8.7 Mass of a Molecule

Calculate the mass in grams for a single molecule of carbon dioxide, CO_2 (given that MM = 44.01 g/mol).

Strategy Plan

Step 1: What unit is asked for in the answer?	**Step 1:** $g \text{ } CO_2/\text{molecule } CO_2$
Step 2: What given value is related to the answer?	**Step 2:** $44.01 \text{ g } CO_2/1 \text{ mol } CO_2$
Step 3: What unit factor(s) should we apply? By definition, $1 \text{ mol } CO_2 = 6.02 \times 10^{23}$ molecules. Thus, the unit factors are shown in Step 3.	**Step 3:** $\dfrac{1 \text{ mol } CO_2}{6.02 \times 10^{23} \text{ molecules } CO_2}$ or $\dfrac{6.02 \times 10^{23} \text{ molecules } CO_2}{1 \text{ mol } CO_2}$

Unit Analysis Map

$$\boxed{\begin{array}{c} \textit{given value} \\ \dfrac{44.01 \text{ g } CO_2}{1 \text{ mol } CO_2} \end{array}} \times \boxed{\begin{array}{c} \textit{unit factor} \\ \dfrac{1 \text{ mol } CO_2}{6.02 \times 10^{23} \text{ molecules } CO_2} \end{array}} \longrightarrow = \boxed{\dfrac{g \text{ } CO_2}{\text{molecule } CO_2}}$$

Solution

We apply the unit factor $1 \text{ mol } CO_2/6.02 \times 10^{23}$ molecules CO_2 to cancel mol CO_2 (mol CO_2).

$$\frac{44.01 \text{ g}}{1 \text{ mol } CO_2} \times \frac{1 \text{ mol } CO_2}{6.02 \times 10^{23} \text{ molecules}} = 7.31 \times 10^{-23} \text{ g /molecule}$$

Practice Exercise

Calculate the mass in grams for a single molecule of carbon monoxide, CO.

Answer: 4.65×10^{-23} g /molecule

Concept Exercise

What is the mass of a carbon monoxide molecule expressed in amu?

Answer: See Appendix G.

▲ **Carbon Dioxide molecule—CO_2**

▶ To state the value for the molar volume of any gas at STP:22.4 L/mol.

▶ To relate the density of a gas at STP to its molar mass and volume.

8.5 MOLAR VOLUME

Recall that 1 mol of any gas contains 6.02×10^{23} molecules. The gas can be hydrogen, oxygen, or any other gas. In 1811, Avogadro proposed that two gases containing equal numbers of molecules occupy equal volumes under similar conditions. This statement is known as **Avogadro's theory**, and is also referred to as Avogadro's law or Avogadro's hypothesis. It naturally follows, therefore, that 1 mol of hydrogen gas and 1 mol of oxygen gas occupy the same volume. Stated differently, 6.02×10^{23} molecules of H_2 occupy the same volume as 6.02×10^{23} molecules of O_2. In fact, 6.02×10^{23} molecules of any gas occupy the same volume as 6.02×10^{23} molecules of hydrogen or oxygen.

What volume of gas contains Avogadro's number of molecules? At **standard temperature and pressure** (symbol STP) the volume is 22.4 L. Standard temperature is 0 °C. Standard pressure is 1 atm, which is the atmospheric pressure exerted by air at sea level. The volume occupied by 1 mol of any gas at STP is called the **molar volume** (Figure 8.1).

Table 8.1 compares 1 mol of five different gases. Notice that the number of molecules and the volume are constant, whereas the molar mass varies.

22.4 L (STP)

1 mole of gas

6.02×10^{23} molecules

▲ **Figure 8.1 Molar Volume of a Gas** A balloon containing 1 mol of gas at STP has a diameter of about 35 cm. A mole of any gas contains Avogadro's number of molecules and occupies a volume of 22.4 L at STP.

TABLE 8.1 MOLE RELATIONSHIPS FOR SELECTED GASES

GAS	NO. OF MOLES	NO. OF MOLECULES	MOLAR MASS	MOLAR VOLUME AT STP
hydrogen, H_2	1.00	6.02×10^{23}	2.02 g/mol	22.4 L/mol
oxygen, O_2	1.00	6.02×10^{23}	32.00 g/mol	22.4 L/mol
carbon dioxide, CO_2	1.00	6.02×10^{23}	44.01 g/mol	22.4 L/mol
ammonia, NH_3	1.00	6.02×10^{23}	17.04 g/mol	22.4 L/mol
argon, Ar*	1.00	6.02×10^{23}	39.95 g/mol	22.4 L/mol

*Argon gas is composed of atoms rather than molecules.

Gas Density

The density of a gas is much less than the density of a liquid or a solid. In Section 2.8 we found that the density of water at 4 °C is 1.00 g/mL. However, the density of air at 4 °C is only 0.00129 g/mL (1.29 g/L). Therefore, the density of water is almost a 1000 times greater than that of air.

We also learned in Section 2.8 that the definition of density is mass divided by volume. The density of a gas, such as hydrogen or oxygen, is its mass divided by its volume. We can easily calculate the density of a gas at STP because 1 mol of any gas has a mass equal to its molar mass and a volume equal to its molar volume. The formula for **gas density** is

$$\frac{\text{molar mass in grams}}{\text{molar volume in liters}} = \text{density, g/L (at STP)}$$

The following example exercises illustrate how density, molar mass, and molar volume of a gas are related:

◄ **The Mole Concept—Molar Volume** The photograph depicts a molar volume of gas. For reference, a basketball contains about 9 liters of air at STP.

Example Exercise 8.8 Density of a Gas at STP

Calculate the density of ammonia gas, NH_3, at STP. (MM = 17.04 g/mol)

Strategy Plan

Step 1: What unit is asked for in the answer?	**Step 1:** g/L
Step 2: What given value is related to the answer?	**Step 2:** 17.04 g/mol
Step 3: What unit factor(s) should we apply? From the molar volume of a gas at STP, 1 mol = 22.4 L; thus, the unit factors are 1 mol/22.4 L, and 22.4 L/1 mol.	**Step 3:** $\dfrac{1\ mol}{22.4\ L}$ or $\dfrac{22.4\ L}{1\ mol}$

Unit Analysis Map

$$\underset{\text{given value}}{\boxed{\dfrac{17.04\ g}{1\ mol}}} \times \underset{\text{unit factor}}{\boxed{\dfrac{1\ mol}{22.4\ L}}} \longrightarrow \underset{\text{unit in answer}}{\boxed{= \dfrac{g}{L}}}$$

Solution

We apply the unit factor 1 mol/22.4 L to cancel moles (mol), which appears in the denominator.

$$\dfrac{17.04\ g}{1\ mol} \times \dfrac{1\ mol}{22.4\ L} = 0.761\ g/L$$

Practice Exercise

Calculate the density of hydrogen sulfide gas, H_2S, at STP.

Answer: 1.52 g/L

Concept Exercise

Why does the balloon filled with helium gas rise, whereas the balloon filled with nitrogen gas does not?

Answer: See Appendix G.

▲ Gas Balloons

Example Exercise 8.9 Molar Mass of a Gas

A fire extinguisher releases 1.96 g of an unknown gas that occupies 1.00 L at STP. What is the molar mass (g/mol) of the unknown gas?

Strategy Plan

Step 1: What unit is asked for in the answer?	**Step 1:** g/mol
Step 2: What given value is related to the answer?	**Step 2:** 1.96 g/1.00 L
Step 3: What unit factor(s) should we apply? From the molar volume of a gas at STP, 1 mol = 22.4 L; thus, the unit factors are 1 mol/22.4 L, and 22.4 L/1 mol.	**Step 3:** $\dfrac{1\ mol}{22.4\ L}$ or $\dfrac{22.4\ L}{1\ mol}$

Unit Analysis Map

| given value
1.96 g
—————
1.00 L | × | unit factor
22.4 L
————
1 mol | → | unit in answer
g
= ———
mol |

Solution

We apply the unit factor 1 mol/22.4 L to cancel liters (L), which appears in the denominator.

$$\frac{1.96 \text{ g}}{1.00 \text{ L}} \times \frac{22.4 \text{ L}}{1 \text{ mol}} = 43.9 \text{ g/mol}$$

Because the unknown gas is from a fire extinguisher, we suspect that it is carbon dioxide. By summing the molar mass for CO_2(44.01 g/mol), we help confirm that the unknown gas is carbon dioxide.

Practice Exercise

Boron trifluoride gas is used in the manufacture of computer chips. Given that 1.505 g of the gas occupies 497 mL at STP, what is the molar mass of boron fluoride gas?

Answer: 67.8 g/mol

Concept Exercise

What is the volume of one mole of any gas at STP?

Answer: See Appendix G.

8.6 MOLE CALCULATIONS III

▶ To relate the volume of a gas at STP to its mass and number of particles.

As mentioned previously, the mole is a central unit in chemical calculations. A mole has three interpretations:

1. A mole is Avogadro's number of particles.
2. A mole of a substance has a mass equal to its atomic mass in grams.
3. A mole of any gas at STP occupies a volume of 22.4 L.

We can state the three interpretations in the form of equations as follows:

1 mol = 6.02×10^{23} particles

1 mol = molar mass

1 mol = 22.4 L at STP

From the preceding mole equations, we can relate the number of particles to the mass or volume of a gaseous substance at STP. The process of interchanging these three quantities involves mole calculations.

The following example exercises illustrate calculations involving the number of moles of a substance. In these calculations, we will use the concepts of Avogadro's number, molar mass, and molar volume.

Example Exercise 8.10 Mole Calculations III

What is the mass of 3.36 L of ozone gas, O_3, at STP?

Strategy Plan

Step 1: What unit is asked for in the answer?   Step 1: $g\ O_3$

Step 2: What given value is related to the answer?   Step 2: $3.36\ L\ O_3$

Step 3: What unit factor(s) should we apply?   Step 3:
From the molar volume of a gas at STP,
$1\ mol\ O_3 = 22.4\ L\ O_3$. The molar mass from the
periodic table is $48.00\ g\ O_3 = 1\ mol\ O_3$. Thus, the
two pairs of unit factors are shown in Step 3.

$$\frac{1\ mol\ O_3}{22.4\ L\ O_3} \quad or \quad \frac{22.4\ L\ O_3}{1\ mol\ O_3}$$

$$\frac{1\ mol\ O_3}{48.00\ g\ O_3} \quad or \quad \frac{48.00\ g\ O_3}{1\ mol\ O_3}$$

Unit Analysis Map

given value	*unit factor 1*	*unit factor 2*	*unit in answer*
$3.36\ L\ O_3$	$\times\ \dfrac{1\ mol\ O_3}{22.4\ L\ O_3}$	$\times\ \dfrac{48.00\ g\ O_3}{1\ mol\ O_3}$	$=\ ?\ g\ O_3$

Solution

We apply the unit factor $1\ mol\ O_3/22.4\ L\ O_3$ to cancel $L\ O_3$ ($\cancel{L\ O_3}$), and $48.00\ g\ O_3/1\ mol\ O_3$ to cancel moles O_3 ($\cancel{mol\ O_3}$)

$$3.36\ \cancel{L\ O_3} \times \frac{1\ \cancel{mol\ O_3}}{22.4\ \cancel{L\ O_3}} \times \frac{48.00\ g\ O_3}{1\ \cancel{mol\ O_3}} = 7.20\ g\ O_3$$

Practice Exercise

What volume is occupied by 0.125 g of methane gas, CH_4, at STP?

Answer: 0.174 L CH_4(174 mL)

Concept Exercise

How many molecules of ozone are in one mole of gas?

Answer: See Appendix G.

Example Exercise 8.11 Mole Calculations III

How many molecules of hydrogen gas, H_2, occupy 0.500 L at STP?

Strategy Plan

Step 1: What unit is asked for in the answer?   Step 1:   molecules H_2

Step 2: What given value is related to the
answer?   Step 2: $0.500\ L\ H_2$

Step 3:

$$\frac{1\ mol\ H_2}{22.4\ L\ H_2} \quad or \quad \frac{22.4\ L\ H_2}{1\ mol\ H_2}$$

Step 3: What unit factor(s) should we apply?
From the molar volume of a gas at STP,
$1\ mol\ H_2 = 22.4\ L\ H_2$ and by definition,
$1\ mol\ H_2 = 6.02 \times 10^{23}$ molecules H_2. Thus, the
two pairs of unit factors are shown in Step 3.

$$\frac{1\ mol\ H_2}{6.02 \times 10^{23}\ molecules\ H_2} \quad or \quad \frac{6.02 \times 10^{23}\ molecules\ H_2}{1\ mol\ H_2}$$

Unit Analysis Map

given value		unit factor 1		unit factor 2		unit in answer
0.500 L H_2	×	$\dfrac{1 \text{ mol } H_2}{22.4 \text{ L } H_2}$	×	$\dfrac{6.02 \times 10^{23} \text{ molecules } H_2}{1 \text{ mol } H_2}$		= ? molecules H_2

Solution

We apply the unit factor 1 mol H_2/22.4 L H_2 to cancel L H_2 (L H_2), and 6.02×10^{23} molecules H_2/1 mol H_2 to cancel moles H_2 (mol H_2). Thus,

$$0.500 \text{ L } H_2 \times \frac{1 \text{ mol } H_2}{22.4 \text{ L } H_2} \times \frac{6.02 \times 10^{23} \text{ molecules } H_2}{1 \text{ mol } H_2} = 1.34 \times 10^{22} \text{ molecules } H_2$$

Practice Exercise

What is the volume occupied by 3.33×10^{21} atoms of helium gas, He, at STP?

Answer: 0.124 L He (124 mL)

Concept Exercise

What is the mass of one mole of hydrogen gas?

Answer: See Appendix G.

8.7 PERCENT COMPOSITION

LEARNING OBJECTIVE

▶ To calculate the percent composition of a compound given its chemical formula.

Previously, we defined percent as parts per 100 parts. Another way to define percent is to say that it is the amount of a given quantity compared to an entire sample. For example, a dime is 10% of a dollar. Now, let's apply the percent concept to the composition of a compound.

The **percent composition** of a compound lists the mass percent of each element. The percent composition of water, H_2O, for example, is 11% hydrogen and 89% oxygen. According to the law of definite composition discussed in Section 3.5, the elements in a compound are always present in the same proportion by mass. Therefore, water always contains 11% hydrogen and 89% oxygen regardless of the amount. A drop of water, a milliliter of water, and a pool of water all contain 11% hydrogen and 89% oxygen.

◀ **Percent Composition** The percent composition of H_2O is the same for a drop of water and a glass of water, that is, 11% hydrogen and 89% oxygen.

The percent of each element in water is given, but how are the values obtained? We can calculate the percent composition of water as follows. Let's begin by assuming that we have 1 mol of H_2O. A mole of H_2O contains 2 mol of hydrogen and 1 mol of oxygen. Thus,

$$2(\text{mol H}) + 1\,\text{mol O} = 1\,\text{mol H}_2O$$

$$2(\text{molar mass H}) + 1\,\text{molar mass O} = 1\,\text{molar mass H}_2O$$

$$2(1.01\,\text{g H}) + 16.00\,\text{g O} = \text{g H}_2O$$

$$2.02\,\text{g H} + 16.00\,\text{g O} = 18.02\,\text{g H}_2O$$

Next, we find the percent composition of water by comparing the molar masses of hydrogen and oxygen to the molar mass of the whole compound:

$$\frac{2.02\,\text{g H}}{18.02\,\text{g H}_2O} \times 100\% = 11.2\%\,\text{H}$$

$$\frac{16.00\,\text{g O}}{18.02\,\text{g H}_2O} \times 100\% = 88.79\%\,\text{O}$$

The following example exercise further illustrates the calculation of the percent composition of a compound.

Example Exercise 8.12 Percent Composition of a Substance

TNT (trinitrotoluene) is a white crystalline substance that explodes at 240 °C. Calculate the percent composition of TNT, $C_7H_5(NO_2)_3$.

Solution

Let's calculate the percent composition assuming there is 1 mol of TNT. For compounds with parentheses, it is necessary to count the number of atoms of each element carefully. That is, 1 mol of $C_7H_5(NO_2)_3$ contains 7 mol of C atoms, 5 mol of H atoms, 3 mol of NO_2 (that is, 3 mol N atoms and 6 mol of O atoms).

We begin the calculation by finding the molar mass of $C_7H_5(NO_2)_3$ as follows:

$$7(12.01\,\text{g C}) + 5(1.01\,\text{g H}) + 3(14.01\,\text{g N} + 32.00\,\text{g O}) = \text{g }C_7H_5(NO_2)_3$$

$$84.07\,\text{g C} + 5.05\,\text{g H} + 42.03\,\text{g N} + 96.00\,\text{g O} = 227.15\,\text{g }C_7H_5(NO_2)_3$$

Now, let's compare the mass of each element to the total molar mass of the compound, that is, 227.15 g.

$$\frac{84.07\,\text{g C}}{227.15\,\text{g }C_7H_5(NO_2)_3} \times 100\% = 37.01\%\,\text{C}$$

$$\frac{5.05\,\text{g H}}{227.15\,\text{g }C_7H_5(NO_2)_3} \times 100\% = 2.22\%\,\text{H}$$

$$\frac{42.03\,\text{g N}}{227.15\,\text{g }C_7H_5(NO_2)_3} \times 100\% = 18.50\%\,\text{N}$$

$$\frac{96.00\,\text{g O}}{227.15\,\text{g }C_7H_5(NO_2)_3} \times 100\% = 42.26\%\,\text{O}$$

The percent composition of TNT reveals that the explosive is mostly oxygen by mass. When we sum the individual percentages (37.01 + 2.22 + 18.50 + 42.26 = 99.99%), we verify our calculation and find that the total is approximately 100%.

Practice Exercise

EDTA (ethylenediaminetetraacetic acid) is used as a food preservative and in the treatment of lead poisoning. Calculate the percent composition of EDTA, $C_{10}H_{16}N_2O_8$.

Answer: 41.09% C, 5.53% H, 9.587% N, and 43.79% O

Concept Exercise

If an analysis of sugar, $C_xH_yO_z$, gave 40.0% C and 6.7% H, what is the percent oxygen?

Answer: See Appendix G.

8.8 EMPIRICAL FORMULA

▶ To calculate the empirical formula of a compound given its mass composition.

▶ To calculate the empirical formula of a compound given its percent composition.

During the late 1700s, chemists experimented to see how elements reacted to form compounds. In particular, they were interested in the reactions of elements with oxygen to form oxides. By measuring the mass of an element and the mass of the oxide after reaction, chemists could determine the formula of the compound.

The **empirical formula** of a compound corresponds to the simplest whole-number ratio of atoms of each element in a molecule, or ions in an ionic compound. The following example illustrates the determination of an empirical formula. A 1.640 g sample of radioactive radium was heated with oxygen to produce 1.755 g of radium oxide. By subtracting the mass of radium from the mass of the oxide (1.755 g − 1.640 g), we find that the mass gain was 0.115 g. Thus, the radium reacted with 0.115 g of oxygen gas.

Now, let's find the empirical formula for radium oxide, $Ra_?O_?$. The empirical formula is the simplest whole-number ratio of radium and oxide ions in an ionic compound. We can determine this ratio from the moles of each reactant. If the molar mass of radium is given as 226.03 g/mol, we can proceed as follows:

$$1.640 \text{ g Ra} \times \frac{1 \text{ mol Ra}}{226.03 \text{ g Ra}} = 0.00726 \text{ mol Ra}$$

We can calculate the moles of oxygen (16.00 g/mol) as follows:

$$0.115 \text{ g O} \times \frac{1 \text{ mol O}}{16.00 \text{ g O}} = 0.00719 \text{ mol O}$$

The mole ratio of the elements in radium oxide is $Ra_{0.00726}O_{0.00719}$. We can simplify the mole ratio by dividing by the smaller number:

$$Ra \frac{0.00726}{0.00719} \quad O \frac{0.00719}{0.00719} = Ra_{1.01}O_{1.00}$$

Because the empirical formula must be a small whole-number ratio, we will round the calculated chemical formula of radium oxide from $Ra_{1.01}O_{1.00}$ to RaO.

Notice that the empirical formula for radium oxide is similar to other Group IIA/2 elements. Magnesium, calcium, and barium are in Group IIA/2 because their compounds have similar empirical formulas. The empirical formulas of the metal oxides all have a metal-to-oxygen ratio of 1:1, that is, MgO, CaO, and BaO. Accordingly, the empirical formula of radium oxide, which has a Group IIA/2 metal, is RaO.

Example Exercise 8.13 Empirical Formula from Mass Composition

In a laboratory experiment, 0.500 g of scandium was heated and allowed to react with oxygen from the air. The resulting product oxide had a mass of 0.767 g. Now, let's find the empirical formula for scandium oxide, $Sc_?O_?$.

Solution

The empirical formula is the simplest whole-number ratio of scandium and oxygen in the compound scandium oxide. This ratio is experimentally determined from the moles of each reactant. The moles of scandium are calculated as follows:

$$0.500 \text{ g Sc} \times \frac{1 \text{ mol Sc}}{44.96 \text{ g Sc}} = 0.0111 \text{ mol Sc}$$

The moles of oxygen are calculated after first subtracting the mass of Sc from the product, $Sc_?O_?$:

$$0.767 \text{ g } Sc_xO_y - 0.500 \text{ g } Sc = 0.267 \text{ g } O$$

The moles of oxygen are calculated from the mass of oxygen that reacted:

$$0.267 \text{ g O} \times \frac{1 \text{ mol O}}{16.00 \text{ g O}} = 0.0167 \text{ mol O}$$

The mole ratio in scandium oxide is $Sc_{0.0111}O_{0.0167}$. To simplify the ratio and obtain small whole numbers, we divide by the smaller number:

$$Sc \frac{0.0111}{0.0111} \quad O \frac{0.0167}{0.0111} = Sc_{1.00}O_{1.50}$$

Because the calculated ratio is not close to whole numbers, we cannot round off the experimental ratio $Sc_{1.00}O_{1.50}$. However, we can double the ratio to obtain whole numbers, that is, $Sc_{2.00}O_{3.00}$. Thus, the empirical formula is Sc_2O_3.

Practice Exercise
Iron can react with chlorine gas to give two different compounds, $FeCl_2$ and $FeCl_3$. If 0.558 g of metallic iron reacts with chlorine gas to yield 1.621 g of iron chloride, which iron compound is produced in the experiment?

Answer: $FeCl_3$

Concept Exercise
If 0.500 mol of yellow powder sulfur reacts with 0.500 mol of oxygen gas, what is the empirical formula of the sulfur oxide?

Answer: See Appendix G.

Empirical Formulas from Percent Composition

Benzene was a common liquid solvent until the Environmental Protection Agency (EPA) discovered that it was a carcinogen. Let's calculate the formula for benzene if its percent composition is 92.2% carbon and 7.83% hydrogen.

The empirical formula expresses the simplest whole-number ratio of carbon to hydrogen atoms in a molecule of benzene. To calculate the moles of each element, let's assume we have 100 g of sample. In 100 g of benzene there are 92.2 g of carbon and 7.83 g of hydrogen. That is, the percentage of each element corresponds to its mass in 100 g of the compound. We find the moles of C and H as we did in the previous examples:

$$92.2 \text{ g C} \times \frac{1 \text{ mol C}}{12.01 \text{ g C}} = 7.68 \text{ mol C}$$

$$7.83 \text{ g H} \times \frac{1 \text{ mol H}}{1.01 \text{ g H}} = 7.75 \text{ mol H}$$

The mole ratio of the elements in benzene is $C_{7.68}H_{7.75}$. We can simplify the mole ratio by dividing both values by the smaller number, 7.68:

$$C \frac{7.68}{7.68} \quad H \frac{7.75}{7.68} = C_{1.00}H_{1.01}$$

Because the ratio $C_{1.00}H_{1.01}$ is close to whole numbers, we can round off to CH to obtain the empirical formula for benzene. The following example exercise further illustrates the calculation of an empirical formula from percent composition data.

Example Exercise 8.14 Empirical Formula from Percent Composition

Glycine is an amino acid found in protein. An analysis of glycine gave the following data: 32.0% carbon, 6.7% hydrogen, 18.7% nitrogen, and 42.6% oxygen. Calculate the empirical formula of the amino acid.

Solution

If we assume a 100-g sample, then the percentage of each element equals its mass in 100 g of glycine, that is, 32.0 g C, 6.7 g H, 18.7 g N, and 42.6 g O. We can determine the empirical formula as follows:

$$32.0 \text{ g C} \times \frac{1 \text{ mol C}}{12.01 \text{ g C}} = 2.66 \text{ mol C}$$

$$6.7 \text{ g H} \times \frac{1 \text{ mol H}}{1.01 \text{ g H}} = 6.6 \text{ mol H}$$

$$18.7 \text{ g H} \times \frac{1 \text{ mol N}}{14.01 \text{ g N}} = 1.33 \text{ mol N}$$

$$42.6 \text{ g O} \times \frac{1 \text{ mol O}}{16.00 \text{ g O}} = 2.66 \text{ mol O}$$

The mole ratio of the elements in the amino acid is $C_{2.66}H_{6.6}N_{1.33}O_{2.66}$. We can find a small whole-number ratio by dividing by the smallest number:

$$C\frac{2.66}{1.33} \quad H\frac{6.6}{1.33} \quad N\frac{1.33}{1.33} \quad O\frac{2.66}{1.33} = C_{2.00}H_{5.0}N_{1.00}O_{2.00}$$

Simplifying, we find that the empirical formula for the amino acid glycine is $C_2H_5NO_2$.

Practice Exercise

Calculate the empirical formula for caffeine given the following percent composition: 49.5% C, 5.15% H, 28.9% N, and 16.5% O.

Answer: $C_4H_5N_2O$

Concept Exercise

If 0.500 mol of yellow powder sulfur reacts with 0.750 mol of oxygen gas, what is the empirical formula of the sulfur oxide?

Answer: See Appendix G.

8.9 MOLECULAR FORMULA

Molecular compounds are represented by individual molecules. In the previous section we found the empirical formula for benzene is CH. However, this does not represent the actual formula for benzene. The actual formula, or **molecular formula**, is a multiple of the empirical formula. We can represent the molecular formula as $(CH)_n$, where n is some multiple of CH, such as 2, 3, 4, 5, or 6.

Now consider acetylene, used in oxyacetylene welding, which also has the empirical formula CH. Even though acetylene and benzene have unrelated properties, each shares the same empirical formula, CH. In addition, the compound styrene, used in manufacturing styrofoam cups, also shares the same empirical formula, CH.

Because benzene, acetylene, and styrene are different compounds, their molecular formulas must be different. Experiments have provided the molar mass for each of these compounds. For benzene, the molar mass is 78 g/mol; for acetylene, it is

LEARNING OBJECTIVE

▶ To calculate the molecular formula for a compound given its empirical formula and molar mass.

26 g/mol; and for styrene, it is 104 g/mol. We can indicate the number of multiples of the empirical formula for each compound as follows:

$$\text{Benzene: } (CH)_n = 78 \text{ g/mol}$$
$$\text{Acetylene: } (CH)_n = 26 \text{ g/mol}$$
$$\text{Styrene: } (CH)_n = 104 \text{ g/mol}$$

The mass of the empirical formula CH is found by adding the molar masses of C and H, that is, 12 g + 1 g = 13 g/mol. Now we can determine how many multiples of the empirical formula are in benzene. We have

$$\text{Benzene: } \frac{(CH)_n}{CH} = \frac{78 \text{ g/mol}}{13 \text{ g/mol}}$$
$$n = 6$$

Therefore, the molecular formula of benzene is $(CH)_6$, which we can write as C_6H_6. Similarly, we can find the molecular formula for acetylene:

$$\text{Acetylene: } \frac{(CH)_n}{CH} = \frac{26 \text{ g/mol}}{13 \text{ g/mol}}$$
$$n = 2$$

The molecular formula of acetylene is $(CH)_2$ or C_2H_2. In a similar fashion, we can find the number of multiples of the empirical formula in styrene:

$$\text{Styrene: } \frac{(CH)_n}{CH} = \frac{104 \text{ g/mol}}{13 \text{ g/mol}}$$
$$n = 8$$

Thus, the molecular formula of styrene is $(CH)_8$ or C_8H_8.

Even though benzene, acetylene, and styrene have the same empirical formula, their molecular formulas are different. Thus, benzene, acetylene, and styrene are different compounds. The following example exercise further illustrates how to determine a molecular formula from an empirical formula:

Example Exercise 8.15 Molecular Formula from Empirical Formula

The empirical formula for fructose, or fruit sugar, is CH_2O. If the molar mass of fructose is 180 g/mol, find the actual molecular formula for the sugar.

Solution
We can indicate the molecular formula of fructose as $(CH_2O)_n$. The molar mass of the empirical formula CH_2O is 12 g C + 2(1 g H) + 16 g O = 30 g/mol. Thus, the number of multiples of the empirical formula is

$$\text{Fructose: } \frac{(CH_2O)_n}{CH_2O} = \frac{180 \text{ g/mol}}{30 \text{ g/mol}}$$
$$n = 6$$

Thus, the molecular formula of fructose is $(CH_2O)_6$ or $C_6H_{12}O_6$.

Practice Exercise
Ethylene dibromide was banned as a grain pesticide in 1983 because it was found to accumulate in groundwater. Laboratory tests showed EDB to be a carcinogen that causes reproductive disorders in test animals. Calculate (a) the empirical formula and (b) the molecular formula for ethylene dibromide given its approximate molar mass of 190 g/mol and its percent composition: 12.7% C, 2.1% H, and 85.1% Br.

Answers:

(a) CH_2Br

(b) $C_2H_4Br_2$

Concept Exercise

If the molecular formula of hydrogen peroxide is H_2O_2, what is the empirical formula?

Answer: See Appendix G.

Note For molecular compounds, the empirical and molecular formulas are usually different. For ionic compounds, the actual formulas are almost always identical to the empirical formulas. For example, the actual formula for sodium chloride is NaCl, not Na_2Cl_2 or some other multiple. The common exception, however, is the mercury(I) compounds. Notice that the actual formula of mercury(I) chloride, Hg_2Cl_2, is twice the empirical formula.

CRITICAL THINKING   Avogadro's Number

Q: What mass of silicon contains Avogadro's number of atoms?

In 1911, Ernest Rutherford determined a value for Avogadro's number. Rutherford counted the alpha particles emitted from radioactive radium using a Geiger counter, which had been invented by his assistant Hans Geiger. As the alpha particles decayed into helium gas, he then measured the volume of the gas. From the data, Rutherford calculated a value of 6.11×10^{23} for Avogadro's number.

The most recent experimental value for Avogadro's number was found using an X-ray method. X-rays were used to determine the spacing of atoms in an ultrapure crystal of silicon. After striking the nuclei of silicon atoms, the path of the X-ray is altered. The volume occupied by a single atom is calculated from the spacing between two X-rays. A precise value for Avogadro's number is obtained by dividing the volume of an individual silicon atom into the volume of a molar mass of pure silicon.

We can illustrate how to calculate a value for Avogadro's number as follows. In the figure notice that the volume occupied by each silicon atom is 0.020116 nm^3 and that the volume of the crystal is 12.114 cm^3. To find Avogadro's number we simply divide the volume of one atom of silicon into the volume of the silicon crystal. However, we must use the same units for the volumes of the atom and the crystal. For example, we can convert the volume of the crystal from cm^3 to nm^3:

$$12.114 \text{ cm}^3 \times \left(\frac{1 \text{ m}}{10^2 \text{ cm}}\right)^3 \times \left(\frac{10^9 \text{ nm}}{1 \text{ m}}\right)^3 = \text{nm}^3$$

$$12.114 \text{ cm}^3 \times \frac{1 \text{ m}^3}{10^6 \text{ cm}^3} \times \frac{10^{27} \text{ nm}^3}{1 \text{ m}^3} = 1.2114 \times 10^{22} \text{ nm}^3$$

When we divide the volume of the silicon atom into the volume of the crystal, we find the number of silicon atoms:

$$1.2114 \times 10^{22} \text{ nm}^3 \times \frac{1 \text{ atom Si}}{0.020116 \text{ nm}^3} = 6.0221 \times 10^{23} \text{ atoms Si}$$

In this example, we obtained an experimental value of 6.0221×10^{23} atoms for Avogadro's number. Currently, the most accurate value for Avogadro's number is 6.0221415×10^{23}.

1 mole of Si = 12.114 cm^3

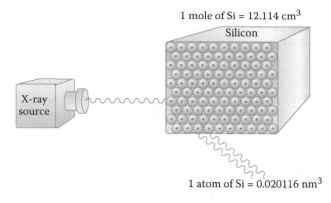

1 atom of Si = 0.020116 nm^3

◀ **X-Ray Diffraction of a Silicon Crystal** We can calculate the volume of a Si atom after using an X-ray method to find the spacing of atoms in a silicon crystal.

A: The mass of silicon containing Avogadro's number of atoms corresponds to the molar mass, that is, 28.09 g.

Summary

LEARNING OBJECTIVES	SEC	EXERCISES
To state the value of Avogadro's number: 6.02×10^{23}.	8.1	Exercises 1–4
To state the mass of Avogadro's number of atoms for any element by referring to the periodic table.	8.1	Exercises 1–4
To relate the moles of a substance to the number of particles.	8.2	Exercises 5–12
To calculate the molar mass of a substance given its chemical formula.	8.3	Exercises 13–16
To relate the mass of a substance to the number of particles.	8.4	Exercises 17–22
To state the value for the molar volume of any gas at STP: 22.4 L/mol.	8.5	Exercises 23–24
To relate the density of a gas at STP to its molar mass and volume.	8.5	Exercises 25–30
To relate the volume of a gas at STP to its mass and number of particles.	8.6	Exercises 31–38
To calculate the percent composition of a compound given its chemical formula.	8.7	Exercises 39–46
To calculate the empirical formula of a compound given its mass composition.	8.8	Exercises 47–52
To calculate the empirical formula of a compound given its percent composition.	8.8	Exercises 53–58
To calculate the molecular formula of a compound given its empirical formula and molar mass.	8.9	Exercises 59–68

Section 8.1 **Avogadro's number** (N) is the value that corresponds to the number of atoms in 12.01 g of carbon. Moreover, the number of atoms in the atomic mass of any element expressed in grams is 6.02×10^{23}.

Section 8.2 A **mole (mol)** is the amount of substance that contains Avogadro's number of particles, that is, 6.02×10^{23} particles. A mole is the central unit in performing chemical formula calculations. These computations, based on moles of substance, are known as mole calculations.

Section 8.3 The mass of 1 mol of any substance is called the **molar mass (MM)**. The molar mass of an element corresponds to the atomic mass of the element. For instance, the molar mass of carbon is 12.01 g/mol, and the molar mass of oxygen is 16.00 g/mol. The molar mass of a compound corresponds to the sum of the atomic masses for all the atoms of each element in the compound. For example, the molar mass of carbon monoxide, CO, equals 28.01 g/mol (12.01 g + 16.00 g).

Section 8.4 The mole is perhaps the most important unit in chemistry. A mole relates the number of particles (atoms, molecules, or formula units) to the amount of a substance. Given the moles of a substance, we can calculate the mass of the substance as well as the number of particles.

Section 8.5 Avogadro's theory states that equal volumes of gases, at the same conditions, contain equal numbers of molecules. The volume of 1 mol of a gaseous substance at standard conditions is called the **molar volume**. The molar volume of any gas at **standard temperature and pressure**

(STP) is 22.4 L/mol. Standard conditions are 0 °C and 1 atm pressure. **Gas density** is found by dividing the molar mass of a gas by the molar volume; that is, we divide the molar mass by 22.4 L/mol.

Section 8.6 The mole concept relates the number of particles, molar mass, and molar volume of a gas. Given the number of liters of a gaseous substance at STP, we can apply the mole concept to find the mass of the substance as well as the number of particles.

Section 8.7 The **percent composition** of a compound is found by comparing the mass contributed by each element to the molar mass of the substance. A list of the resulting percentages of each element is the percent composition of the compound.

Section 8.8 The **empirical formula** is the simplest whole-number ratio of the atoms of the elements in a compound. The empirical formula can be calculated from (1) experimental synthesis data, or (2) the percent composition of the compound. After calculating the moles of each element in a compound, the mole ratio is simplified to small whole numbers.

Section 8.9 The **molecular formula** is the actual ratio of the atoms in a molecular compound. For example, lactic acid and glucose each have the empirical formula CH_2O. The molecular formula of lactic acid, $C_3H_6O_3$, is three times the empirical formula. The actual formula of glucose, $C_6H_{12}O_6$, is six times the empirical formula.

PROBLEM–SOLVING ORGANIZER

TOPIC	PROCEDURE	EXAMPLE
Avogadro's Number Sec. 8.1	Express the atomic mass of an element in grams to find the mass of Avogadro's number of atoms.	Avogadro's number of Fe atoms has a mass of 55.85 g.
Mole Calculations I Sec. 8.2	1. Write down the unit asked for in the answer. 2. Write down the related given value. 3. Apply a unit factor to convert the given unit to the unit in the answer.	How many iron atoms are in 0.500 mol of Fe? $$0.500 \text{ mol} \times \frac{6.02 \times 10^{23} \text{ atoms}}{1 \text{ mol}} = 3.01 \times 10^{23} \text{ atoms}$$
Molar Mass Sec. 8.3	Sum the masses of each atom of each element in a compound to calculate the molar mass.	What is the molar mass of iron(III) oxide, Fe_2O_3? $$2(55.85 \text{ g/mol}) + 3(16.00 \text{ g/mol}) = 159.70 \text{ g/mol}$$
Mole Calculations II Sec. 8.4	1. Write down the unit asked for in the answer. 2. Write down the related given value. 3. Apply a unit factor to convert the given unit to the unit in the answer.	What is the mass of 5.00×10^{23} formula units of Fe_2O_3? $$5.00 \times 10^{23} \text{ formula units} \times \frac{1 \text{ mol}}{6.02 \times 10^{23} \text{ formula units}}$$ $$\times \frac{159.70 \text{ g } Fe_2O_2}{1 \text{ mol}} = 133 \text{ g } Fe_2O_3$$
Molar Volume Sec. 8.5	The volume occupied by 1 mol of any gas at STP is 22.4 L.	Volume of 1.00 mol of O_2 at STP is 22.4 L.
Mole Calculations III Sec. 8.6	1. Write down the unit asked for in the answer. 2. Write down the related given value. 3. Apply a unit factor to convert the given unit to the unit in the answer.	What is the mass of 2.50 L of O_2 gas at STP? $$2.50 \text{ L} \times \frac{1 \text{ mol}}{22.4 \text{ L}} \times \frac{32.00 \text{ g } O_2}{1 \text{ mol}} = 3.57 \text{ g } O_2$$
Percent Composition Sec. 8.7	Find the mass of each element compared to the total molar mass of the compound, all multiplied by 100%.	What is the percent composition of hydrogen peroxide, H_2O_2 (MM = 34.02 g/mol)? $$\frac{2(1.01) \text{ g}}{34.02 \text{ g}} \times 100\% = 5.94\% \text{ H}$$ $$\frac{2(16.00) \text{ g}}{34.02 \text{ g}} \times 100\% = 94.06\% \text{ O}$$
Empirical Formula Sec. 8.8	Find the mole ratio of each element in the compound, and simplify to whole numbers.	What is the empirical formula of hydrogen peroxide, given 2.25 mol H and 2.22 mol O? $$H \frac{2.25}{2.22} O \frac{2.22}{2.22} = H_{1.01}O_{1.00}$$ thus, H_1O_1
Molecular Formula Sec. 8.9	Find the ratio of the molar mass of the compound to the molar mass of the empirical formula unit. Use this ratio as a multiplier for the subscripts in the empirical formula unit.	What is the molecular formula of hydrogen peroxide, given the molar mass is about 34 g/mol? $$\frac{(HO)_n}{HO} = \frac{34 \text{ g/mol}}{17 \text{ g/mol}} = 2$$ thus, H_2O_2

Key Terms   *Answers to Key Terms are in Appendix H.*

Select the key term that corresponds to each of the following definitions.

_____ 1. the value that corresponds to the number of atoms in 12.01 g of carbon, that is, 6.02×10^{23} particles

_____ 2. the amount of substance that contains 6.02×10^{23} particles

_____ 3. the mass of 1 mol of pure substance expressed in grams

_____ 4. the volume occupied by 1 mol of any gas at standard conditions

_____ 5. a temperature of 0 °C and 1 atm pressure that have been chosen as standard conditions

_____ 6. equal volumes of gases, under the same conditions of temperature and pressure, contain equal numbers of molecules

_____ 7. the ratio of mass per unit volume for a gas, expressed in grams per liter

_____ 8. a list of the mass percent of each element in a compound

_____ 9. a chemical formula that expresses the simplest whole-number ratio of atoms of each element in a molecule, or ions in an ionic compound

_____ 10. a chemical formula that expresses the actual number of atoms of each element in a molecule

(a) Avogadro's number (*N*) (*Sec. 8.1*)

(b) Avogadro's theory (*Sec. 8.5*)

(c) empirical formula (*Sec. 8.8*)

(d) gas density (*Sec. 8.5*)

(e) molar mass (MM) (*Sec. 8.3*)

(f) molar volume (*Sec. 8.5*)

(g) mole (mol) (*Sec. 8.2*)

(h) molecular formula (*Sec. 8.9*)

(i) percent composition (*Sec. 8.7*)

(j) standard temperature and pressure (STP) (*Sec. 8.5*)

Exercises   *Answers to odd-numbered Exercises are in Appendix I.*

Avogadro's Number (Sec. 8.1)

1. Refer to the periodic table and state the atomic mass (in amu) of one atom for each of the following metals:
   (a) lithium **(b)** titanium
   (c) gold **(d)** bismuth

2. Refer to the periodic table and state the atomic mass (in amu) of one atom for each of the following nonmetals:
   (a) carbon **(b)** sulfur
   (c) selenium **(d)** iodine

3. Refer to the periodic table and state the mass of 6.02×10^{23} atoms of each of the following metals:
   (a) lithium **(b)** titanium
   (c) gold **(d)** bismuth

4. Refer to the periodic table and state the mass of 6.02×10^{23} atoms of each of the following nonmetals:
   (a) carbon **(b)** sulfur
   (c) selenium **(d)** iodine

Mole Calculations I (Sec. 8.2)

5. State the number of particles in each of the following:
   (a) 1 mol of carbon atoms, C
   (b) 1 mol of methane molecules, CH_4

6. State the number of particles in each of the following:
   (a) 1 mol of silicon atoms, Si
   (b) 1 mol of silane molecules, SiH_4

7. State the number of moles represented by each of the following:
   (a) 6.02×10^{23} atoms of lithium, Li
   (b) 6.02×10^{23} molecules of bromine, Br_2

8. State the number of moles represented by each of the following:
   (a) 6.02×10^{23} atoms of sulfur, S
   (b) 6.02×10^{23} molecules of sulfur dioxide, SO_2

9. Calculate the number of particles in each of the following:
   (a) 0.100 mol zinc atoms, Zn
   (b) 0.200 mol chlorine molecules, Cl_2
   (c) 0.300 mol zinc chloride formula units, $ZnCl_2$

10. Calculate the number of particles in each of the following:
    (a) 0.250 mol calcium atoms, Ca
    (b) 0.500 mol fluorine molecules, F_2
    (c) 0.750 mol calcium fluoride formula units, CaF_2

11. Calculate the number of moles containing each of the following:
    (a) 1.00×10^{22} atoms of manganese, Mn
    (b) 2.00×10^{23} molecules of sulfur trioxide, SO_3
    (c) 3.00×10^{24} formula units of manganese(II) sulfate, $MnSO_4$

12. Calculate the number of moles containing each of the following:
    (a) 2.50×10^{22} atoms of iron, Fe
    (b) 5.00×10^{23} molecules of carbon dioxide, CO_2
    (c) 7.50×10^{24} formula units of iron(II) carbonate, $FeCO_3$

Molar Mass (Sec. 8.3)

13. State the molar mass for each of the following:
    (a) aluminum, Al **(b)** silicon, Si
    (c) oxygen, O_2 **(d)** sulfur, S_8

14. State the molar mass for each of the following:
    (a) arsenic, As **(b)** germanium, Ge
    (c) ozone, O_3 **(d)** phosphorus, P_4

15. Calculate the molar mass for each of the following:
    (a) calcium sulfide, CaS
    (b) calcium sulfate, $CaSO_4$
    (c) iron(II) acetate, $Fe(C_2H_3O_2)_2$
    (d) iron(II) phosphate, $Fe_3(PO_4)_2$

16. Calculate the molar mass for each of the following:
 (a) bromine iodide, BrI
 (b) tribromine octaoxide, Br_3O_8
 (c) glycerin, $C_3H_5(OH)_3$
 (d) nitroglycerin, $C_3H_5O_3(NO_2)_3$

Mole Calculations II (Sec. 8.4)

17. Calculate the mass in grams for each of the following:
 (a) 2.95×10^{23} atoms of mercury, Hg
 (b) 1.16×10^{22} molecules of nitrogen, N_2
 (c) 5.05×10^{21} formula units of barium chloride, $BaCl_2$

18. Calculate the mass in grams for each of the following:
 (a) 1.21×10^{24} atoms krypton, Kr
 (b) 6.33×10^{22} molecules of dinitrogen oxide, N_2O
 (c) 4.17×10^{21} formula units of magnesium perchlorate, $Mg(ClO_4)_2$

19. Calculate the number of particles in each of the following:
 (a) 1.50 g potassium, K (b) 0.470 g oxygen, O_2
 (c) 0.555 g silver chlorate, $AgClO_3$

20. Calculate the number of particles in each of the following:
 (a) 7.57 g platinum, Pt (b) 3.88 g ethane, C_2H_6
 (c) 0.152 g aluminum chloride, $AlCl_3$

21. Calculate the mass in grams for a single atom of the following elements:
 (a) beryllium, Be (b) sodium, Na
 (c) cobalt, Co (d) arsenic, As

22. Calculate the mass in grams for a single molecule of the following compounds:
 (a) methane, CH_4 (b) ammonia, NH_3
 (c) sulfur trioxide, SO_3 (d) nitrogen dioxide, NO_2

Molar Volume (Sec. 8.5)

23. State standard conditions for a gas in degrees Celsius and atmospheres.

24. State standard conditions for a gas in Kelvin units and atmospheres.

25. Calculate the density for each of the following gases at STP:
 (a) argon, Ar (b) chlorine, Cl_2
 (c) methane, CH_4 (d) ethane, C_2H_6

26. Calculate the density for each of the following gases at STP:
 (a) xenon, Xe (b) fluorine, F_2
 (c) propane, C_3H_8 (d) butane, C_4H_{10}

27. Calculate the molar mass for each of the following gases given the STP density:
 (a) oxygen, 1.43 g/L   (b) phosphine, 1.52 g/L
 (c) nitrous oxide, 1.97 g/L (d) Freon-12, 5.40 g/L

28. Calculate the molar mass for each of the following gases given the STP density:
 (a) ozone, 2.14 g/L   (b) silane, 1.43 g/L
 (c) nitric oxide, 1.34 g/L (d) Freon-22, 3.86 g/L

29. Given 1 mol of each gas listed, complete the following table:

Gas	Molecules	Mass	Volume at STP
nitrogen, N_2			
oxygen, O_2			
nitrogen dioxide, NO_2			

30. Given 1 mol of each gas listed, complete the following table:

Gas	Molecules	Mass	Volume at STP
nitrogen, N_2			
hydrogen, H_2			
ammonia, NH_3			

Mole Calculations III (Sec. 8.6)

31. Calculate the volume in liters for each of the following gases at STP:
 (a) 0.250 g of helium, He (b) 5.05 g of nitrogen, N_2

32. Calculate the volume in liters for each of the following gases at STP:
 (a) 2.22×10^{22} molecules of methane, CH_4
 (b) 4.18×10^{24} molecules of ethane, C_2H_6

33. Calculate the mass in grams for each of the following gases at STP:
 (a) 1.05 L of hydrogen sulfide, H_2S
 (b) 5.33 L of dinitrogen trioxide, N_2O_3

34. Calculate the mass in grams for each of the following gases at STP:
 (a) 5.42×10^{22} molecules of propane, C_3H_8
 (b) 1.82×10^{23} molecules of butane, C_4H_{10}

35. Calculate the number of molecules in each of the following gases at STP:
 (a) 100.0 mL of hydrogen, H_2
 (b) 70.5 mL of ammonia, NH_3

36. Calculate the number of molecules in each of the following gases at STP:
 (a) 0.150 g of carbon monoxide, CO
 (b) 2.75 g of nitrogen monoxide, NO

37. Use the given quantity for each gas listed to complete the following table:

Gas	Molecules	Mass	Volume at STP
methane, CH_4	1.50×10^{23}		
ethane, C_2H_6		7.50 g	
propane, C_3H_8			5.58 L

38. Use the given quantity for each gas listed to complete the following table:

Gas	Molecules	Mass	Volume at STP
ozone, O_3	2.50×10^{22}		
carbon dioxide, CO_2		1.83 g	
carbon monoxide, CO			0.930 L

Percent Composition (Sec. 8.7)

39. If the percent hydrogen in a drop of water is 11%, what is the percent hydrogen in a kilogram of water?

40. If the percent oxygen in a drop of water is 89%, what is the percent oxygen in a liter of water?

41. Lactose is a sugar found in milk. Calculate the percent composition of lactose, $C_{12}H_{22}O_{11}$.

42. Benzoyl peroxide is the active ingredient in an acne cream. Calculate the percent composition of benzoyl peroxide, $C_{14}H_{10}O_4$.

43. Methionine is an essential amino acid in protein. Calculate the percent composition of methionine, $C_5H_{11}NSO_2$.

44. Monosodium glutamate (MSG) is added to food to enhance the flavor. Calculate the percent composition of MSG, $NaC_5H_8NO_4$.

45. Mercurochrome dissolved in water is a reddish liquid formerly used as an antiseptic. Calculate the percent composition of mercurochrome, $HgNa_2C_{20}H_8Br_2O_6$.

46. Chlorophyll is a dark green plant pigment. Calculate the percent composition of chlorophyll, $C_{55}H_{70}MgN_4O_6$.

Empirical Formula (Sec. 8.8)

47. In an experiment 0.500 g of tin reacted with nitric acid to give tin oxide. If the oxide had a mass of 0.635 g, what is the empirical formula of tin oxide?

48. In an experiment 0.500 g of nickel reacted with air to give 0.704 g of nickel oxide. What is the empirical formula of the oxide?

49. In an experiment 2.410 g of copper oxide produced 1.925 g of copper metal after heating with hydrogen gas. What is the empirical formula of copper oxide?

50. In an experiment 1.550 g of mercury oxide decomposed to give oxygen gas and 1.435 g of liquid mercury. What is the empirical formula of mercury oxide?

51. A 1.115 g sample of cobalt was heated with sulfur to give 2.025 g of cobalt sulfide. What is the empirical formula of cobalt sulfide?

52. A 0.715 g sample of titanium was heated with chlorine gas to give 2.836 g of titanium chloride. What is the empirical formula of titanium chloride?

53. The percent composition of copper chloride is 64.1% Cu and 35.9% Cl. Calculate the empirical formula.

54. The percent composition of vanadium oxide is 68.0% V and 32.0% O. Calculate the empirical formula.

55. The percent composition of tin bromide is 42.6% Sn and 57.4% Br. Calculate the empirical formula.

56. The percent composition of bismuth oxide is 89.7% Bi and 10.3% O. Calculate the empirical formula.

57. Trichloroethylene (TCE) is a common solvent used to degrease machine parts. Calculate the empirical formula for TCE if the percent composition is 18.25% C, 0.77% H, and 80.99% Cl.

58. Dimethyl sulfoxide (DMSO) is a liniment for horses and has been used in the treatment of arthritis for humans. Calculate the empirical formula for DMSO, given that the percent composition is 30.7% C, 7.74% H, 20.5% O, and 41.0% S.

Molecular Formula (Sec. 8.9)

59. Aspirin has a molar mass of 180 g/mol. If the empirical formula is $C_9H_8O_4$, what is the molecular formula of aspirin?

60. Quinine is used to treat malaria and has a molar mass of 325 g/mol. If the empirical formula is $C_{10}H_{12}NO$, what is the molecular formula of quinine?

61. Hexamethylene diamine is used to make nylon. If the molar mass is 115 g/mol and the empirical formula is C_3H_8N, what is the molecular formula of the compound?

62. Adipic acid is used to make nylon. If the molar mass is 147 g/mol and the empirical formula is $C_3H_5O_2$, what is the molecular formula of the compound?

63. Ethylene glycol is used as permanent antifreeze. If the molar mass is 62 g/mol and the percent composition is 38.7% C, 9.74% H, and 51.6% O, what is the molecular formula of ethylene glycol?

64. Dioxane is a common solvent for plastics. If the molar mass is 88 g/mol and the percent composition is 54.5% C, 9.15% H, and 36.3% O, what is the molecular formula of dioxane?

65. Lindane is an insecticide. If the molar mass is 290 g/mol and the percent composition is 24.8% C, 2.08% H, and 73.1% Cl, what is the molecular formula of lindane?

66. Mercurous chloride is a fungicide. If the molar mass is 470 g/mol and the percent composition is 85.0% Hg and 15.0% Cl, what is the molecular formula of mercurous chloride?

67. Nicotine has a molar mass of 160 g/mol. If the percent composition is 74.0% C, 8.70% H, and 17.3% N, what is the molecular formula of nicotine?

68. Allose is a sugar with a molar mass of 180 g/mol. If the percent composition is 40.0% C, 6.72% H, and 53.3% O, what is the molecular formula of allose?

General Exercises

69. A quadrillion, 1×10^{15}, is the approximate number of red blood cells in 50,000 people. Which is greater: a quadrillion red blood cells or the number of nickel atoms in a 5-g nickel coin?

70. By rubbing the Lincoln profile on a penny coin, a student removed just enough mass to be detected by an electronic balance, 0.0001 g. How many copper atoms were rubbed off the coin?

71. If the mass of Earth is 6×10^{24} kg and an average rodent mole has a mass of 100 g, which weighs more, Earth or a mole of furry moles?

72. If a light year, 9.5×10^{12} km, is the distance light travels in a year and an average rodent mole has a length of 17 cm, which is longer, a light year or a mole of furry moles?

73. In 1871 Mendeleev predicted the undiscovered element *ekaaluminum*. In 1875 the element was discovered in Gaul (France) and was given the name gallium. If 0.500 g of gallium reacts with oxygen gas to give 0.672 g of gallium oxide, what is its empirical formula?

74. In 1871 Mendeleev predicted the undiscovered element *ekasilicon*. In 1886 the element was discovered in Germany and was given the name germanium. If 0.500 g of germanium reacts with chlorine gas to give 1.456 g of germanium chloride, what is its empirical formula?

75. Calculate the volume in cubic centimeters occupied by one molecule of water in a beaker of water. Recall that the density of water is 1.00 g/cm^3.

76. Calculate the volume in milliliters occupied by one molecule of ethyl alcohol, C_2H_5OH, in a beaker of alcohol. The density of ethyl alcohol is 0.789 g/mL.

77. Calculate the number of carbon atoms in 1.00 g of table sugar, $C_{12}H_{22}O_{11}$.

78. Calculate the number of carbon atoms in 1.00 g of blood sugar, $C_6H_{12}O_6$.

79. What is the mass of cuprite, Cu_2O, that contains 10.0 g of copper?

80. What is the mass of rust, Fe_2O_3, that contains 10.0 g of iron?

Challenge Exercises

81. The volume occupied by each copper atom in a 1-mole crystal is $0.0118 \ nm^3$. If the density of the copper crystal is $8.92 \ g/cm^3$, what is the experimental value of Avogadro's number?

82. Each atom in a crystal of aluminum metal occupies a theoretical cube that is 0.255 nm on a side. If the density of the aluminum crystal is $2.70 \ g/cm^3$, what is the experimental value of Avogadro's number?

Online Exercises

Research each of the following using an Internet search engine (e.g., Google.com or Yahoo.com) and cite your URL reference.

83. How many photons are in an Einstein?

84. How many electrons are in a Faraday?

▲ **The Mole Concept** The photograph shows a mole of sugar, water, mercury, sulfur, salt, copper, lead (clockwise), and orange potassium dichromate (center). Each sample contains 6.02×10^{23} particles; however, the molar masses differ as follows: 342.34 g/mol $C_{12}H_{22}O_{11}$, 18.02 g/mol H_2O, 200.59 g/mol Hg, 32.07 g/mol S, 58.44 g/mol NaCl, 63.55 g/mol Cu, 207.2 g/mol Pb, and 294.20 g/mol $K_2Cr_2O_7$.

8 Chapter Self-Test   *Answers to Self-Test are in Appendix J.*

1. How many atoms of silver equal a mass of 107.87 amu? (Sec. 8.1)
   (a) 1   (b) 47
   (c) 107.87   (d) 108
   (e) 6.02×10^{23}

2. How many atoms of silver are in 2.50 mol of Ag metal? (Sec. 8.2)
   (a) 1.51×10^{22} atoms   (b) 1.51×10^{23} atoms
   (c) 1.51×10^{24} atoms   (d) 2.41×10^{23} atoms
   (e) 2.41×10^{24} atoms

3. What is the molar mass of ammonium dichromate, $(NH_4)_2Cr_2O_7$? (Sec. 8.3)
   (a) 238.09 g/mol   (b) 252.10 g/mol
   (c) 260.18 g/mol   (d) 372.18 g/mol
   (e) 386.19 g/mol

4. What is the mass of 3.30×10^{23} atoms of silver, Ag? (Sec. 8.4)
   (a) 0.549 g   (b) 25.8 g
   (c) 59.1 g   (d) 85.7 g
   (e) 197 g

5. How many ozone molecules are in 22.4 liters of O_3 gas at STP? (Sec. 8.5)
   (a) 1.20×10^{24} (b) 1.35×10^{25}
   (c) 1.81×10^{24} (d) 2.69×10^{22}
   (e) 6.02×10^{23}

6. What is the volume of 1.20×10^{22} molecules of ozone gas, O_3, at STP? (Sec. 8.6)
   (a) 0.0199 L   (b) 0.447 L
   (c) 2.24 L   (d) 5.02 L
   (e) 1120 L

7. An emerald has the chemical formula $Be_3Al_2Si_{16}O_{18}$. What is the percentage of aluminum in the gemstone? (Sec. 8.7)
   (a) 3.30%   (b) 3.37%
   (c) 6.59%   (d) 35.2%
   (e) 54.9%

8. If 0.500 mol of silver combines with 0.250 mol of sulfur, what is the empirical formula of the silver sulfide product? (Sec. 8.8)
   (a) AgS   (b) Ag_2S
   (c) AgS_2 (d) Ag_5S_5
   (e) none of the above

9. A common name for fructose is *fruit sugar*. What is the molecular formula of fructose if the empirical formula is CH_2O, and the approximate molar mass is 180 g/mol? (Sec. 8.9)
   (a) CHO   (b) CH_2O
   (c) CH_2O_6 (d) $C_6H_{12}O_6$
   (e) $C_{12}H_{22}O_{11}$

Key Concepts

10. Given that F–19 is the only natural isotope of fluorine, what is the mass of one F atom and Avogadro's number of F atoms, respectively?

11. Given 1 mol of fluorine gas at STP, what is the mass, volume, and number of F_2 molecules?

12. Given Avogadro's number of shotput balls, which of the following is the best estimate of the total mass: an automobile, the Empire State building, or Earth?

13. Given Avogadro's number of marbles, which of the following is the best estimate of the total volume: a basketball, Dallas Cowboys Stadium, or the Moon?

Critical Thinking

14. If an ultrasensitive balance can weigh samples having a mass of 1 μg or greater, can it weigh 10 trillion copper atoms?

15. A 1-carat diamond is pure, crystalline carbon and has a mass of 0.200 g. Which has more atoms, a 1-carat diamond or a googol (1×10^{100}) of atoms?

9

Chemical Equation Calculations

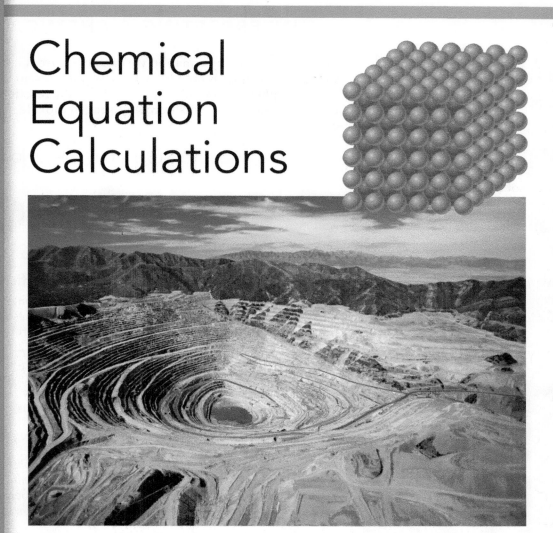

Copper in the Environment Copper is unreactive and the native metal is found naturally in the environment. Most copper is extracted from open-pit mines (shown). Rich deposits of copper are found worldwide, and the United States has large deposits in Utah, Colorado, and West Virginia.

"In the middle of difficulty lies opportunity."
Albert Einstein, German/Swiss/American Physicist (1879–1955)

The manufacturing of chemicals is one of the most important industries in the United States. Millions of tons of chemicals are produced each year for use both in the United States and in other countries. These chemicals are used to manufacture cars, computer chips, electronic instruments, prescription drugs, glass, paper, fertilizers, pesticides, plumbing supplies, synthetic fibers, and other products.

Chemists and chemical engineers routinely perform calculations based on balanced chemical equations to determine the cost of producing chemicals. These calculations are critical to many industries. The amounts of chemicals manufactured are published annually, and sulfuric acid, found in automobile batteries, consistently tops this list. The amount of sulfuric acid produced indicates the general activity of manufacturing and for that reason is referred to as the barometer of the chemical industry. However, sulfuric acid is an environmental problem that results from burning low-grade coal containing sulfur. Sulfur dioxide is released into the atmosphere and is converted to sulfuric acid. So-called "acid rain" contains sulfuric acid, which is a corrosive chemical that harms plants, birds animals, and aquatic life.

▸ To relate the coefficients in a balanced chemical equation to
(a) moles of reactants and products, and
(b) liters of gaseous reactants and products.

▸ To verify the coefficients of a balanced chemical equation using the conservation of mass law.

9.1 INTERPRETING A CHEMICAL EQUATION

Let's examine the information we can obtain from a balanced chemical equation. Consider nitrogen monoxide gas, which is present in automobile emissions. In the atmosphere, ultraviolet light catalyzes the reaction of nitrogen monoxide and oxygen to produce reddish-brown nitrogen dioxide smog. The balanced chemical equation is

$$2\,NO(g) + O_2(g) \xrightarrow{\text{UV}} 2\,NO_2(g)$$

▲ **Nitrogen Oxides** This photo shows a smoggy day in Los Angeles as a result of automobile emissions and the release of nitrogen oxides into the atmosphere.

The Mole Interpretation of Equation Coefficients

The coefficients in the balanced equation indicate that 2 molecules of NO react with 1 molecule of O_2 to produce 2 molecules of NO_2. These coefficients indicate relative numbers of reactant and product molecules. It therefore follows that multiples of these coefficients are in the same ratios. For example, 2000 molecules of NO react with 1000 molecules of O_2 to give 2000 molecules of NO_2. Let's consider a number even larger than 2000; let's consider Avogadro's number (symbol N) of molecules, that is, 6.02×10^{23} molecules. When we substitute this very large number of molecules for the coefficients, the equation remains balanced. That is,

$$2\,N\,NO + 1\,N\,O_2 \longrightarrow 2\,N\,NO_2$$

We read the equation as *two times Avogadro's number of nitrogen monoxide molecules reacts with Avogadro's number of oxygen molecules to produce two times Avogadro's number of nitrogen dioxide molecules.* Because Avogadro's number is the number of molecules in 1 mol, we can write the equation in terms of moles of substance:

$$2\,mol\,NO + 1\,mol\,O_2 \longrightarrow 2\,mol\,NO_2$$

Similarly, this equation reads *two moles of nitrogen monoxide react with one mole of oxygen to give two moles of nitrogen dioxide.* Furthermore, the coefficients indicate the ratio of moles, or the **mole ratio**, of reactants and products in every balanced chemical equation.

The Volume Interpretation of Equation Coefficients

According to **Avogadro's theory**, there are equal numbers of molecules in equal volumes of gas at the same temperature and pressure. It therefore follows that twice the number of molecules occupies twice the volume of gas. In the preceding equation, 2 molecules of NO react with 1 molecule of O_2 to give 2 molecules of NO_2. Accordingly, 2 volumes of NO react with 1 volume of O_2 gas to give 2 volumes of NO_2 gas. If we choose the liter as our unit of volume, we can write the ratio of volumes of gas for the reaction.

$$2\,L\,NO + 1\,L\,O_2 \longrightarrow 2\,L\,NO_2$$

Regardless of the units, the numbers in the ratio of volumes correspond to the coefficients of the balanced chemical equation, that is, 2:1:2. For example, 2 mL of NO reacts with 1 mL of O_2 to give 2 mL of NO_2. Similarly, 20 mL of NO reacts with 10 mL of O_2 to give 20 mL of NO_2. Although the ratio of gaseous volumes is 20:10:20, the smallest whole-number ratio is 2:1:2. Table 9.1 summarizes the information that can be obtained from the coefficients of a balanced chemical equation.

TABLE 9.1 INTERPRETATION OF CHEMICAL EQUATION COEFFICIENTS

FOR THE GENERAL EQUATION	2 A	+	3 B	→	C	+	2 D
The ratio of molecules	2 :		3 :		1 :		2
The ratio of moles	2 :		3 :		1 :		2
The ratio of volumes of gas	2 :		3 :		1 :		2

The following example exercise illustrates the information that can be obtained by interpreting the coefficients in a balanced chemical equation:

Example Exercise 9.1 Interpreting Chemical Equation Coefficients

Given the chemical equation for the combustion of methane, CH_4, balance the equation and interpret the coefficients in terms of (a) moles and (b) liters:

$$CH_4(g) + O_2(g) \xrightarrow{\text{spark}} CO_2(g) + H_2O(g)$$

Solution
The balanced chemical equation is

$$CH_4(g) + 2\,O_2(g) \xrightarrow{\text{spark}} CO_2(g) + 2\,H_2O(g)$$

(a) The coefficients in the equation (1:2:1:2) indicate the ratio of moles as well as molecules.

$$1 \text{ mol } CH_4 + 2 \text{ mol } O_2 \longrightarrow 1 \text{ mol } CO_2 + 2 \text{ mol } H_2O$$

(b) The coefficients in the equation (1:2:1:2) indicate the ratio of volumes of gases. If we express the volume in liters, we have

$$1\,L\,CH_4 + 2\,L\,O_2 \longrightarrow 1\,L\,CO_2 + 2\,L\,H_2O$$

Practice Exercise
Given the chemical equation for the combustion of propane, C_3H_8, balance the equation and interpret the coefficients in terms of (a) moles and (b) milliliters:

$$C_3H_8(g) + O_2(g) \xrightarrow{\text{spark}} CO_2(g) + H_2O(g)$$

Answers:

(a) $1 \text{ mol } C_3H_8 + 5 \text{ mol } O_2 \longrightarrow 3 \text{ mol } CO_2 + 4 \text{ mol } H_2O$
(b) $1 \text{ ml } C_3H_8 + 5 \text{ ml } O_2 \longrightarrow 3 \text{ ml } CO_2 + 4 \text{ mL } H_2O$

Concept Exercise
Which of the following is in the same ratio as the coefficients in a balanced equation: moles of gas, mass of gas, volume of gas?

Answer: See Appendix G.

Verifying the Conservation of Mass Law

In 1787 after conducting numerous experiments, Antoine Lavoisier formulated the **law of conservation of mass**. He stated that mass is neither created nor destroyed during a chemical reaction. As a result, the combined masses of the reactants must equal the combined masses of the products.

We can verify the conservation of mass law for any balanced equation. Let's consider the previous equation for the formation of nitrogen dioxide:

$$2\,NO(g) + O_2(g) \xrightarrow{\text{UV}} 2\,NO_2(g)$$

According to the coefficients in the balanced equation, the ratio of the substances is 2:1:2. Therefore, the mole ratio of each substance is 2:1:2.

$$2\,mol\,NO + 1\,mol\,O_2 \longrightarrow 2\,mol\,NO_2$$

By summing the atomic masses for each substance, we find that the **molar mass** for NO is 30.01 g/mol; for O_2, 32.00 g/mol; and for NO_2, 46.01 g/mol. Substituting the molar mass for a mole of each substance gives

$$2\,(30.01\,g) + 1\,(32.00\,g) \longrightarrow 2\,(46.01\,g)$$

$$\text{Simplifying, } 60.02\,g + 32.00\,g \longrightarrow 92.02\,g$$

$$\text{and, } 92.02\,g \longrightarrow 92.02\,g$$

In this example, the total mass of the reactants is 92.02 g, which is equal to the total mass of the products. Thus from our calculation, we have verified the conservation of mass law.

9.2 MOLE–MOLE RELATIONSHIPS

LEARNING OBJECTIVE

▶ To relate the number of moles of two substances in a balanced chemical equation.

As we demonstrated in Section 9.1, the coefficients in a chemical equation indicate the mole ratio of the reactants and products. Consider the combination reaction of nitrogen and oxygen to give nitrogen monoxide. The equation is

$$N_2(g) + O_2(g) \xrightarrow{\Delta} 2\,NO(g)$$

From the coefficients in the balanced equation, we see that 1 mol of nitrogen reacts with 1 mol of oxygen to produce 2 mol of nitrogen monoxide. We can write several mole ratios for this equation.

Because 1 mol of N_2 reacts with 1 mol of O_2, the corresponding mole ratios are

$$\frac{1\,mol\,N_2}{1\,mol\,O_2} \quad \text{and} \quad \frac{1\,mol\,O_2}{1\,mol\,N_2}$$

Because 1 mol of N_2 produces 2 mol of NO, the corresponding mole ratios are

$$\frac{1\,mol\,N_2}{2\,mol\,NO} \quad \text{and} \quad \frac{2\,mol\,NO}{1\,mol\,N_2}$$

Because 1 mol of O_2 produces 2 mol of NO, the corresponding mole ratios are

$$\frac{1\,mol\,O_2}{2\,mol\,NO} \quad \text{and} \quad \frac{2\,mol\,NO}{1\,mol\,O_2}$$

Suppose we want to find out how many moles of oxygen react with 2.25 mol of nitrogen. As usual, we apply the unit analysis method of problem solving:

$$2.25\,mol\,N_2 \times \frac{\text{unit}}{\text{factor}} = mol\,O_2$$

To cancel units, we select the mole ratio 1 mol O_2/1 mol N_2 as our unit factor:

$$2.25\,mol\,N_2 \times \frac{1\,mol\,O_2}{1\,mol\,N_2} = 2.25\,mol\,O_2$$

We can also calculate the moles of nitrogen monoxide produced by the reaction. To cancel units, we select the mole ratio 2 mol NO/1 mol N_2 as our unit factor:

$$2.25 \text{ mol N}_2 \times \frac{2 \text{ mol NO}}{1 \text{ mol N}_2} = 4.50 \text{ mol NO}$$

Whenever we have a balanced chemical equation, we can always convert from moles of one substance to moles of another substance using a mole ratio as a unit factor. Example Exercise 9.2 further illustrates the relationship between moles of reactants and moles of products.

Example Exercise 9.2 Mole–Mole Relationships

Carbon monoxide is produced in a blast furnace by passing oxygen gas over hot coal. How many moles of oxygen react with 2.50 mol of carbon, according to the balanced equation?

$$2 \text{ C}(s) + \text{O}_2(g) \xrightarrow{\Delta} 2 \text{ CO}(g)$$

Strategy Plan

Step 1: What unit is asked for in the answer?   **Step 1:** | mol O_2

Step 2: What given value is related to the answer?   **Step 2:** | 2.50 mol C

Step 3: What unit factor(s) should we apply? **Step 3:** $\dfrac{2 \text{ mol C}}{1 \text{ mol O}_2}$ or $\dfrac{1 \text{ mol O}_2}{2 \text{ mol C}}$
Using the balanced equation, we see that 2 mol C = 1 mol O_2. Thus, the mole ratio and the two unit factors are

given value	*unit factor*	*unit in answer*
2.50 mol C	$\times \dfrac{1 \text{ mol O}_2}{2 \text{ mol C}}$	$= ? \text{ mol O}_2$

Unit Analysis Map

Solution

We select the unit factor that cancels the unit in the given value (mol C). Thus,

$$2.50 \text{ mol C} \times \frac{1 \text{ mol O}_2}{2 \text{ mol C}} = 1.25 \text{ mol O}_2$$

Practice Exercise

Iron is produced from iron ore in a blast furnace by passing carbon monoxide gas through molten iron(III) oxide. The balanced equation is

$$\text{Fe}_2\text{O}_3(l) + 3 \text{ CO}(g) \xrightarrow{\Delta} 2 \text{ Fe}(l) + 3 \text{ CO}_2(g)$$

(a) How many moles of carbon monoxide react with 2.50 mol of Fe_2O_3?
(b) How many moles of iron are produced from 2.50 mol of Fe_2O_3?

Answers:

(a) 7.50 mol CO   (b) 5.00 mol Fe

Concept Exercise

How many unit factors are required to solve a mole–mole problem?

Answer: See Appendix G.

CRITICAL THINKING   Iron versus Steel

Q: What is the difference between iron and steel?

The Iron Age began about 1000 B.C. in western Asia and Europe. The Iron Age followed the Bronze Age after it was discovered that iron could be made by heating iron ore with coal. Interestingly, iron is still obtained by a similar method.

Today, an industrial blast furnace converts iron ore to iron. In the process, iron ore, coke (a form of coal), and limestone, $CaCO_3$, are added into the top of a heated furnace while a blast of hot air is blown in at the bottom.

Many reactions take place in the process, but first, oxygen in the hot air reacts with carbon in coke to produce carbon monoxide:

$$2\,C(s) + O_2(g) \xrightarrow{\Delta} 2\,CO(g)$$

▲ **Blast Furnace** Molten pig iron reacts with a "blast" of oxygen gas that converts carbon and sulfur impurities into CO_2 and SO_2 gases.

Iron ore is an impure mixture of hematite, Fe_2O_3, and magnetite, Fe_3O_4. In the blast furnace hematite and magnetite are converted to iron by reaction with carbon monoxide gas. The reactions are as follows:

$$Fe_2O_3(l) + 3\,CO(g) \longrightarrow 2\,Fe(l) + 3\,CO_2(g)$$

$$Fe_3O_4(l) + 4\,CO(g) \longrightarrow 3\,Fe(l) + 4\,CO_2(g)$$

The iron ore also contains silicon impurities that must be removed. This is done by reacting the impurities with CaO, which is produced from limestone, that is, $CaCO_3$. Silicon compounds such as $CaSiO_3$ form and are referred to as "slag." This less dense slag is easily removed, as it floats on the molten iron at the bottom of the furnace.

The molten iron obtained from the blast furnace is still not pure and is referred to as "pig iron." Pig iron contains impurities such as carbon and sulfur. In a second stage of the process, these impurities are removed by blowing oxygen gas through the molten pig iron. The impurities are converted to oxides, and are released as gases such as CO_2 and SO_2.

The iron obtained after the oxygen process contains a trace amount of carbon. Manganese is then often added for strength and flexibility, and the resulting product is referred to as "steel." A large number of alloy steels can be produced by adding other metals. For example, stainless steel contains about 10% chromium.

A: Iron is an element, whereas steel is an alloy of iron with traces of carbon and metals, such as manganese, nickel, and chromium, which impart special properties.

LEARNING OBJECTIVE

▶ To classify the three basic types of stoichiometry problems: mass–mass, mass–volume, and volume–volume.

9.3 TYPES OF STOICHIOMETRY PROBLEMS

In Chapter 8, we performed mole calculations based on chemical formulas. In this chapter, we will perform mole calculations based on chemical equations. That is, we will apply mole ratios to relate quantities of reactants and products. The term **stoichiometry** (stoy-kee-AHM-uh-tree) is used to refer to the relationship between quantities in a chemical reaction according to the balanced chemical equation. The term is derived from the Greek words *stoicheion*, meaning "element," and *metron*, meaning "measure."

Some stoichiometry calculations relate a given amount of reactant to an unknown amount of product. Conversely, other stoichiometry calculations relate a given amount of product to an unknown amount of reactant. Whether we relate a reactant to a product, or vice versa, the calculations use the same basic method of problem solving.

We can classify three types of stoichiometry problems based on the given quantity and the quantity to be calculated. Consider the general equation for any reaction, where *a*, *b*, *c*, and *d* are the respective coefficients for the substances A, B, C, and D:

$$a\,A + b\,B \longrightarrow c\,C + d\,D$$

If we are given grams of A and asked to find how many grams of C are produced, we classify this as a **mass–mass problem**. If we are given grams of A and asked to calculate the milliliters of a gas D, we classify this as a **mass–volume problem**. If we are given liters of a gas A and asked to find the liters of a gas D, we classify this as a **volume–volume problem**. In summary, stoichiometry problems can be classified as one of these basic types: mass–mass, mass–volume, or volume–volume.

After classifying a stoichiometry problem, we can apply the unit analysis method of problem solving to its solution. Example Exercise 9.3 offers practice in classifying types of stoichiometry problems.

Example Exercise 9.3 Classifying Stoichiometry Problems

Classify the type of stoichiometry problem for each of the following:

(a) How many grams of Zn metal react with hydrochloric acid to give 0.500 g of zinc chloride?
(b) How many liters of H_2 gas react with chlorine gas to yield 50.0 cm^3 of hydrogen chloride gas?
(c) How many kilograms of Fe react with sulfuric acid to produce 50.0 mL of hydrogen gas?

Solution

After analyzing a problem for the unknown quantity and the relevant given value, we classify the type of problem.

(a) The problem asks for grams of Zn (mass) that react to give 0.500 g of $ZnCl_2$ (mass). This is a *mass–mass* type of problem.
(b) The problem asks for liters of H_2 gas (volume) that react to yield 50.0 cm^3 of HCl gas (volume). This is a *volume–volume* type of problem.
(c) The problem asks for kilograms of Fe (mass) that react to produce 50.0 mL of H_2 gas (volume). This is a *mass–volume* type of problem.

Practice Exercise

Classify the type of stoichiometry problem for each of the following:

(a) How many grams of HgO decompose to give 0.500 L of oxygen gas at STP?
(b) How many grams of AgCl are produced from the reaction of 0.500 g of solid sodium chloride with silver nitrate solution?
(c) How many milliliters of H_2 gas react with nitrogen gas to yield 1.00 L of ammonia gas?

Answers:

(a) mass–volume   (b) mass–mass   (c) volume–volume

Concept Exercise

What are the three types of stoichiometry problems?

Answer: See Appendix G.

▲ **Reaction of Zn Metal** Zinc metal reacts with hydrochloric acid to give $ZnCl_2$ and H_2 bubbles.

9.4 MASS–MASS PROBLEMS

A mass–mass stoichiometry problem is so named because an *unknown mass* of substance is calculated from a *given mass* of reactant or product in a chemical equation. After balancing the chemical equation, we proceed as follows:

(a) Convert the given mass of substance to moles using the molar mass of the substance as a unit factor.
(b) Convert the moles of the given to moles of the unknown using the mole ratio from the coefficients in the balanced equation.
(c) Convert the moles of the unknown to grams using the molar mass of the substance as a unit factor.

To see how to solve a mass–mass problem, consider the high-temperature conversion of 14.4 g of iron(II) oxide to elemental iron with aluminum metal. The balanced equation for the reaction is

$$3\,FeO(l) + 2\,Al(l) \xrightarrow{\Delta} 3\,Fe(l) + Al_2O_3(l)$$

LEARNING OBJECTIVE

▶ To perform mass–mass stoichiometry calculations.

To calculate the mass of aluminum necessary for the reaction, we must first find the moles of iron(II) oxide. Given that the molar mass of FeO is 71.85 g/mol, the unit factor conversion is as follows:

(a)
$$14.4 \text{ g FeO} \times \frac{1 \text{ mol FeO}}{71.85 \text{ g FeO}} = 0.200 \text{ mol FeO}$$

Next, we convert the moles of FeO to moles of Al by applying a mole ratio using the coefficients in the balanced equation. Because 3 mol FeO = 2 mol Al, the mole ratio unit factor is

(b)
$$0.200 \text{ mol FeO} \times \frac{2 \text{ mol Al}}{3 \text{ mol FeO}} = 0.134 \text{ mol Al}$$

Last, we use the molar mass of aluminum (26.98 g/mol) as a unit factor to obtain the mass of Al reacting with 14.4 g of FeO.

(c)
$$0.134 \text{ mol Al} \times \frac{26.98 \text{ g Al}}{1 \text{ mol Al}} = 3.60 \text{ g Al}$$

After you gain confidence in solving stoichiometry problems, it will be more convenient to perform one continuous calculation. For example, the solution to the preceding problem can be shown as

$$14.4 \text{ g FeO} \times \underbrace{\frac{1 \text{ mol FeO}}{71.85 \text{ g FeO}}}_{(a)} \times \underbrace{\frac{2 \text{ mol Al}}{3 \text{ mol FeO}}}_{(b)} \times \underbrace{\frac{26.98 \text{ g Al}}{1 \text{ mol Al}}}_{(c)} = 3.60 \text{ g Al}$$

The following example exercises give additional illustrations of mass–mass stoichiometry calculations using unit factors.

▲ **Decomposition of HgO**
Orange mercury(II) oxide decomposes by heating to give droplets of silver Hg liquid and O₂ gas.

Example Exercise 9.4 **Mass–Mass Stoichiometry**

Calculate the mass of mercury produced from the decomposition of 1.25 g of orange mercury(II) oxide (MM = 216.59 g/mol):

$$2 \text{ HgO}(s) \xrightarrow{\Delta} 2 \text{ Hg}(l) + O_2(g)$$

Strategy Plan

Step 1: What unit is asked for in the answer?

Step 1:
> g Hg

Step 2: What given value is related to the answer?

Step 2:
> 1.25 g HgO

Step 3: What unit factor(s) should we apply?
We are given that 1 mol HgO = 216.59 g HgO; the mole ratio from the balanced equation is 2 mol HgO = 2 mol Hg. From the periodic table, we find that 1 mol Hg = 200.59 g Hg. Thus, the unit factors are

Step 3:

$$\frac{1 \text{ mol HgO}}{216.59 \text{ g HgO}} \quad \text{or} \quad \frac{216.59 \text{ g HgO}}{1 \text{ mol HgO}}$$

$$\frac{2 \text{ mol HgO}}{2 \text{ mol Hg}} \quad \text{or} \quad \frac{2 \text{ mol Hg}}{2 \text{ mol HgO}}$$

$$\frac{1 \text{ mol Hg}}{200.59 \text{ g Hg}} \quad \text{or} \quad \frac{200.59 \text{ g Hg}}{1 \text{ mol Hg}}$$

Unit Analysis Map

given value		*unit factor 1*		*unit factor 2*		*unit factor 3*		*unit in answer*
1.25 g HgO	×	$\dfrac{1 \text{ mol HgO}}{216.59 \text{ g HgO}}$	×	$\dfrac{2 \text{ mol Hg}}{2 \text{ mol HgO}}$	×	$\dfrac{200.59 \text{ g Hg}}{1 \text{ mol Hg}}$		= ? g Hg

Solution

We select from each of the three pairs of ratios a unit factor that cancels the previous units. Thus,

$$1.25 \text{ g HgO} \times \frac{1 \text{ mol HgO}}{216.59 \text{ g HgO}} \times \frac{2 \text{ mol Hg}}{2 \text{ mol HgO}} \times \frac{200.59 \text{ g Hg}}{1 \text{ mol Hg}} = 1.16 \text{ g Hg}$$

Practice Exercise

Calculate the mass of carbon dioxide released from 10.0 g of cobalt(III) carbonate given the *unbalanced* equation for the reaction:

$$Co_2(CO_3)_3(s) \xrightarrow{\Delta} Co_2O_3(s) + CO_2(g)$$

Answer: 4.43 g CO_2

Concept Exercise

What are the three steps in the unit analysis method of problem solving?

Answer: See Appendix G.

▲ **Precipitation of HgI₂**
Potassium iodide and mercury(II) nitrate react to give an orange precipitate of HgI₂.

Example Exercise 9.5 Mass–Mass Stoichiometry

Calculate the mass of potassium iodide (166.00 g/mol) required to yield 1.78 g of mercury(II) iodide precipitate (454.39 g/mol):

$$2 \text{ KI}(s) + Hg(NO_3)_2(aq) \longrightarrow HgI_2(s) + 2 \text{ KNO}_3(aq)$$

Strategy Plan

Step 1: What unit is asked for in the answer?

Step 1: | g KI

Step 2: What given value is related to the answer?

Step 2: | 1.78 g HgI₂

Step 3: What unit factor(s) should we apply? From the given molar mass, we see that 1 mol HgI₂ = 454.39 g HgI₂. The mole ratio from the balanced equation is 2 mol KI = 1 mol HgI₂, and from the given molar mass, 1 mol KI = 166.00g KI. Thus, the three pairs of unit factors are

Step 3:

$$\frac{1 \text{ mol HgI}_2}{454.39 \text{ g HgI}_2} \quad \text{or} \quad \frac{454.39 \text{ g HgI}_2}{1 \text{ mol HgI}_2}$$

$$\frac{2 \text{ mol KI}}{1 \text{ mol HgI}_2} \quad \text{or} \quad \frac{1 \text{ mol HgI}_2}{2 \text{ mol KI}}$$

$$\frac{1 \text{ mol KI}}{166.00 \text{ g KI}} \quad \text{or} \quad \frac{166.00 \text{ g KI}}{1 \text{ mol KI}}$$

Unit Analysis Map

given value	unit factor 1	unit factor 2	unit factor 3	unit in answer
1.78 g HgI₂	$\times \dfrac{1 \text{ mol HgI}_2}{454.39 \text{ g HgI}_2}$	$\times \dfrac{2 \text{ mol KI}}{1 \text{ mol HgI}_2}$	$\times \dfrac{166.00 \text{ g KI}}{1 \text{ mol KI}}$	= ? g KI

Solution

We select from each of the three pairs of ratios a unit factor that cancels the previous units. Thus,

$$1.78 \text{ g HgI}_2 \times \frac{1 \text{ mol HgI}_2}{454.39 \text{ g HgI}_2} \times \frac{2 \text{ mol KI}}{1 \text{ mol HgI}_2} \times \frac{166.00 \text{ g KI}}{1 \text{ mol KI}} = 1.30 \text{ g KI}$$

Practice Exercise

Calculate the mass of iron filings required to produce 0.455 g of silver metal given the *unbalanced* equation for the reaction:

$$Fe(s) + AgNO_3(aq) \longrightarrow Fe(NO_3)_3(aq) + Ag(s)$$

Answer: 0.0785 g Fe

Concept Exercise

In general, how many unit factors are required to solve a mass–mass stoichiometry problem?

Answer: See Appendix G.

▶ To perform mass–volume stoichiometry calculations.

9.5 MASS–VOLUME PROBLEMS

A mass–volume stoichiometry problem is so named because an *unknown volume* of substance is calculated from a *given mass* of reactant or product in a chemical equation. After balancing the chemical equation, we proceed as follows:

(a) Convert the given mass of substance to moles using the molar mass of the substance as a unit factor.

(b) Convert the moles of the given to moles of the unknown using the coefficients in the balanced equation.

(c) Convert the moles of the unknown to liters using the **molar volume** of a gas as a unit factor. At **standard temperature and pressure (STP)**, the molar volume of a gas is 22.4 L/mol.

Of course, it is also possible to perform the reverse calculation; that is, we can find the mass of an unknown substance from a given volume of gas. For simplicity, this reverse process is also referred to as a mass–volume stoichiometry problem.

To understand how to solve a mass–volume stoichiometry problem, consider the reaction of 0.165 g of aluminum metal with dilute hydrochloric acid. The balanced equation for the reaction is

$$2 Al(s) + 6 HCl(aq) \longrightarrow 2 AlCl_3(aq) + 3 H_2(g)$$

Let's calculate the volume of hydrogen gas produced by the reaction at STP. This is a mass–volume stoichiometry problem. First, we calculate the moles of aluminum whose molar mass is 26.98 g/mol:

(a) $$0.165 \text{ g Al} \times \frac{1 \text{ mol Al}}{26.98 \text{ g Al}} = 0.00611 \text{ mol Al}$$

Next, we use the coefficients in the balanced equation to find the moles of hydrogen gas. According to the balanced equation, 2 mol Al = 3 mol H_2. Applying the mole ratio unit factor, we have

(b) $$0.00611 \text{ mol Al} \times \frac{3 \text{ mol } H_2}{2 \text{ mol Al}} = 0.00917 \text{ mol } H_2$$

Last, we multiply by the molar volume, 22.4 L/mol, to obtain the volume of H_2 gas produced at STP:

(c) $$0.00917 \text{ mol } H_2 \times \frac{22.4 \text{ L } H_2}{1 \text{ mol } H_2} = 0.205 \text{ L } H_2$$

The solution to the preceding problem can also be shown as one continuous calculation:

$$0.165 \text{ g Al} \times \frac{1 \text{ mol Al}}{26.98 \text{ g Al}} \times \frac{3 \text{ mol } H_2}{2 \text{ mol Al}} \times \frac{22.4 \text{ L } H_2}{1 \text{ mol } H_2} = 0.205 \text{ L } H_2$$

$$\text{(a)} \qquad \text{(b)} \qquad \text{(c)}$$

Example Exercise 9.6 Mass–Volume Stoichiometry

In an automobile collision, sodium azide, NaN_3, decomposes and fills an air bag with nitrogen gas. If an air bag contains 100.0 g of NaN_3 (65.02 g/mol), what is the volume of nitrogen gas produced at STP? The equation for the reaction is

$$2\ NaN_3(s) \xrightarrow{\text{spark}} Na(s) + 3\ N_2(g)$$

Strategy Plan

Step 1: What unit is asked for in the answer?

Step 1: | $L\ N_2$

Step 2: What given value is related to the answer?

Step 2: | 100.0 g NaN_3

Step 3: What unit factor(s) should we apply? Given the molar mass, 1 mol NaN_3 = 65.02 g NaN_3. The mole ratio from the balanced equation is 2 mol NaN_3 = 3 mol N_2, and the molar volume of a gas is 1 mol N_2 = 22.4 L N_2. Thus, the unit factors are

Step 3:

$$\frac{1\ mol\ NaN_3}{65.02\ g\ NaN_3} \quad \text{or} \quad \frac{65.02\ g\ NaN_3}{1\ mol\ NaN_3}$$

$$\frac{2\ mol\ NaN_3}{3\ mol\ N_2} \quad \text{or} \quad \frac{3\ mol\ N_2}{2\ mol\ NaN_3}$$

$$\frac{1\ mol\ N_2}{22.4\ L\ N_2} \quad \text{or} \quad \frac{22.4\ L\ N_2}{1\ mol\ N_2}$$

Unit Analysis Map

given value	×	unit factor 1	×	unit factor 2	×	unit factor 3		unit in answer
100.0 g NaN_3		$\dfrac{1\ mol\ NaN_3}{65.02\ g\ NaN_3}$		$\dfrac{3\ mol\ N_2}{2\ mol\ NaN_3}$		$\dfrac{22.4\ L\ N_2}{1\ mol\ N_2}$		$= ?\ L\ N_2$

Solution

We select from each of the three pairs of ratios a unit factor that cancels the previous units. Thus,

$$100.0\ g\ \cancel{NaN_3} \times \frac{1\ \cancel{mol\ NaN_3}}{65.02\ g\ \cancel{NaN_3}} \times \frac{3\ \cancel{mol\ N_2}}{2\ \cancel{mol\ NaN_3}} \times \frac{22.4\ L\ N_2}{1\ \cancel{mol\ N_2}} = 51.7\ L\ N_2$$

Practice Exercise

Calculate the volume of hydrogen gas produced at STP from 1.55 g of sodium metal in water, given the *unbalanced* equation for the reaction:

$$Na(s) + H_2O(l) \longrightarrow NaOH(aq) + H_2(g)$$

Answer: 0.755 L H_2

Concept Exercise

What are the three steps in the unit analysis method of problem solving?

Answer: See Appendix G.

▲ **Automobile Air Bag** The decomposition of sodium azide releases N_2 gas, which inflates the air bag.

Example Exercise 9.7 Mass–Volume Stoichiometry

Baking soda can be used as a fire extinguisher. When heated, it decomposes to carbon dioxide gas, which can smother a fire. If a sample of $NaHCO_3$ (84.01 g/mol) produces 0.500 L of carbon dioxide gas at STP, what is the mass of the sample?

$$2\,NaHCO_3(s) \xrightarrow{\Delta} Na_2CO_3(s) + H_2O(g) + CO_2(g)$$

Strategy Plan

Step 1: What unit is asked for in the answer?

Step 1:   g $NaHCO_3$

Step 2: What given value is related to the answer?

Step 2:   0.500 L CO_2

Step 3: What unit factor(s) should we apply? From molar volume, we know that 1 mol CO_2 = 22.4 L CO_2. The mole ratio from the balanced equation is 2 mol $NaHCO_3$ = 1 mol CO_2, and from the given molar mass, 1 mol $NaHCO_3$ = 84.01 g $NaHCO_3$. Thus, the unit factors are

Step 3:

$$\frac{1\ mol\ CO_2}{22.4\ L\ CO_2} \quad or \quad \frac{22.4\ L\ CO_2}{1\ mol\ CO_2}$$

$$\frac{2\ mol\ NaHCO_3}{1\ mol\ CO_2} \quad or \quad \frac{1\ mol\ CO_2}{2\ mol\ NaHCO_3}$$

$$\frac{1\ mol\ NaHCO_3}{84.01\ g\ NaHCO_3} \quad or \quad \frac{84.01\ g\ NaHCO_3}{1\ mol\ NaHCO_3}$$

Unit Analysis Map

given value	unit factor 1	unit factor 2	unit factor 3	unit in answer
0.500 L CO_2	× $\dfrac{1\ mol\ CO_2}{22.4\ L\ CO_2}$	× $\dfrac{2\ mol\ NaHCO_3}{1\ mol\ CO_2}$	× $\dfrac{84.01\ g\ NaHCO_3}{1\ mol\ NaHCO_3}$	= ? g $NaHCO_3$

Solution

We select from each of the three pairs of ratios a unit factor that cancels the previous units. Thus,

$$0.500\ L\ \cancel{CO_2} \times \frac{1\ \cancel{mol\ CO_2}}{22.4\ L\ \cancel{CO_2}} \times \frac{2\ \cancel{mol\ NaHCO_3}}{1\ \cancel{mol\ CO_2}} \times \frac{84.01\ g\ NaHCO_3}{1\ \cancel{mol\ NaHCO_3}} = 3.75\ g\ NaHCO_3$$

Practice Exercise

Calculate the mass of aluminum metal required to release 2160 mL of hydrogen gas at STP from sulfuric acid given the *unbalanced* equation for the reaction:

$$Al(s) + H_2SO_4(aq) \longrightarrow Al_2(SO_4)_3(aq) + H_2(g)$$

Answer: 1.73 g Al

Concept Exercise

In general, how many unit factors are required to solve a mass–volume stoichiometry problem?

Answer: See Appendix G.

◀ **Baking Soda, $NaHCO_3$**
Ordinary baking soda can be used to extinguish a fire. When heated, it decomposes and releases carbon dioxide gas, which is more dense than air and displaces oxygen from the flame.

9.6 VOLUME–VOLUME PROBLEMS

In 1804, the French chemist Joseph Gay-Lussac ascended to 23,000 feet in a hydrogen-filled balloon. During his record-setting ascent, he took samples of the atmosphere and later studied their composition.

In 1808, Gay-Lussac proposed the **law of combining volumes**. This law states that volumes of gases, under similar conditions, combine in small whole-number ratios. For example, 10.0 mL of hydrogen gas combines with 10.0 mL of chlorine gas to give 20.0 mL of hydrogen chloride gas:

$$H_2(g) \quad + \quad Cl_2(g) \longrightarrow \quad 2\,HCl(g)$$

$$\textit{10.0 mL} \qquad \textit{10.0 mL} \qquad \textit{20.0 mL}$$

Notice that the volumes of gas (10.0 mL:10.0 mL:20.0 mL) are in the ratio of small whole numbers (1:1:2). Moreover, the ratio of the volumes is identical to the mole ratio in the balanced chemical equation (1:1:2).

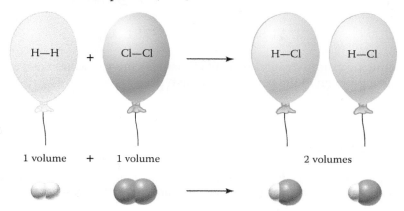

Similarly, 100.0 mL of hydrogen gas reacts with 50.0 mL of oxygen gas to produce 100.0 mL of water vapor:

$$2\,H_2(g) \quad + \quad O_2(g) \longrightarrow 2\,H_2O(g)$$

$$\textit{100.0 mL} \qquad \textit{50.0 mL} \qquad \textit{100.0 mL}$$

In this example, the volumes of gas (100.0 mL:50.0 mL:100.0 mL) are also in the ratio of small whole numbers (2:1:2). Once again, the ratio of the volumes is identical to the mole ratio in the balanced equation (2:1:2).

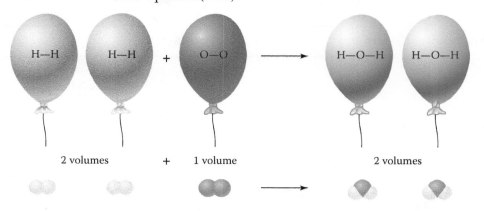

The law of combining volumes states that gases combine in small whole-number ratios. The volume ratio is identical to the coefficients in the balanced equation, so we can convert from a given volume to an unknown volume of gas in a single conversion using the mole ratio. A volume–volume stoichiometry problem is so named because an *unknown volume* of gas is calculated from a *given volume* of gaseous reactant or product in a chemical equation.

▲ **Ammonia, NH₃** Aqueous ammonia, NH_3, is found in laboratory reagent bottles labeled "ammonium hydroxide," NH_4OH.

We can illustrate a volume–volume problem using the industrial method for preparing sulfuric acid. Sulfuric acid is manufactured by the Contact process, which begins with the conversion of sulfur dioxide to sulfur trioxide using heat and a catalyst. The sulfur trioxide gas is then passed through water to produce sulfuric acid. The balanced equation for the conversion of SO_2 to SO_3 is

$$2\,SO_2(g) + O_2(g) \xrightarrow{\Delta} 2\,SO_3(g)$$

Let's calculate the liters of oxygen gas that react with 37.5 L of sulfur dioxide. From the balanced equation, we see that 2 volumes of SO_2 = 1 volume of O_2. When we express the volume in liters, we have $2\,L\,SO_2 = 1\,L\,O_2$. Using the volume ratio as a unit factor, we have

$$37.5\;L\;SO_2 \times \frac{1\;L\;O_2}{2\;L\;SO_2} = 18.8\;L\;O_2$$

Now let's calculate the volume, in liters, of sulfur trioxide produced. From the balanced equation we see that 2 volumes of SO_2 = 2 volumes of SO_3. Therefore,

$$37.5\;L\;SO_2 \times \frac{2\;L\;SO_3}{2\;L\;SO_2} = 37.5\;L\;SO_3$$

The following example exercise further illustrates the application of stoichiometry principles to a problem of the volume–volume type:

Example Exercise 9.8 Volume–Volume Stoichiometry

In the Haber process, nitrogen and hydrogen gases combine to give ammonia gas. If 5.55 L of nitrogen gas is available, calculate the volume of ammonia that is produced. Assume that all volumes of gas are measured under constant conditions of 500 °C and 300 atm pressure:

$$N_2(g) + 3\,H_2(g) \xrightarrow{Fe/Al_2O_3} 2\,NH_3(g)$$

Strategy Plan

Step 1: What unit is asked for in the answer?   **Step 1:** | L NH₃ |

Step 2: What given value is related to the answer?   **Step 2:** | 5.55 L N₂ |

Step 3: What unit factor(s) should we apply? Using the balanced equation, we see that 1 mol N_2 = 2 mol NH_3. The volumes of gas have the same ratio as the mole ratio, so the unit factors are   **Step 3:** $\dfrac{1\;L\;N_2}{2\;L\;NH_3}$ **or** $\dfrac{2\;L\;NH_3}{1\;L\;N_2}$

Unit Analysis Map

given value	unit factor(s)	unit in answer
5.55 L N₂	$\times\;\dfrac{2\;L\;NH_3}{1\;L\;N_2}$	$=\;?\;L\;NH_3$

Solution

We select the unit factor that cancels the unit in the given value (L N$_2$). Thus,

$$5.55 \text{ L N}_2 \times \frac{2 \text{ L NH}_3}{1 \text{ L N}_2} = 11.1 \text{ L NH}_3$$

Practice Exercise

Calculate the volumes of (a) hydrogen chloride gas and (b) oxygen gas that react to yield 50.00 mL of chlorine gas given the following unbalanced equation. Assume that all gases are at the same temperature and pressure.

$$\text{HCl}(g) + \text{O}_2(g) \longrightarrow \text{Cl}_2(g) + \text{H}_2\text{O}(g)$$

Answers:

(a) 100.0 mL HCl   (b) 25.00 mL O$_2$

Concept Exercise

In general, how many unit factors are required to solve a volume–volume stoichiometry problem?

Answer: See Appendix G.

CHEMISTRY CONNECTION   Manufacturing Ammonia

Q: What are the main uses of ammonia, NH$_3$, which is one of the 10 most important industrial chemicals?

Over 15 million tons of ammonia are produced annually in the United States. Ammonia, NH$_3$, is primarily used in agriculture to fertilize the soil and replenish nitrogen depleted by crops. Although our atmosphere is a vast potential source of nitrogen, the gaseous element is unreactive and does not readily combine with other elements. Nitrogen is essentially a colorless, odorless, inert gas.

In 1905, the German chemist Fritz Haber (1868–1934) successfully prepared ammonia in the laboratory for the first time. He discovered that nitrogen and hydrogen gases combine directly at high temperatures and pressures in the presence of metal oxide catalysts. The Haber process thus provides a method for converting unreactive atmospheric

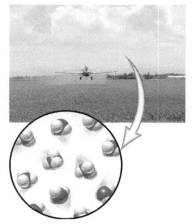

▲ **Soil Nitrogen** Spraying anhydrous ammonia provides nitrogen to soil for optimum crop yields.

nitrogen into the versatile compound ammonia, NH$_3$. Ammonia is easily converted to important ammonium compounds and nitric acid, HNO$_3$. Today, the Haber process is the main source for manufacturing nitrogen compounds throughout the world.

Until the beginning of the 1900s, the bulk of the world's nitrate was supplied by the rich saltpeter (KNO$_3$) deposits in South America. Although nitrates were used principally as fertilizer, they were also used to make explosives. Indirectly, the Haber process had a pronounced effect on World War I. Soon after the outbreak of the war, the British blockade halted the supply of Chilean saltpeter to Germany. Without a source of nitrate, Germany would have soon run out of ammunition. But by late 1914, Germany had built factories that applied the Haber process for the manufacture of ammonia and nitrate compounds.

During World War I, Haber helped to develop weapons used in chemical warfare, such as chlorine gas and even more lethal mustard gas. Haber's wife was so troubled by his crimes against humanity that she committed suicide at a dinner party honoring his role in the use of poison gas. She shot herself with his service revolver, but did not die until the following morning as Haber was leaving for the Eastern front to personally oversee the use of poison gas against the Russians. In 1918, the same year World War I ended, Haber was awarded the Nobel Prize in chemistry. Following the announcement of the Nobel Prize, he was denounced by American, English, and French scientists for his involvement in the war.

Ironically, the patriotic Haber was later condemned by his own country. When the Nazis rose to power in 1933, Haber had to resign as director of the Kaiser Wilhelm Institute because he was of Jewish descent. In distress, he fled to Cambridge University in England where he spent a few months before passing away while traveling in Switzerland.

A: The chief use of ammonia is as an agricultural fertilizer, but it is also used in explosives and household products such as ordinary window cleaner.

▶ To explain the concept of a limiting reactant.

▶ To identify the limiting reactant in a chemical reaction given the number of moles of each reactant.

▲ **Producing FeS** Heating a mixture of iron powder and sulfur powder produces iron(II) sulfide; either the iron or the sulfur can be the limiting reactant.

9.7 LIMITING REACTANT CONCEPT

In world-class cycling, competitors carry extra bicycle frames and tires. If a cyclist participating in the Tour de France bicycle race has 5 frames and 20 tires, how many complete bicycles can be assembled? Because 5 complete frames require 10 tires, there are 10 spare tires. In this example, the frames limit the number of bicycles that can be assembled. Similarly, we will learn that one of the reactants in a chemical reaction can limit the amount of product.

We have learned how to perform calculations using information from a balanced chemical equation. For example, we can calculate the amount of iron(II) sulfide produced by the reaction of metallic iron and powdered sulfur:

$$\text{Fe}(s) + \text{S}(s) \xrightarrow{\Delta} \text{FeS}(s)$$

Previously, we assumed that there is sufficient iron and sulfur to react completely with each other. However, this assumption may not be true. What if there is not enough sulfur to react with the iron? If that were the case, the sulfur would *limit* the amount of FeS produced. In a stoichiometry problem, the reactant that controls the amount of product is called the **limiting reactant** and must be identified to correctly calculate the amount of product. Figure 9.1 is an example model to help you visualize the concept of a limiting reactant.

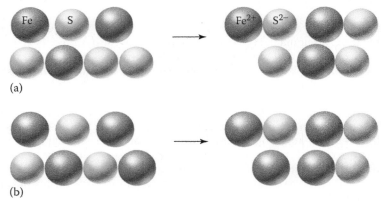

▲ **Figure 9.1 Limiting Reactant Concept** (a) In this reaction there is excess S; thus, Fe is the limiting reactant. Notice that an unreacted S atom remains. (b) In another reaction, there is excess Fe; thus, S is the limiting reactant. Notice that an unreacted Fe atom remains.

Determining the Limiting Reactant

Now that we have a visual model for the limiting reactant concept, let's examine data from an experiment and solve a problem. Suppose we heat 2.50 mol of iron with 3.00 mol of sulfur. How many moles of FeS are formed? We will analyze the problem by considering the amount of each substance before and after the reaction.

Before the reaction begins, there are 2.50 mol of Fe, 3.00 mol of S, and 0.00 mol of FeS. According to the balanced equation, 1 mol of Fe reacts with 1 mol of S to give 1 mol of FeS. Therefore, 2.50 mol of Fe reacts with 2.50 mol of S to give 2.50 mol of FeS. At the outset we have 3.00 mol of S, so there is not enough iron to react with all the sulfur. Therefore, iron is the limiting reactant and sulfur is the excess reactant. After the reaction, the excess sulfur is 0.50 mol (3.00 mol − 2.50 mol). Table 9.2 summarizes the amounts of each substance before and after the reaction.

TABLE 9.2 SUMMARY OF EXPERIMENTAL SYNTHESIS OF FES

EXPERIMENT	MOL FE	MOL S	MOL FES
before reaction:	2.50	3.00	0.00
after reaction:	0.00	0.50	2.50

Example Exercise 9.9 Limiting Reactant Concept

A 1.00 mol sample of iron(II) oxide is heated with 1.00 mol of aluminum metal and converted to molten iron. Identify the limiting reactant, and calculate the moles of iron produced:

$$3\, FeO(l) + 2\, Al(l) \xrightarrow{\Delta} 3\, Fe(l) + Al_2O_3(s)$$

Strategy Plan

Step 1: What unit is asked for in the answer?

Step 1: mol Fe

Step 2: What given value is related to the answer?

Step 2: 1.00 mol FeO and 1.00 mol Al

Step 3: What unit factor(s) should we apply? From the balanced equation, we have the mole ratio 3 mol FeO/3 mol Fe, and 2 mol Al/3 mol Fe.

Step 3:

$$\frac{3\ mol\ FeO}{3\ mol\ Fe} \quad or \quad \frac{3\ mol\ Fe}{3\ mol\ FeO}$$

$$\frac{2\ mol\ Al}{3\ mol\ Fe} \quad or \quad \frac{3\ mol\ Fe}{2\ mol\ Al}$$

Unit Analysis Map

given value
1.00 mol FeO

× *unit factor*
$\dfrac{3\ mol\ Fe}{3\ mol\ FeO}$

unit in answer
= ? mol Fe

given value
1.00 mol Al

× *unit factor*
$\dfrac{3\ mol\ Fe}{2\ mol\ Al}$

unit in answer
= ? mol Fe

Solution

We select the unit factor that cancels the unit in the given value (mol FeO). Thus,

$$1.00\ mol\ FeO \times \frac{3\ mol\ Fe}{3\ mol\ FeO} = 1.00\ mol\ Fe$$

Second, we select the unit factor that cancels the unit in the given value (mol Al). Thus,

$$1.00\ mol\ Al \times \frac{3\ mol\ Fe}{2\ mol\ Al} = 1.50\ mol\ Fe$$

Notice that FeO produces 1.00 mol Fe, whereas Al produces 1.50 mol Fe. Thus, FeO is the *limiting reactant* and the amount of product is **1.00 mol Fe**.

Practice Exercise

A 5.00 mol sample of iron(III) oxide is heated with 5.00 mol aluminum metal and converted to molten iron. Identify the limiting reactant, and calculate the moles of iron produced given the *unbalanced* equation for the reaction:

$$Fe_2O_3(l) + Al(l) \xrightarrow{\Delta} Fe(l) + Al_2O_3(s)$$

Answer: The limiting reactant is Al, which produces 5.00 mol of Fe.

Concept Exercise

A Tour de France cyclist has 10 tires and 3 frames. How many complete bicycles can be assembled?

Answer: See Appendix G.

▲ **Thermite Reaction** The thermite reaction of iron oxide and aluminum metal produces molten iron and a shower of sparks.

▶ To perform mass–
mass stoichiometry
calculations involving a
limiting reactant.

▶ To perform volume–
volume stoichiometry
calculations involving a
gaseous limiting reactant.

9.8 LIMITING REACTANT PROBLEMS

Suppose we wish to find how much molten iron is produced from the reaction of 25.0 g of FeO with 25.0 g of Al. The balanced equation for the reaction is

$$3\,FeO(l) + 2\,Al(l) \xrightarrow{\Delta} 3\,Fe(l) + Al_2O_3(s)$$

Because the mass of each reactant is given, it is not obvious whether FeO or Al limits the amount of iron produced. In problems where we are given the amounts of two reactants, we can determine the limiting reactant in three steps.

I. *Calculate the mass of product that can be produced from the first reactant.*
  (a) Calculate the moles of reactant.
  (b) Calculate the moles of product.
  (c) Calculate the mass of product.

II. *Calculate the mass of product that can be produced from the second reactant.*
  (a) Calculate the moles of reactant.
  (b) Calculate the moles of product.
  (c) Calculate the mass of product.

III. *State the limiting reactant and the corresponding mass of product formed.* The limiting reactant gives the least amount of product. The actual mass of product obtained from the chemical reaction is the lesser of the two product masses calculated in Steps I and II.

Applying I: We can calculate the amount of iron produced from iron(II) oxide in the preceding problem. Using the balanced equation for the reaction, we can find the mass of Fe produced from 25.0 g of FeO. Let's outline the solution to the problem:

$$\text{g FeO} \longrightarrow \text{mol FeO} \longrightarrow \text{mol Fe} \longrightarrow \text{g Fe}$$
$$\text{I(a)} \qquad\qquad \text{I(b)} \qquad\qquad \text{I(c)}$$

From the periodic table, we find that for Fe, the molar mass is 55.85 g/mol, and for FeO, the molar mass is 71.85 g/mol. The unit analysis solution to the problem is

$$25.0\ \text{g FeO} \times \frac{1\ \text{mol FeO}}{71.85\ \text{g FeO}} \times \frac{3\ \text{mol Fe}}{3\ \text{mol FeO}} \times \frac{55.85\ \text{g Fe}}{1\ \text{mol Fe}} = 19.4\ \text{g Fe}$$

Applying II: We calculate the amount of iron that can be produced by the aluminum. Using the balanced equation, we can find the mass of Fe produced from 25.0 g of Al. We can outline the solution to the problem as follows:

$$\text{g Al} \longrightarrow \text{mol Al} \longrightarrow \text{mol Fe} \longrightarrow \text{g Fe}$$
$$\text{II(a)} \qquad\qquad \text{II(b)} \qquad\qquad \text{II(c)}$$

From the periodic table, we find that for Al, the molar mass is 26.98 g/mol. The unit analysis solution to the problem is

$$25.0\ \text{g Al} \times \frac{1\ \text{mol Al}}{26.98\ \text{g Al}} \times \frac{3\ \text{mol Fe}}{2\ \text{mol Al}} \times \frac{55.85\ \text{g Fe}}{1\ \text{mol Fe}} = 77.6\ \text{g Fe}$$

Applying III: We compare the grams of Fe produced from each of the reactants:

$$25.0\ \text{g FeO} \longrightarrow 19.4\ \text{g Fe}$$
$$25.0\ \text{g Al} \longrightarrow 77.6\ \text{g Fe}$$

We see that the FeO yields less mass of product; thus, FeO is the *limiting reactant.* Conversely, aluminum metal is the excess reactant, because not all the Al is used in the reaction. Therefore, the maximum yield of metallic iron from the reaction is limited to 19.4 g of Fe.

Example Exercise 9.10 provides additional practice in solving a limiting reactant problem.

Example Exercise 9.10 Mass–Mass Limiting Reactant

In a reaction, 50.0 g of manganese(IV) oxide reacts with 25.0 g of aluminum. Identify the limiting reactant and calculate the mass of manganese metal produced. The equation for the reaction is

$$3\ MnO_2(l) + 4\ Al(l) \xrightarrow{\Delta} 3\ Mn(l) + 2\ Al_2O_3(s)$$

Solution

Step1: We calculate the mass of Mn produced from 50.0 g of MnO_2. We can outline the solution as follows:

$$g\ MnO_2 \longrightarrow mol\ MnO_2 \longrightarrow mol\ Mn \longrightarrow g\ Mn$$

From the periodic table, we find the molar mass of MnO_2 is 86.94 g/mol and Mn is 54.94 g/mol. The unit analysis solution to the problem is

$$50.0\ g\ MnO_2 \times \frac{1\ mol\ MnO_2}{86.94\ g\ MnO_2} \times \frac{3\ mol\ Mn}{3\ mol\ MnO_2} \times \frac{54.94\ g\ Mn}{1\ mol\ Mn} = 31.6\ g\ Mn$$

Step2: We calculate the mass of Mn produced from 25.0 g of Al. We can outline the solution as follows:

$$g\ Al \longrightarrow mol\ Al \longrightarrow mol\ Mn \longrightarrow g\ Mn$$

From the periodic table, we find that the molar mass of Al is 26.98 g/mol. Starting with 25.0 g of Al, the unit analysis solution is

$$25.0\ g\ Al \times \frac{1\ mol\ Al}{26.98\ g\ Al} \times \frac{3\ mol\ Mn}{4\ mol\ Al} \times \frac{54.94\ g\ Mn}{1\ mol\ Mn} = 38.2\ g\ Mn$$

Step3: We compare the mass of product obtained from each of the reactants:

$$50.0\ g\ MnO_2 \longrightarrow 31.6\ g\ Mn$$
$$25.0\ g\ Al \longrightarrow 38.2\ g\ Mn$$

In this example, MnO_2 is the *limiting reactant* because it yields less product. Al is the excess reactant and is not completely consumed in the reaction. Thus, the maximum amount of product from the reaction is 31.6 g of Mn.

Practice Exercise

In a reaction, 75.0 g of manganese(IV) oxide react with 30.0 g of aluminum. Identify the limiting reactant and calculate the mass of aluminum oxide produced:

$$3\ MnO_2(l) + 4\ Al(l) \xrightarrow{\Delta} 3\ Mn(l) + 2\ Al_2O_3(s)$$

Answer: The limiting reactant is Al, which gives 56.7 g of Al_2O_3.

Concept Exercise

Indicate the limiting reactant shown in the following illustration:

$$Zn(s) + S(s) \xrightarrow{\Delta} ZnS(s)$$

Answer: See Appendix G.

Limiting Reactants Involving Volumes of Gas

Now let's try a limiting reactant problem that involves reactants and products in the gaseous state. For example, consider the reaction of nitrogen monoxide and oxygen to give nitrogen dioxide. The balanced equation for the reaction is

$$2\,NO(g) + O_2(g) \xrightarrow{\text{UV}} 2\,NO_2(g)$$

Suppose 5.00 L of NO gas reacts with 5.00 L of O_2 gas. The volumes of both reactants are given, so it is not obvious which gas limits the amount of product. We will assume that the temperature and pressure remain constant and use the following three steps to determine the limiting reactant:

I. *Calculate the volume of product that can be produced from the first reactant.*

Recall that the coefficients in the balanced equation are in the same mole ratio as the volumes of gas.

II. *Calculate the volume of product that can be produced from the second reactant.*

Again, the coefficients in the balanced equation are in the same mole ratio as the volumes of gas.

III. *State the limiting reactant and the corresponding volume of product.*

The limiting reactant is the gas that gives the least amount of product. The actual volume of product obtained from the chemical reaction is the lesser of the two volumes calculated in Steps I and II.

Applying I: We calculate the volume of nitrogen dioxide produced from 5.00 L of nitrogen monoxide gas. From the balanced equation, we see that 2 mol of NO produce 2 mol of NO_2. Accordingly, 2 L of NO produce 2 L of NO_2. Hence,

$$5.00\ \text{L NO} \times \frac{2\ \text{L NO}_2}{2\ \text{L NO}} = 5.00\ \text{L NO}_2$$

Applying II: We calculate the volume of nitrogen dioxide produced from 5.00 L of oxygen gas. From the balanced equation, we see that 1 mol of O_2 produces 2 mol of NO_2. Accordingly, 1 L of O_2 produces 2 L of NO_2. Thus,

$$5.00\ \text{L O}_2 \times \frac{2\ \text{L NO}_2}{1\ \text{L O}_2} = 10.0\ \text{L NO}_2$$

Applying III: We compare the liters of NO_2 gas from each of the reactants.

$$5.00\ \text{L NO} \longrightarrow 5.00\ \text{L NO}_2$$

$$5.00\ \text{L O}_2 \longrightarrow 10.0\ \text{L NO}_2$$

We see that the NO yields less volume of product; thus, NO is the *limiting reactant.* Conversely, O_2 is the excess reactant, and not all the O_2 gas is used in the reaction. Therefore, the maximum yield of product from the reaction is 5.00 L of NO_2. The following example exercise provides additional practice in solving a limiting reactant problem involving gases.

▲ **Oxyacetylene Welding** The reaction of oxygen and acetylene gases releases enough heat to melt iron.

Example Exercise 9.11   Volume–Volume Limiting Reactant

In oxyacetylene welding, acetylene reacts with oxygen to give carbon dioxide and water. If 25.0 mL of C_2H_2 reacts with 75.0 mL of O_2, what is the limiting reactant? Assuming constant conditions, what is the volume of CO_2 produced?

$$2\,C_2H_2(g) + 5\,O_2(g) \xrightarrow{\text{spark}} 4\,CO_2(g) + 2\,H_2O(g)$$

Strategy Plan

Step1: What unit is asked for in the answer? **Step 1:** mL CO_2

Step2: What given value is related to the answer? **Step 2:** 25.0 mL C_2H_2 and 75.0 mL O_2

Step3: What unit factor(s) should we apply? From the balanced equation, we have the mole ratio so the volume ratio is 2 mL C_2H_2/4 mL CO_2, and 5 mL O_2/4 mL CO_2.

Step 3:

$$\frac{2 \text{ mL } C_2H_2}{4 \text{ mL } CO_2} \quad \text{or} \quad \frac{4 \text{ mL } CO_2}{2 \text{ mL } C_2H_2}$$

$$\frac{5 \text{ mL } O_2}{4 \text{ mL } CO_2} \quad \text{or} \quad \frac{4 \text{ mL } CO_2}{5 \text{ mL } O_2}$$

Unit Analysis Map

given value		*unit factor*		*unit in answer*
25.0 mL C_2H_2	$\times$	$\dfrac{4 \text{ mL } CO_2}{2 \text{ mL } C_2H_2}$		$= ?$ mL CO_2

given value		*unit factor*		*unit in answer*
75.0 mL O_2	$\times$	$\dfrac{4 \text{ mL } CO_2}{5 \text{ mL } O_2}$		$= ?$ mL CO_2

Solution

First, we find the amount of product that can be produced from the first reactant (mL C_2H_2). Thus,

$$25.0 \text{ mL } C_2H_2 \times \frac{4 \text{ mL } CO_2}{2 \text{ mL } C_2H_2} = 50.0 \text{ mL } CO_2$$

Second, we find the amount of product that can be produced from the second reactant (mL O_2):

$$75.0 \text{ mL } O_2 \times \frac{4 \text{ mL } CO_2}{5 \text{ mL } O_2} = 60.0 \text{ mL } CO_2$$

Third, we compare the amount of product from each reactant and see that C_2H_2 produces 50.0 mL CO_2, whereas O_2 produces 60.0 mL CO_2. Thus, C_2H_2 is the *limiting reactant* and the amount of product is limited to 50.0 mL CO_2.

Practice Exercise

Ethane undergoes combustion to give carbon dioxide and water. If 10.0 L of C_2H_6 reacts with 25.0 L of O_2, what is the limiting reactant? Assuming constant conditions, what is the volume of CO_2 produced? The equation is

$$2 \text{ } C_2H_6(g) + 7 \text{ } O_2(g) \xrightarrow{\text{spark}} 4 \text{ } CO_2(g) + 6 \text{ } H_2O(g)$$

Answer: The limiting reactant is O_2, which gives 14.3 L of CO_2.

Concept Exercise

Indicate the limiting reactant shown in the following illustration:

$$Zn(s) + S(s) \xrightarrow{\Delta} ZnS(s)$$

Answer: See Appendix G.

9.9 PERCENT YIELD

To understand the concept of yield, consider the following laboratory experiment. First, a student weighs a 1.00-g sample of cadmium chloride and dissolves it in water. Then, the student adds aqueous sodium sulfide solution to obtain a precipitate of cadmium sulfide, CdS. The balanced equation for the reaction is

$$CdCl_2(aq) + Na_2S(aq) \longrightarrow CdS(s) + 2\,NaCl(aq)$$

The student collects the insoluble CdS precipitate in filter paper and determines its mass on a balance. The mass of the precipitate is called the **actual yield**.

The mass of cadmium sulfide obtained, starting with the 1.00-g sample of cadmium chloride, can also be calculated as a mass–mass problem. The calculated amount of precipitate is called the **theoretical yield**. In practice, there is always inherent experimental error. Thus, we compare the actual and theoretical yields and express the results in terms of percent yield. The **percent yield** is the amount of the actual yield compared to the theoretical yield expressed as a percent:

$$\frac{\text{actual yield}}{\text{theoretical yield}} \times 100\% = \text{percent yield}$$

To find the percent yield for this laboratory experiment, we start with the 1.00-g sample of cadmium chloride. Applying stoichiometry to the balanced equation, we calculate that the amount of cadmium sulfide precipitate is 0.788 g. Suppose the student weighs the CdS precipitate and finds that it has an actual mass of 0.775 g. To find the percent yield, we compare the actual yield (0.775 g) to the theoretical yield (0.788 g) as follows:

$$\frac{0.775\ \cancel{g}}{0.788\ \cancel{g}} \times 100\% = 98.4\%$$

Suppose that the student performs a second trial for the same experiment, using a 1.00-g sample of cadmium chloride. In this second trial, the precipitate has a mass of 0.805 g. Since the student started with 1.00 g of cadmium chloride, the theoretical yield for the two trials is the same, 0.788 g. As before, to find the percent yield we compare the actual yield to the theoretical yield.

$$\frac{0.805\ \cancel{g}}{0.788\ \cancel{g}} \times 100\% = 102\%$$

Notice that the percent yield for this second trial is greater than 100%. Although surprising, this result is possible. In an experiment, some errors lead to high results and other errors lead to low results. In the two trials, the student made different types of experimental errors. For example, high results will be obtained when impurities are trapped, or when the precipitate is not completely dry.

The following example exercise provides additional practice in calculating percent yield:

▲ **Percent Yield of CdS** The aqueous solution reaction of $CdCl_2$ and Na_2S yields a yellow precipitate of CdS.

▲ **Percent Yield of CuCO₃** The aqueous solution reaction of $Cu(NO_3)_2$ and Na_2CO_3 yields a precipitate of $CuCO_3$.

> **Example Exercise 9.12**   Percent Yield

A student dissolves 1.50 g of copper(II) nitrate in water. After adding aqueous sodium carbonate solution, the student obtains 0.875 g of $CuCO_3$ precipitate. If the theoretical yield is 0.988 g, what is the percent yield?

$$Cu(NO_3)_2(aq) + Na_2CO_3(aq) \longrightarrow CuCO_3(s) + 2\,NaNO_3(aq)$$

Solution

The percent yield is the ratio of the actual yield compared to the theoretical yield. In this experiment, the actual yield is 0.875 g and the theoretical yield is 0.988 g. The percent yield, therefore, is

$$\frac{\text{actual yield}}{\text{theoretical yield}} \times 100\% = \text{percent yield}$$

$$\frac{0.875 \text{ g}}{0.988 \text{ g}} \times 100\% = 88.6\%$$

The percent yield obtained by the student is 88.6%.

Practice Exercise

Ammonium nitrate is used in explosives and is produced by the reaction of ammonia, NH_3, and nitric acid. The equation for the reaction is

$$NH_3(g) + HNO_3(aq) \longrightarrow NH_4NO_3(s)$$

If 15.0 kg of ammonia gives an actual yield of 65.3 kg of ammonium nitrate, what is the percent yield? The calculated yield of ammonium nitrate for the experiment is 70.5 kg.

Answer: 92.6%

Concept Exercise

Is it possible to have a percent yield greater than 100%?

Answer: See Appendix G.

Summary

LEARNING OBJECTIVES	SEC	EXERCISES
To relate the coefficients in a balanced chemical equation to (a) moles of reactants and products, and (b) liters of gaseous reactants and products.	9.1	Exercises 1–4
To verify the coefficients of a balanced chemical equation using the conservation of mass law.	9.1	Exercises 5–6
To relate the number of moles of two substances in a balanced equation.	9.2	Exercises 7–12
To classify the three basic types of stoichiometry problems: mass–mass, mass–volume, and volume–volume.	9.3	Exercises 13–18
To perform mass–mass stoichiometry calculations.	9.4	Exercises 19–28
To perform mass–volume stoichiometry calculations.	9.5	Exercises 29–36
To perform volume–volume stoichiometry calculations.	9.6	Exercises 37–48
To explain the concept of a limiting reactant.	9.7	Exercises 49–50
To identify the limiting reactant in a chemical reaction given the number of moles of each reactant.	9.7	Exercises 51–58
To perform mass–mass stoichiometry calculations involving a limiting reactant.	9.8	Exercises 59–66
To perform volume–volume stoichiometry calculations involving a gaseous limiting reactant.	9.8	Exercises 67–74
To calculate the percent yield for a reaction given the actual yield and theoretical yield.	9.9	Exercises 75–78

Section 9.1 We learned to interpret the coefficients in a balanced equation as a **mole ratio**. We also showed that by applying **Avogadro's theory** we can express the mole ratio in terms of volumes of gases. Furthermore, we illustrated the **law of conservation of mass** by substituting the **molar mass** for a mole of each reactant and product into a balanced chemical equation.

Section 9.2 We learned to relate the moles of reactants to the moles of products by simply applying the coefficients in the balanced chemical reaction.

Section 9.3 **Stoichiometry** relates the quantities of substances involved in a chemical reaction. There are three basic types of stoichiometry problems. In a **mass–mass problem**, the mass of one substance is related to the mass of another substance according to a balanced chemical equation. In a **mass–volume problem**, the mass of a substance is related to the volume of a gas. In a **volume–volume problem**, the volumes of two gaseous substances are related.

Section 9.4 In a mass–mass problem, we first convert the given mass of a substance to the number of moles using the molar mass. If the molar mass is not shown in the problem, we refer to the periodic table and add up the gram atomic masses for each element in the substance. Next, we apply the mole ratio to convert the moles of the given substance to the moles of the unknown substance using the coefficients from the balanced equation. Finally, we determine the mass of the unknown by multiplying by the molar mass of the unknown.

Section 9.5 In a mass–volume problem, we first convert the given mass of substance to the number of moles using the molar mass. Next, we apply the mole ratio to convert the moles of the given substance to the moles of the unknown substance using the coefficients from the balanced equation. Finally, we determine the volume of the unknown gas at STP by multiplying by the **molar volume**. The volume occupied by 1 mol of gas is 22.4 L at STP, that is, 0 °C and 1 atm pressure.

Section 9.6 In a volume–volume problem, we can take advantage of Gay-Lussac's **law of combining volumes**. Since the volumes of gases combine in the same whole-number ratio as the coefficients in the balanced equation, we can solve this type of problem in one conversion step. We simply multiply the given volume by the ratio of the coefficients in the equation.

Section 9.7 In more difficult stoichiometry problems, we cannot assume that there is a sufficient quantity of each reactant available. The amount of one reactant may not be sufficient to completely consume another reactant that is in excess. The reactant that controls the reaction and limits the amount of product formed is referred to as the **limiting reactant**.

Section 9.8 If we are given the amounts of two reactants, we can determine the limiting reactant by finding the amount of product yield from each of the reactants. The reactant that produces the least amount of product controls the reaction and is the limiting reactant. A limiting reactant problem may involve the masses of two reacting substances as well as the volumes of two gases.

Section 9.9 The percent yield provides an evaluation of the laboratory method and the skill of the analyst. A **percent yield** from an experiment expresses the amount of the **actual yield** compared to the **theoretical yield**.

PROBLEM-SOLVING ORGANIZER

TOPIC	PROCEDURE	EXAMPLE
Interpreting a Chemical Equation Sec. 9.1	Express the mole ratio and volume ratio of gaseous substances in a balanced equation using the coefficients.	Given that $N_2(g) + O_2(g) \longrightarrow 2NO(g)$, interpret the mole ratio and the volume ratio in liters. $1 \text{ mol } N_2 + 1 \text{ mol } O_2 \longrightarrow 2 \text{ mol } NO$ $1 \text{ L } N_2 + 1 \text{ L } O_2 \longrightarrow 2 \text{ L } NO$
Mole–Mole Relationships Sec. 9.2	Convert moles of a given substance to moles of an unknown using the mole ratio.	How many moles of NO are produced from 0.500 mol N_2? $0.500 \text{ mol } N_2 \times \dfrac{2 \text{ mol NO}}{1 \text{ mol } N_2} = 1.00 \text{ mol NO}$
Types of Stoichiometry Problems Sec. 9.3	Classify a stoichiometry problem as a mass–mass, mass–volume, or volume–volume type of problem.	What type of problem is the following: How many grams of NO are produced from 11.2 L N_2? This is a mass–volume type problem.
Mass–Mass Problems Sec. 9.4	(a) Convert mass of given to moles of given. (b) Convert moles of given to moles of unknown. (c) Convert moles of unknown to mass of unknown.	How many grams of NO are produced from 10.0 g N_2? $10.0 \text{ g } N_2 \times \dfrac{1 \text{ mol } N_2}{28.02 \text{ g } N_2} \times \dfrac{2 \text{ mol NO}}{1 \text{ mol } N_2} \times \dfrac{30.01 \text{ g NO}}{1 \text{ mol NO}}$ $= 21.4 \text{ g NO}$
Mass–Volume Problems Sec. 9.5	(a) Convert mass of given to moles of given. (b) Convert moles of given to moles unknown. (c) Convert moles unknown to volume unknown.	How many liters of NO at STP are produced from 10.0 g N_2? $10.0 \text{ g } N_2 \times \dfrac{1 \text{ mol } N_2}{28.02 \text{ g } N_2} \times \dfrac{2 \text{ mol NO}}{1 \text{ mol } N_2} \times \dfrac{22.4 \text{ L NO}}{1 \text{ mol NO}}$ $= 16.0 \text{ L NO}$
Volume–Volume Problems Sec. 9.6	Convert volume of given to volume of unknown.	How many liters of NO at STP are produced from 10.0 L N_2? $10.0 \text{ L } N_2 \times \dfrac{2 \text{ L NO}}{1 \text{ L } N_2} = 20.0 \text{ L NO}$

Key Terms *Answers to Key Terms are in Appendix H.*

Select the key term that corresponds to each of the following definitions.

_____ **1.** the ratio of moles of reactants and products according to the coefficients in the balanced chemical equation

_____ **2.** the principle that equal volumes of gases contain equal numbers of molecules, at the same temperature and pressure

_____ **3.** the principle that mass is neither gained nor lost during a chemical reaction

_____ **4.** the mass in grams of 1 mol of substance

_____ **5.** the relationship of quantities (i.e., mass of a substance, or volume of a gas) in a chemical reaction according to the balanced equation

_____ **6.** a type of stoichiometry calculation that relates the masses of two substances

_____ **7.** a type of stoichiometry calculation that relates the mass of a substance to the volume of a gas

_____ **8.** a type of stoichiometry calculation that relates the volumes of two gases at the same temperature and pressure

_____ **9.** the volume of 1 mol of gas at STP, that is, 22.4 L/mol

_____ **10.** a temperature of 0 °C and a pressure of 1 atm

_____ **11.** the principle that states that the volumes of gases that react in a chemical reaction are in the ratio of small whole numbers

_____ **12.** the substance in a chemical reaction that controls the maximum amount of product formed

_____ **13.** the amount of product experimentally obtained from a given amount of reactant

_____ **14.** the amount of product calculated to be obtained from a given amount of reactant

_____ **15.** the actual yield compared to the theoretical yield expressed as a percent

(a) actual yield *(Sec. 9.9)*
(b) Avogadro's theory *(Sec. 9.1)*
(c) law of combining volumes *(Sec. 9.6)*
(d) law of conservation of mass *(Sec. 9.1)*
(e) limiting reactant *(Sec. 9.7)*
(f) mass–mass problem *(Sec. 9.3)*
(g) mass–volume problem *(Sec. 9.3)*
(h) molar mass *(Sec. 9.1)*
(i) molar volume *(Sec. 9.5)*
(j) mole ratio *(Sec. 9.1)*
(k) percent yield *(Sec. 9.9)*
(l) standard temperature and pressure (STP) *(Sec. 9.5)*
(m) stoichiometry *(Sec. 9.3)*
(n) theoretical yield *(Sec. 9.9)*
(o) volume–volume problem *(Sec. 9.3)*

Exercises *Answers to odd-numbered Exercises are in Appendix I.*

Interpreting a Chemical Equation (Sec. 9.1)

1. Consider the general chemical equation
   $A + 2B \longrightarrow 3C + 2D$.
   (a) How many moles of C are produced from 1 mol of A?
   (b) How many liters of gas B must react to give 2 L of gas D at the same temperature and pressure?

2. Consider the general chemical equation
   $2A + 3B \longrightarrow 2C + D$.
   (a) How many moles of C are produced from 2 mol of A?
   (b) How many liters of gas B must react to give 1 L of gas D at the same temperature and pressure?

3. Consider the general chemical equation $2A + 3B \longrightarrow C$.
   (a) If 1.00 g of A reacts with 1.50 g of B, what is the mass of C?
   (b) If 2.00 g of A reacts to produce 5.00 g of C, what is the mass of B?

4. Consider the general chemical equation $3A + B \longrightarrow 2C$.
   (a) If 1.50 g of A reacts with 1.65 g of B, what is the mass of C?
   (b) If 4.50 g of A reacts to produce 9.45 g of C, what is the mass of B?

5. Verify the conservation of mass law using the molar masses of reactants and products for each substance in the following balanced equations:
   (a) $2 N_2(g) + O_2(g) \longrightarrow 2 N_2O(g)$
   (b) $N_2(g) + 2 O_2(g) \longrightarrow N_2O_4(g)$

6. Verify the conservation of mass law using the molar masses of reactants and products for each substance in the following balanced equations:
   (a) $P_4(s) + 3 O_2(g) \longrightarrow 2 P_2O_3(s)$
   (b) $P_4(s) + 5 O_2(g) \longrightarrow 2 P_2O_5(s)$

Mole–Mole Relationships (Sec. 9.2)

7. Given the decomposition of hydrogen peroxide, calculate the moles of oxygen gas produced from 5.00 mol of H_2O_2.
   $$2 H_2O_2(l) \longrightarrow 2 H_2O(l) + O_2(g)$$

8. Given the reaction of hydrogen and chlorine gases, calculate the moles of hydrogen that react to produce 5.00 mol of HCl.
   $$H_2(g) + Cl_2(g) \longrightarrow 2 HCl(g)$$

9. How many moles of chlorine gas react with 0.100 mol of metallic iron? How many moles of iron(III) chloride are produced?

$$Fe(s) + Cl_2(g) \longrightarrow FeCl_3(s)$$

10. How many moles of barium metal react to produce 0.100 mol of barium nitride? How many moles of nitrogen gas react?

$$Ba(s) + N_2(g) \longrightarrow Ba_3N_2(s)$$

11. How many moles of propane gas, C_3H_8, react with 2.50 mol of oxygen gas? How many moles of carbon dioxide are produced?

$$C_3H_8(g) + O_2(g) \longrightarrow CO_2(g) + H_2O(g)$$

◄ **Propane Torch** The reaction of propane gas, C_3H_8, and oxygen in the air releases heat energy.

12. How many moles of butane gas, C_4H_{10}, react to produce 2.50 mol of water? How many moles of oxygen gas react?

$$C_4H_{10}(g) + O_2(g) \longrightarrow CO_2(g) + H_2O(g)$$

Types of Stoichiometry Problems (Sec. 9.3)

13. Classify the type of stoichiometry problem: How many liters of carbon dioxide gas are produced from the decomposition of 25.0 g NaHCO₃?

14. Classify the type of stoichiometry problem: How many grams of baking soda must decompose to give 25.0 mL CO_2 gas?

15. Classify the type of stoichiometry problem: How many milliliters of hydrogen bromide gas are produced from 25.0 mL of H_2 gas and excess bromine liquid?

16. Classify the type of stoichiometry problem: How many milliliters of hydrogen gas react with bromine liquid to yield 25.0 cm³ of HBr gas?

17. Classify the type of stoichiometry problem: How many grams of ferric oxide are produced from steam and 1.00 g of iron?

18. Classify the type of stoichiometry problem: How many grams of potassium chlorate must decompose to give 1.00 g of KCl?

Mass–Mass Problems (Sec. 9.4)

19. What is the mass of silver that can be prepared from 1.00 g of copper metal?

$$Cu(s) + 2\,AgNO_3(aq) \longrightarrow Cu(NO_3)_2(aq) + 2\,Ag(s)$$

20. How many grams of silver nitrate must react to give 1.00 g of Ag according to the equation in Exercise 19?

21. Given the balanced equation, calculate the mass of product that can be prepared from 1.00 g of zinc metal.

$$2\,Zn(s) + O_2(g) \longrightarrow 2\,ZnO(s)$$

22. How many grams of oxygen gas must react to give 1.00 g of ZnO according to the equation in Exercise 21?

23. Given the balanced equation, calculate the mass of product that can be prepared from 3.45 g of bismuth metal.

$$2\,Bi(s) + 3\,Cl_2(g) \longrightarrow 2\,BiCl_3(s)$$

24. How many grams of chlorine gas must react to give 3.52 g of BiCl₃ according to the equation in Exercise 23?

25. What is the mass of mercury that can be prepared from 1.25 g of cobalt metal?

$$Co(s) + HgCl_2(aq) \longrightarrow CoCl_3(aq) + Hg(l)$$

26. How many grams of mercuric chloride must react to give 5.11 g of Hg according to the equation in Exercise 25?

27. What is the mass of calcium phosphate that can be prepared from 1.78 g of Na₃PO₄?

$$Na_3PO_4(aq) + Ca(OH)_2(aq) \longrightarrow Ca_3(PO_4)_2(s) + NaOH(aq)$$

28. How many grams of calcium hydroxide must react to give 2.39 g of Ca₃(PO₄)₂ according to the equation in Exercise 27?

Mass–Volume Problems (Sec. 9.5)

29. How many milliliters of carbon dioxide gas at STP are produced from the decomposition of 1.59 g of lithium hydrogen carbonate?

$$2\,LiHCO_3(s) \longrightarrow Li_2CO_3(s) + H_2O(l) + CO_2(g)$$

30. How many milliliters of carbon dioxide gas at STP are produced from the decomposition of 5.00 g of iron(III) carbonate?

$$Fe_2(CO_3)_3(s) \longrightarrow Fe_2O_3(s) + 3\,CO_2(g)$$

31. How many milliliters of oxygen gas at STP are released from heating 5.00 g of calcium chlorate?

$$Ca(ClO_3)_2(s) \longrightarrow CaCl_2(s) + 3\,O_2(g)$$

32. How many milliliters of oxygen gas at STP are released from heating 2.50 g of mercuric oxide?

$$2\,HgO(s) \longrightarrow 2\,Hg(l) + O_2(g)$$

33. What mass of magnesium metal reacts with sulfuric acid to produce 225 mL of hydrogen gas at STP?

$$Mg(s) + H_2SO_4(aq) \longrightarrow MgSO_4(aq) + H_2(g)$$

34. What mass of manganese(II) chloride must react with sulfuric acid to release 49.5 mL of hydrogen chloride gas at STP?

$$MnCl_2(s) + H_2SO_4(aq) \longrightarrow MnSO_4(aq) + 2\,HCl(g)$$

35. How many grams of sodium metal react with water to give 75.0 mL of hydrogen gas at STP?

$$Na(s) + H_2O(l) \longrightarrow NaOH(aq) + H_2(g)$$

36. How many grams of hydrogen peroxide must decompose to give 55.0 mL of oxygen gas at STP?

$$H_2O_2(l) \longrightarrow H_2O(l) + O_2(g)$$

◀ **Hydrogen Peroxide**
Hydrogen peroxide is unstable and breaks down to give water and oxygen gas. When H_2O_2 is poured on a wound, the fizzing bubbles are O_2 gas.

Volume–Volume Problems (Sec. 9.6)

37. Assuming all gases are at the same temperature and pressure, how many milliliters of iodine vapor react with 125 mL of hydrogen gas?

$$H_2(g) + I_2(g) \longrightarrow 2\,HI(g)$$

38. Assuming all gases are at the same temperature and pressure, how many milliliters of hydrogen iodide are produced from 125 mL of H_2 according to the equation in Exercise 37?

39. Assuming all gases are at the same temperature and pressure, how many milliliters of nitrogen gas react to give 45.0 mL of ammonia gas?

$$3\,H_2(g) + N_2(g) \longrightarrow 2\,NH_3(g)$$

40. Assuming all gases are at the same temperature and pressure, how many milliliters of hydrogen gas must react to give 45.0 mL of NH_3 according to the equation in Exercise 39?

41. Assuming all gases are at the same temperature and pressure, how many liters of oxygen gas react with 10.0 L of carbon monoxide?

$$2\,CO(g) + O_2(g) \longrightarrow 2\,CO_2(g)$$

42. Assuming all gases are at the same temperature and pressure, how many liters of carbon dioxide are produced from 10.0 L of CO according to the equation in Exercise 41?

43. Assuming all gases are at the same temperature and pressure, how many milliliters of chlorine gas react to yield 1.75 L of dichlorine trioxide?

$$Cl_2(g) + O_2(g) \longrightarrow Cl_2O_3(g)$$

44. Assuming all gases are at the same temperature and pressure, how many milliliters of oxygen gas must react to give 1.75 L of Cl_2O_3 according to the equation in Exercise 43?

45. What volume of sulfur trioxide gas is produced from 25.0 L of oxygen gas? The volume of each gas is measured at 875 °C and 1.00 atm pressure.

$$SO_2(g) + O_2(g) \longrightarrow SO_3(g)$$

46. What volume of sulfur dioxide gas reacts with 25.0 L of O_2 according to the equation in Exercise 45? The reaction conditions are 875 °C and 1.00 atm pressure.

47. What volume of nitrogen gas reacts to yield 500.0 cm^3 of dinitrogen pentaoxide? The volume of each gas is measured at 350 °C and 2.50 atm pressure.

$$N_2(g) + O_2(g) \longrightarrow N_2O_5(g)$$

48. What volume of oxygen gas reacts to yield 500.0 cm^3 of N_2O_5 according to the equation in Exercise 47? The reaction conditions are 350 °C and 2.50 atm pressure.

The Limiting Reactant Concept (Sec. 9.7)

49. If 1.00 mol of nitrogen monoxide gas and 1.00 mol of oxygen gas react, what is the limiting reactant and how many moles of NO_2 are produced from the reaction?

$$2\,NO(g) + O_2(g) \longrightarrow 2\,NO_2(g)$$

50. If 1.00 mol of nitrogen monoxide gas and 2.00 mol of oxygen gas react, what is the limiting reactant and how many moles of NO_2 are produced according to the equation in Exercise 49?

▲ **Tour de France** The relationship between bicycle frames and tires illustrates the limiting reactant concept. If 5 frames and 20 tires are available, the number of frames limits the number of bicycles to 5.

51. If 5.00 mol of nitrogen gas and 5.00 mol of oxygen gas react, what is the limiting reactant and how many moles of NO are produced from the reaction?

$$N_2(g) + O_2(g) \longrightarrow 2\,NO(g)$$

52. If 0.125 mol of nitrogen gas and 0.125 mol of oxygen gas react, what is the limiting reactant and how many moles of NO are produced according to the equation in Exercise 51?

53. If 5.00 mol of hydrogen gas and 5.00 mol of oxygen gas react, what is the limiting reactant and how many moles of water are produced from the reaction?

$$2\,H_2(g) + O_2(g) \longrightarrow 2\,H_2O(l)$$

54. If 5.00 mol of hydrogen gas and 1.50 mol of oxygen gas react, what is the limiting reactant and how many moles of water are produced according to the equation in Exercise 53?

55. If 1.00 mol of ethane gas and 5.00 mol of oxygen gas react, what is the limiting reactant and how many moles of water are produced from the reaction?

$$2\,C_2H_6(g) + 7\,O_2(g) \longrightarrow 4\,CO_2(g) + 6\,H_2O(g)$$

56. If 1.00 mol of ethane gas and 3.00 mol of oxygen gas react, what is the limiting reactant and how many moles of water are produced according to the equation in Exercise 55?

57. Complete the following table for the reaction of cobalt and sulfur and calculate the moles of Co, S, and CoS after reaction according to the balanced equation:

$$Co(s) + S(s) \longrightarrow CoS(s)$$

Experiment	mol Co	mol S	mol CoS
(a) before reaction:	1.00	1.00	0.00
after reaction:			
(b) before reaction:	2.00	3.00	0.00
after reaction:			

58. Complete the following table for the reaction of cobalt and sulfur and calculate the moles of Co, S, and Co_2S_3 after reaction according to the balanced equation:

$$2\,Co(s) + 3\,S(s) \longrightarrow Co_2S_3(s)$$

Experiment	mol Co	mol S	mol Co_2S_3
(a) before reaction:	1.00	1.00	0.00
after reaction:			
(b) before reaction:	2.00	3.00	0.00
after reaction:			

Limiting Reactant Problems (Sec. 9.8)

59. If 40.0 g of molten iron(II) oxide reacts with 10.0 g of magnesium, what is the mass of iron produced?

$$FeO(l) + Mg(l) \longrightarrow Fe(l) + MgO(s)$$

60. If 10.0 g of molten iron(II) oxide reacts with of 40.0 g of magnesium according to the equation in Exercise 59, what is the mass of iron produced?

61. If 175 g of molten iron(III) oxide reacts with 37.5 g of aluminum, what is the mass of iron produced?

$$Fe_2O_3(l) + Al(l) \longrightarrow Fe(l) + Al_2O_3(s)$$

62. If 37.5 g of molten iron(III) oxide reacts with 175 g of aluminum according to the equation in Exercise 61, what is the mass of iron produced?

63. If 1.00 g of magnesium hydroxide reacts with 0.605 g of sulfuric acid, what is the mass of magnesium sulfate produced?

$$Mg(OH)_2(s) + H_2SO_4(l) \longrightarrow MgSO_4(s) + H_2O(l)$$

64. If 0.605 g of magnesium hydroxide reacts with 1.00 g of sulfuric acid according to the equation in Exercise 63, what is the mass of magnesium sulfate produced?

65. If 1.00 g of aluminum hydroxide reacts with 3.00 g of sulfuric acid, what is the mass of water produced?

$$Al(OH)_3(s) + H_2SO_4(l) \longrightarrow Al_2(SO_4)_3(aq) + H_2O(l)$$

66. If 3.00 g of aluminum hydroxide reacts with 1.00 g of sulfuric acid according to the equation in Exercise 65, what is the mass of water produced?

67. If 45.0 mL of nitrogen gas reacts with 95.0 mL of oxygen gas, what is the volume of NO_2 produced? Assume all gases are at the same temperature and pressure.

$$N_2(g) + O_2(g) \longrightarrow NO_2(g)$$

68. If 95.0 mL of nitrogen gas reacts with 45.0 mL of oxygen gas according to the equation in Exercise 67, what is the volume of NO_2 produced? Assume all gases are at the same temperature and pressure.

69. If 70.0 mL of nitrogen gas reacts with 45.0 mL of oxygen gas, what is the volume of N_2O_3 produced? Assume all gases are at the same temperature and pressure.

$$N_2(g) + O_2(g) \longrightarrow N_2O_3(g)$$

70. If 45.0 mL of nitrogen gas reacts with 70.0 mL of oxygen gas according to the equation in Exercise 69, what is the volume of N_2O_3 produced? Assume all gases are at the same temperature and pressure.

71. If 3.00 L of sulfur dioxide gas reacts with 1.25 L of oxygen gas, what is the volume of sulfur trioxide gas produced? Assume all gases are at the same temperature and pressure.

$$SO_2(g) + O_2(g) \longrightarrow SO_3(g)$$

72. If 1.25 L of sulfur dioxide gas reacts with 3.00 L of oxygen gas according to the equation in Exercise 71, what is the volume of sulfur trioxide gas produced? Assume all gases are at the same temperature and pressure.

73. If 50.0 L of hydrogen chloride gas reacts with 10.0 L of oxygen gas, what is the volume of chlorine gas produced? Assume all gases are at the same temperature and pressure.

$$HCl(g) + O_2(g) \longrightarrow Cl_2(g) + H_2O(g)$$

74. If 10.0 L of hydrogen chloride gas reacts with 50.0 L of oxygen gas according to the equation in Exercise 73, what is the volume of chlorine gas produced? Assume all gases are at the same temperature and pressure.

Percent Yield (Sec. 9.9)

75. A chemistry student prepared lead(II) iodide from 10.0 g of lead(II) nitrate and aqueous potassium iodide. If the student collected 12.5 g of PbI_2 and the theoretical yield is 13.9 g, what is the percent yield?

76. A chemistry student prepared acetone by decomposing 10.0 g of calcium acetate. If the student collected 3.50 g of acetone and the theoretical yield is 3.67 g, what is the percent yield?

77. A 1.50-g sample of sodium nitrate is decomposed by heating. If the resulting sodium nitrite has a mass of 1.29 g and the calculated yield is 1.22 g, what is the percent yield?

78. A 1.00-g sample of potassium bicarbonate is decomposed by heating. If the resulting potassium carbonate weighs 0.725 g and the calculated yield is 0.690 g, what is the percent yield?

General Exercises

79. What units are associated with molar mass?

80. What units are associated with molar volume?

81. The "volcano reaction" produces chromium(III) oxide, water, and nitrogen gas from the decomposition of ammonium dichromate. Calculate the mass of chromium(III) oxide produced by the decomposition of 1.54 g of ammonium dichromate.

82. What STP volume of nitrogen gas is produced in the "volcano reaction" from the decomposition of 1.54 g of ammonium dichromate according to the reaction described in Exercise 81?

83. Manganese metal and aluminum oxide are produced by the reaction of manganese(IV) oxide and aluminum metal. Calculate the mass of aluminum that is necessary to yield 1.00 kg of manganese metal.

84. What mass of aluminum oxide must react to produce 1.00 kg of manganese metal according to the reaction described in Exercise 83?

85. The mineral stibnite, antimony(III) sulfide, is treated with hydrochloric acid to give antimony(III) chloride and hydrogen sulfide gas. What STP volume of H_2S is produced from a 3.00-g sample of stibnite?

86. What mass of $SbCl_3$ is produced from a 3.00-g sample of stibnite according to the reaction described in Exercise 85?

Challenge Exercises

87. Recreational vehicles use propane for cooking and heating. The combustion of propane and oxygen produces carbon dioxide and water. What mass of water is produced from the combustion of 10.0 g of propane, C_3H_8?

88. What STP volume of carbon dioxide gas is produced from the combustion of 10.0 g of propane according to the reaction described in Exercise 87?

89. When an electric current is passed through water, hydrogen and oxygen gases are liberated. What STP volume of hydrogen gas is obtained from the electrolysis of 100.0 mL of water? (*Hint:* The density of water is 1.00 g/mL.)

90. What STP volume of oxygen gas is obtained from the electrolysis of 100.0 mL of water according to the reaction described in Exercise 89?

 Online Exercises

Research each of the following using an Internet search engine (e.g., Google.com or Yahoo.com) and cite your URL reference.

91. Which planet in our solar system has a sulfuric acid atmosphere?

92. Which country produced the most sulfuric acid for industry in 2000?

9 Chapter Self-Test *Answers to Self-Test are in Appendix J.*

1. Hydrogen gas reacts with 5.00 g of oxygen gas to give 5.63 g of water. Use the conservation of mass law to predict the mass of reacting hydrogen. (Sec. 9.1)

$$2 H_2(g) + O_2(g) \longrightarrow 2 H_2O(l)$$

(a) 0.63 g
(b) 5.00 g
(c) 5.63 g
(d) 10.63 g
(e) none of the above

2. How many moles of water must decompose to yield 5.00 mol of oxygen gas? (Sec. 9.2)

$$2 H_2O(l) \longrightarrow 2 H_2(g) + O_2(g)$$

(a) 1.00 mol
(b) 2.00 mol
(c) 5.00 mol
(d) 10.0 mol
(e) none of the above

3. Classify the following type of stoichiometry problem:

How many liters of oxygen are produced from decomposing 5.00 g of water? (Sec. 9.3)

(a) mass–mass problem
(b) mass–volume problem
(c) volume–volume problem
(d) mole–mole problem
(e) none of the above

4. What mass of oxygen gas is produced from decomposing 5.00 g of water (18.02 g/mol)? (Sec. 9.4)

$$2 H_2O(l) \longrightarrow 2 H_2(g) + O_2(g)$$

(a) 2.22 g
(b) 2.50 g
(c) 4.44 g
(d) 5.00 g
(e) 8.88 g

5. What STP volume of hydrogen gas is produced from decomposing 5.00 g of water (18.02 g/mol)? (Sec. 9.5)
$$2 H_2O(l) \longrightarrow 2 H_2(g) + O_2(g)$$
   (a) 1.55 L
   (b) 3.11 L
   (c) 5.00 L
   (d) 6.22 L
   (e) 12.4 L

6. What volume of oxygen gas is released from decomposing water if 5.00 mL of hydrogen gas is produced (assume constant temperature and pressure)? (Sec. 9.6)
$$2 H_2O(l) \longrightarrow 2 H_2(g) + O_2(g)$$
   (a) 2.50 mL
   (b) 5.00 mL
   (c) 7.50 mL
   (d) 10.0 mL
   (e) 20.0 mL

7. Consider the limiting reactant concept and predict how many moles of steam are released from the reaction of 5.00 mol of hydrogen gas and 5.00 mol of oxygen gas (assume constant temperature and pressure). (Sec. 9.7)
$$2 H_2(g) + O_2(g) \longrightarrow 2 H_2O(g)$$
   (a) 2.50 mol
   (b) 5.00 mol

   (c) 10.0 mol
   (d) 15.0 mol
   (e) none of the above

8. Consider the limiting reactant concept and predict how many liters of steam are released from the reaction of 5.00 L of hydrogen gas and 5.00 L of oxygen gas (assume constant temperature and pressure). (Sec. 9.8)
$$2 H_2(g) + O_2(g) \longrightarrow 2 H_2O(g)$$
   (a) 2.50 L
   (b) 5.00 L
   (c) 10.0 L
   (d) 15.0 L
   (e) none of the above

9. The decomposition of 5.00 g of water releases 4.00 g of oxygen gas. If the calculated mass of oxygen is 4.44 g, what is the percent yield? (Sec. 9.9)
$$2 H_2O(l) \longrightarrow 2 H_2(g) + O_2(g)$$
   (a) 80.0%
   (b) 88.8%
   (c) 90.1
   (d) 111%
   (e) 125%

Key Concepts

10. What must be done first before applying unit analysis to solve a stoichiometry problem?

11. How many unit factors are typically required to solve a mass–mass problem?

12. How many unit factors are typically required to solve a mass–volume problem?

13. How many unit factors are typically required to solve a volume–volume problem?

Critical Thinking

14. Gasoline and air undergo a combustion reaction in an automobile engine. What is the limiting reactant? What is the excess reactant?

16. Silver metal heated with yellow sulfur powder gives Ag₂S.
$$2 Ag(s) + S(s) \xrightarrow{\Delta} Ag_2S(s)$$

Complete the following illustrations by drawing the product and excess reactant. Indicate the element that is the limiting reactant in each example.

10

Gases

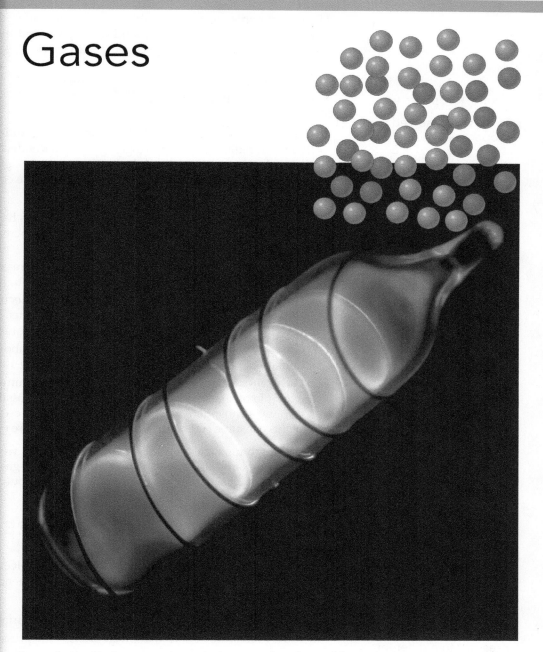

Argon in the Environment Argon is the most abundant noble gas in the atmosphere and is inert to chemical reaction even at high temperatures. When excited electrically, argon gas emits a violet glow.

"When we attempt to conceive the number of particles in an atmosphere, it is somewhat like attempting to conceive the number of stars in the universe."
John Dalton, English Chemist (1766–1844)

English chemist Robert Boyle is best known for establishing the scientific method and his work with gases. He studied the atmosphere and found that a volume of air could be compressed. He envisioned air as being composed of invisible particles that can be squeezed closer together. Furthermore, he found that other gases could be compressed and reasoned that all gases were composed of tiny, discrete particles.

His experiments were remarkable because they offered the first evidence of the particle nature of matter. In 1803, John Dalton proposed the atomic theory, which in part was supported by Boyle's experiments with gases.

▲ **Hot Air Balloon** The hot air inside the balloon is less dense than the air surrounding the balloon. As the less dense air rises, the balloon ascends.

10.1 PROPERTIES OF GASES

In the late 1700s, high-altitude ballooning became popular in France. Even French scientists filled balloons with hydrogen gas and ascended miles into the sky. Ballooning in turn helped to create a great deal of interest in the study of gases. After numerous experiments, scientists concluded that all gases have common characteristics. We can summarize these properties as follows.

1. **Gases have a variable shape and volume.** A gas has the same shape and volume as its container. If the volume of the container increases or decreases, the volume of the gas increases or decreases.
2. **Gases expand uniformly.** When a container increases its volume, a gas expands, and the gas molecules distribute uniformly throughout the container.
3. **Gases compress uniformly.** When a container decreases its volume, a gas compresses, and gas molecules are closer to each other. If the volume of the container is reduced sufficiently, the gas will eventually liquefy.
4. **Gases have a low density.** The density of air is about 1 g/L (0.001 g/mL). The density of water is 1 g/mL. Thus, water is about 1000 times more dense than air.
5. **Gases mix uniformly with other gases in the same container.** Air is a common example of a gaseous mixture. The burning of fossil fuels releases carbon dioxide into the atmosphere where it mixes with the gases in air. During photosynthesis, plants consume carbon dioxide from air and release oxygen gas into the atmosphere.

Although most gases are colorless and invisible, we can observe their behavior indirectly. For example, if we decrease the volume of a gas, we observe an increase in gas pressure. Thus, it is possible to gather information about a gas by studying its properties.

10.2 ATMOSPHERIC PRESSURE

Gas pressure is the result of constantly moving molecules striking the inside surface of their container. The pressure that a gas exerts depends on how often and how hard these molecules strike the walls of the container.

1. If the molecules collide more often, the gas pressure *increases*.
2. If the molecules collide with more energy, the pressure *increases*.

As the temperature increases, the molecules move faster and collide more frequently and with more energy. Thus, the gas pressure increases (Figure 10.1).

▶ Figure 10.1 **Gas Pressure and Temperature** (a) The molecules are moving faster and colliding more frequently with the container. (b) The molecules are moving slower and colliding less frequently with the container.

**(a) Higher temperature
Higher pressure**

**(b) Lower temperature
Lower pressure**

CHEMISTRY CONNECTION   The Greenhouse Effect

Q: Why has planting millions of trees been suggested as a means of reducing global warming?

When we read about the greenhouse effect, we may be alarmed and in fear that it is life-threatening to our planet. However, the greenhouse effect is necessary for life on Earth as it helps to maintain a moderately mild climate. The current concern is that our atmosphere has an abundance of so-called greenhouse gases that will cause drastic global warming. Although carbon dioxide is singled out as the chief offender, other gases such as chlorofluorocarbons, CFCs, methane, CH_4, and the oxides of nitrogen, NO_x, also contribute to global warming.

Scientists explain the greenhouse effect as follows: Earth's atmosphere is transparent to short-wavelength radiation from the Sun. After striking Earth's surface, the radiation from the Sun is emitted back into space as long-wavelength heat energy. Long-wavelength heat energy can be absorbed by carbon dioxide and other trace gases in the atmosphere.

Subsequently, these gas molecules release heat energy in all directions, some of which is radiated back toward Earth. The net effect is that carbon dioxide and other gases in the atmosphere form an invisible canopy that traps heat energy.

Our present concern is that additional gases in the atmosphere are increasing the temperature of our planet at an alarming rate. Global warming can result from high concentrations of carbon dioxide in the atmosphere. Carbon dioxide is produced by burning fossil fuels (coal, oil, and gas) in automobiles, homes, and power plants. The problem is further accelerated by massive deforestation, especially in South America. The loss of forests is especially harmful because trees convert carbon dioxide in the atmosphere to oxygen.

Some scientists think global warming is a severe threat and believe we must do something immediately. One futuristic suggestion is to add chemicals to the oceans that will stimulate the growth of plankton. Plankton remove carbon dioxide from the air through the process of photosynthesis. Currently, our efforts are directed at reforestation and reducing the emission of greenhouse gases into the atmosphere.

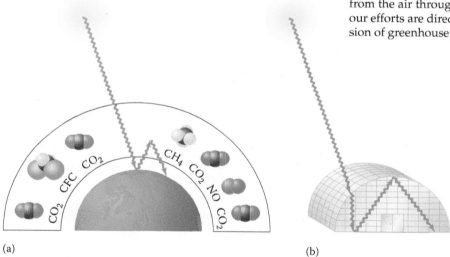

(a)   (b)

◀ **Greenhouse Effect** Greenhouse gases trap heat energy from the Sun in much the same way as a plant greenhouse.

A: The greenhouse gas that contributes most to global warming is carbon dioxide. The planting of millions of trees will allow the process of photosynthesis to reduce the amount of carbon dioxide and return more oxygen to the atmosphere.

Atmospheric Pressure

Italian scientist Evangelista Torricelli (1608–1647) published the first scientific explanation of a vacuum. He proposed that a "sea of air" surrounds Earth and argued that this sea of air exerts a pressure on everything it contacts. We now understand that there are no gas molecules in a **vacuum** and that the gas pressure is therefore zero.

By the end of the 1600s, the concept of atmospheric pressure was well established. Today, we understand that **atmospheric pressure** is the result of air molecules in the environment. The pressure of the atmosphere is considerable, about 15 pounds on every square inch of surface. In fact, the atmosphere exerts a total weight of nearly 20 tons on an average-size human body! More effects of atmospheric pressure are illustrated in Figure 10.2.

In 1643, Torricelli invented the **barometer** to measure atmospheric pressure (Figure 10.3). He showed that at sea level, the height of mercury measures 29.9 inches, which we define as standard atmospheric pressure, that is, 1 atmosphere (symbol atm). Above sea level, the height of mercury is less than 29.9 inches, indicating that atmospheric pressure is less at higher elevations.

▶ Figure 10.2 **Atmospheric Pressure** (a) The pressure of air molecules in the atmosphere supports a 34-foot column of water. (b) Because atmospheric pressure operates in all directions, air molecules strike the bottom of the card and support the water in the inverted glass.

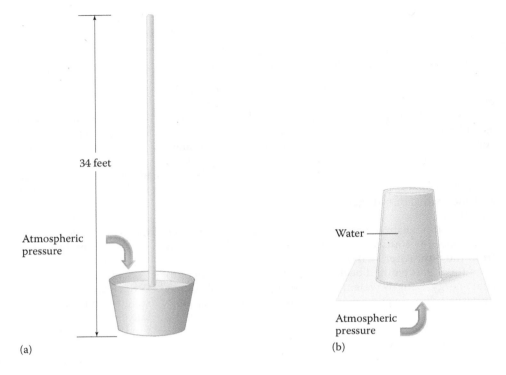

34 feet

Atmospheric pressure

(a)

Water

Atmospheric pressure

(b)

Glass tube

Atmospheric pressure

29.9 in. (760 mm)

Mercury

▲ Figure 10.3 **Torricelli's Mercury Barometer** A sealed glass tube is filled with liquid mercury, inverted, and placed into a dish of mercury. No gas molecules are above the column of mercury inside the glass tube. The pressure of the atmosphere at sea level supports a column of mercury 29.9 inches (760 mm) high.

We can express standard pressure in many units besides atmospheres and inches of mercury. For example, 29.9 in. of Hg is equivalent to 760 mm Hg. In honor of Torricelli, standard pressure is stated as 760 torr, where 1 **torr** equals 1 mm Hg. Table 10.1 lists units that are frequently used to express pressure.

TABLE 10.1 UNITS OF GAS PRESSURE

UNIT	STANDARD PRESSURE
atmosphere	1 atm (exactly)
inches of mercury	29.9 in. Hg
centimeters of mercury	76 cm Hg (exactly)
millimeters of mercury	760 mm Hg (exactly)
torr[1]	760 torr (exactly)
pounds per square inch	14.7 psi
kilopascal[2]	101 kPa

[1]A torr is defined as exactly equal to 1 mm Hg pressure; thus, standard pressure is 760 torr.
[2]The kilopascal (kPa) is the official SI unit of pressure.

Each of the values in Table 10.1 is an expression for the same standard pressure, so we can relate one unit to another. For example, if the pressure of propane gas in a steel tank is 2550 torr, we can relate the pressure to atmospheres. We can perform the conversion by applying the unit analysis method. The unknown unit is atm, and the given value is 2550 torr. Thus,

$$2550 \text{ torr} \times \frac{\text{unit}}{\text{factor}} = \text{atm}$$

To convert from one unit of pressure to another, we derive a unit factor from the relationship among units of standard pressure. Because 1 atm = 760 torr, the two related unit factors are 1 atm/760 torr, and its reciprocal 760 torr/1 atm. We select the first unit factor to cancel units.

$$2550 \text{ torr} \times \frac{1 \text{ atm}}{760 \text{ torr}} = 3.36 \text{ atm}$$

The following example exercise further illustrates the conversion of gas pressures.

Example Exercise 10.1 Gas Pressure Conversion

Meteorologists state that a "falling" barometer indicates an approaching storm. Given a barometric pressure of 27.5 in. Hg, express the pressure in each of the following units of pressure:

(a) atm   (b) mm Hg   (c) psi   (d) kPa

Solution

For each conversion, we apply a unit conversion factor related to units of standard pressure.

(a) To express the pressure in atmospheres, we derive a unit factor related to the equivalent relationship 29.9 in. Hg = 1 atm.

$$27.5 \text{ in. Hg} \times \frac{1 \text{ atm}}{29.9 \text{ in. Hg}} = 0.920 \text{ atm}$$

(b) To convert to millimeters of mercury, we derive a unit factor related to the equivalent relationship 29.9 in. Hg = 760 mm Hg.

$$27.5 \text{ in. Hg} \times \frac{760 \text{ mm Hg}}{29.9 \text{ in. Hg}} = 699 \text{ mm Hg}$$

(c) To calculate the pressure in pounds per square inch, we derive a unit factor related to the equivalent relationship 29.9 in. Hg = 14.7 psi.

$$27.5 \text{ in. Hg} \times \frac{14.7 \text{ psi}}{29.9 \text{ in. Hg}} = 13.5 \text{ psi}$$

(d) To find the pressure in kilopascals, we derive a unit factor related to the equivalent relationship 29.9 in. Hg = 101 kPa.

$$27.5 \text{ in. Hg} \times \frac{101 \text{ kPa}}{29.9 \text{ in. Hg}} = 92.9 \text{ kPa}$$

Because 1 atm and 760 mm Hg are exact values, the answers have been rounded to three significant digits, which is consistent with the given value, 27.5 in. Hg.

Practice Exercise

Given that the air pressure inside an automobile tire is 34.0 psi, express the pressure in each of the following units:

(a) atm   (b) cm Hg   (c) torr   (d) kPa

Answers:

(a) 2.31 atm   (b) 176 cm Hg   (c) 1760 torr   (d) 234 kPa

Concept Exercise

Which of the following expresses the greatest gas pressure: 1 atm, 1 in. Hg, 1 torr, 1 cm Hg, 1 mm Hg, or 1 psi?

Answer: See Appendix G.

▲ Adding air to an automobile tire increases the pressure because there are more molecules, which cause an increase in the number of collisions inside the tire.

10.3 VARIABLES AFFECTING GAS PRESSURE

In Section 10.2, we learned that gas pressure is related to the frequency and energy of gas molecule collisions. Experimentally, there are only three ways to change the number of collisions, and hence the pressure.

1. **Increase or decrease the volume of the container.** When we increase the volume, gas molecules are farther apart and collide less frequently, and the pressure decreases. When we decrease the volume, gas molecules are closer together and collide more frequently, and the pressure increases. The pressure is said to be *inversely* related to the volume. That is, when the volume increases, the pressure decreases. When the volume decreases, the pressure increases.

LEARNING OBJECTIVES

▸ To identify the three variables that affect the pressure of a gas.

▸ To state whether gas pressure increases or decreases for a given change in volume, temperature, or the number of moles of gas.

2. **Increase or decrease the temperature of the gas.** When we increase the temperature, gas molecules move faster and collide with a greater frequency and energy. When we decrease the temperature, the gas molecules move slower and collide less frequently. The pressure is said to be *directly* related to the temperature. When the temperature increases, the pressure increases. When the temperature decreases, the pressure decreases.

3. **Increase or decrease the number of molecules in the container. Avogadro's theory**, also called Avogadro's law, states that equal volumes of gases, at the same temperature and pressure, contain equal numbers of molecules. When we increase the number of gas molecules, there are more collisions and the pressure increases. When we decrease the number of gas molecules, there are fewer collisions and the pressure decreases. The pressure is said to be *directly* related to the number of moles of gas, or the number of gas molecules. When the number of gas molecules increases, the pressure increases. When the number of molecules decreases, the pressure decreases.

The effects of these three variables (volume, temperature, and number of molecules) on pressure are illustrated in Figure 10.4.

▲ Figure 10.4 **Variables Affecting Gas Pressure** A gas is contained in a cylinder with a moving piston. The gas pressure, *P*, is affected by (a) changing volume, *V*; (b) changing temperature, *T*; and (c) changing the number of gas molecules in the cylinder.

> **Example Exercise 10.2** Gas Pressure Changes

State whether the pressure of a gas in a sealed container increases or decreases with each of the following changes:

(a) The volume changes from 250 mL to 500 mL.
(b) The temperature changes from 20 °C to −80 °C.
(c) The moles of gas change from 1.00 mol to 1.50 mol.

Solution

For each of the changes we must consider whether the number of molecular collisions increases or decreases.

(a) The volume increases, and so the number of collisions decreases; thus the *pressure decreases*.
(b) The temperature decreases, and so the number of collisions decreases; thus, the *pressure decreases*.
(c) When the moles of gas increase, the number of molecules increases. With more molecules, there are more collisions, and the *pressure increases*.

Practice Exercise

Indicate whether gas pressure increases or decreases with each of the following changes in a sealed container:

(a) increasing the temperature   (b) increasing the volume
(c) increasing the number of gas molecules

Answers:

(a) pressure increases   (b) pressure decreases   (c) pressure increases

Concept Exercise

Which of the following decreases gas pressure: increasing volume, increasing temperature, or increasing the number of molecules?

Answer: See Appendix G.

10.4 BOYLE'S LAW: PRESSURE–VOLUME RELATIONSHIPS

LEARNING OBJECTIVES

We have mentioned that Robert Boyle was the founder of the scientific method. In one of his experiments, Boyle trapped air in a J-shaped tube with liquid mercury. As he added mercury into the tube, he found that the volume of trapped air decreased (Figure 10.5). When he doubled the pressure, the volume was reduced to half. When he tripled the pressure, the volume was reduced to a third. Thus, Boyle established the relationship between the pressure and the volume of a gas.

▸ To sketch a graph of the pressure–volume relationship for a gas.

▸ To calculate the pressure or volume of a gas after a change in conditions.

Atmospheric pressure (760 mm Hg)

Atmospheric pressure (760 mm Hg)

Air

760 mm

Volume = 30 mL

Volume = 60 mL

(a)

(b)

◀ **Figure 10.5 Boyle's Law**
(a) The initial volume of gas at atmospheric pressure is 60 mL. (b) After adding mercury, the volume of gas is 30 mL. Note that the volume is halved when the pressure is doubled. Initially, the pressure is 760 mm Hg; after adding mercury, the pressure is 1520 mm Hg (760 mm Hg + 760 mm Hg).

▲ Figure 10.6 **Gas Pressure versus Volume** As the volume of a gas increases, the pressure decreases. Conversely, as the volume decreases, the pressure increases. The volume and the pressure of a gas are inversely proportional.

The results of Boyle's experiments are known as **Boyle's law**, which states that the volume of a gas is inversely proportional to the pressure when the temperature remains constant. **Inversely proportional** means that two variables have a reciprocal relationship. As one variable gets larger, the other variable gets smaller. We can express Boyle's law mathematically, where the symbol $\propto$ is read as "proportional to."

$$V \propto \frac{1}{P} \qquad (T \text{ remains constant})$$

That is, the volume (V) is proportional to the reciprocal pressure $(1/P)$ when the temperature (T) remains constant. Using experimental data, we can plot pressure versus volume and obtain the curve shown in Figure 10.6.

The relationship between pressure and volume can be written as an equation by using a proportionality constant (k):

$$V = k \times \frac{1}{P}$$

Multiplying both sides of the equation by P, we see that the product of pressure and volume is equal to the constant (k). The equation becomes

$$PV = k$$

We can consider a sample of a gas under changing conditions but with temperature remaining the same. Let the initial conditions of pressure and volume be P_1 and V_1, respectively. After a change in conditions, we can indicate the final pressure and volume as P_2 and V_2. Because the product of pressure and volume is a constant, we write

$$P_1 V_1 = k = P_2 V_2$$

Solving Boyle's Law Problems

In this textbook, we will present two methods for solving gas law problems. First, we will solve problems using a conceptual approach and a reasoning method. Second, we will solve problems using an algebraic method.

Because the pressure and the volume of a gas are inversely related, we can apply a proportionality factor to find an unknown variable. To find the gas pressure after a change in volume, we apply a volume factor to the initial pressure (P_1).

$$\boxed{P_1 \times V_{\text{factor}} = P_2}$$

Similarly, to find the volume after a change in gas pressure, we apply a pressure factor to the initial volume (V_1).

$$\boxed{V_1 \times P_{\text{factor}} = V_2}$$

Let's consider the following Boyle's law gas problem. In an experiment, 5.00 L of propane gas is compressed and the pressure increases from 1.00 atm to 1.50 atm. To calculate the final volume (V_2), we write

$$5.00 \, \text{L} \times P_{\text{factor}} = V_2$$

The pressure of the propane gas increases from 1.00 atm to 1.50 atm, so the final volume must decrease. Therefore, the P_{factor} must be less than 1. That is, the smaller pressure value must appear in the numerator.

$$5.00 \, \text{L} \times \frac{1.00 \, \text{atm}}{1.50 \, \text{atm}} = 3.33 \, \text{L}$$

Notice that the cancellation of units takes place in the unit factor (P_{factor}). Although the numerator and the denominator are not equal, this method uses a format very much like that of the unit analysis method of problem solving. Now, let's reinforce our understanding of Boyle's law with an example exercise.

Example Exercise 10.3 Boyle's Law

A 1.50-L sample of methane gas exerts a pressure of 1650 mm Hg. Calculate the final pressure if the volume changes to 7.00 L. Assume the temperature remains constant.

Conceptual Solution
We can find the final pressure (P_2) by applying Boyle's law and using the relationship

$$P_1 \times V_{\text{factor}} = P_2$$

The volume increases from 1.50 L to 7.00 L. Thus, the pressure decreases. The V_{factor} must be less than 1. Hence,

$$1650 \text{ mm Hg} \times \frac{1.50 \text{ L}}{7.00 \text{ L}} = 354 \text{ mm Hg}$$

We can visually summarize the Boyle's law solution as follows:

Algebraic Solution
Alternatively, we can solve this problem using the equation

$$P_1 V_1 = P_2 V_2$$

Solving for P_2 gives

$$\frac{P_1 V_1}{V_2} = P_2$$

Substituting for each variable and simplifying, we obtain

$$\frac{1650 \text{ mm Hg} \times 1.50 \text{ L}}{7.00 \text{ L}} = 354 \text{ mm Hg}$$

Practice Exercise
A sample of ethane gas has a volume of 125 mL at 20 °C and 725 torr. What is the volume of the gas at 20 °C when the pressure decreases to 475 torr?

Answer: 191 mL

Concept Exercise
When air in a steel cylinder is compressed from 10 L to 5 L, and temperature remains constant, the gas pressure inside the cylinder (increases/decreases).

Answer: See Appendix G.

Note A conceptual solution for solving gas law problems is valuable because it emphasizes reason and a deeper understanding of gaseous behavior. A conceptual solution requires that we understand how changes in pressure, volume, and temperature of a gas affect each other. On the other hand, mathematics is a powerful tool for solving problems, and an algebraic solution is valuable where the concepts are initially difficult to grasp.

Robert Boyle

Q. What instrument did Robert Boyle invent that demonstrated a feather and a lump of lead are affected identically by gravity?

Robert Boyle (1627–1691) was a child prodigy who was studying Latin and Greek by the age of 8. He was the son of wealthy English aristocrats and traveled throughout Europe with a private tutor to gain a broad education. When he was 18 years old, his father died and left him with a lifetime income. At 27, he enrolled in Oxford University to continue his studies. There he became interested in experimentation, although laboratory work was considered to be of minor importance at the time. Most influential scientists believed, like the Greeks, that reason was far superior to experimentation.

In 1657, Boyle designed a vacuum pump that was an improvement over the first one developed a few years earlier. In one experiment, he evacuated most of the air from a sealed chamber and showed that a ticking clock could not be heard in a vacuum. He then correctly concluded that sound does not exist in the absence of air. Boyle was fascinated by the behavior of gases and formulated the law stating that pressure and volume of a gas are inversely related.

In 1661, Boyle published *The Sceptical Chymist* and argued that theories were no better than the experiments on which they were based. Gradually, this point of view was accepted, and his text marked a turning point for recognition of the importance of experimentation. Because of his numerous contributions to chemistry and physics, Boyle is generally regarded as the founder of the modern scientific method.

Boyle felt strongly about keeping meticulous notes and reporting experimental results. He thought that everyone should be able to learn from published accounts of laboratory inquiry. Boyle felt that experiments should be held up to scientific scrutiny and that others should have the opportunity to confirm or disprove the results. This practice has become a cornerstone of science and, except for information involving military and industrial secrets, research experiments are published and made available to the scientific community and to the public at large.

◀ Robert Boyle
(1627–1691)

A: Boyle invented a vacuum pump to remove air from a cylinder. When he released a feather and a lump of lead from the same height in the cylinder, he found that they landed simultaneously at the bottom of the cylinder.

10.5 CHARLES'S LAW: VOLUME–TEMPERATURE RELATIONSHIPS

▶ To sketch a graph of the volume–temperature relationship for a gas.

▶ To calculate the volume or temperature of a gas after a change in conditions.

In 1783, the French scientist Jacques Charles (1746–1823) filled a balloon with hydrogen gas and ascended to 10,000 feet—nearly two miles! Although hot air ballooning had been pioneered by the Montgolfier brothers, Jacques Charles was the first to make an ascent in a hydrogen-filled balloon.

In 1787, Charles discovered the effect of temperature on the volume of a gas. From his experiments, he correctly deduced that the volume of a gas is **directly proportional** to the Kelvin temperature. That is, when we double the Kelvin temperature of a gas, we double its volume. When we halve the Kelvin temperature of a gas, we halve its volume. We can state **Charles's law** as follows: The volume of a gas is directly proportional to the Kelvin temperature if the pressure remains constant. Using experimental data, we can plot volume versus Kelvin temperature and obtain the straight-line graph shown in Figure 10.7.

We can express the direct relationship between volume and Kelvin temperature as

$$V \propto T \qquad (P \text{ remains constant})$$

The relationship of volume and Kelvin temperature can also be written as an equation using a proportionality constant (k).

$$V = kT$$

Dividing both sides of the equation by T, we see that the ratio of volume to temperature equals the constant k. The equation becomes

$$\frac{V}{T} = k$$

Let's consider a sample of gas under changing conditions, but with pressure remaining the same. We indicate the initial conditions of volume and temperature as V_1 and T_1, respectively. After a change in conditions, we indicate the final volume and temperature as V_2 and T_2. Because the ratio of volume to temperature equals the constant k, we write

$$\frac{V_1}{T_1} = k = \frac{V_2}{T_2}$$

Solving Charles's Law Problems

The volume and temperature of a gas are directly related, so we can apply a proportionality factor to find an unknown variable. To find the volume after a change in temperature, we apply a temperature factor to the initial volume (V_1):

$$V_1 \times T_{\text{factor}} = V_2$$

Similarly, to find the temperature after a change in volume, we apply a volume factor to the initial temperature (T_1):

$$T_1 \times V_{\text{factor}} = T_2$$

Let's consider the following Charles's law gas problem. In an experiment, a sample of argon gas at 225 K is heated and the volume increases from 3.50 L to 12.5 L. To calculate the final temperature (T_2), we write

$$225 \text{ K} \times V_{\text{factor}} = T_2$$

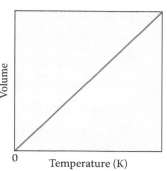

▲ Figure 10.7 **Gas Volume versus Temperature** As the Kelvin temperature decreases, the volume of a gas decreases. The Kelvin temperature and the volume of a gas are directly proportional.

(a)　　　　(b)

◀ **Illustration of Charles's Law** (a) A balloon contains air at room temperature. (b) As liquid nitrogen at −196 °C is poured on the balloon, the air inside the balloon cools, causing it to decrease in volume.

Because the volume of argon gas increases from 3.50 L to 12.5 L, the final temperature must increase. Therefore, the V_{factor} must be greater than 1. That is, the larger value must appear in the numerator.

$$225 \text{ K} \times \frac{12.5 \, \cancel{L}}{3.50 \, \cancel{L}} = 804 \text{ K}$$

The final temperature is 804 K, or 531 °C. Now, let's reinforce our understanding of Charles's law with an example exercise.

Example Exercise 10.4 Charles's Law

A 275 L helium balloon is heated from 20 °C to 40 °C. Calculate the final volume assuming the pressure remains constant.

Conceptual Solution
We first convert the Celsius temperatures to Kelvin by adding 273 units.

$$20 \text{ °C} + 273 = 293 \text{ K}$$

$$40 \text{ °C} + 273 = 313 \text{ K}$$

We can find the final volume, V_2, by applying Charles's law and using the relationship

$$V_1 \times T_{factor} = V_2$$

The temperature increases from 293 K to 313 K. It follows that the volume increases and the T_{factor} must be greater than 1.

$$275 \text{ L} \times \frac{313 \text{ K}}{293 \text{ K}} = 294 \text{ L}$$

We can visually summarize the Charles's law solution as follows:

Algebraic Solution
Alternatively, we can solve this problem using the equation

$$\frac{V_1}{T_1} = \frac{V_2}{T_2}$$

Solving for V_2 gives

$$\frac{V_1 T_2}{T_1} = V_2$$

Substituting for each variable and simplifying, we obtain

$$\frac{275 \text{ L} \times 313 \text{ K}}{293 \text{ K}} = 294 \text{ L}$$

Practice Exercise
A krypton balloon has a volume of 555 mL at 21 °C. If the balloon is cooled and the volume decreases to 475 mL, what is the final temperature? Assume that the pressure remains constant.

Answer: −21 °C

Concept Exercise
When air in an elastic balloon cools from 25 °C to 20 °C, the volume of the balloon (increases/decreases).

Answer: See Appendix G.

Note In Charles's law problems we can state the volume in any units, but all volumes must be expressed in the same units. For example, we can express the volume in liters or cubic centimeters. However, we must *always* express the temperature in Kelvin units.

10.6 GAY-LUSSAC'S LAW: PRESSURE–TEMPERATURE RELATIONSHIPS

LEARNING OBJECTIVES

▸ To sketch a graph of the pressure–temperature relationship for a gas.

▸ To calculate the pressure or temperature of a gas after a change in conditions.

Like Jacques Charles, French scientist Joseph Gay-Lussac (1778–1850) was also interested in ballooning and made a record ascent to 23,000 feet in a hydrogen-filled balloon. During his ascent, he collected samples of the atmosphere for study in his laboratory.

In 1802, Gay-Lussac established the relationship between pressure and temperature. He correctly interpreted his experiments to mean that the pressure of a gas is directly proportional to the Kelvin temperature. That is, when we double the Kelvin temperature of a gas, we double its pressure. When we halve the Kelvin temperature of a gas, we halve its pressure. We can state **Gay-Lussac's law** as follows: The pressure of a gas is directly proportional to the Kelvin temperature if the volume remains constant. Using experimental data, we can plot pressure versus Kelvin temperature and obtain the straight-line graph shown in Figure 10.8.

We can express the relationship between pressure and Kelvin temperature as

$$P \propto T \qquad (V \text{ remains constant})$$

The relationship between pressure and temperature can also be written as an equation using the proportionality constant (k):

$$P = kT$$

Dividing both sides of the equation by T, we see that the ratio of pressure to temperature equals the constant k. The equation becomes

$$\frac{P}{T} = k$$

Let's consider a sample of a gas under changing conditions, but with volume remaining the same. We indicate the initial conditions of pressure and temperature as P_1 and T_1, respectively. After a change in conditions, we indicate the final pressure and temperature as P_2 and T_2. Because the ratio of pressure to temperature equals the constant (k), we can write

$$\frac{P_1}{T_1} = k = \frac{P_2}{T_2}$$

▲ Figure 10.8 **Gas Pressure versus Temperature** As the Kelvin temperature decreases, the pressure of a gas decreases. The Kelvin temperature and the pressure exerted by a gas are directly proportional.

Solving Gay-Lussac's Law Problems

The pressure and temperature of a gas are directly related, so we can apply a proportionality factor to find an unknown variable. To find the pressure after a change in temperature, we apply a temperature factor to the initial pressure (P_1).

$$P_1 \times T_{\text{factor}} = P_2$$

Similarly, to find the temperature after a change in pressure, we apply a pressure factor to the initial temperature (T_1).

$$T_1 \times P_{\text{factor}} = T_2$$

Let's consider the following problem involving Gay-Lussac's law. An automobile tire is inflated to 28.0 psi at a temperature of 20 °C. After it has traveled at high speed, the tire pressure is 36.0 psi. To calculate the final temperature (T_2), we first convert the initial temperature to Kelvin (20 °C + 273 = 293 K), and then write

$$293 \text{ K} \times P_{\text{factor}} = T_2$$

$P = 1.00$ atm

$T = 300$ K

(a)

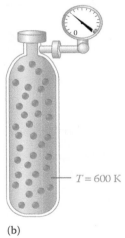

$P = 2.00$ atm

$T = 600$ K

(b)

▲ **Illustration of Gay-Lussac's Law** (a) A cylinder contains helium gas at 300 K and a pressure of 1.00 atm. (b) After doubling the temperature of the helium gas to 600 K, the pressure doubles to 2.00 atm.

Because the volume of the tire remains constant and the pressure increases from 28.0 psi to 36.0 psi, the final temperature must increase. Therefore, the P_{factor} must be greater than 1. That is, the larger pressure value must appear in the numerator.

$$293 \text{ K} \times \frac{36.0 \text{ psi}}{28.0 \text{ psi}} = 377 \text{ K}$$

The final temperature is 377 K, or 104 °C. Now, let's reinforce our understanding of Gay-Lussac's law with an example exercise.

Example Exercise 10.5 Gay-Lussac's Law

A steel container filled with nitrous oxide at 15.0 atm is cooled from 25 °C to −40 °C. Calculate the final pressure, assuming the volume remains constant.

Conceptual Solution
We must first convert the Celsius temperatures to Kelvin by adding 273.

$$25 \text{ °C} + 273 = 298 \text{ K}$$

$$-40 \text{ °C} + 273 = 233 \text{ K}$$

We can find the final pressure (P_2) by applying Gay-Lussac's law and using the relationship

$$P_1 \times T_{factor} = P_2$$

The volume of the container remains constant, but the temperature decreases from 298 K to 233 K. Therefore, the pressure decreases. The T_{factor} must be less than 1. Hence,

$$15.0 \text{ atm} \times \frac{233 \text{ K}}{298 \text{ K}} = 11.7 \text{ atm}$$

We can visually summarize the Gay-Lussac's law solution as follows:

15.0 atm → Temperature Factor → 11.7 atm

Algebraic Solution
Alternatively, we can solve this problem using the equation

$$\frac{P_1}{T_1} = \frac{P_2}{T_2}$$

Solving for P_2 gives

$$\frac{P_1 T_2}{T_1} = P_2$$

Substituting for each variable and simplifying, we have

$$\frac{15.0 \text{ atm} \times 233 \text{ K}}{298 \text{ K}} = 11.7 \text{ atm}$$

Practice Exercise
A copper container has a volume of 555 mL and is filled with air at 25 °C. The container is immersed in dry ice, and the pressure of the gas drops from 761 torr to 495 torr. What is the final temperature of the air in the copper container?

Answer: 194 K (−79 °C)

Concept Exercise
When air in a rigid steel tank cools from 25 °C to 20 °C, the pressure inside the tank (increases/decreases).

Answer: See Appendix G.

10.7 COMBINED GAS LAW

LEARNING OBJECTIVE

▶ To calculate the pressure, volume, or temperature of a gas after a change in conditions.

We began our discussion of gas laws with a simplifying assumption. In discussing Boyle's, Charles's, and Gay-Lussac's laws, we assumed that we could limit our treatment of gases to two variables. Experimentally, all three variables (pressure, volume, and temperature) usually change simultaneously. Now, we will bring all three variables together in a single expression. The resulting expression is called the **combined gas law**, and the equation is

$$\frac{P_1 V_1}{T_1} = \frac{P_2 V_2}{T_2}$$

Because the variables P, V, and T are proportional, we can solve combined gas law problems using the unit analysis approach. To calculate a final pressure (P_2), we apply a volume factor and a temperature factor to the initial pressure (P_1).

$$P_1 \times V_{\text{factor}} \times T_{\text{factor}} = P_2$$

To calculate a final volume (V_2), we apply a pressure factor and a temperature factor to the initial volume (V_1).

$$V_1 \times P_{\text{factor}} \times T_{\text{factor}} = V_2$$

To calculate a final temperature (T_2), we apply a pressure factor and a volume factor to the initial temperature (T_1).

$$T_1 \times P_{\text{factor}} \times V_{\text{factor}} = T_2$$

In a combined gas law problem, we have three variables at initial and final conditions. That gives us six pieces of data, and so it is helpful to use a table. We place the data in a table and organize the information as follows:

CONDITIONS	P	V	T
initial	P_1	V_1	T_1
final	P_2	V_2	T_2

Let's apply the combined gas law to 10.0 L of carbon dioxide gas at 300 K and 1.00 atm. When both the volume and the Kelvin temperature double, what is the final pressure in atmospheres? The initial conditions are 300 K and 1.00 atm. Doubling the temperature gives 600 K; doubling the volume gives 20.0 L. Now let's enter the data in a table:

CONDITIONS	P	V	T
initial	1.00 atm	10.0 L	300 K
final	P_2	20.0 L	600 K

We calculate the final pressure (P_2) by applying a V_{factor} and a T_{factor} to the initial pressure, 1.00 atm.

$$1.00 \text{ atm} \times V_{\text{factor}} \times T_{\text{factor}} = P_2$$

The volume of the gas increases from 10.0 L to 20.0 L, so P_2 must decrease. The V_{factor} is less than 1 and the smaller value is placed in the numerator.

$$1.00 \text{ atm} \times \frac{10.0 \text{ L}}{20.0 \text{ L}} \times T_{\text{factor}} = P_2$$

The temperature of the gas increases from 300 K to 600 K; therefore, P_2 increases. The T_{factor} is greater than 1 and the larger value is placed in the numerator.

$$1.00 \text{ atm} \times \frac{10.0 \text{ L}}{20.0 \text{ L}} \times \frac{600 \text{ K}}{300 \text{ K}} = 1.00 \text{ atm}$$

In this problem the pressure did not change even though both the volume and the temperature each doubled. The pressure remained unchanged because pressure and volume are inversely proportional, whereas pressure and temperature are directly proportional. Thus, in effect the volume and temperature changes cancel and the pressure remains constant.

Standard Conditions of Temperature and Pressure

The **standard temperature and pressure** (symbol **STP**) for a gas are 0 °C and 1 atm. We could also express standard temperature as 273 K and standard pressure in other units such as 760 mm Hg, 760 torr, or 76 cm Hg. The following example exercise illustrates how to convert a set of conditions to STP conditions.

Example Exercise 10.6 Combined Gas Law

A nitrogen gas sample occupies 50.5 mL at −80 °C and 1250 torr. What is the volume at STP?

Conceptual Solution
Although the final conditions are not given, we know that STP conditions are 273 K and 760 torr. We can summarize the information as follows:

CONDITIONS	P	V	T
initial	1250 torr	50.5 mL	−80 °C + 273 = 193 K
final	760 torr	V_2	273 K

We can calculate the final volume by applying a P_{factor} and a T_{factor} to the initial volume.

$$V_1 \times P_{factor} \times T_{factor} = V_2$$

The pressure decreases, and so the volume increases; thus, the P_{factor} is greater than 1. The temperature increases, and so the volume increases; thus, the T_{factor} is also greater than 1.

$$50.5 \text{ mL} \times \frac{1250 \text{ torr}}{760 \text{ torr}} \times \frac{273 \text{ K}}{193 \text{ K}} = 117 \text{ mL}$$

We can visually summarize the combined gas law solution as follows:

50.5 mL	Pressure Factor →	Temperature Factor →	117 mL

Algebraic Solution
Alternatively, we can solve this problem using the equation

$$\frac{P_1 V_1}{T_1} = \frac{P_2 V_2}{T_2}$$

Rearranging variables and solving for V_2,

$$\frac{P_1 V_1 T_2}{T_1 P_2} = V_2$$

Substituting for each variable and simplifying, we obtain

$$\frac{1250 \text{ torr} \times 50.5 \text{ mL} \times 273 \text{ K}}{193 \text{ K} \times 760 \text{ torr}} = 117 \text{ mL}$$

Practice Exercise

An oxygen gas sample occupies 50.0 mL at 27 °C and 765 mm Hg. What is the final temperature if the gas is cooled to a volume of 35.5 mL and a pressure of 455 mm Hg?

Answer: 127 K (−146 °C)

Concept Exercise

A sample of air is at an initial pressure of 1.00 atm. If both the volume and Kelvin temperature each double, what is the final pressure?

Answer: See Appendix G.

10.8 THE VAPOR PRESSURE CONCEPT

LEARNING OBJECTIVES

▶ To state the relationship between vapor pressure and temperature.

Everyone has observed that water in an open container evaporates. Vaporization occurs when molecules have enough energy to escape from the liquid. When the container is enclosed, the vapor molecules are trapped above the liquid. We should note that molecules continuously escape from the liquid into the vapor. Simultaneously, other molecules return from the vapor to the liquid. The **vapor pressure** is the pressure exerted by the gaseous vapor above a liquid when the rates of evaporation and condensation are equal (Figure 10.9).

Liquid ethanol
(a) Initial

Vapor pressure

Liquid + vapor
(b) Final

◀ Figure 10.9 **Vapor Pressure of a Liquid** (a) Initially, ethanol is placed in a sealed container and molecules begin to escape from the liquid. After awhile, some of the ethanol molecules in the vapor return to the liquid. (b) Eventually, the ethanol molecules are evaporating and condensing at the same rate. The vapor pressure is measured by the difference in the height of mercury in the side tube.

The vapor pressure of a liquid can be determined with a mercury barometer (Figure 10.10). A drop of liquid is introduced at the bottom of the barometer. The less dense liquid droplet floats to the top of the mercury and partially vaporizes. The vaporized liquid exerts a gas pressure, thus driving the column of mercury down. *The decrease in the mercury level corresponds to the increase in vapor pressure.* If the mercury level drops from 760 mm to 740 mm, the vapor pressure of the liquid is recorded as 20 mm Hg.

We can observe that vapor pressure increases as the temperature increases. This is because molecules in the liquid evaporate faster at a higher temperature and the vapor molecules have more kinetic energy. At 25 °C the vapor pressure of water is 23.8 mm Hg. At 50 °C the vapor pressure increases to 92.5 mm Hg. Table 10.2 lists selected values for the vapor pressure of water.

▶ Figure 10.10 **Measuring Vapor Pressure** (a) Initially, a single drop of water is introduced into the tube of mercury. As molecules of the liquid evaporate, the gaseous vapor molecules exert a pressure on the column of mercury. (b) Eventually, molecules are evaporating and condensing at the same rate. The difference in the height of the mercury before and after a drop of liquid is added is the vapor pressure of the liquid at the given temperature.

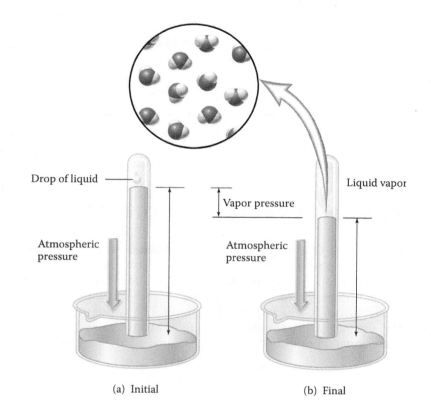

Drop of liquid

Atmospheric pressure

Liquid vapor

Vapor pressure

Atmospheric pressure

(a) Initial

(b) Final

TABLE 10.2 VAPOR PRESSURE OF WATER

TEMPERATURE (°C)	PRESSURE (mm Hg)	TEMPERATURE (°C)	PRESSURE (mm Hg)
5	6.5	55	118.0
10	9.2	60	149.4
15	12.8	65	187.5
20	17.5	70	233.7
25	23.8	75	289.1
30	31.8	80	355.1
35	41.2	85	433.6
40	55.3	90	525.8
45	71.9	95	633.9
50	92.5	100	760.0

LEARNING OBJECTIVE

▶ To apply Dalton's law of partial pressures to a mixture of gases.

10.9 DALTON'S LAW OF PARTIAL PRESSURES

When John Dalton proposed the atomic theory, his evidence was largely based on experiments with gases. His knowledge of gases was related to his interest in meteorology, and in fact he kept daily records of the weather throughout his life. In 1801, Dalton proposed that each gas in a mixture of gases contributes to the total pressure of the mixture. He then formulated a law, now called **Dalton's law of partial pressures**, that states that the total pressure of a gaseous mixture is equal to the sum of the individual pressures of each gas. We can express this law as follows:

$$P_1 + P_2 + P_3 + \ldots = P_{total}$$

The pressure exerted by each gas in a mixture of gases is called the **partial pressure**. In the equation, P_1, P_2, and P_3 represent the partial pressures of each of the gases in the mixture; P_{total} symbolizes the total of all the partial pressures.

In 1952, Stanley Miller conducted a historic experiment at the University of Chicago. In an attempt to prove the chemical evolution of life, Miller attempted to simulate Earth's primordial atmosphere. He placed hydrogen, ammonia, methane, and water vapor in a glass container and energized the mixture with ultraviolet light and electric sparks. After a week, Miller analyzed the contents of the glass container. In the "primordial soup," he found amino acids and nucleic acids—the basic building blocks of life! Biologists frequently cite this famous experiment as evidence for the chemical evolution of life. Miller won a Nobel Prize for his work.

We can use Stanley Miller's gas mixture to explore Dalton's law in more detail. Using a mixture of gases, we can write an expression for the total pressure of the gaseous mixture:

$$P_{hydrogen} + P_{ammonia} + P_{methane} + P_{water\ vapor} = P_{total}$$

If the partial pressures of hydrogen, ammonia, and methane were 275 torr, 125 torr, and 340 torr, respectively, what was the partial pressure of the water vapor? Assuming the pressure in the container was standard pressure, 760 torr, we have

$$275\ torr + 125\ torr + 340\ torr + P_{water\ vapor} = 760\ torr$$

Subtracting the partial pressures of hydrogen, ammonia, and methane from each side of the equation, we have

$$P_{water\ vapor} = 760\ torr - (275\ torr + 125\ torr + 340\ torr)$$

$$P_{water\ vapor} = 760\ torr - 740\ torr = 20\ torr$$

The following example exercise illustrates an application of Dalton's law.

▲ **Primordial Soup** Stanley Miller (shown) placed H_2, NH_3, CH_4, and H_2O vapor in his apparatus and energized the gaseous mixture with ultraviolet light and electric sparks.

Example Exercise 10.7 · Dalton's Law of Partial Pressures

An atmospheric sample contains nitrogen, oxygen, argon, and traces of other gases. If the partial pressure of nitrogen is 587 mm Hg, oxygen is 158 mm Hg, and argon is 7 mm Hg, what is the observed pressure as read on the barometer?

Solution
The sum of the individual partial pressures equals the total atmospheric pressure; therefore,

$$P_{nitrogen} + P_{oxygen} + P_{argon} = P_{total}$$

Substituting the values for the partial gas pressures, we have

$$587\ mm\ Hg + 158\ mm\ Hg + 7\ mm\ Hg = 752\ mm\ Hg$$

Thus, the atmospheric pressure as read on the barometer is 752 mm Hg.

Practice Exercise
The regulator on a steel scuba tank containing compressed air indicates that the pressure is 2250 psi. If the partial pressure of nitrogen is 1755 psi and that of argon is 22 psi, what is the partial pressure of oxygen in the tank?

Answer: 473 psi

Concept Exercise
A rigid steel cylinder contains N_2, O_2, and NO at a total pressure of 2.50 atm. What is the partial pressure of NO gas if N_2 and O_2 are each 1.00 atm?

Answer: See Appendix G.

Collecting a Gas over Water

One way of measuring the volume of a gas is to measure the amount of water it displaces. This method is called determining **volume by displacement**. The volume of gas equals the volume of water displaced.

Let's consider a laboratory experiment that produces hydrogen gas from the reaction of zinc metal and sulfuric acid.

$$Zn(s) + H_2SO_4(aq) \rightarrow ZnSO_4(aq) + H_2(g)$$

To collect the hydrogen gas produced in a laboratory experiment, we can invert a graduated cylinder filled with water over the zinc metal. Figure 10.11 shows the experimental apparatus.

▶ Figure 10.11 **Collecting a Gas over Water** Zinc metal reacts with sulfuric acid to give bubbles of hydrogen gas. A graduated cylinder full of water is placed over the metal to collect the gas bubbles. The volume of water displaced from the graduated cylinder equals the volume of hydrogen gas liberated from the acid.

Hydrogen gas and water vapor

Water

Sulfuric acid solution

Zinc metal

When the reaction is complete, the pressure exerted by the hydrogen gas inside the graduated cylinder is balanced by the atmospheric pressure outside. That is, the hydrogen gas pressure on the water inside the graduated cylinder is equal to the atmospheric pressure on the surface of the solution in the beaker.

However, there are actually two gases inside the graduated cylinder. Because the hydrogen gas is collected over an aqueous solution, water vapor is also present. We can use Dalton's law to determine the partial pressure of the hydrogen gas.

$$P_{hydrogen} + P_{water\ vapor} = P_{atmosphere}$$

If the reaction takes place at 25 °C and the barometer reads 767 mm Hg, what is the partial pressure of the hydrogen gas? We refer to Table 10.2 and find that the vapor pressure of water is 23.8 mm Hg at 25 °C. Then we calculate the pressure of the hydrogen gas.

$$P_{hydrogen} + 23.8 \text{ mm Hg} = 767 \text{ mm Hg}$$

After rearranging, we have

$$P_{hydrogen} = 767 \text{ mm Hg} - 23.8 \text{ mm Hg} = 743 \text{ mm Hg}$$

Note When a gas is collected over water it is often called a "wet" gas; that is, the collected gas contains water vapor. A gas that does not contain water vapor is sometimes referred to as a "dry" gas.

10.10 IDEAL GAS BEHAVIOR

LEARNING OBJECTIVES

▸ To list five characteristics of an ideal gas according to the kinetic theory of gases.

▸ To determine the value of absolute zero from a graph of volume or pressure versus temperature.

By the early 1800s, experiments had provided a lot of information about the gaseous state. There was, however, no clear way to interpret this information. By 1850, scientists had enough data to begin to construct a theory to explain the behavior of gases. British physicist James Joule (1818–1889) suggested that the temperature of a gas is related to the energy of its molecules. Joule proposed that temperature and the motion of molecules in a gas are related. At higher temperatures, gas molecules move faster, and at lower temperatures, gas molecules move slower.

Kinetic Theory of Gases

In the period from 1850 to 1870, scientists attempted to construct a model that would explain the behavior of individual gas molecules. They reasoned that given a theoretical model, they would be able to explain the behavior of real gases. This model would also allow predictions of ideal gas behavior. An **ideal gas** is a gas that always behaves in a consistent and predictable manner. Experimentally, a **real gas**, such as hydrogen or oxygen, does not behave ideally under all conditions. Specifically, a real gas does not behave ideally at low temperatures and high pressures.

In due time, the behavior of an ideal gas was described by a model called the *kinetic molecular theory*, or simply the **kinetic theory** of gases. According to the kinetic theory, an ideal gas has the following characteristics:

1. **Gases are made up of tiny molecules.** The size of gas molecules is tiny, and the distance between molecules is quite large. Therefore, gases are mostly empty space. Gas molecules occupy zero volume in an ideal gas.

2. **Gas molecules demonstrate rapid motion, move in straight lines, and travel in random directions.**

3. **Gas molecules have no attraction for one another.** After colliding with each other, molecules simply bounce off in different directions.

4. **Gas molecules collide without losing energy.** Two gas molecules are said to have an **elastic collision**. If a high-energy molecule strikes a less energetic molecule, part of the energy can be transferred. However, the total kinetic energy of both molecules, before and after the collision, does not change.

5. **The average kinetic energy of gas molecules is proportional to the Kelvin temperature that is, $KE \propto T$.** At the same temperature, all gas molecules have equal kinetic energy.

Even for different gases, the average kinetic energy is equal at the same temperature. For example, the kinetic energy of hydrogen and oxygen gases is equal at 25 °C. Although the kinetic energy is equal, hydrogen molecules move faster than oxygen molecules because they are lighter. Given the equation for kinetic energy, $KE = \frac{1}{2}mv^2$, we can explain this mathematically. If the kinetic energy of the two gases is equal, then the lighter hydrogen molecules ($m = 2$ amu) must have a greater velocity (v) than the heavier oxygen molecules ($m = 32$ amu).

At higher temperatures, molecules have more kinetic energy, move faster, and collide more frequently. At lower temperatures, molecules have less kinetic energy, move slower, and collide less frequently. The following example exercise further illustrates the characteristics of an ideal gas according to the kinetic theory.

Example Exercise 10.8 Ideal Gas Behavior

Suppose we have two 5.00-L samples of gas at 25 °C. One sample is ammonia, NH_3, and the other nitrogen dioxide, NO_2. Which gas has the greater kinetic energy? Which gas has the faster molecules?

Solution

Because the temperature of each gas is 25 °C, we know that the kinetic energy is the same for NH_3 and NO_2. At the same temperature, we know that lighter molecules move faster than heavier molecules. The molecular mass of NH_3 is 17 amu and NO_2 is 46 amu. Because NH_3 is lighter than NO_2, the ammonia molecules have a higher velocity than the nitrogen dioxide molecules.

Practice Exercise

Which of the following statements is *not* true according to the kinetic theory of gases?
(a) Molecules occupy a negligible volume.
(b) Molecules move in straight-line paths.
(c) Molecules are attracted to each other.
(d) Molecules undergo elastic collisions.
(e) Molecules of different gases at the same temperature have the same average kinetic energy.

Answer: All these statements are true except (c). Molecules of an ideal gas are not attracted to each other and behave as independent particles.

Concept Exercise

Which of the following is an example of an ideal gas: H_2, O_2, or He?

Answer: See Appendix G.

Absolute Zero

The temperature at which the pressure and volume of a gas theoretically reach zero is referred to as **absolute zero**. Absolute zero is the coldest possible temperature and corresponds to $-273\,°C$, or 0 K. An ideal gas at absolute zero has no kinetic energy, and therefore no molecular motion.

How do we determine the value of absolute zero if $-273\,°C$ is impossible to attain experimentally? We determine absolute zero from the data for the volume of a gas over a range of temperatures above 0 K. When we plot the volume and temperature data points and extend the graph to zero volume, we have the temperature corresponding to absolute zero. Figure 10.12 illustrates an extrapolated value for absolute zero.

▶ Figure 10.12 **Absolute Zero at Zero Volume** As the temperature of the gas decreases, the volume decreases. As an ideal gas approaches zero volume, the temperature approaches absolute zero.

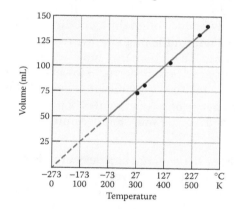

We can also determine absolute zero by obtaining data for the pressure and temperature of a gas. We can plot the pressure and temperature data and extrapolate the graph to absolute zero. Figure 10.13 illustrates the determination of absolute zero.

▶ Figure 10.13 **Absolute Zero at Zero Pressure** As the temperature of the gas decreases, the pressure decreases. As an ideal gas approaches zero pressure, the temperature approaches absolute zero.

10.11 IDEAL GAS LAW

LEARNING OBJECTIVE

▸ To calculate the pressure, volume, temperature, or moles of gas from the ideal gas equation.

In Section 10.3 we learned that the pressure (P) of a gas is inversely proportional to the volume (V). We also learned that pressure is directly proportional to the number of molecules, or moles of gas (n), and directly proportional to the Kelvin temperature (T). We can therefore write a relationship that pressure is proportional to the moles of gas, multiplied by the temperature, divided by the volume:

$$P \propto \frac{nT}{V}$$

By introducing the proportionality constant, R, we can write this relationship as an equation:

$$P = \frac{RnT}{V}$$

After rearranging,

$$PV = nRT$$

This equation is called the **ideal gas law**. The constant R is the **ideal gas constant** and can be expressed as $0.0821 \ L \cdot atm/mol \cdot K$. To use this value of R in a gas law calculation, the pressure must be expressed in atmospheres, the volume in liters, and the temperature in Kelvin. The ideal gas law is a powerful equation that summarizes the behavior of gases. That is, any change in the pressure, volume, temperature, or amount of a gas (moles of gas) is related through this single equation.

Let's try a calculation using the ideal gas law. If a sealed container holds 1.10 mol of nitrogen gas at 25 °C and 3.75 atm, what is the volume in liters? We need to find volume, so we begin by rearranging the ideal gas equation to solve for volume, V. If $PV = nRT$, then

$$V = \frac{nRT}{P}$$

To convert the temperature to Kelvin, we add 273 to 25 °C which gives 298 K. Now we can substitute for each variable in the ideal gas equation.

$$V = \frac{1.10 \ \text{mol} \times \dfrac{0.0821 \ L \cdot atm}{1 \ \text{mol} \cdot K} \times 298 \ K}{375 \ atm} = 7.18 \ L$$

CRITICAL THINKING   Conceptualizing Gases

Q: Can you describe the distribution of helium atoms in a steel tank containing helium gas at 200 °C, −200 °C, and −273 °C?

One of the first studies to offer evidence that most students can solve traditional gas law problems, but many students find it difficult to describe the behavior of gases, was *Concept Learning versus Problem Solving: Is There a Difference.*[1] Research carried out at the University of Wisconsin, Stout, and the University of Missouri, Kansas City, found that most chemistry students could correctly answer a traditional gas law problem, but only one-third gave a correct response to the corresponding conceptual question.

Three years later, in *Concept Learning versus Problem Solving: Revisited,*[2] a more detailed study at the University of California, San Diego, confirmed the research. At UCSD, a study of 285 freshman chemistry students found that nearly 90% answered a traditional gas law problem correctly, but only about 30% of the students gave a correct response to a related conceptual question.

[1] *Journal of Chemical Education*, 64, 508–510.
[2] *Journal of Chemical Education*, 67, 253–54.

Conceptual Questions

Now, let's see if you can answer three conceptual questions about a gas at different temperatures. The following diagram represents a steel tank filled with helium gas at 20 °C and 1 atm pressure. The dots represent helium atoms in the steel container.

Initial Conditions:

Diagram of a steel tank with helium gas at 20 °C and 1 atm pressure.

(1) Which of the following diagrams represents the steel container filled with helium gas heated to 200 °C?

(a)   (b)   (c)   (d)   (e)

(2) Which of the following diagrams represents the steel container filled with helium gas cooled to −200 °C? (The boiling point of helium is −269 °C.)

(a)   (b)   (c)   (d)   (e)

(3) Which of the following diagrams represents the steel container filled with helium gas cooled to −273 °C? (Recall the concept of absolute zero.)

(a)   (b)   (c)   (d)   (e)

A: (1) At 200 °C, the helium atoms are moving faster, but still distributed randomly as shown in (a). (2) At −200 °C, the atoms are moving slower, but still distributed randomly as shown in (a). (3) At absolute zero, −273 °C, the helium atoms are not moving and the gas condenses as shown in (b).

The following example exercise further illustrates the ideal gas law.

Example Exercise 10.9 Ideal Gas Law

How many moles of hydrogen gas occupy a volume of 0.500 L at STP?

Solution

We begin by rearranging the ideal gas equation, $PV = nRT$, and solving for n:

$$n = \frac{PV}{RT}$$

The temperature at STP is 273 K, and the pressure is 1 atm. Then we substitute for each variable in the ideal gas equation:

$$n = \frac{1\ \text{atm} \times 0.500\ \text{L}}{\dfrac{0.0821\ \text{L} \cdot \text{atm}}{1\ \text{mol} \cdot \text{K}} \times 273\ \text{K}} = 0.0223\ \text{mol}$$

Alternatively, we can display the value for the ideal gas constant separately to more clearly show the cancellation of units:

$$n = \frac{1\text{ atm} \times 0.500\text{ L}}{273\text{ K}} \times \frac{1\text{ mol} \cdot \text{K}}{0.0821\text{ L} \cdot \text{atm}} = 0.0223\text{ mol}$$

Practice Exercise

What is the temperature of 0.250 mol of chlorine gas at 655 torr if the volume is 3.50 L?

Answer: 147 K ($-126\,°\text{C}$)

Concept Exercise

Solve for the proportionality constant, R, in the ideal gas law.

Answer: See Appendix G.

Summary

LEARNING OBJECTIVES	SEC	EXERCISES
To list five observed properties of a gas.	10.1	Exercises 1–2
To state standard atmospheric pressure in the following units: atm, mm Hg, torr, cm Hg, in. Hg, psi, and kPa.	10.2	Exercises 3–4
To convert a given gas pressure to a different unit of measurement.	10.2	Exercises 5–8
To identify the three variables that affect the pressure of a gas.	10.3	Exercises 9–10
To state whether gas pressure increases or decreases for a given change in volume, temperature, or number of moles of gas.	10.3	Exercises 11–14
To sketch a graph of the pressure–volume relationship for a gas.	10.4	Exercises 15–16
To calculate the pressure or volume of a gas after a change in conditions.	10.4	Exercises 17–20
To sketch a graph of the volume–temperature relationship for a gas.	10.5	Exercises 21–22
To calculate the volume or temperature of a gas after a change in conditions.	10.5	Exercises 23–26
To sketch a graph of the pressure–temperature relationship for a gas.	10.6	Exercises 27–28
To calculate the pressure or temperature of a gas after a change in conditions.	10.6	Exercises 29–32
To calculate the pressure, volume, or temperature of a gas after a change in conditions.	10.7	Exercises 33–42
To state the relationship between vapor pressure and temperature.	10.8	Exercises 43–46
To apply Dalton's law of partial pressures to a mixture of gases.	10.9	Exercises 47–54
To list five characteristics of an ideal gas according to the kinetic theory of gases.	10.10	Exercises 55–56
To determine the value of absolute zero from a graph of volume or pressure versus temperature.	10.10	Exercises 57–62
To calculate the pressure, volume, temperature, or moles of gas from the ideal gas equation.	10.11	Exercises 63–66

Section 10.1 The shape and volume of a gas are variable and occupy the entire volume of a sealed container. A gas can expand and compress, and the gaseous state has a density much less than that of the liquid state. A gas mixes completely with other gases in the same container.

Section 10.2 **Gas pressure** results from gas molecules striking the inside surface of their container. The pressure exerted by a gas depends on how often and how hard the molecules strike the container. In a **vacuum**, there are no gas molecules and the pressure is zero. **Atmospheric pressure** results from molecules in the air and is measured with a **barometer**.

Standard pressure can be expressed as 1 atm, 760 mm Hg, 760 **torr**, 76 cm Hg, 29.9 in. Hg, 14.7 psi, or 101 kPa.

Section 10.3 We can increase gas pressure by changing one of three variables. First, if we *decrease the volume*, molecules will collide more frequently with the inner surface of the container and the pressure will increase. Second, if we *increase the temperature*, molecules will collide more frequently with the walls of the container and the pressure will increase. Third, if we *increase the number of molecules*, there will be more collisions against the walls of the container and the pressure will increase. **Avogadro's theory** states that equal volumes of gases, at the same temperature and pressure, contain equal numbers of molecules.

Section 10.4 The relationship between the pressure and the volume of a gas is **inversely proportional**. In solving problems involving **Boyle's law**, the pressure increases when the volume decreases, while the temperature remains constant.

Section 10.5 The relationship between the volume and the temperature of a gas is **directly proportional**. In solving problems involving **Charles's law**, the volume increases when the temperature increases, while the pressure remains constant.

Section 10.6 The relationship between the pressure and the temperature of a gas is directly proportional. In solving problems involving **Gay-Lussac's law**, the pressure increases when the temperature increases, while the volume remains constant. We can summarize all the relationships for the gas laws as shown in Table 10.3.

Section 10.7 **Standard temperature and pressure (STP)** is 273 K and exactly 1 atm. In solving problems involving the **combined gas law**, simultaneous changes occur in pressure, volume, and temperature.

TABLE 10.3 SUMMARY OF GAS LAW VARIABLES

GAS LAW	PRESSURE	VOLUME	TEMPERATURE
Boyle's	increases	decreases	*constant*
	decreases	increases	*constant*
Charles's	*constant*	increases	increases
	constant	decreases	decreases
Gay-Lussac's	increases	*constant*	increases
	decreases	*constant*	decreases

Section 10.8 **Vapor pressure** is the pressure exerted by gaseous vapor above a liquid in a sealed container, when the rates of evaporation and condensation are equal. A familiar example is the pressure of H_2O molecules in the vapor above water in a sealed bottle. When the temperature increases, the vapor pressure increases. Conversely, when the temperature decreases, the vapor pressure decreases.

Section 10.9 **Dalton's law of partial pressures** states that the total pressure of gases in a sealed container is equal to the sum of the **partial pressure** of each gas in the mixture. We can collect a gas over water to determine the **volume by displacement**. A "wet" gas collected over water contains water vapor. The partial pressure of the gas is found by subtracting the vapor pressure of water from the total pressure.

Section 10.10 According to the **kinetic theory**, a gas is made up of individual molecules behaving ideally. Molecules in an **ideal gas** move about rapidly and randomly in straight-line paths. Gas molecules show no attraction for one another and undergo **elastic collisions**. The kinetic energy is directly proportional to the Kelvin temperature. At **absolute zero** (0 K), the pressure of an ideal gas is zero. The velocity of gas molecules increases with the temperature and decreases with the molecular mass. The behavior of a **real gas** can deviate substantially at low temperatures and high pressures from that predicted by the kinetic theory.

Section 10.11 A more mathematical method for solving gas problems involves the **ideal gas law**. In the equation $PV = nRT$, the **ideal gas constant** (symbol R) has a value of $0.0821 \ \text{L} \cdot \text{atm}/\text{mol} \cdot \text{K}$.

PROBLEM–SOLVING ORGANIZER

TOPIC	PROCEDURE	EXAMPLE
Properties of Gases Sec. 10.1	Predict the shape and volume of a gas.	The shape and volume of argon gas are variable.
Atmospheric Pressure Sec. 10.2	Express a given gas pressure in units of atm, mm Hg, torr, cm Hg, in. Hg, psi, or kPa.	If argon gas is at 655 mm Hg, what is the pressure in atm? $$655 \text{ mm Hg} \times \frac{1 \text{ atm}}{760 \text{ mm Hg}} = 0.862 \text{ atm}$$
Variables Affecting Gas Pressure Sec. 10.3	Predict an increase or decrease in gas pressure for a change in volume, temperature, or number of molecules.	An increase in which variable causes a decrease in pressure? Answer: *volume*
Boyle's Law Sec. 10.4	Calculate a final pressure after a change in volume (temperature constant). Pressure and volume are inversely proportional.	If a gas is at 1.00 atm, what is the pressure when the volume decreases from 5.00 L to 2.00 L? $$1.00 \text{ atm} \times \frac{5.00 \text{ L}}{2.00 \text{ L}} = 2.50 \text{ atm}$$
Charles's Law Sec. 10.5	Calculate a final volume after a change in temperature (pressure constant). Volume and temperature are directly proportional.	If a gas occupies 50.0 mL, what is the volume when the gas is heated from 300 K to 450 K? $$50.0 \text{ mL} \times \frac{450 \text{ K}}{300 \text{ K}} = 75.0 \text{ mL}$$
Gay-Lussac's Law Sec. 10.6	Calculate a final pressure after a change in temperature (volume constant). Pressure and temperature are directly proportional.	If a gas is at 1.00 atm, what is the pressure when the gas is heated from 300 K to 450 K? $$1.00 \text{ atm} \times \frac{450 \text{ K}}{300 \text{ K}} = 1.50 \text{ atm}$$
Combined Gas Law Sec. 10.7	Calculate a final volume after a change in pressure and temperature. Volume and pressure are inversely proportional; volume and temperature are directly proportional.	If 50.0 mL of gas is at 1.50 atm and 450 K, what is the volume at 1.00 atm and 273 K? $$50.0 \text{ mL} \times \frac{1.50 \text{ atm}}{1.00 \text{ atm}} \times \frac{273 \text{ K}}{450 \text{ K}} = 45.5 \text{ mL}$$
Dalton's Law Sec. 10.9	Calculate the total pressure of a gas mixture by summing the individual partial pressures.	If a gas sample contains He at 0.25 atm and Ar at 1.50 atm, what is the total pressure? $$P_1 + P_2 + P_3 + \ldots = P_{total}$$ $$0.25 \text{ atm} + 1.50 \text{ atm} = 1.75 \text{ atm}$$

Key Terms *Answers to Key Terms are in Appendix H.*

Select the key term that corresponds to each of the following definitions.

_____ 1. a measure of the frequency and energy of molecules colliding against the walls of a container

_____ 2. a volume of space that does not contain gas molecules

_____ 3. the pressure exerted by the molecules in air

_____ 4. an instrument for measuring atmospheric pressure

_____ 5. a unit of pressure equal to 1 mm Hg

_____ 6. the statement that equal volumes of gases, under the same conditions of temperature and pressure, contain equal numbers of molecules

_____ 7. a relationship between two variables such that when one variable doubles, the other variable halves

_____ 8. a relationship between two variables such that when one variable doubles, the other variable doubles

_____ 9. the statement that the pressure and volume of a gas are inversely proportional at constant temperature

_____ 10. the statement that the volume and the Kelvin temperature of a gas are directly proportional at constant pressure

_____ 11. the statement that the pressure and the Kelvin temperature of a gas are directly proportional at constant volume

_____ 12. the statement that the pressure exerted by a gas is inversely proportional to its volume and directly proportional to its Kelvin temperature

_____ 13. the conditions of a gas at 273 K and 760 mm Hg

_____ 14. the pressure exerted by gaseous molecules above a liquid in a sealed container when the rates of evaporation and condensation are equal

_____ 15. the statement that the pressure exerted by a mixture of gases is equal to the sum of the individual pressures exerted by each gas

_____ 16. the pressure exerted by an individual gas in a mixture of two or more gases

_____ 17. a technique for determining the volume of gas from the volume of water it displaces

_____ 18. a theoretical description of gas molecules demonstrating ideal behavior

_____ 19. a theoretical gas that obeys the kinetic theory under all conditions

_____ 20. a gas that deviates from ideal behavior at low temperature and high pressure

_____ 21. an impact between gas molecules with no change in total energy

_____ 22. the theoretical temperature at which the kinetic energy of a gas is zero

_____ 23. the principle stated by the relationship $PV = nRT$

_____ 24. the proportionality constant R in the equation $PV = nRT$

(a) absolute zero (*Sec. 10.10*)

(b) atmospheric pressure (*Sec. 10.2*)

(c) Avogadro's theory (*Sec. 10.3*)

(d) barometer (*Sec. 10.2*)

(e) Boyle's law (*Sec. 10.4*)

(f) Charles's law (*Sec. 10.5*)

(g) combined gas law (*Sec. 10.7*)

(h) Dalton's law of partial pressures (*Sec. 10.9*)

(i) directly proportional (*Sec. 10.5*)

(j) elastic collision (*Sec. 10.10*)

(k) gas pressure (*Sec. 10.2*)

(l) Gay-Lussac's law (*Sec. 10.6*)

(m) ideal gas (*Sec. 10.10*)

(n) ideal gas constant (*Sec. 10.11*)

(o) ideal gas law (*Sec. 10.11*)

(p) inversely proportional (*Sec. 10.4*)

(q) kinetic theory (*Sec. 10.10*)

(r) partial pressure (*Sec. 10.9*)

(s) real gas (*Sec. 10.10*)

(t) standard temperature and pressure (*Sec. 10.7*)

(u) torr (*Sec. 10.2*)

(v) vacuum (*Sec. 10.2*)

(w) vapor pressure (*Sec. 10.8*)

(x) volume by displacement (*Sec. 10.9*)

Exercises *Answers to odd-numbered Exercises are in Appendix I.*

Properties of Gases (Sec. 10.1)

1. Which of the following are observed properties of gases?
   (a) variable shape   (b) expand uniformly
   (c) compress infinitely   (d) mix with other gases
2. Which of the following are observed properties of gases?
   (a) variable volume   (b) expand infinitely
   (c) compress uniformly   (d) low density

Atmospheric Pressure (Sec. 10.2)

3. Give the value for standard atmospheric pressure in each of the following units:
   (a) millimeters of mercury
   (b) centimeters of mercury
4. Give the value for standard atmospheric pressure in each of the following units:
   (a) inches of mercury   (b) pounds per square inch

◀ **The Atmosphere** The atmospheric pressure progressively decreases at higher altitudes. By way of example, the atmospheric pressure on Mt. Everest is about one-third the atmospheric pressure at sea level.

5. If oxygen gas in a steel container is at a pressure of 5.00 atm, what is the pressure expressed in each of the following units?
   (a) psi   (b) cm Hg
6. If a piston in an automobile engine compresses a fuel–air mixture to a pressure of 9.50 atm, what is the pressure expressed in each of the following units?
   (a) in. Hg   (b) mm Hg
7. An American newscast states that the barometer reads 30.8 in. Hg. Express the atmospheric pressure in each of the following units:
   (a) kPa   (b) torr
8. A Canadian newscast states that the barometer reads 104 kPa. Express the atmospheric pressure in each of the following units:
   (a) psi   (b) cm Hg

Variables Affecting Gas Pressure (Sec. 10.3)

9. Indicate what happens to the pressure of a gas with the following changes:
   (a) The volume increases.
   (b) The temperature increases.
   (c) The moles of gas increase.

10. Indicate what happens to the pressure of a gas with the following changes:
    (a) The volume decreases.
    (b) The temperature decreases.
    (c) The moles of gas decrease.
11. State whether the pressure of a gas in a sealed container increases or decreases with the following changes:
    (a) The volume changes from 2.50 L to 5.00 L.
    (b) The temperature changes from 20 °C to 100 °C.
    (c) The moles of gas change from 0.500 mol to 0.250 mol.
12. State whether the pressure of a gas in a sealed container increases or decreases with the following changes:
    (a) The volume changes from 75.0 mL to 50.0 mL.
    (b) The temperature changes from 0 °C to −195 °C.
    (c) The moles of gas change from 1.00 mol to 5.00 mol.
13. Explain how increasing the volume of a gas decreases its pressure.
14. Explain how increasing the temperature of a gas increases its pressure.

◀ **Tire Pressure** The pressure inside the bicycle tire increases as the number of air molecules increases.

Boyle's Law: Pressure–Volume Relationships (Sec. 10.4)

15. Sketch a graph of pressure versus volume, assuming temperature is constant. Label the vertical axis P and the horizontal axis V.
16. Sketch a graph of pressure versus inverse volume, assuming temperature is constant. Label the vertical axis P and the horizontal axis 1/V.
17. A sample of air at 5.00 atm expands from 1.75 L to 2.50 L. If the temperature remains constant, what is the final pressure in atm?
18. A sample of air at 15.0 psi compresses from 555 mL to 275 mL. If the temperature remains constant, what is the final pressure in psi?
19. Calculate the final volume when 5.00 L of argon gas undergoes a pressure change from 1.55 atm to 6.50 atm. Assume that the temperature remains constant.

20. Calculate the final volume when 125 mL of argon gas undergoes a pressure change from 705 mm Hg to 385 mm Hg. Assume that the temperature remains constant.

Charles's Law: Volume–Temperature Relationships (Sec. 10.5)

21. Sketch a graph of volume versus Kelvin temperature, assuming pressure is constant. Label the vertical axis V and the horizontal axis T (K).

22. Sketch a graph of volume versus Celsius temperature, assuming pressure is constant. Label the vertical axis V and the horizontal axis t (°C). Assume the Celsius temperature approaches zero at the origin.

23. A 555 mL sample of nitrous oxide at 25 °C is heated to 50 °C. If the pressure remains constant, what is the final volume?

24. A 2.50 L sample of nitric oxide gas at 100 °C is cooled to 20 °C. If the pressure remains constant, what is the final volume?

25. Calculate the final Celsius temperature when 125 mL of chlorine gas at 25 °C is heated to give a volume of 175 mL. Assume that the pressure remains constant.

26. Calculate the final Celsius temperature when 5.00 L of fluorine gas at 50 °C is cooled to give a volume of 3.75 L. Assume that the pressure remains constant.

Gay-Lussac's Law: Pressure–Temperature Relationships (Sec. 10.6)

27. Sketch a graph of pressure versus Kelvin temperature, assuming volume is constant. Label the vertical axis P and the horizontal axis T (K).

28. Sketch a graph of pressure versus Celsius temperature, assuming volume is constant. Label the vertical axis P and the horizontal axis t (°C). Assume the Celsius temperature approaches zero at the origin.

29. A 1.00-L sample of argon gas at 1.00 atm is heated from 20 °C to 110 °C. If the volume remains constant, what is the final pressure?

30. A 25.0-mL sample of neon gas at 455 mm Hg is cooled from 100 °C to 10 °C. If the volume remains constant, what is the final pressure?

31. Calculate the final Celsius temperature of sulfur dioxide gas if 50.0 mL of the gas at 20 °C and 0.450 atm is heated until the pressure is 0.750 atm. Assume that the volume remains constant.

32. Calculate the final Celsius temperature of nitrogen dioxide gas if 1.95 L of the gas at 0 °C and 375 mm Hg is cooled until the pressure is 225 mm Hg. Assume that the volume remains constant.

Combined Gas Law (Sec. 10.7)

33. A 5.00-L sample of air is collected at 500 °C and 5.00 atm. What is the volume of air at STP?

34. A 100.0-mL sample of air is collected at 21 °C and 772 mm Hg. What is the volume of air at STP?

35. If a sample of hydrogen gas occupies 2.00 L at −50 °C and 155 mm Hg, what is the volume at 75 °C and 365 mm Hg?

36. If a sample of oxygen gas occupies 25.0 mL at −25 °C and 650 mm Hg, what is the volume at 25 °C and 350 mm Hg?

37. A sample of hydrogen chloride gas occupies 0.750 L at STP. What is the pressure in atm if the volume is 0.100 L at 25 °C?

38. A sample of hydrogen fluoride gas occupies 1250 mL at STP. What is the pressure in mm Hg if the volume is 255 mL at 300 °C?

39. A sample of nitrogen gas has a volume of 1.00 L at STP. What is the temperature in °C if the volume is 10.0 L at 2.00 atm?

40. A sample of ammonia gas has a volume of 50.0 mL at STP. What is the Celsius temperature if the volume is 350.0 mL at 350 mm Hg?

41. A sample of argon gas occupies 0.500 L at −125 °C and 225 mm Hg. Calculate the pressure in mm Hg if the gas occupies 0.375 L at 100 °C.

42. A sample of xenon gas occupies 500.0 mL at −185 °C and 75.0 cm Hg. Calculate the Celsius temperature if the volume is 225.0 mL at 55.0 cm Hg.

The Vapor Pressure Concept (Sec. 10.8)

43. What is the relationship between the vapor pressure of a liquid and temperature?

44. Which of the following liquids has the higher vapor pressure at 25 °C: water or mercury?

45. Refer to Table 10.2 and state the vapor pressure for water in mm Hg at each of the following temperatures:
   (a) 25 °C   (b) 50 °C

46. Refer to Table 10.2 and state the vapor pressure for water in atm at each of the following temperatures:
   (a) 75 °C   (b) 100 °C

Dalton's Law of Partial Pressures (Sec. 10.9)

47. Air contains nitrogen, oxygen, argon, and trace gases. If the partial pressure of nitrogen is 592 mm Hg, oxygen is 160 mm Hg, argon is 7 mm Hg, and trace gas is 1 mm Hg, what is the atmospheric pressure?

48. Air contains nitrogen, oxygen, argon, and trace gases. If the partial pressure of nitrogen is 587 mm Hg, oxygen is 158 mm Hg, argon is 7 mm Hg, and trace gas pressure is negligible, what is the atmospheric pressure?

49. A steel cylinder with sulfur dioxide, sulfur trioxide, and oxygen gases is at 825 °C and 1.00 atm. If the partial pressure of sulfur dioxide is 150 mm Hg and sulfur trioxide is 475 mm Hg, what is the partial pressure of oxygen in mm Hg?

50. A steel cylinder with nitrogen, hydrogen, and ammonia gases is at 500 °C and 5.00 atm. If the partial pressure of nitrogen is 1850 mm Hg and hydrogen is 1150 mm Hg, what is the partial pressure of ammonia in mm Hg?

51. Describe the meaning of the expression "collecting a gas over water."

52. Distinguish between a "wet" gas and a "dry" gas.

53. If oxygen is collected over water at 20 °C and 766 mm Hg, what is the partial pressure of the oxygen? Refer to Table 10.2 for the vapor pressure of water.

54. If xenon is collected over water at 30 °C and 755 mm Hg, what is the partial pressure of the xenon? Refer to Table 10.2 for the vapor pressure of water.

Ideal Gas Behavior (Sec. 10.10)

55. State five characteristics of an ideal gas according to the kinetic theory.

56. Distinguish between a real gas and an ideal gas.

57. Under what conditions of temperature and pressure does a real gas behave most like an ideal gas?

58. At what Celsius temperature does a gas possess zero kinetic energy?

59. A sealed container holds the gases He, Ne, and Ar. Which of these gases corresponds to each of the following descriptions?
 (a) highest kinetic energy
 (b) lowest kinetic energy
 (c) fastest atoms
 (d) slowest atoms

60. A sealed container holds the gases H_2, N_2, and O_2. Which of these gases corresponds to each of the following descriptions?
 (a) highest kinetic energy
 (b) lowest kinetic energy
 (c) fastest molecules
 (d) slowest molecules

61. What pressure is exerted by an ideal gas at absolute zero?

62. What volume is occupied by an ideal gas at absolute zero?

Ideal Gas Law (Sec. 10.11)

63. If 0.500 mol of hydrogen gas occupies 5.00 L at 25 °C, what is the pressure in atmospheres?

64. If 1.25 mol of oxygen gas exerts a pressure of 1200 mm Hg at 25 °C, what is the volume in liters?

65. If 10.0 L of neon gas exerts a pressure of 125 psi at 373 K, what is the number of moles of gas?

66. If 0.100 mol of argon gas occupies 2.15 L at 725 mm Hg, what is the temperature in degrees Celsius?

General Exercises

67. If the surface area of a human body is 255 square inches, what is the total weight of the atmosphere on a human body expressed in pounds?

68. If the surface area of a human hand is 165 square centimeters, what is the total weight of the atmosphere on a human hand expressed in pounds?

69. What is standard atmospheric pressure (in cm) measured by a barometer filled with water (given that mercury is 13.6 times more dense than water)?

70. What is standard atmospheric pressure (in cm) measured by a barometer filled with alcohol (given that mercury is 19.2 times more dense than alcohol)?

71. A deep-sea scuba tank contains oxygen and helium gases. If the partial pressures of the gases are 35 atm and 125 atm, what is the total pressure (in psi)?

72. A bicycle tire contains nitrogen, oxygen, and argon gases. If the partial pressures are 51.0 psi, 13.5 psi, and 0.5 psi, what is the total pressure (in atm)?

73. The decomposition of baking soda produces carbon dioxide gas. If 42.5 mL of wet gas is collected over water at 22 °C and 764 mm Hg, what is the volume of dry gas at STP conditions? (The vapor pressure of water at 22 °C is 19.8 mm Hg.)

74. Calcium metal and water produce hydrogen gas. If the volume of wet gas collected over water is 95.0 mL at 20 °C and 758 mm Hg, what is the volume of dry gas at STP conditions? (The vapor pressure of water at 20 °C is 17.5 mm Hg.)

75. What pressure (in atm) is exerted by 1.51×10^{23} oxygen molecules at 25 °C in a 5.00-L container?

76. What volume (in liters) is occupied by 3.38×10^{22} nitrogen molecules at 100 °C and 255 mm Hg?

77. Natural gas contains methane, CH_4, ethane, C_2H_6, and hydrogen sulfide, H_2S. Which molecules have the fastest velocity?

78. Bottled gas for recreational vehicles contains propane, C_3H_8, and butane, C_4H_{10}. Which molecules have the faster velocity?

79. A sample of chlorine gas occupies 1550 mL at 0.945 atm and 50 °C. What is the mass of the sample?

80. A sample of fluorine gas occupies 855 mL at 710 mm Hg and 155 °C. What is the mass of the sample?

Challenge Exercises

81. Which of the following gases has a density of 2.14 g/L at STP: H_2, O_2, O_3?

82. Which of the following gases has a density of 5.40 g/L at STP: H_2S, SO_3, CF_2Cl_2?

83. A sample of unknown gas has a mass of 1.95 g and occupies 3.00 L at 1.25 atm and 20 °C. What is the molar mass of the unknown gas?

84. A sample of unknown gas has a mass of 2.85 g and occupies 750 mL at 760 mm Hg and 100 °C. What is the molar mass of the unknown gas?

Online Exercises

Research each of the following using an Internet search engine (e.g., Google.com or Yahoo.com) and cite your URL reference.

85. Which two planets in our solar system, in addition to Earth, exhibit the "greenhouse effect"?

86. What are the amounts of the two gases in a "heliox" mixture used by deep-sea divers?

◀ **Deep-Sea Divers**
These divers are breathing a "heliox" gas mixture.

10 Chapter Self-Test *Answers to Self-Test are in Appendix J.*

1. Which of the following is *not* an observed property of gases? (Sec. 10.1)
   (a) Gases vary in shape and volume.
   (b) Gases expand infinitely.
   (c) Gases compress infinitely.
   (d) Gases have low density.
   (e) Gases mix completely.

2. Which of the following expresses standard atmospheric pressure? (Sec. 10.2)
   (a) 29.9 in. Hg
   (b) 76.0 cm Hg
   (c) 760 mm Hg
   (d) 14.7 psi
   (e) all of the above

3. Which of the following changes decreases the pressure of a gas? (Sec. 10.3)
   (a) increasing the volume
   (b) increasing temperature
   (c) increasing the number of molecules
   (d) all of the above
   (e) none of the above

4. A volume of hydrogen gas at 1.00 atm increases from 0.250 L to 0.500 L. If the temperature remains constant, what is the final pressure? (Sec. 10.4)
   (a) 0.250 atm
   (b) 0.500 atm
   (c) 1.00 atm
   (d) 2.00 atm
   (e) none of the above

5. A 1.00 L volume of oxygen gas is cooled from 50.0 °C to 25.0 °C. If the pressure remains constant, what is the final volume? (Sec. 10.5)
   (a) 0.500 L   (b) 0.923 L
   (c) 1.00 L   (d) 1.08 L
   (e) 2.00 L

6. A sample of nitrogen gas at 1.00 atm is heated from 250 K to 500 K. If the volume remains constant, what is the final pressure? (Sec. 10.6)
   (a) 0.250 atm
   (b) 0.500 atm
   (c) 1.00 atm
   (d) 2.00 atm
   (e) none of the above

7. A sample of air occupies a volume of 10.0 L. If both the pressure and Kelvin temperature each double, what is the final volume? (Sec. 10.7)
   (a) 2.50 L
   (b) 5.00 L
   (c) 10.0 L
   (d) 20.0 L
   (e) 40.0 L

8. If the temperature of a liquid increases from 20.0 °C to 50.0 °C, what happens to the vapor pressure? (Sec. 10.8)
   (a) increases
   (b) decreases
   (c) remains constant
   (d) unpredictable
   (e) none of the above

9. What is the partial pressure of a gas collected over water at 25 °C and 775 mm Hg? The vapor pressure of water at 25 °C is 23.8 mm Hg. (Sec. 10.9)
   (a) 750 torr
   (b) 751 torr
   (c) 760 torr
   (d) 775 torr
   (e) 799 torr

10. Which of the following is true for an ideal gas? (Sec. 10.10)
    (a) All molecules have the same velocity.
    (b) All molecules have the same kinetic energy.
    (c) All molecular collisions have the same energy.
    (d) all of the above
    (e) none of the above

11. How many moles of helium occupy a volume of 5.00 L at 227 °C and 5.00 atm (given that R = 0.0821 atm · L/mol · K)? (Sec. 10.11)
    (a) 0.609 mol
    (b) 1.64 mol
    (c) 5.00 mol
    (d) 25.0 mol
    (e) 6090 mol

Key Concepts

12. A few drops of water in a gallon can are heated to steam, and the can is sealed with a cap. As the steam cools from 100 °C to 20 °C, the can is crushed, as shown in the diagram. Explain the observation.

No cap

Steam
100 °C

Cap

Water

20 °C

13. If you check automobile tire pressure on a cold morning before leaving home, and check it again after driving a few miles, would you expect the tire pressure to increase or decrease?

14. Methyl acetate, $C_3H_6O_2$, smells fragrant, and hydrogen sulfide gas, H_2S, smells like rotten eggs. Would you be attracted or repulsed first, if both gases escaped from the same container at the same time?

Critical Thinking

15. When you heat the air inside an open hot air balloon, why does the balloon rise? (Assume that the air pressure inside the balloon equals that of the surrounding air.)

16. If you release a helium balloon into the air, why does the volume increase as the balloon ascends into the atmosphere? (Assume that the temperature stays constant.)

17. A plastic water bottle in a car on a hot day bulges after an hour. Explain the observation.

18. A plastic water bottle in a car on a cold night is crushed in the morning. Explain the observation.

19. Before starting to climb a mountain, you drink water from a plastic bottle, and replace the cap tightly. Describe the water bottle when you reach the top of the mountain.

Liquids and Solids

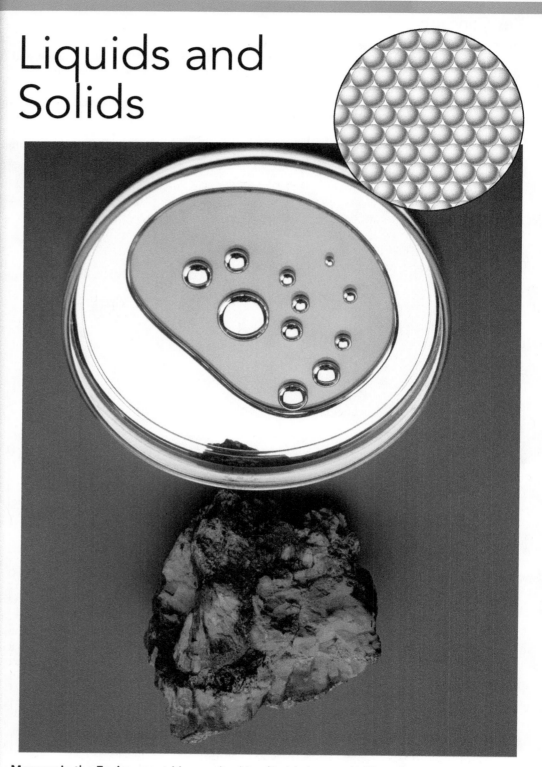

Mercury in the Environment Mercury (top) is a liquid above −40 °C, and its most common ore is cinnabar (bottom). In January, 2012, the Environmental Protection Agency (EPA), issued new regulations limiting the emission of mercury from coal-burning power plants. The EPA estimates the new regulations will prevent thousands of premature deaths and heart attacks each year.

"If I have ever made any valuable discoveries it has been owing more to patient attention, than to any other talent."
Sir Isaac Newton, English Scientist (1643–1727)

In Chapter 10 we discussed the gaseous state of matter, where individual molecules are relatively distant from one another. In this chapter, we will discuss the liquid and solid states of matter in which particles contact one another. We will use water in much of our discussion to reinforce the topics of nomenclature, mole calculations, and stoichiometry that we discussed in earlier chapters.

Water is the most important liquid on Earth and covers about three-fourths of the surface of our planet. It is necessary for all the chemical reactions that support plant and animal life, and about two-thirds of the mass of the human body is water. With the exception of oxygen, water is our most critical substance. We can survive quite some time without food, but only a few days without water.

The physical properties of water are unusual in several ways. One unusual property is its density. The density of a substance is generally greater in the solid state than in the liquid state. The two exceptions to this generalization are water and ammonia. Because the density of solid ice is less than that of liquid water, ice floats on water. If ice were more dense than water, marine life would not survive. Rivers and lakes would freeze into solid chunks of ice in wintry climates. Initially, ice would form on the surface and then sink, and eventually the entire body of water would change to solid ice. This, of course, would destroy aquatic life.

11.1 PROPERTIES OF LIQUIDS

LEARNING OBJECTIVE

▶ To identify five observed properties of a liquid.

Unlike gases, liquids do not respond significantly to temperature and pressure changes. Also, the mathematical relationships that apply to gases, such as the combined gas law, do not apply to liquids. Rather, when we study the liquid state, we observe the following general properties:

1. **Liquids have a variable shape, but a fixed volume.** The shape of a liquid conforms to the shape of its container.
2. **Liquids usually flow readily.** Liquids flow at different rates; for example, petroleum flows more slowly than water.
3. **Liquids do not compress or expand significantly.** The volume of a liquid varies very little with changes in temperature or pressure.
4. **Liquids have a high density compared to gases.** Gases and liquids are both fluids; that is, the shape is not fixed and individual particles are free to move throughout the container. However, the liquid state is about 1000 times more dense than the gaseous state because particles in a liquid are closer together. For example, the density of water is 1.00 g/mL, whereas the density of air at sea level is about 0.001 g/mL.
5. **Liquids that are soluble mix homogeneously.** Liquids diffuse more slowly than gases. However, liquids that are soluble eventually form a homogeneous mixture. For example, when food coloring is added to water, the liquids diffuse slowly and mix uniformly.

▲ **Scientific Misconception** It is a misconception that stained glass windows are thicker at the bottom due to liquid flow; the thickness varies owing to the glassmaking process.

11.2 THE INTERMOLECULAR BOND CONCEPT

LEARNING OBJECTIVES

▶ To explain the concept of an intermolecular bond.

▶ To describe three types of attraction between molecules in a liquid.

The Internet is an international network for computers, whereas an Intranet is a localized network; and highways are designated interstate (between states) or intrastate (in state). Similarly, an intermolecular bond indicates an attraction between molecules, whereas an intramolecular bond is between atoms in a molecule.

Some properties of liquids, such as vapor pressure, are determined by the strength of attraction between molecules. This attraction is called an *intermolecular bond*, and it is much weaker than an intramolecular bond between atoms. The three types of intermolecular attraction are based on temporary dipoles, permanent dipoles, and hydrogen bonds.

Temporary Dipole Attraction

In molecules, positive and negative charges are concentrated in different regions of individual molecules. These two charged regions are created by an uneven distribution of electrons in the molecule. A molecule having regions of positive and negative charge is said to possess a *dipole*.

Let's first consider temporary dipole attraction. Even though atoms in a molecule may share electrons equally, the electrons are constantly shifting about. This shifting about of electrons produces regions in the molecule that are temporarily "electron rich" and slightly negative. Simultaneously, another region of the molecule is temporarily "electron poor" and slightly positive. A negative region in one molecule has a weak attraction for a positive region in another molecule. This temporary attraction between molecules is referred to as a **dispersion force**.

Although dispersion forces last for only brief periods of time, they occur frequently between molecules. Figure 11.1 illustrates temporary intermolecular dispersion forces.

▶ Figure 11.1 **Intermolecular Dispersion Forces** (a) Two molecules are shown. (b) The molecule on the left forms a temporary dipole, which can induce a dipole in the molecule on the right. (c) The two molecules are temporarily attracted to each other. In turn, these molecules induce temporary dipole attractions in the surrounding molecules in the liquid.

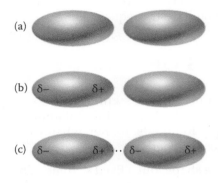

Permanent Dipoles and Hydrogen Bonds

Atoms of different elements vary in their attraction for electrons. This gives rise to regions of positive and negative charge in a molecule. As a result, similar to magnets, individual molecules are attracted to each other. In contrast to temporary dipole attraction, permanent dipole attraction operates continuously. That is, a permanent **dipole force** operates between molecules as shown in Figure 11.2.

(a)   (b)

▲ Figure 11.2 **Intermolecular Dipole Forces** (a) A dipole force results from a dipole–dipole attraction between two molecules. (b) Dipole forces between several molecules in a liquid are shown.

When a hydrogen atom is bonded to an oxygen atom or a nitrogen atom in a molecule, an especially strong dipole results. This strong dipole produces an attraction between molecules that is typically about 10% of the strength of an intramolecular bond. This special type of permanent dipole attraction is called a **hydrogen bond** (Figure 11.3). Hydrogen bonds are important in living organisms where they maintain the structure of protein molecules, and the double-helix structure of DNA molecules.

▲ Figure 11.3 **Intermolecular Hydrogen Bonds** Water molecules form intermolecular hydrogen bonds. Notice that the hydrogen atom is attracted to the nonbonding electrons on the highly electronegative oxygen atom.

The following example exercise illustrates the characteristics of intermolecular bonds:

Example Exercise 11.1 Intermolecular Attraction

If molecules in a liquid have a permanent dipole, what is the strongest type of intermolecular attraction?

Solution

In a liquid, intermolecular attraction is the result of both permanent and temporary dipoles. Molecules that contain either $H-O$ or $H-N$ bonds have the strongest type of intermolecular attraction, that is, hydrogen bonds. Water, H_2O, and ammonia, NH_3, are examples of liquids with hydrogen bonds.

Practice Exercise

If molecules in a liquid do not have a permanent dipole, what is the strongest type of intermolecular attraction?

Answer: The intermolecular attraction between molecules in a liquid not having a permanent dipole is a dispersion force resulting from temporary dipoles.

Concept Exercise

Which of the following liquids has the stronger intermolecular attraction between molecules: CH_3-CH_2-OH or CH_3-O-CH_3?

Answer: See Appendix G.

11.3 VAPOR PRESSURE, BOILING POINT, VISCOSITY, AND SURFACE TENSION

In the previous chapter, we introduced the kinetic theory of gases to explain the behavior of gases. Now, we will extend this theory to explain the properties of liquids.

According to the kinetic theory the attraction between gas molecules is negligible. This is not the case for liquids. Molecules in the liquid state are in contact with each other, and their attraction restricts their movement. Individual molecules do have enough energy to move about one another; that is, a liquid is free to flow. The liquid state and the gaseous state are analogous to honeybees swarming in a hive (liquid state), and individual bees flying off to gather pollen (gaseous state). Now let's consider some properties of liquids.

Vapor Pressure

The kinetic theory relates the average energy of molecules to temperature. The higher the temperature, the greater the kinetic molecular energy. However, not all molecules at the same temperature have identical energies. Some are more energetic than others.

LEARNING OBJECTIVES

▶ To understand the concepts of vapor pressure, boiling point, viscosity, and surface tension.

▶ To relate the vapor pressure, boiling point, viscosity, and surface tension of a liquid to the strength of attraction between molecules.

At the surface of a liquid, for example, some molecules have enough energy to completely escape the attraction of neighboring molecules. The molecules that escape enter the gaseous state, which is referred to as *vapor*. This process is called *vaporization*. In the reverse process, some molecules in the vapor return to the liquid. This process is called *condensation*.

When the rates of vaporization and condensation are equal, the pressure exerted by the gas molecules above a liquid is called the **vapor pressure**. However, the vapor pressure above a liquid depends on the attraction between molecules in the liquid. Water molecules have a strong attraction for each other, and ethyl ether molecules have a relatively weak attraction. Because of the lesser attraction between molecules, ether molecules escape from the liquid state more readily than water molecules. Therefore, the vapor pressure of ether is greater than that of water at the same temperature (Figure 11.4).

▶ Figure 11.4 **Vapor Pressure of Water and Ether** (a) At 0 °C neither water nor ether has sufficient vapor pressure to affect the balloons. (b) At 35 °C the vapor pressure of water is still low; however, the vapor pressure of ether is considerable and inflates the balloon.

Table 11.1 compares the attraction between molecules, that is, *intermolecular attraction*, and the vapor pressure for a few selected liquids. In general, as the attraction between molecules increases, the vapor pressure decreases. In Table 11.1 we see that propionic acid and butyl alcohol both have a strong intermolecular attraction. Thus, their vapor pressures at 20 °C are quite low. Conversely, propyl chloride and ethyl ether each has a weak intermolecular attraction. Thus, their vapor pressures are considerably higher. When comparing vapor pressure values, it is necessary to choose two liquids that have approximately the same molar mass. Note that in these comparisons, each liquid, except water, has an approximate molar mass of 74 g/mol.

TABLE 11.1 VAPOR PRESSURE OF SELECTED LIQUIDS

LIQUID	APPROXIMATE MOLAR MASS	INTERMOLECULAR ATTRACTION	VAPOR PRESSURE AT 20 °C
water	18 g/mol	strong	18 mm Hg
propionic acid, C_2H_5COOH	74 g/mol	strong	5 mm Hg
butyl alcohol, C_4H_9OH	74 g/mol	strong	6 mm Hg
propyl chloride, C_3H_7Cl	79 g/mol	weak	300 mm Hg
ethyl ether, $C_2H_5OC_2H_5$	74 g/mol	weak	450 mm Hg

Boiling Point

As the temperature of a liquid increases, its vapor pressure increases. At 30 °C the vapor pressure of water is about 30 mm Hg, and at 60 °C it is 150 mm Hg. Figure 11.5 shows the relationship between vapor pressure and temperature for ether, ethanol, and water.

◀ **Figure 11.5 Vapor Pressure versus Temperature** The vapor pressure of a liquid increases as the temperature increases. The vapor pressure of water equals 760 mm Hg at 100 °C. Thus, at 100 °C the vapor pressure of water equals the standard atmospheric pressure (760 mm Hg), and water begins to boil.

A liquid begins to boil when the pressure of the vapor above the liquid equals the pressure of the atmosphere. Thus, we define the normal **boiling point** (symbol **Bp**) as the temperature at which the vapor pressure equals standard atmospheric pressure. Accordingly, liquids that have *high* boiling points must have *low* vapor pressures. The following example exercise illustrates the determination of boiling points from vapor pressure data.

Example Exercise 11.2 Boiling Point Predictions

Refer to Figure 11.5 and determine the approximate boiling point of ether.

Solution
The normal boiling point of a liquid is the temperature at which the vapor pressure equals standard atmospheric pressure, that is, 760 mm Hg. From the graph, we find that the vapor pressure of ether is 760 mm Hg at about 35 °C. Thus, the normal boiling point of ether is about 35 °C. The actual observed value for the boiling point of ether is 36 °C.

Practice Exercise
Refer to Figure 11.5 and determine the approximate boiling point of ethanol.

Answer: ~80 °C (The actual boiling point of ethanol is 78 °C.)

Concept Exercise
Which of the following liquids has the higher boiling point: $CH_3—CH_2—OH$ or $CH_3—O—CH_3$?

Answer: See Appendix G.

Viscosity

Some liquids are easier to pour than others. Water pours easily, whereas honey does not. The resistance of a liquid to flow is a property called **viscosity**. Viscosity is the result of an attraction between molecules. It is also affected by factors such as the size and shape of the molecules. In principle, the greater the attraction between molecules, the higher the viscosity. Table 11.2 compares the attraction between molecules and the viscosity for a few selected liquids.

TABLE 11.2 VISCOSITY OF SELECTED LIQUIDS

LIQUID	APPROXIMATE MOLAR MASS	INTERMOLECULAR ATTRACTION	VISCOSITY* AT 20 °C
water	18 g/mol	strong	1.00
propionic acid, C_2H_5COOH	74 g/mol	strong	1.10
butyl alcohol, C_4H_9OH	74 g/mol	strong	2.95
propyl chloride, C_3H_7Cl	79 g/mol	weak	0.35
ethyl ether, $C_2H_5OC_2H_5$	74 g/mol	weak	0.23

*Values are expressed in centipoise, a common unit of viscosity.

▲ **Viscosity** The motor oil on the left is more viscous and flows more slowly than the motor oil on the right.

In Table 11.2 we see that propionic acid and butyl alcohol have a strong intermolecular attraction and that the viscosity of both is greater than that of water. We also see that propyl chloride and ethyl ether have a weak attraction between molecules and that the viscosity of both is much lower than that of water. Honey is an example of a viscous liquid. We can therefore predict that there is a strong attraction between molecules in honey.

Surface Tension

At some time you have probably noticed a small insect floating on water. For an insect or any object to sink in a liquid, it has to break through the surface. But the molecules on the surface of a liquid resist being pushed apart. The attraction between the surface molecules in a liquid is called **surface tension**. There are other factors to consider, but in general the greater the intermolecular attraction, the higher the surface tension. Table 11.3 compares the intermolecular attraction and surface tension for a few selected liquids.

TABLE 11.3 SURFACE TENSION OF SELECTED LIQUIDS

LIQUID	APPROXIMATE MOLAR MASS	INTERMOLECULAR ATTRACTION	SURFACE TENSION* AT 20 °C
water	18 g/mol	strong	70
propionic acid, C_2H_5COOH	74 g/mol	strong	27
butyl alcohol, C_4H_9OH	74 g/mol	strong	25
propyl chloride, C_3H_7Cl	79 g/mol	weak	18
ethyl ether, $C_2H_5OC_2H_5$	74 g/mol	weak	17

*Values are expressed in dynes per square centimeter, a common unit of surface tension.

Hydrogen bonds

▶ **Surface Tension** Water has a high surface tension owing to hydrogen bonds, and this allows the insect to "walk" on water.

We all know that rain forms drops as it falls. In fact, when we spray any liquid, it forms drops, and each drop has the shape of a small sphere. Drops of liquid are spherical because surface tension causes them to have the smallest possible surface area, and that area corresponds to a spherical droplet. Table 11.3 shows that water has an unusually high surface tension.

Example Exercise 11.3 illustrates the relationships between the properties of liquids and intermolecular attraction.

Example Exercise 11.3 Physical Property Predictions

Consider the following properties of liquids. State whether the value for each property is high or low for a liquid with a strong intermolecular attraction:

(a) vapor pressure
(b) boiling point
(c) viscosity
(d) surface tension

Solution

For a liquid having a strong attraction between molecules, properties (b), (c), and (d) are generally high; property (a) is low.

(a) Molecular attraction slows vaporization. Therefore, vapor pressure is *low* for liquids with a strong intermolecular attraction.
(b) Attraction between molecules inhibits boiling. Thus, the boiling point is *high* for liquids with a strong intermolecular attraction.
(c) Molecular attraction increases the resistance of a liquid to flow. Viscosity is *high* for liquids with a strong intermolecular attraction.
(d) Attraction between molecules causes a drop of liquid to form a sphere. Surface tension is *high* for liquids with a strong intermolecular attraction.

Practice Exercise

The intermolecular attraction is greater in isopropyl alcohol, C_3H_7OH, than in pentane, C_5H_{12}. Predict which liquid has the higher value for each of the following:

(a) vapor pressure
(b) boiling point
(c) viscosity
(d) surface tension

Answers:

(a) C_5H_{12}
(b) C_3H_7OH
(c) C_3H_7OH
(d) C_3H_7OH

Concept Exercise

Explain why the paper clip can float on water even though its density is much greater than the density of water.

Answer: See Appendix G.

Hydrogen bonds

▲ **Surface Tension** A paper clip can float on water.

11.4 PROPERTIES OF SOLIDS

LEARNING OBJECTIVE

▶ To identify five observed properties of a solid.

Unlike liquids, solids have a fixed shape. The reason for this is that the individual particles of the solid are not free to move. Unlike gases, the volume of a solid shows very little response to changes in temperature or pressure. The observed properties of the solid state are as follows:

1. **Solids have a fixed shape and a fixed volume.** Unlike liquids, solids are rigid and their shape is fixed.
2. **Solids are either crystalline or noncrystalline.** A **crystalline solid** contains particles arranged in a regular repeating pattern. Each particle occupies a fixed position in the crystal. The high degree of order of the molecules can produce a beautiful clear crystal, for example, a diamond or a ruby. An ordinary stone is a noncrystalline solid and is not transparent.

3. **Solids do not compress or expand to any degree.** Assuming no change in physical state, temperature and pressure have a negligible effect on the volume of a solid.

4. **Solids have a slightly higher density than their corresponding liquids.** For example, solid chunks of iron sink in a high-temperature furnace containing molten iron. One important exception to this rule is water; ice is less dense than liquid water. As a result, ice floats on water.

5. **Solids do not mix by diffusion.** In a solid heterogeneous mixture, the particles are not free to diffuse and they cannot mix uniformly. In an alloy, which is a homogeneous mixture, the metals mix uniformly in the molten liquid state before cooling to a solid.

LEARNING OBJECTIVE

▶ To describe three types of crystalline solids: ionic, molecular, and metallic.

11.5 CRYSTALLINE SOLIDS

Chemists know that the particles of a crystalline solid are arranged in a regular geometric pattern. However, the particles can be of different types. They can be ionic, molecular, or metallic. In ionic solids the crystals are composed of regular patterns of ions. In molecular solids the molecules, not ions, form repeating patterns. In metallic solids, individual metal atoms are arranged geometrically.

Ionic Solids

A crystalline **ionic solid** is an ionic compound composed of positive and negative ions. Salt, for example, is a crystalline solid of NaCl. Here, sodium ions, Na^+, and chloride ions, Cl^-, are arranged in a regular three-dimensional structure referred to as a *crystal lattice*. Notice the clear crystal of table salt shown in Figure 11.6 has the shape of a cube. Other ionic crystalline compounds, such as NaF, CaF_2, and $CaCO_3$, have different geometric shapes.

▶ Figure 11.6 **A Crystalline Ionic Solid** A sodium chloride crystal, NaCl, is an example of a crystalline ionic solid.

Molecular Solids

A crystalline **molecular solid** has molecules arranged in a particular configuration. Crystalline sucrose (table sugar), for example, is composed of $C_{12}H_{22}O_{11}$ molecules. The sucrose molecules are arranged in a regular order that allows light to pass through the crystal. Therefore, a large crystal of sucrose appears transparent. Other molecular solids are sulfur and phosphorus. Sulfur crystals (Figure 11.7) are made from S_8 molecules held together by intramolecular bonds. Phosphorus powder is made from P_4 molecules.

◀ Figure 11.7 **A Crystalline Molecular Solid** A sulfur crystal, S_8, is an example of a crystalline molecular solid.

Metallic Solids

A crystalline **metallic solid** has atoms of metals arranged in a definite pattern. That is, a metallic crystal is made up of positive metal ions surrounded by valence electrons. Metals are good conductors of electricity because the valence electrons are free to move about the crystal. This arrangement of atoms and freely moving electrons is referred to as the "electron sea" model. The flow of electricity is associated with the movement of electrons through a metal. Figure 11.8 shows a crystal of gold.

Classifying Crystalline Solids

It is helpful to classify crystalline solids to predict their properties. In general, the properties of ionic solids such as melting point, hardness, electrical conductivity, and water solubility are similar. The properties of molecular solids are usually similar as well. Metals show a range of physical properties, but all are malleable (form thin foils) and ductile (drawn into wire) and are good conductors of electricity. Table 11.4 lists the general properties for each of the three types of crystalline solids.

▲ Figure 11.8 **A Crystalline Metallic Solid** A gold nugget is an example of a crystalline metallic solid.

TABLE 11.4 GENERAL PROPERTIES OF CRYSTALLINE SOLIDS

TYPE OF SOLID	GENERAL PROPERTIES	EXAMPLES
ionic	high melting point, hard, brittle, at least slightly soluble in water, conductor of electricity when melted or in solution	$NaCl$, $CaCO_3$, $MgSO_4$
molecular	low melting point, generally insoluble in water, nonconductor of electricity	S_8, $C_{10}H_8$, $C_6H_{12}O_6$
metallic	low to high melting point, malleable, ductile, conductor of electricity, insoluble in most solvents	Cu, Ag, Au

Diamond, a form of carbon, is a special type of crystalline solid that has intramolecular bonds between atoms (Figure 11.9). This type of crystalline solid is referred to as a *network solid*. Diamond is a hard, brittle, crystalline network solid with unusual properties, including a very high melting point (above 3500 °C).

The following example exercise further illustrates the classification of ionic, molecular, and metallic types of crystalline solids.

▲ Figure 11.9 **A Crystalline Network Solid** A diamond is a crystalline network solid of carbon atoms.

> **Example Exercise 11.4** Classifying Crystalline Solids

Classify each of the following crystalline solids as ionic, molecular, or metallic:

(a) nickel, Ni   (b) nickel(II) oxide, NiO

Solution

The type of crystalline solid is dictated by the type of particle in the solid.

(a) Nickel is a metal composed of atoms; thus, Ni is a *metallic solid*.

(b) Nickel(II) oxide contains ions and is therefore an *ionic solid*.

Practice Exercise

Classify each of the following crystalline solids as ionic, molecular, or metallic:

(a) iodine, I_2

(b) silver iodide, AgI

Answers: (a) molecular   (b) ionic

Concept Exercise

Which type of crystalline solid has a high melting point and is a nonconductor of electricity in the solid state, but a good conductor of electricity when melted?

Answer: See Appendix G.

LEARNING OBJECTIVES

▶ To understand the concepts of specific heat, heat of fusion, and heat of vaporization.

▶ To calculate heat changes that involve the specific heat, heat of fusion, and heat of vaporization.

11.6 CHANGES OF PHYSICAL STATE

Heat is necessary to change the physical state of a substance. Specific heat is the amount of heat required to raise one gram of substance one degree Celsius. Every substance has a unique value for its specific heat. Water is considered a reference and its specific heat is 1.00 calorie per gram per degree Celsius, that is, $1.00 \text{ cal}/(g \times {}^\circ C)$. The specific heats for ice and steam are approximately half that of liquid water.

Next, let's consider a substance changing state from a solid to a liquid at its melting point. The amount of heat required to melt 1.00 g of substance is called the **heat of fusion** (H_{fusion}). For water, the heat of fusion is 80.0 cal/g. Water releases the same amount of heat energy, 80 cal/g, when it changes from the liquid to the solid state. This heat change is called the *heat of solidification* (H_{solid}). For any substance, the heats of fusion and solidification are equal. That is, the amount of heat to melt a substance equals the amount of heat released when the substance solidifies.

A substance rapidly changes state from a liquid to a vapor at its boiling point. The amount of heat required to vaporize 1.00 g of a substance is called the **heat of vaporization** (H_{vapor}). For water, it is 540 cal/g. Conversely, water releases the same amount of heat energy, 540 cal/g, when it condenses from a gas to a liquid. This heat change is called the *heat of condensation* (H_{cond}). For any substance, the heats of vaporization and condensation are equal. Table 11.5 lists the heat values for water, ice, and steam.

TABLE 11.5 HEAT VALUES FOR WATER

SUBSTANCE	SPECIFIC HEAT [cal/(g × °C)]	H_{fusion} (cal/g)	H_{solid} (cal/g)	H_{vapor} (cal/g)	H_{cond} (cal/g)
ice, $H_2O(s)$	0.50	80.0			
water, $H_2O(l)$	1.00		80.0	540	
steam, $H_2O(g)$	0.48				540

To see the change in temperature with a constant application of heat, we draw a temperature–energy graph, sometimes called a *heating curve*. The heating curve for water is shown in Figure 11.10.

◀ **Figure 11.10**
Temperature–Energy Graph
As heat is continuously added
to a substance, the substance
eventually changes its physical
state. Notice the temperature
remains constant during fusion
(solid to liquid), vaporization
(liquid to gas), condensation
(gas to liquid), and solidification (liquid to solid).

Let's combine the concept of a heating curve with the heat values in Table 11.5. For example, let's find the amount of heat energy necessary to convert 25.5 g of ice at −5.0 °C to steam at 100.0 °C. This problem requires four steps: (1) heat the ice from −5.0 °C to 0.0 °C, (2) convert the ice to liquid water at 0.0 °C, (3) heat the water from 0.0 °C to 100.0 °C, and (4) convert the water to steam at 100.0 °C.

1. To calculate the amount of energy required to heat the ice we use its mass (25.5 g), the temperature change (−5.0 °C to 0.0 °C), and the specific heat of ice (0.50 cal/(g × °C)). Using 0.50 cal/(g × °C) as a unit factor, we have

$$25.5 \; \cancel{g} \times \frac{0.50 \; \text{cal}}{1 \; \cancel{g} \times °\cancel{C}} \times [0.0 - (-5.0)] \; °\cancel{C} = 64 \; \text{cal}$$

2. The heat of fusion for ice, 80.0 cal/g, is found in Table 11.5. The energy required to melt 25.5 g of ice is

$$25.5 \; \cancel{g} \times \frac{80.0 \; \text{cal}}{1 \; \cancel{g}} = 2040 \; \text{cal}$$

3. To calculate the amount of energy required to heat the liquid water we must know its mass, the temperature change (0.0 °C to 100.0 °C), and the specific heat of water; therefore, we have

$$25.5 \; \cancel{g} \times \frac{1.00 \; \text{cal}}{1 \; \cancel{g} \times °\cancel{C}} \times (100.0 - 0.0) \; °\cancel{C} = 2550 \; \text{cal}$$

4. The heat of vaporization, 540 cal/g, is found in Table 11.5. The energy required to vaporize the water to steam is

$$25.5 \; \cancel{g} \times \frac{540 \; \text{cal}}{1 \; \cancel{g}} = 13{,}800 \; \text{cal}$$

The total heat energy required to heat and vaporize the ice is equal to the sum of the values obtained in Steps 1–4.

$$64 \; \text{cal} + 2040 \; \text{cal} + 2550 \; \text{cal} + 13{,}800 \; \text{cal} = 18{,}500 \; \text{cal}$$

The heat required to raise the temperature of the ice at −5.0 °C to steam at 100.0 °C is 18,500 cal, or 18.5 kcal. The following example exercise illustrates the heat changes associated with the cooling of water and its solidification to ice.

> **Example Exercise 11.5** Change in Heat Problem

Calculate the amount of heat released when 15.5 g of liquid water at 22.5 °C cools to ice at −10.0 °C.

Solution

In this problem we have to consider (1) the specific heat of water, (2) the heat of solidification, and (3) the specific heat of ice.

1. To calculate the amount of heat released when cooling the water, consider the mass, the temperature change (22.5 °C to 0.0 °C), and the specific heat of water, 1.00 cal/(g × °C).

$$15.5 \text{ g} \times \frac{1.00 \text{ cal}}{1 \text{ g} \times °C} \times (22.5 - 0.0) \ °C = 349 \text{ cal}$$

We can summarize the solution visually as follows:

2. The heat of solidification, found in Table 11.5, is 80.0 cal/g. The heat released when water solidifies to ice is

$$15.5 \text{ g} \times \frac{80.0 \text{ cal}}{1 \text{ g}} = 1240 \text{ cal}$$

3. The specific heat of ice is 0.50 cal/(g × °C). The heat released as the ice cools to −10.0 °C is found as follows:

$$15.5 \text{ g} \times \frac{0.50 \text{ cal}}{1 \text{ g} \times °C} \times [0.0 - (-10.0)]°C = 78 \text{ cal}$$

The total heat energy released when the water cools to ice at −10.0 °C equals the sum of the values obtained in Steps 1–3.

$$349 \text{ cal} + 1240 \text{ cal} + 78 \text{ cal} = 1670 \text{ cal}$$

Thus, the heat released when the water cools is 1670 cal, or 1.67 kcal.

Practice Exercise

Calculate the amount of heat required to convert 50.0 g of steam at 100.0 °C to ice at 0.0 °C.

Answer: 3.60×10^4 cal (36.0 kcal)

Concept Exercise

Which of the following changes involves more heat energy: (a) heating 1 g of ice at 0 °C to water at 0 °C, or (b) heating 1 g of water at 100 °C to steam at 100 °C.

Answer: See Appendix G.

LEARNING OBJECTIVE

▶ To illustrate the bond angle and net dipole in a water molecule.

11.7 STRUCTURE OF WATER

We learned in Section 11.3 that the boiling point and surface tension of water are unusually high. We also saw that water has a strong intermolecular attraction because of hydrogen bonding. To understand these properties more completely, let's review the water molecule. Specifically, let's examine the structural formula, bond angle, and net dipole for a water molecule.

Structural Formula and Bond Angle

The structural formula for a molecule uses dashes to represent bonds between atoms. We will draw the water molecule with the two hydrogen atoms at an angle to each other. Experimental evidence shows that the angle between the two hydrogen atoms is 104.5°. The angle formed by the central atom and two attached atoms is referred to as the **bond angle**.

$$H—O$$
$$104.5 \rightarrow H$$

Dipoles and Net Dipole

In a water molecule, each of the two bonds is a dipole. That is, the oxygen atom is slightly negative and each hydrogen atom is slightly positive. We can indicate this using delta notation (δ^+ and δ^-).

$$\delta^+ \ H—O \ ^{\delta^-}$$
$$H \ \delta^+$$

Notice that a water molecule has two dipoles, and the central oxygen atom is pulling electrons toward the O atom. The two dipoles create a single dipole passing through the center of the molecule. The single, overall dipole for a molecule having two or more dipoles is called the **net dipole**.

$$H—O$$
$$H$$

The net dipole produces a negative end and a positive end in the water molecule. The negative end of the molecule is indicated by the tip of the arrow. The positive end is indicated by the plus sign on the opposite end of the net dipole arrow. The positive and negative ends of different water molecules form hydrogen bonds. This strong intermolecular attraction between water molecules explains water's unusual properties, including a high boiling point and high surface tension.

CHEMISTRY CONNECTION | **Water Purification**

Q: What is the process for changing hard water into soft water?

In some areas of the country, the minerals dissolved in water give it a high concentration of various ions that make the water suitable neither for drinking nor for agriculture. Such water is called **hard water**. Sometimes the mineral content in hard water is so great that it causes plumbing and corrosion problems. Hard water typically contains a high concentration of the following ions: Ca^{2+}, Mg^{2+}, Fe^{3+}, Cl^-, CO_3^{2-}, SO_4^{2-}, and PO_4^{3-}.

In homes having hard water, soap rings are sometimes found in bathtubs. A soap ring is formed by the cations in hard water reacting with soap to create a compound that deposits as an insoluble film. This problem can be eliminated by removing Ca^{2+}, Mg^{2+}, and Fe^{3+} from water by passing hard water through a water softener. A water softener replaces Ca^{2+}, Mg^{2+}, and Fe^{3+} with Na^+; compounds containing Na^+ are generally soluble. Note, however, that although a water softener removes ions, **soft water** still has a high concentration of other ions. In addition to Na^+, soft water contains Cl^-, CO_3^{2-}, SO_4^{2-}, and PO_4^{3-}.

Soft water can interfere with the results of a chemical analysis. Therefore, chemists routinely use water that contains no ions. Chemists may use distilled water that is made by boiling water and collecting the condensed vapor. Alternatively, chemists use water with the minerals removed using an ion exchange system. Water purified by this method is called **deionized water**, or *demineralized water*. Deionized water is made by passing hard water through a system that exchanges both cations and anions. First, cations such as Na^+ in the water are exchanged for hydrogen ions on the resin. Second, anions such as Cl^- in the water are exchanged for hydroxide ions.

$$Na^+(aq) + H(resin) \longrightarrow Na(resin) + H^+(aq)$$
$$Cl^-(aq) + (resin)OH \longrightarrow (resin)Cl + OH^-(aq)$$

Notice that the ion exchange resin produces both hydrogen ions and hydroxide ions, which combine to give water.

$$H^+(aq) + OH^-(aq) \longrightarrow H_2O(l)$$

The net result is that the resin removes *all ions* from water passing through the ion exchange resin.

▲ Deionized Water The cations in hard water are exchanged for
H^+. The anions in hard water are exchanged for OH^-. The H^+
and OH^- combine to produce deionized H_2O.

A: Hard water is changed to soft water using an ion-exchange resin, which exchanges Na^+ ions for Ca^{2+}, Mg^{2+}, and Fe^{3+}.

LEARNING OBJECTIVE

▶ To explain the unusual
physical properties of
water.

11.8 PHYSICAL PROPERTIES OF WATER

Water is a colorless, odorless, tasteless liquid and a powerful solvent. At room temperature water has the highest specific heat, heat of fusion (except for ammonia), and heat of vaporization of any liquid.

Density

Generally, a substance in the solid state has a higher density than one in the liquid state. Therefore, we would predict that the density of ice is greater than that of water. But, we know that ice floats in water. That is, the solid form of water is *less dense* than the liquid form. The reason solid ice is less dense than liquid water relates to hydrogen bonding. Figure 11.11 illustrates three-dimensional hydrogen bonding in water.

▶ **Figure 11.11 Hydrogen
Bonding** Each water molecule
is attracted to four other water
molecules. These intermolecular hydrogen bonds are about
50% longer than an ordinary
covalent bond. Because a
hydrogen bond is longer, it is
weaker and requires much less
energy to break.

When water freezes to ice, the hydrogen bonds produce a three-dimensional crystal. Figure 11.12 illustrates the structure of an ice crystal. Because of the arrangement of water molecules, however, the crystal has holes. These holes create a volume for ice that is greater than that for an equal mass of water. Thus, the density of solid ice is less than that of liquid water. At 0 °C, the density of ice is 0.917 g/mL, and the density of water is 1.00 g/mL.

◀ Figure 11.12 **Structure of Ice Crystals** Water molecules hydrogen bond to form six-member rings. The rings in turn hydrogen bond to other rings, producing large, three-dimensional crystalline structures.

Melting and Boiling Points

Water has an unusually high melting point and boiling point for a small molecule. To see how unusual these properties are, compare them with those of some hydrogen compounds of Group VIA/16 as outlined in Table 11.6.

TABLE 11.6 GROUP VIA /16 HYDROGEN COMPOUNDS

COMPOUND	MOLAR MASS (g/mol)	Mp (°C)	Bp (°C)	H_{fusion} (cal/mol)	H_{vapor} (cal/mol)
H_2O	18	0.0	100.0	1440	9720
H_2S	34	−85.5	−60.7	568	4450
H_2Se	81	−60.4	−41.5	899	4620
H_2Te	130	−48.9	−2.2	1670	5570

If we ignore water, we see a clear trend in the melting and boiling points of Group VIA/16 hydrogen compounds. First, notice the increase in molar mass for H_2S through H_2Te. Next, notice that the values for the melting point and the boiling point increase simultaneously. As with density, the properties of water are unusual because of hydrogen bonding. Hydrogen bonding produces a strong intermolecular attraction that resists the movement of molecules. Therefore, a higher temperature is needed to melt ice and to boil water. Figure 11.13 illustrates the melting and boiling points of Group VIA/16 hydrogen compounds.

◀ Figure 11.13 **Mp and Bp of Group VIA/16 Hydrogen Compounds** Notice the systematic trend in melting point and boiling point as the molar mass increases. Water is a striking exception because of strong intermolecular hydrogen bonds.

Heats of Fusion and Vaporization

Water also has surprisingly high values for heat of fusion and heat of vaporization. This is illustrated in Table 11.6. Excluding water, we notice that as the molar mass of H_2S through H_2Te increases, the values for the heat of fusion and heat of vaporization increase. The explanation for this trend is that as the molecular size increases, the attractive forces increase slightly. Therefore, more energy is required to melt a solid or vaporize a liquid. The unusually high values for water are due to hydrogen bonding.

LEARNING OBJECTIVE

▸ To write chemical equations for the chemical reactions of water.

11.9 CHEMICAL PROPERTIES OF WATER

Previously, we studied five basic types of chemical reactions. Water is usually the solvent for these chemical reactions, although water can also be a reactant. One example is the passing of an electric current through water, which decomposes H_2O into hydrogen and oxygen gases. This process is called the **electrolysis** of water. From the balanced chemical equation, we notice that two volumes of hydrogen are produced for every volume of oxygen.

$$2\,H_2O(l) \xrightarrow{\text{electricity}} 2\,H_2(g) + O_2(g)$$

One of the five basic types of reactions is a replacement reaction. In this reaction an active metal (Li, Na, K, Ca, Sr, or Ba) reacts directly with water to give a metal hydroxide and hydrogen gas. These reactions occur rapidly at room temperature. For example, potassium metal reacts violently with water as follows:

$$2\,K(s) + 2\,H_2O(l) \longrightarrow 2\,KOH(aq) + H_2(g)$$

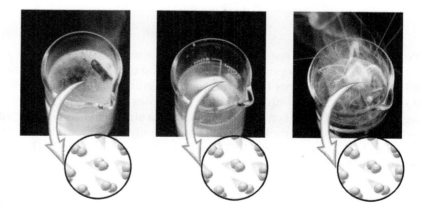

▸ **Alkali Metals in Water** The reaction of Li, Na, and K in water (left to right) produces hydrogen gas, which is flammable.

The oxides of many metals can react with water to yield a metal hydroxide. Hydroxide compounds are said to be basic, or alkaline. A **metal oxide** reacts with water to yield a basic solution, so a metal oxide is referred to as a *basic oxide*. For example, calcium oxide reacts with water as follows:

$$CaO(s) + H_2O(l) \longrightarrow Ca(OH)_2(aq) \quad (a\ base)$$

The oxides of most nonmetals react with water to yield an acidic solution. A **nonmetal oxide** reacts with water to yield an acid, so a nonmetal oxide is referred to as an *acidic oxide*. For example, carbon dioxide reacts with water as follows:

$$CO_2(g) + H_2O(l) \longrightarrow H_2CO_3(aq) \quad (an\ acid)$$

Reactions That Produce Water

Water is produced by several types of reactions. The simplest reaction is the formation of water directly from hydrogen and oxygen. In this reaction, hydrogen and oxygen gases react to give H_2O. The reaction takes place very slowly at room temperature but explosively if exposed to a flame or spark. From the balanced chemical equation, we note that two volumes of hydrogen react with one volume of oxygen.

$$2\,H_2(g) + O_2(g) \xrightarrow{\text{spark}} 2\,H_2O(l)$$

Another reaction that produces water is the combustion of hydrocarbons. Hydrocarbons are organic compounds containing hydrogen and carbon. They burn in oxygen to give carbon dioxide and water. For example, propane, C_3H_8, undergoes combustion as follows:

$$C_3H_8(g) + 5\,O_2(g) \xrightarrow{\text{spark}} 3\,CO_2(g) + 4\,H_2O(g)$$

Organic compounds containing hydrogen and oxygen also undergo combustion to give carbon dioxide and water. Ethanol, C_2H_5OH, for example, is currently blended with gasoline to produce gasohol. It undergoes combustion to give carbon dioxide and water as follows:

$$C_2H_5OH(g) + 3\,O_2(g) \xrightarrow{\text{spark}} 2\,CO_2(g) + 3\,H_2O(g)$$

Recall that neutralization reactions also produce water. An acid neutralizes a base to produce an aqueous salt and water. For example, battery acid, H_2SO_4, reacts with aqueous lye, $NaOH$, to produce sodium sulfate and water.

$$H_2SO_4(aq) + 2\,NaOH(aq) \longrightarrow Na_2SO_4(aq) + 2\,H_2O(l)$$

The decomposition of a hydrate compound also produces water. A **hydrate** is a crystalline compound that contains a specific number of water molecules. Gypsum is a hydrate of calcium sulfate, $CaSO_4$. The formula $CaSO_4 \cdot 2H_2O$ indicates that two water molecules are attached to each $CaSO_4$ formula unit. Heating a hydrate releases water from the compound. For example, heat decomposes gypsum to give $CaSO_4$ and two molecules of water. Thus,

$$CaSO_4 \cdot 2H_2O(s) \xrightarrow{\Delta} CaSO_4(s) + 2\,H_2O(g)$$

11.10 HYDRATES

A hydrate is a crystalline compound containing a specific number of water molecules. Common examples of hydrates include borax, $Na_2B_4O_7 \cdot 10H_2O$, and Epsom salts, $MgSO_4 \cdot 7H_2O$. The dot ($\cdot$) in the hydrate formula indicates that water molecules are attached to each unit of hydrate. In Epsom salts, $MgSO_4 \cdot 7H_2O$, seven molecules of water are attached to each $MgSO_4$ formula unit.

Heating a hydrate drives off the water and produces an **anhydrous compound** (without water). For example, when we heat copper(II) sulfate pentahydrate, it decomposes to give anhydrous copper(II) sulfate and water. The equation for the reaction is

$$CuSO_4 \cdot 5H_2O(s) \xrightarrow{\Delta} CuSO_4(s) + 5\,H_2O(g)$$

The water molecules in the hydrate are referred to as the **water of hydration**, or *water of crystallization*. Thus, the water of hydration for copper(II) sulfate pentahydrate is 5. Figure 11.14 shows the hydrate and anhydrous forms of copper(II) sulfate.

IUPAC prescribes rules for the nomenclature of hydrate compounds. According to these rules, the name of the anhydrous compound appears first, followed by the number for the water of hydration (as indicated by a Greek prefix) and the word "hydrate." For example, gypsum, $CaSO_4 \cdot 2H_2O$, is systematically named calcium sulfate dihydrate; the *di*–indicates the water of hydration is 2. The following example exercise further illustrates how to name hydrate compounds:

LEARNING OBJECTIVES

▶ To calculate the percentage of water in a hydrate.

▶ To determine the water of hydration for a hydrate.

▲ **Mineral Turquoise** The mineral turquoise is an example of a tetrahydrate that contains copper, $CuAl_6(PO_4)_4(OH)_8 \cdot 4H_2O$.

▶ Figure 11.14 **Hydrate and Anhydrous Copper(II) Sulfate** Copper(II) sulfate pentahydrate, $CuSO_4 \cdot 5H_2O$, crystals are deep blue, whereas anhydrous copper(II) sulfate, $CuSO_4$, is a white powder. A few drops of water produce the blue color of the hydrate.

Example Exercise 11.6 Naming Hydrates

Supply a systematic name for each of the following hydrate compounds:

(a) $Co(CN)_3 \cdot 3H_2O$ (b) $FeSO_4 \cdot H_2O$

Solution

First, name the anhydrous compound and then indicate the water of hydration by a Greek prefix. (Refer to Table 7.4 if necessary.)

(a) $Co(CN)_3$ is named cobalt(III) cyanide according to the Stock system, and cobaltic cyanide according to the Latin system. The Greek prefix for 3 is *tri–*, so the hydrate is named *cobalt(III) cyanide trihydrate,* or *cobaltic cyanide trihydrate.*

(b) $FeSO_4$ is named iron(II) sulfate according to the Stock system, and ferrous sulfate according to the Latin system. The Greek prefix for 1 is *mono–*, so the hydrate is named *iron(II) sulfate monohydrate,* or *ferrous sulfate monohydrate.*

Practice Exercise

Provide the chemical formula for each of the following hydrate compounds:

(a) zinc sulfate heptahydrate   (b) sodium chromate tetrahydrate

Answers:

(a) $ZnSO_4 \cdot 7H_2O$ (b) $Na_2CrO_4 \cdot 4H_2O$

Concept Exercise

What is the systematic name for the following hydrates: $CaCl_2 \cdot H_2O$, $CaCl_2 \cdot 2H_2O$, and $CaCl_2 \cdot 6H_2O$?

Answer: See Appendix G.

Percent Water in a Hydrate

In Section 8.7 we studied the percent composition of compounds. Here, we see that the percent water in a hydrate is the ratio of the mass of water in the hydrate to the mass of the hydrate, all multiplied by 100%.

$$\frac{\text{mass of water}}{\text{mass of hydrate}} \times 100\% = \% \, H_2O$$

As an example, we'll find the percentage of water in gypsum, $CaSO_4 \cdot 2H_2O$. Using the periodic table, we find the molar mass of H_2O to be 18.02 g, and that of $CaSO_4$ to be 136.15 g. We find the percentage of water from the following ratio:

$$\frac{2(18.02)\,g}{136.15\,g + 2(18.02)\,g} \times 100\% = 20.93\%$$

Notice that in the numerator we multiplied the molar mass of water by 2 because the compound is a dihydrate. In the denominator, we added twice the molar mass of water to that of the anhydrous compound. The following example exercise provides additional practice in calculating the percent water in a hydrate.

Example Exercise 11.7 Percentage of Water in Hydrates

Calculate the percentage of water in each of the following hydrates:

(a) $CuSO_4 \cdot 5H_2O$ (b) $Na_2B_4O_7 \cdot 10H_2O$

Solution

In each example, first obtain the molar mass of the anhydrous compound from the periodic table. The molar mass of water is 18.02 g.

(a) Using the periodic table, we calculate that the molar mass of $CuSO_4$ is 159.62 g. Because the water of hydration for the hydrate is 5, we have

$$\frac{5(18.02)\ g}{159.62\ g\ +\ 5(18.02)\ g} \times 100\% = \%\ H_2O$$

$$= 36.08\%$$

(b) Using the periodic table, we calculate that the molar mass of $Na_2B_4O_7$ is 201.22 g. The water of hydration for the hydrate is 10, so we have

$$\frac{10(18.02)\ g}{201.22\ g\ +\ 10(18.02)\ g} \times 100\% = \%H_2O$$

$$= 47.24\%$$

Practice Exercise

Calculate the percentage of water in each of the following hydrates:

(a) $NaC_2H_3O_2 \cdot 3H_2O$ (b) $Na_2S_2O_3 \cdot 5H_2O$

Answers:

(a) 39.72%   (b) 36.30%

Concept Exercise

Which of the following hydrates has the highest percentage of water: $CaCl_2 \cdot H_2O$, $CaCl_2 \cdot 2H_2O$, or $CaCl_2 \cdot 6H_2O$?

Answer: See Appendix G.

Determining the Chemical Formula of a Hydrate

In Section 8.8 we calculated the empirical formula for a compound from its percent composition. To determine the water of hydration for a hydrate we will proceed in a similar fashion.

The empirical formula of a compound is the simplest whole-number ratio of its elements. Similarly, the formula of a hydrate is the simplest whole-number ratio of water molecules to the anhydrous compound. In the chemical formula for washing soda, $Na_3PO_4 \cdot XH_2O$, X represents the water of hydration. To determine the value of X we must know the percent water. Let's assume that $Na_3PO_4 \cdot XH_2O$ is found by experiment to contain 52.3% water. The equation for the decomposition reaction is as follows:

$$Na_3PO_4 \cdot XH_2O(s) \xrightarrow{\Delta} Na_3PO_4(s) + XH_2O(g)$$

Because the hydrate contains 52.3% water, the percentage of Na_3PO_4 is 47.7% ($100.0 - 52.3 = 47.7\%$). As in an empirical formula, let's assume we have a 100.0-g sample of hydrate. Therefore, our sample has 52.3 g of water and 47.7 g of anhydrous compound. The next step is to calculate the moles of water.

$$52.3\ g\ H_2O \times \frac{1\ mol\ H_2O}{18.02\ g\ H_2O} = 2.90\ mol\ H_2O$$

Using the periodic table, we calculate that the molar mass of Na_3PO_4 is 163.94 g. The moles of the anhydrous compound are

$$47.7 \text{ g } Na_3PO_4 \times \frac{1 \text{ mol } Na_3PO_4}{163.94 \text{ g } Na_3PO_4} = 0.291 \text{ mol } Na_3PO_4$$

We can write the mole ratio of the hydrate as $Na_3PO_4 \cdot (2.90/0.291) H_2O$, where the water of hydration is 2.90/0.291. This ratio simplifies to 10/1, meaning that the water of hydration is 10 and the formula of the hydrate is $Na_3PO_4 \cdot 10H_2O$.

Example Exercise 11.8 Water of Hydration for a Hydrate

Determine the water of hydration for a hydrate of magnesium iodide. In an experiment, $MgI_2 \cdot XH_2O$ was found to contain 34.0% water.

Solution

We begin by writing an equation for the decomposition.

$$MgI_2 \cdot XH_2O(s) \xrightarrow{\Delta} MgI_2(s) + XH_2O(g)$$

Because the hydrate contains 34.0% water, the percentage of MgI_2 is 66.0% ($100.0 - 34.0 = 66.0\%$). Assume that we have a 100.0-g sample of hydrate. Therefore, we have 34.0 g of water and 66.0 g of anhydrous compound. The moles of water are

$$34.0 \text{ g } H_2O \times \frac{1 \text{ mol } H_2O}{18.02 \text{ g } H_2O} = 1.89 \text{ mol } H_2O$$

Using the periodic table, we calculate the molar mass of MgI_2 as 278.11 g. We find the moles of the anhydrous compound as follows:

$$66.0 \text{ g } MgI_2 \times \frac{1 \text{ mol } MgI_2}{278.11 \text{ g } MgI_2} = 0.237 \text{ mol } MgI_2$$

We can write the mole ratio of the hydrate as $MgI_2 \cdot (1.89/0.237) H_2O$. The ratio 1.89/0.237 reduces to 7.97 and rounds off to the whole number 8. The water of hydration is 8 and the chemical formula is $MgI_2 \cdot 8H_2O$. The name of the hydrate is *magnesium iodide octahydrate*.

Practice Exercise

Determine the water of hydration for the hydrate of copper(II) fluoride. In an experiment, $CuF_2 \cdot XH_2O$ was found to contain 26.2% water.

Answer: $CuF_2 \cdot 2H_2O$

Concept Exercise

Which of the following hydrates has the highest water of hydration: $CaCl_2 \cdot H_2O$, $CaCl_2 \cdot 2H_2O$, or $CaCl_2 \cdot 6H_2O$?

Answer: See Appendix G.

CRITICAL THINKING Bottled Water

Q: What is the difference between bottled water and tap water?

Recently, bottled water has become a huge industry and Americans consume nearly six billion gallons of bottled water each year. One survey found that more than half of all Americans drink bottled water, and about a third of the public consumes it regularly. Many different types of bottled water are now available including purified water, spring water, mineral water, and vitamin-enriched bottled water.

The water we drink from a home faucet is referred to as *tap water*. It comes from a city source and must be chlorinated for sanitation purposes. Tap water that has been processed by distillation or deionization is referred to as *purified water*.

Some brands of purified water add minerals to mimic the taste of drinking water. Water obtained from natural springs that lie deep within the Earth is referred to as *spring water*. Although spring water does not require purification, the transportation of spring water can jeopardize purity. This fact has led some spring water suppliers to bottle the water directly at the source of the natural spring.

Consumers have been led to believe that bottled water is superior to tap water in terms of purity and health benefits. Surprisingly, in most cases bottled water adheres to purity standards that are less strict than tap water. Although the

◄ **Bottled Water**
Aquafina, Perrier, and Dasani are popular brands of bottled water.

Environmental Protection Agency (EPA) regulates the quality of public water supplies, the EPA has no authority over bottled water. Bottled water that crosses state lines is considered a food product and is overseen by the Food and Drug Administration (FDA), which does require that the water be bottled in sanitary conditions.

In a study by the Natural Resources Defense Council that tested 38 brands of California bottled water, eight samples were found to have measurable levels of contamination. In a study at Case Western Reserve University and Ohio State University, 57 samples of bottled water were compared to Cleveland's tap water. Although 39 of the bottled water samples were purer than the tap water, 15 of the bottles had significantly higher bacteria levels. However, the scientists stated that all of the water was safe to drink.

An example of a sparkling mineral water is Perrier®, which comes from a source in the south of France. A distinguishing characteristic of sparkling mineral water is its natural carbonation. Carbonation is the result of volcanic activity within Earth. Heat from a volcano produces steam that passes through limestone ($CaCO_3$), which in turn releases carbon dioxide gas into the mineral water.

A: The difference between bottled water and tap water depends on the source. Some bottled water originates from natural springs; whereas, other bottled water is distilled or deionized tap water, sometimes with minerals added.

Summary

LEARNING OBJECTIVES	SEC	EXERCISES
To identify five observed properties of a liquid.	11.1	Exercises 1–4
To explain the concept of an intermolecular bond.	11.2	Exercises 5–6
To describe three types of attraction between molecules in a liquid.	11.2	Exercises 5–6
To understand the concepts of vapor pressure, boiling point, viscosity, and surface tension.	11.3	Exercises 7–12
To relate the vapor pressure, boiling point, viscosity, and surface tension of a liquid to the strength of attraction between molecules.	11.3	Exercises 13–22
To identify five observed properties of a solid.	11.4	Exercises 23–26
To describe three types of crystalline solids: ionic, molecular, and metallic.	11.5	Exercises 27–32
To understand the concepts of specific heat, heat of fusion, and heat of vaporization.	11.6	Exercises 33–34
To calculate heat changes that involve specific heat, heat of fusion, and heat of vaporization.	11.6	Exercises 35–44
To illustrate the bond angle and net dipole in a water molecule.	11.7	Exercises 45–50
To explain the unusual physical properties of water.	11.8	Exercises 51–60
To write chemical equations for the chemical reactions of water.	11.9	Exercises 61–70
To calculate the percentage of water in a hydrate.	11.10	Exercises 71–76
To determine the water of hydration for a hydrate.	11.11	Exercises 77–78

Section 11.1 The liquid state has a variable shape but a fixed volume. Liquids usually flow readily but do not compress or expand as do gases. The densities of liquids vary but are approximately 1000 times greater than the densities of gases. Liquids mix and diffuse uniformly in a container, similar to gases.

Section 11.2 There are three basic types of intermolecular attraction: dispersion forces, dipole forces, and hydrogen bonds. A **dispersion force** has the weakest attraction and results from temporary dipoles in molecules. A **dipole force** has a stronger attraction and results from permanent dipoles in molecules. A **hydrogen bond** exerts the strongest intermolecular attraction, and occurs between molecules having H—O, or H—N bonds.

Section 11.3 When the **vapor pressure** of a liquid equals the atmospheric pressure, the liquid is at its **boiling point**. The normal boiling point of a liquid is the temperature at which the vapor pressure is 760 mm Hg. Liquids have a resistance to flow, and this property is called **viscosity**. The attraction between molecules at the surface of a liquid is called **surface tension**. Each of these properties is affected by the degree of attraction between molecules in the liquid. If the attraction is low, the vapor pressure is high. Conversely, if the attraction is high, the values for the boiling point, viscosity, and surface tension are also high.

Section 11.4 The solid state has a fixed shape and a fixed volume. A solid that has a highly defined structure is called a **crystalline solid**. Solids do not compress or expand to any large degree. The density of a substance in the solid state is usually higher than that in the liquid state. Water and ammonia are two interesting exceptions to this rule. Solid ice and solid ammonia float on their respective liquids. Because the solid state contains particles in fixed positions, solids do not mix or diffuse.

Section 11.5 There are three basic types of crystalline solids. **Ionic solids** are made up of ions. The ions are attracted to each other and form repeating geometric patterns. **Molecular solids** form crystals made up of molecules. **Metallic solids** are made up of metal atoms arranged in a definite pattern. The properties of ionic, molecular, and metallic solids differ. Metallic solids are good conductors of electricity. Ionic solids conduct electricity only when they are melted or are in an aqueous solution. As a rule, molecular solids do not conduct electricity.

Section 11.6 **Specific heat** is the heat required to raise one gram of substance one degree Celsius. The heat required to melt a substance is called the **heat of fusion**. The heat released when a substance freezes to a solid is called the *heat of solidification*. The heat of solidification of a substance has the same value as its heat of fusion. The heat required to convert a liquid to a gas at its boiling point is the **heat of vaporization**. When a vapor condenses to a liquid, it releases the same amount of heat energy that was necessary to vaporize the liquid. This energy is termed the *heat of condensation*.

Section 11.7 Water has unusual properties because of the two O—H bonds separated by a **bond angle** of 104.5°. The oxygen atom has a partial negative charge, and each hydrogen atom has a partial positive charge. These two dipoles create an overall **net dipole** for a water molecule.

Section 11.8 Hydrogen bonds between water molecules explain why water has extraordinarily high values for boiling point, viscosity, and surface tension. Hydrogen bonding also explains why the density of ice is less than that of water. For a small molecule, water has an unusually high melting point, boiling point, heat of fusion, and heat of vaporization.

Section 11.9 Water undergoes the following chemical reactions: (1) An electric current decomposes water into hydrogen and oxygen gases by **electrolysis**. (2) The active metals of Groups IA/1 and IIA/2 react with water to give a metal hydroxide and hydrogen gas. (3) A **metal oxide** reacts with water to give a metal hydroxide. (4) A **nonmetal oxide** combines with water to yield an acidic solution. (See Table 11.7.)

TABLE 11.7 SUMMARY OF THE CHEMICAL REACTIONS OF WATER

water	$\xrightarrow{\text{electricity}}$	hydrogen + oxygen
active metal + water	$\longrightarrow$	metal hydroxide + hydrogen
metal oxide + water	$\longrightarrow$	basic solution
nonmetal oxide + water	$\longrightarrow$	acidic solution

Water is produced from (1) the reaction of hydrogen and oxygen gases, (2) burning hydrocarbons, (3) neutralizing an acid with a base, and (4) heating a **hydrate**. (See Table 11.8.)

TABLE 11.8 SUMMARY OF THE CHEMICAL REACTIONS PRODUCING WATER

hydrogen + oxygen	$\xrightarrow{\text{spark}}$	water
hydrocarbon + oxygen	$\xrightarrow{\text{spark}}$	carbon dioxide + water
acid + base	$\longrightarrow$	salt + water
hydrate	$\xrightarrow{\Delta}$	anhydrous compound + water

Section 11.10 The name of a hydrate consists of the name of the **anhydrous compound** followed by a Greek prefix and the word "hydrate"; for example, $BaCl_2 \cdot 2H_2O$ is named barium chloride dihydrate. Determining the chemical formula of a hydrate is similar to determining an empirical formula. From the percent water in a hydrate, we can calculate the moles of water and anhydrous compound. The ratio of moles of water to moles of the anhydrous compound gives the **water of hydration**, which is also termed *water of crystallization*.

Key Terms   *Answers to Key Terms are in Appendix H.*

Select the key term that corresponds to each of the following definitions.

_____ 1. an intermolecular attraction based on temporary dipoles

_____ 2. an intermolecular attraction based on permanent dipoles

_____ 3. an intermolecular attraction based on permanent dipoles involving a H atom bonded to O or N

_____ 4. the pressure exerted by gaseous molecules above a liquid in a closed container when the rates of vaporization and condensation are equal

_____ 5. the temperature at which the vapor pressure of a liquid is equal to the atmospheric pressure

_____ 6. the resistance of a liquid to flow

_____ 7. the tendency of a liquid to form spherical drops

_____ 8. a solid substance composed of ions or molecules that repeat in a regular geometric pattern

_____ 9. a crystalline solid composed of ions that repeat in a regular pattern

_____ 10. a crystalline solid composed of molecules that repeat in a regular pattern

_____ 11. a crystalline solid composed of metal atoms that repeat in a regular pattern

_____ 12. the heat required to raise 1 g of any substance 1 °C

_____ 13. the heat required to convert a solid to a liquid at its melting point

_____ 14. the heat required to vaporize a liquid to a gas at its boiling point

_____ 15. the angle formed by two atoms bonded to a central atom in a molecule

_____ 16. the overall direction of partial negative charge in a molecule having two or more dipoles

_____ 17. the chemical reaction produced by the passage of electric current through an aqueous solution

_____ 18. a compound that reacts with water to form a basic solution; also termed a *basic oxide*

_____ 19. a compound that reacts with water to form an acidic solution; also termed an *acidic oxide*

_____ 20. a substance that contains a specific number of water molecules in a crystalline compound

_____ 21. refers to a compound that does not contain water

_____ 22. the number of water molecules in a hydrate

_____ 23. water containing a variety of cations and anions such as Ca^{2+}, Mg^{2+}, Fe^{3+}, CO_3^{2-}, SO_4^{2-}, and PO_4^{3-}

_____ 24. water containing sodium ions and a variety of anions

_____ 25. water purified by removing ions using an ion exchange method; also termed *demineralized water*

_____ 26. water purified by boiling and collecting the condensed vapor

(a) anhydrous compound (*Sec. 11.10*)

(b) boiling point (Bp) (*Sec. 11.3*)

(c) bond angle (*Sec. 11.7*)

(d) crystalline solid (*Sec. 11.4*)

(e) deionized water (*Sec. 11.7*)

(f) dipole force (*Sec. 11.2*)

(g) dispersion force (*Sec. 11.2*)

(h) distilled water (*Sec. 11.7*)

(i) electrolysis (*Sec. 11.9*)

(j) hard water (*Sec. 11.7*)

(k) heat of fusion (*Sec. 11.6*)

(l) heat of vaporization (*Sec. 11.6*)

(m) hydrate (*Sec. 11.9*)

(n) hydrogen bond (*Sec. 11.2*)

(o) ionic solid (*Sec. 11.5*)

(p) metal oxide (*Sec. 11.9*)

(q) metallic solid (*Sec. 11.5*)

(r) molecular solid (*Sec. 11.5*)

(s) net dipole (*Sec. 11.7*)

(t) nonmetal oxide (*Sec. 11.9*)

(u) soft water (*Sec. 11.7*)

(v) specific heat (*Sec. 11.6*)

(w) surface tension (*Sec. 11.3*)

(x) vapor pressure (*Sec. 11.3*)

(y) viscosity (*Sec. 11.3*)

(z) water of hydration (*Sec. 11.10*)

Exercises *Answers to odd-numbered Exercises are in Appendix I.*

Properties of Liquids (Sec. 11.1)

◀ **The Liquid State**
Maple syrup can be poured and its rate of flow depends on its viscosity.

1. Which of the following are observed general properties of liquids?
   (a) variable shape   (b) flow readily
   (c) compress significantly (d) more dense than gases

2. Which of the following are observed general properties of liquids?
   (a) fixed volume   (b) mix homogeneously
   (c) expand significantly (d) less dense than gases

3. Indicate the physical state (solid, liquid, gas) for each of the following noble gases at the designated temperature:
   (a) Ne at -225 °C   (b) Ne at -255 °C
   (c) Ar at -175 °C   (d) Ar at -200 °C
   (e) Kr at -155 °C   (f) Kr at -150 °C
   The melting points and boiling points for neon, argon, and krypton are as follows:

Element	Melting Point	Boiling Point
neon, Ne	-249 °C	-246 °C
argon, Ar	-189 °C	-186 °C
krypton, Kr	-157 °C	-152 °C

4. Indicate the physical state (solid, liquid, or gas) for each of the following at the designated temperature:
   (a) H_2O at -10 °C   (b) H_2O at 110 °C
   (c) NH_3 at -100 °C   (d) NH_3 at -50 °C
   (e) $CHCl_3$ at 100 °C   (f) $CHCl_3$ at 50 °C
   The melting points and boiling points for water, ammonia, and chloroform are as follows:

Compound	Melting Point	Boiling Point
water, H_2O	0 °C	100 °C
ammonia, NH_3	-78 °C	-33 °C
chloroform, $CHCl_3$	-64 °C	62 °C

The Intermolecular Bond Concept (Sec. 11.2)

5. Distinguish temporary dipole attraction from permanent dipole attraction between molecules in a liquid.

6. Distinguish permanent dipole attraction from hydrogen bond attraction between molecules in a liquid.

Vapor Pressure, Boiling Point, Viscosity, and Surface Tension (Sec. 11.3)

7. Describe and illustrate the concept of vapor pressure using water as an example.

8. Describe and illustrate the concept of boiling point using water as an example.

9. Describe and illustrate the concept of viscosity using water as an example.

10. Describe and illustrate the concept of surface tension using water as an example.

11. If the molecules in a liquid are weakly attracted, which of the following properties has a high value?
    (a) vapor pressure   (b) boiling point
    (c) viscosity   (d) surface tension

12. If the molecules in a liquid are strongly attracted, which of the following properties has a high value?
    (a) vapor pressure   (b) boiling point
    (c) viscosity   (d) surface tension

13. Predict which liquid in each pair has the higher vapor pressure:
    (a) CH_3COOH or C_2H_5Cl (b) C_2H_5OH or CH_3OCH_3

14. Predict which liquid in each pair has the higher boiling point:
    (a) CH_3COOH or C_2H_5Cl (b) C_2H_5OH or CH_3OCH_3

15. Predict which liquid in each pair has the higher viscosity:
    (a) CH_3COOH or C_2H_5Cl (b) C_2H_5OH or CH_3OCH_3

16. Predict which liquid in each pair has the higher surface tension:
    (a) CH_3COOH or C_2H_5Cl (b) C_2H_5OH or CH_3OCH_3

17. What is the general relationship for the vapor pressure of a liquid and its temperature?

18. What is the general relationship for the boiling point of a liquid and its vapor pressure?

19. Refer to Figure 11.5 and estimate the vapor pressure of ethanol at each of the following temperatures:
    (a) 45 °C   (b) 60 °C

20. Refer to Figure 11.5 and estimate the vapor pressure of ether at each of the following temperatures:
    (a) 15 °C   (b) 30 °C

21. The vapor pressure of acetone is 1 mm Hg at -59 °C, 10 mm Hg at -31 °C, 100 mm Hg at 8 °C, 400 mm Hg at 40 °C, and 760 mm Hg at 56 °C. What is the normal boiling point of acetone?

22. The vapor pressure of methanol is 1 atm at 65 °C, 2 atm at 84 °C, 5 atm at 112 °C, 10 atm at 138 °C, and 20 atm at 168 °C. What is the normal boiling point of methanol?

Properties of Solids (Sec. 11.4)

23. Which of the following are observed general properties of solids?
    (a) fixed shape   (b) crystalline structure
    (c) do not compress   (d) less dense than liquids

24. Which of the following are observed general properties of solids?
   (a) fixed volume **(b)** noncrystalline structure
   (c) do not expand **(d)** alloys mix by diffusion

25. Indicate the physical state (solid, liquid, or gas) for gallium given its melting point (30 °C) and boiling point (2403 °C) under the following conditions:
   (a) Ga in ice water **(b)** Ga in boiling water

26. Indicate the physical state (solid, liquid, or gas) for mercury given its melting point (−40 °C) and boiling point (357 °C) under the following conditions:
   (a) Hg in ice water **(b)** Hg in boiling water

Crystalline Solids (Sec. 11.5)

27. List three examples of crystalline solids.

28. List three examples of noncrystalline solids.

29. State the type of particles that compose each of the following:
   (a) ionic solid **(b)** molecular solid
   (c) metallic solid

▲ **A Molecular Solid, H_2O**

30. State whether the following list of properties is most descriptive of an ionic, a molecular, or a metallic solid:
   (a) malleable, ductile, insoluble in water
   (b) high melting point, conductor of electricity when melted
   (c) low melting point, nonconductor of electrical current

31. Classify each of the following crystalline solids as ionic, molecular, or metallic:
   (a) zinc, Zn **(b)** zinc oxide, ZnO
   (c) phosphorus, P_4 **(d)** iodine monobromide, IBr

32. Classify each of the following crystalline solids as ionic, molecular, or metallic:
   (a) sulfur, S_8 **(b)** sulfur dioxide, SO_2
   (c) copper, Cu **(d)** silver nitrate, $AgNO_3$

◄ **A Metallic Solid, Cu**

Changes of Physical State (Sec. 11.6)

33. Draw the general shape of the temperature–energy graph for the heating of ethanol from −120 °C to 120 °C. (Given: Mp = −117.3 °C; Bp = 78.5 °C)

34. Draw the general shape of the temperature–energy graph for the cooling of acetone from 100 °C to −100 °C. (Given: Mp = −95.4 °C; Bp = 56.2 °C)

35. Calculate the heat required to melt 50.0 g of ice at 0 °C.

36. Calculate the heat released when 75.0 g of water freezes to ice at 0 °C.

37. Calculate the heat required to convert 25.0 g of water at 25.0 °C to steam at 100.0 °C.

38. Calculate the heat released when 65.5 g of water at 55.5 °C cools to ice at 0.0 °C.

39. Calculate the heat required to convert 115 g of ice at 0.0 °C to steam at 100.0 °C.

40. Calculate the heat released when 155 g of steam at 100.0 °C cools to ice at 0.0 °C.

41. Calculate the heat required to convert 38.5 g of ice at −20.0 °C to steam at 100.0 °C.

42. Calculate the heat released when 90.5 g of steam at 110.0 °C cools to ice at 0.0 °C.

43. Calculate the heat required to convert 100.0 g of ice at −40.0 °C to steam at 125.0 °C.

44. Calculate the heat released when 0.500 kg of steam at 150.0 °C cools to ice at −50.0 °C.

Structure of Water (Sec. 11.7)

45. Is the boiling point of water unusually high or low?

46. Is the surface tension of water unusually high or low?

47. What is the observed bond angle in a water molecule?

48. What type of intermolecular bond exists between water molecules?

49. Draw the two dipoles in a water molecule using delta convention.

50. Draw the net dipole for a water molecule using standard convention.

Physical Properties of Water (Sec. 11.8)

51. Which liquid has the highest specific heat?

52. Which liquid has the highest heat of fusion and heat of vaporization?

53. A solid cube of ice floats in water. Which is more dense: ice or water?

54. A solid cube of ammonia floats in liquid ammonia. Which is more dense: solid or liquid ammonia?

55. Without referring to Table 11.6, predict which compound in each of the following pairs has the higher melting point:
   (a) H_2O or H_2S **(b)** H_2S or H_2Se

56. Without referring to Table 11.6, predict which compound in each of the following pairs has the higher boiling point:
   (a) H_2O or H_2Se **(b)** H_2S or H_2Te

57. Without referring to Table 11.6, predict which compound in each of the following pairs has the higher heat of fusion (cal/mol):
   (a) H_2O or H_2S **(b)** H_2S or H_2Se

58. Without referring to Table 11.6, predict which compound in each of the following pairs has the higher heat of vaporization (cal/mol):
(a) H_2O or H_2Se **(b)** H_2S or H_2Te

59. In general, as the molar mass of Group VIA/16 hydrogen compounds increases, does each of the following increase or decrease?
(a) melting point   **(b)** boiling point
(c) heat of fusion   **(d)** heat of vaporization

60. Refer to the trends in Table 11.6 and estimate a value for the physical properties of radioactive H_2Po; that is, predict a value for the Mp, Bp, H_{fusion}, and H_{vapor}.

Chemical Properties of Water (Sec. 11.9)

61. Write a balanced equation for the reaction of hydrogen and oxygen gases.

62. Write a balanced equation for the decomposition of water by electrolysis.

63. Complete and balance the following equations:
(a) $Li(s) + H_2O(l) \longrightarrow$
(b) $Na_2O(s) + H_2O(l) \longrightarrow$
(c) $CO_2(g) + H_2O(l) \longrightarrow$

64. Complete and balance the following equations:
(a) $Rb(s) + H_2O(l) \longrightarrow$
(b) $Cs_2O(s) + H_2O(l) \longrightarrow$
(c) $P_2O_5(s) + H_2O(l) \longrightarrow$

65. Complete and balance the following equations:
(a) $Mg(s) + H_2O(l) \longrightarrow$
(b) $SrO(s) + H_2O(l) \longrightarrow$
(c) $N_2O_5(g) + H_2O(l) \longrightarrow$

66. Complete and balance the following equations:
(a) $Ba(s) + H_2O(l) \longrightarrow$
(b) $CaO(s) + H_2O(l) \longrightarrow$
(c) $N_2O_3(g) + H_2O(l) \longrightarrow$

67. Complete and balance the following equations:
(a) $C_3H_6(g) + O_2(g) \xrightarrow{spark}$
(b) $Na_2Cr_2O_7 \cdot 2H_2O(s) \xrightarrow{\Delta}$
(c) $HF(aq) + Ca(OH)_2(aq) \longrightarrow$

68. Complete and balance the following equations:
(a) $C_3H_7OH(l) + O_2(g) \xrightarrow{spark}$
(b) $Ca(NO_3)_2 \cdot 4H_2O(s) \xrightarrow{\Delta}$
(c) $H_2CO_3(aq) + KOH(aq) \longrightarrow$

69. Complete and balance the following equations:
(a) $C_4H_{10}(g) + O_2(g) \xrightarrow{spark}$
(b) $Co(C_2H_3O_2)_2 \cdot 4H_2O(s) \xrightarrow{\Delta}$
(c) $HNO_3(aq) + Ba(OH)_2(aq) \longrightarrow$

70. Complete and balance the following equations:
(a) $C_4H_9OH(l) + O_2(g) \xrightarrow{spark}$
(b) $KAl(SO_4)_2 \cdot 12H_2O(s) \xrightarrow{\Delta}$
(c) $H_3PO_4(aq) + NaOH(aq) \longrightarrow$

Hydrates (Sec. 11.10)

71. Supply a systematic name for each of the following hydrate compounds:
(a) $MgSO_4 \cdot 7H_2O$ **(b)** $Co(CN)_3 \cdot 3H_2O$
(c) $MnSO_4 \cdot H_2O$ **(d)** $Na_2Cr_2O_7 \cdot 2H_2O$

72. Supply a systematic name for each of the following hydrate compounds:
(a) $Sr(NO_3)_2 \cdot 6H_2O$ **(b)** $Co(C_2H_3O_2)_2 \cdot 4H_2O$
(c) $CuSO_4 \cdot 5H_2O$ **(d)** $Cr(NO_3)_3 \cdot 9H_2O$

73. Provide the chemical formula for each of the following hydrate compounds:
(a) sodium carbonate decahydrate
(b) nickel(II) nitrate hexahydrate
(c) cobalt(III) iodide octahydrate
(d) chromium(III) acetate monohydrate

74. Provide the chemical formula for each of the following hydrate compounds:
(a) sodium acetate trihydrate
(b) calcium sulfate dihydrate
(c) potassium chromate tetrahydrate
(d) zinc sulfate heptahydrate

75. Calculate the percentage of water in each of the following hydrates:
(a) $SrCl_2 \cdot 6H_2O$
(b) $K_2Cr_2O_7 \cdot 2H_2O$
(c) $Co(CN)_3 \cdot 3H_2O$
(d) $Na_2CrO_4 \cdot 4H_2O$

76. Calculate the percentage of water in each of the following hydrates:
(a) $MnSO_4 \cdot H_2O$
(b) $Sr(NO_3)_2 \cdot 6H_2O$
(c) $Co(C_2H_3O_2)_2 \cdot 4H_2O$
(d) $Cr(NO_3)_3 \cdot 9H_2O$

77. Determine the water of hydration for the following hydrates and write the chemical formula:
(a) $NiCl_2 \cdot XH_2O$ is found to contain 21.7% water.
(b) $Sr(NO_3)_2 \cdot XH_2O$ is found to contain 33.8% water.
(c) $CrI_3 \cdot XH_2O$ is found to contain 27.2% water.
(d) $Ca(NO_3)_2 \cdot XH_2O$ is found to contain 30.5% water.

78. Determine the water of hydration for the following hydrates and write the chemical formula:
(a) $SrCl_2 \cdot XH_2O$ is found to contain 18.5% water.
(b) $Ni(NO_3)_2 \cdot XH_2O$ is found to contain 37.2% water.
(c) $CoSO_4 \cdot XH_2O$ is found to contain 10.4% water.
(d) $Na_2B_4O_7 \cdot XH_2O$ is found to contain 30.9% water.

General Exercises

79. State the approximate percent of Earth's surface that is covered by water.

80. State the approximate percent of the human body that is water.

81. What is the strongest type of intermolecular attraction that exists in each of the following liquids?
(a) C_6H_{14} **(b)** C_2H_5-F
(c) CH_3-OH **(d)** CH_3-O-CH_3

82. What is the strongest type of intermolecular attraction that exists in each of the following liquids?
(a) C_8H_{18} **(b)** C_2H_5-Cl
(c) $HCOOH$ **(d)** $C_2H_5-O-C_2H_5$

83. Refer to Figure 11.5 and determine the boiling point of water at an elevation where the atmospheric pressure is 0.500 atm.

84. Refer to Figure 11.5 and determine the boiling point of ethanol at an elevation where the atmospheric pressure is 0.500 atm.

85. Venus has clouds of sulfuric acid, H_2SO_4. Why is it reasonable to predict that Venus "raindrops" are spheres?

86. Saturn has clouds of ammonia, NH_3. Why is it reasonable to predict that Saturn "raindrops" are spheres?

Challenge Exercises

87. Methanol can be used in automobiles as antifreeze. Calculate the heat required to vaporize 5.00 L of the liquid at 25.0 °C. (For methanol: density = 0.792 g/mL; specific heat = 0.610 cal/(g × °C); Bp = 65.0 °C; H_{vapor} = 263 cal/g.)

88. Ethylene glycol is used in automobiles as antifreeze. Calculate the heat required to vaporize 5.00 L of the liquid at 25.0 °C. (For ethylene glycol: density = 1.11 g/mL; specific heat = 0.561 cal/(g × °C); Bp = 197.6 °C; H_{vapor} = 201 cal/g.)

  ## Online Exercises

Research each of the following using an Internet search engine (e.g., Google.com or Yahoo.com) and cite your URL reference.

89. Which planet is more massive: Earth or Saturn? Which planet is more dense: Earth or Saturn?

90. What is the chemical composition of the atmosphere surrounding Saturn?

11

Chapter Self-Test   *Answers to Self-Test are in Appendix J.*

1. Which of the following is an observed property of liquids? (Sec. 11.1)
 (a) Liquids are more dense than gases.
 (b) Liquids expand and compress significantly.
 (c) Liquids have a fixed shape and variable volume.
 (d) Liquids that are insoluble mix homogeneously.
 (e) all of the above

2. What is the strongest intermolecular force in a liquid containing molecules with H—O bonds? (Sec. 11.2)
 (a) dipole forces
 (b) dispersion forces
 (c) hydrogen bonds
 (d) all of the above
 (e) none of the above

3. If the molecules in a liquid have a strong attraction for each other, which of the following properties has a relatively high value? (Sec. 11.3)
 (a) boiling point
 (b) viscosity
 (c) surface tension
 (d) all of the above
 (e) none of the above

4. Which of the following is an observed property of solids? (Sec. 11.4)
 (a) Solids have a variable shape and fixed volume.
 (b) Solids are usually less dense than liquids.
 (c) Solids can have noncrystalline structures.
 (d) Solids compress and expand significantly.
 (e) none of the above

5. Which of the following is an example of a molecular crystalline solid? (Sec. 11.5)
 (a) cuprite, Cu_2O
 (b) dry ice, CO_2
 (c) limestone, $CaCO_3$
 (d) iron pyrite, FeS_2
 (e) none of the above

◀ **Dry Ice** Solid carbon dioxide, CO_2, is undergoing sublimation from a solid to a gas.

6. Calculate the heat required to convert 10.0 g of water at 100 °C to steam at 100 °C. The specific heat of water is 1.00 cal/(g × °C); the heat of fusion is 80.0 cal/g; and the heat of vaporization is 540.0 cal/g. (Sec. 11.6)
 (a) 8.0 cal
 (b) 10.0 cal
 (c) 54.0 cal
 (d) $8.00 × 10^2$ cal
 (e) $5.40 × 10^3$ cal

7. How many dipoles are in a water molecule? (Sec. 11.7)
 (a) 0   **(b)** 1
 (c) 2   **(d)** 3
 (e) 4

8. Which of the following explains why ice floats on water? (Sec. 11.8)
   (a) Ice has a greater density than water.
   (b) Ice has a greater heat of fusion than water.
   (c) Ice has a greater molar mass than water.
   (d) Ice has a greater specific heat than water.
   (e) Ice has a greater volume than an equal mass of water.

9. What is the product from the reaction of water and a nonmetal oxide? (Sec. 11.9)
   (a) an acid
   (b) a base
   (c) a nonmetal hydroxide and hydrogen gas
   (d) a nonmetal hydroxide and oxygen gas
   (e) none of the above

10. An unknown hydrate of cobalt(II) cyanide, $Co(CN)_2 \cdot XH_2O$, is heated to give 32.7% water. What is the water of crystallization (X) for the hydrate?
    (a) 2
    (b) 3
    (c) 4
    (d) 6
    (e) 10

Key Concepts

11. Which physical state can be described by the following analogy? A beehive is surrounded by honey bees, which fly faster when approached by fire.

12. If a water bottle is filled completely and capped, what will happen if the water in the bottle freezes?

Critical Thinking

13. Why does hard-boiling an egg take more time in Denver, CO, than Miami, FL?

14. Observe the photograph closely and note water has a concave surface and mercury is convex. Explain this observation in terms of the attractive forces between the glass test tube and each liquid.

▶ **Water versus Mercury** The concave surface of water in a test tube is shown on the left, and the convex surface of mercury is shown on the right.

Chemical Bonding

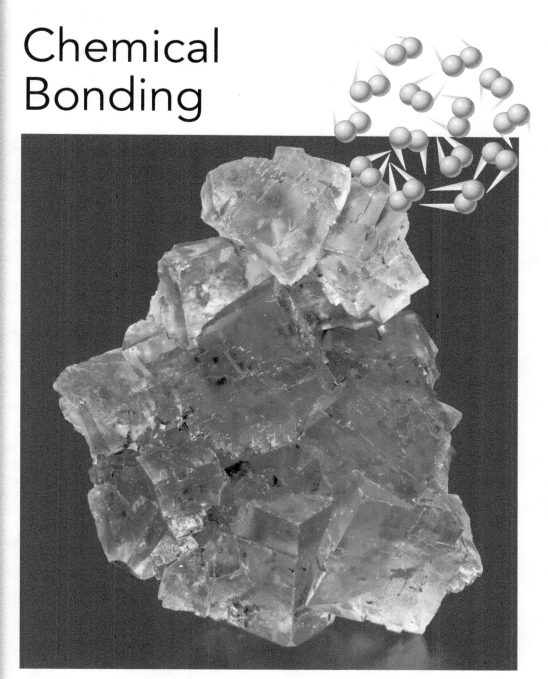

Fluorine in the Environment Fluorine is a greenish-yellow, extremely reactive gas, F_2. Elemental fluorine is not found naturally, but occurs in the mineral flluorspar, CaF_2 (shown). Sodium fluoride, NaF, helps prevent dental cavities and is found naturally in some water supplies and is added to others.

"The best way to have a good idea is to have lots of ideas."
Linus Pauling, American Chemist (1901–1994)

At the beginning of the twentieth century, scientists were rapidly unraveling the mysteries of the atom. In 1897, J. J. Thomson discovered the electron and, shortly thereafter, the proton. In 1911, Ernest Rutherford unveiled the atomic nucleus. And in 1913, Niels Bohr offered evidence that electrons occupied orbits and circled the nucleus. During this same period of time, scientists began to speculate that electrons were responsible for holding molecules together. They suggested that electrons provided the "glue" that bonded one atom to another.

In 1916, American chemist G. N. Lewis (1875–1946) formulated one of the first theories of chemical bonding. He noted that the noble gases were unusually stable and that, with the exception of helium, all these gases had eight electrons in their outer shell. Lewis theorized that atoms bonded together to attain a stable noble gas electron structure. This principle, referred to as the *octet rule*, states that atoms bond in such a way that each atom attains eight electrons in its outer shell.

12.1 THE CHEMICAL BOND CONCEPT

LEARNING OBJECTIVES

▸ To explain how valence electrons create a chemical bond.

▸ To predict whether a bond is ionic or covalent.

In Section 5.7, we learned that an atom has core electrons and valence electrons. Core electrons are found closer to the nucleus, whereas **valence electrons** are found in the most distant s and p energy subshells. Valence electrons are responsible for holding two or more atoms together in a **chemical bond**.

The **octet rule** states that an atom tends to bond in such a way that it acquires eight electrons in its outer shell. In the words of G. N. Lewis, the chemical bond concept can be described as follows:

> Two atoms may conform to the rule of eight, or the octet rule, not only by the transfer of electrons from one atom to another, but also by sharing one or more pairs of electrons. These electrons which are held in common by two atoms may be considered to belong to the outer shells of both atoms.

> The simplest explanation of the predominant occurrence of an even number of electrons in the valence shells of molecules is that the electrons are definitely paired with one another. Two electrons thus coupled together, when lying between two atomic centers, and held jointly in the shells of the two atoms, I have considered to be the chemical bond.

In an **ionic bond**, a metal cation is attracted to a nonmetal anion. The positively charged cation and negatively charged anion are held together by the attraction of opposite charges. A fundamental particle held together by an ionic bond is a **formula unit**. We can easily identify a formula unit by the fact that it contains metal and nonmetal ions. NaCl, MgO, and AlN all contain a metal cation and a nonmetal anion and are examples of formula units.

In a **covalent bond**, two nonmetal atoms share valence electrons. A fundamental particle held together by covalent bonds is a **molecule**. We can easily identify a molecule by the fact that it contains nonmetal atoms. H_2O, NH_3, and CH_4 all contain nonmetal atoms and are examples of molecules. The formation of an ionic bond and a covalent bond is shown in Figure 12.1.

(a)   (b)

▲ Figure 12.1 **Chemical Bonds** (a) An ionic bond forms when a metal cation (M^+) is attracted to a nonmetal anion (N^-). (b) A covalent bond forms when valence electrons are shared by two nonmetal atoms (N).

A substance can be composed of either formula units or molecules. The distinction between the types of representative particles found in a substance is shown in Figure 12.2.

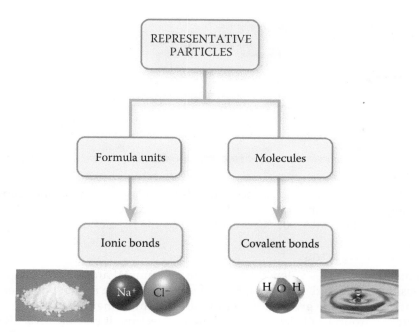

◀ Figure 12.2 **Classification of Representative Particles**
Particles can be formula units (for example, NaCl) held together by ionic bonds or they can be molecules (for example, H_2O) held together by covalent bonds.

The following example exercise further illustrates the relationship between bonding and the type of fundamental particles.

Example Exercise 12.1 Bond Predictions

Predict whether each of the following is held together by ionic or by covalent bonds:

(a) ammonia, NH_3 (b) magnesium nitride, Mg_3N_2

Solution

A metal ion and nonmetal ion are attracted in ionic bonds; two or more nonmetal atoms are attracted in covalent bonds.

(a) Ammonia contains the nonmetals nitrogen and hydrogen. It follows that NH_3 has *covalent* bonds.

(b) Magnesium nitride contains a metal (Mg) and a nonmetal (N). It follows that Mg_3N_2 has *ionic* bonds.

Practice Exercise

Predict whether each of the following is held together by ionic or by covalent bonds:

(a) aluminum oxide, Al_2O_3 (b) sulfur dioxide, SO_2

Answers:

(a) ionic   (b) covalent

Concept Exercise

What type of chemical bond results from the attraction between a metal cation and a nonmetal anion? between two nonmetal atoms?

Answer: See Appendix G.

12.2 IONIC BONDS

An ionic bond results from the attraction between a positively charged cation and a negatively charged anion. In a crystal of table salt, NaCl, there is an attraction between Na^+ ions and Cl^- ions. This attraction between ions is similar to the attraction between the ends of two magnets. Figure 12.3 illustrates the attraction between ions, and the similar attraction between two magnets.

LEARNING OBJECTIVE

▶ To describe the formation of an ionic bond between a metal atom and a nonmetal atom.

▶ **Figure 12.3 Electrostatic Attraction** Opposite ends of ordinary magnets are attracted to each other in much the same way that oppositely charged cations and anions are attracted. Notice that attraction can take place vertically as well as horizontally.

▲ **Figure 12.4 Crystalline Structure of Sodium Chloride** A crystal of sodium chloride is composed of sodium and chloride ions that repeat regularly. Notice that each sodium ion is attracted to several nearby chloride ions. The alternating pattern of cations and anions gives rise to a three-dimensional crystalline structure.

In ordinary table salt, NaCl, the ionic bonds between sodium ion and chloride ion are so strong that they can create a rigid crystalline structure (Figure 12.4). In fact, the high melting point of NaCl, 801 °C, is explained by the rigid crystal structure.

Formation of Cations

When a metal atom loses valence electrons to a nonmetal atom, the metal atom becomes positively charged. In Section 5.7, we learned that the number of valence electrons corresponds to the group number of the element in the periodic table. When a sodium atom (Group IA/1) loses its one valence electron, it becomes Na^+. Referring to the periodic table, we notice that Na^+ has 10 electrons ($11 - 1 = 10\,e-$). This is the same number of electrons found in the preceding noble gas neon ($10\,e-$).

Although there are exceptions, main group metals usually achieve a noble gas electron configuration after losing their valence electrons. Stated differently, main group metal ions are generally *isoelectronic* with a noble gas as explained in Section 5.10. When a magnesium atom (Group IIA/2) loses its 2 valence electrons, it becomes Mg^{2+}. A magnesium ion has 10 electrons ($12 - 2 = 10\,e-$) and is also isoelectronic with neon.

In Section 5.8 we learned how to write electron dot formulas for atoms of elements. We can now use electron dot diagrams to clarify the formation of ions. Electron dot diagrams allow us to focus our attention on valence electrons involved in this process of forming ions. Figure 12.5 illustrates the formation of ions by third-period metals.

▶ **Figure 12.5 Formation of Metal Ions** The atoms of the metals in Period 3 form cations by losing 1, 2, and 3 electrons, respectively. In each case the metal atom becomes isoelectronic with the preceding noble gas neon, [Ne].

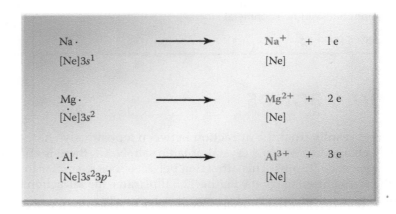

Note Notice that the electron dot diagrams of atoms in Figure 12.5 show electron dots, whereas the ions in Figure 12.5 do not show electron dots. Each of the ions has the electron configuration of neon. And each of these ions, like neon, has a stable electron configuration consisting of eight electrons. By convention, chemists do not draw the underlying octet of electrons because they are not valence electrons.

Formation of Anions

When a nonmetal atom gains valence electrons from a metal atom, the nonmetal atom becomes negatively charged. When a chlorine atom (Group VIIA/17) gains one valence electron, it becomes Cl^-. Referring to the periodic table, we notice that Cl^- has 18 electrons ($17 + 1 = 18\,e-$). This is the same number of electrons found in the next noble gas argon ($18\,e-$). When a sulfur atom (Group VIA/16) gains two valence electrons, it becomes S^{2-}. A sulfide ion has 18 electrons ($16 + 2 = 18\,e-$) and is also isoelectronic with argon. Figure 12.6 illustrates the formation of ions by third-period nonmetals.

◀ **Figure 12.6 Formation of Nonmetal Ions** The nonmetals in Period 3 gain 1, 2, and 3 electrons, respectively. In each case the nonmetal ion becomes isoelectronic with the next noble gas argon, [Ar].

The following example exercise further illustrates the formation of cations and anions.

Example Exercise 12.2 Electron Configuration of Ions

Which noble gas has an electron configuration identical to that of each of the following ions?
(a) lithium ion
(b) oxide ion
(c) calcium ion
(d) bromide ion

Solution

Refer to the group number in the periodic table for the number of valence electrons.

(a) Lithium (Group IA/1) forms an ion by losing one valence electron; Li^+ has only 2 electrons remaining and is isoelectronic with *He*.
(b) Oxygen (Group VIA/16) forms an ion by gaining 2 electrons; thus, O^{2-} has 10 electrons and is isoelectronic with *Ne*.

(c) Calcium (Group IIA/2) forms an ion by losing 2 electrons; Ca^{2+} has 18 electrons remaining and is isoelectronic with *Ar*.

(d) Bromine (Group VIIA/17) forms an ion by gaining one electron; Br^- has 36 electrons and is isoelectronic with *Kr*.

Practice Exercise

Which noble gas element has an electron configuration identical to that of each of the following ions?

(a) potassium ion   (b) nitride ion

(c) strontium ion   (d) iodide ion

Answers:

(a) K^+ is isoelectronic with Ar.   (b) N^{3-} is isoelectronic with Ne.

(c) Sr^{2+} is isoelectronic with Kr.   (d) I^- is isoelectronic with Xe.

Concept Exercise

Which noble gas is isoelectronic with a barium ion? with an iodide ion?

Answer: See Appendix G.

Ionic Radii versus Atomic Radii

To visualize an ionic bond more clearly, we can picture a sodium atom becoming smaller after losing its valence electron. The radius of a sodium atom is 0.186 nm, whereas the radius of the sodium ion is 0.095 nm. The reason for this decrease in radius is that the sodium atom has lost its 3s energy sublevel. Moreover, in the sodium ion the positive nuclear charge (11+) is greater than the negative electron charge (10−) and pulls the electrons closer to the nucleus; thus, the radius decreases.

Conversely, we can picture a chlorine atom becoming larger after gaining a valence electron. The radius of a chlorine atom is 0.099 nm, whereas the radius of the chloride ion is 0.181 nm. The reason for this increase in radius is that the additional electron repels the electrons already present. In fact, the radius of the charged chloride ion is almost twice as large as that of the neutral chlorine atom.

The behavior of sodium and chlorine atoms show the same general trend observed for all metals and nonmetals with respect to atomic radius. The radius of a *cation is smaller* than that of the corresponding metal atom; the radius of an *anion is larger* than that of the corresponding nonmetal atom. The specific changes in the radius of a sodium atom and a chlorine atom are depicted in Figure 12.7.

▶ Figure 12.7 **Formation of Sodium and Chloride Ions** The radius of the sodium atom decreases (a and c) as a result of losing an electron, whereas the radius of the chlorine atom increases (b and d) after gaining an electron.

(a)   (b)   (c)   (d)

Na atom   Cl atom   Na⁺   Cl⁻
r = 0.186 nm   r = 0.099 nm   r = 0.095 nm   r = 0.181 nm

The following example exercise further illustrates the characteristics associated with the formation of an ionic bond.

Example Exercise 12.3   Characteristics of Ionic Bonds

Which of the following statements are true regarding an ionic bond between an iron ion and a sulfide ion in an FeS formula unit?

(a) The iron atom loses electrons and the sulfur atom gains electrons.

(b) The iron atom has a larger radius than the iron ion.

(c) Iron and sulfide ions form a bond by electrostatic attraction.

Solution

All of these statements are true regarding an ionic bond.

(a) An iron atom loses electrons and a sulfur atom gains electrons.
(b) The radius of an iron atom is greater than its ionic radius.
(c) An ionic bond is from the attraction of positive and negative ions.

Practice Exercise

Which of the following statements are true regarding an ionic bond between a zinc ion and an oxide ion in a ZnO formula unit?

(a) Zinc and oxygen form a bond by sharing electrons.
(b) The oxygen atom is larger in radius than the oxide ion.
(c) Zinc and oxide ions form a bond by the repulsion of ions.

Answers:

(a) False, zinc and oxygen bond by transferring electrons.
(b) False, the radius of an oxygen atom is smaller than its ionic radius.
(c) False, zinc and oxygen form a bond by the attraction of ions.

Concept Exercise

Which of the following statements are true regarding the formation of an ionic bond between a metal and a nonmetal?

(a) The atomic radius of a metal atom is greater than its ionic radius.
(b) The atomic radius of a nonmetal atom is less than its ionic radius.
(c) Energy is released in the formation of an ionic bond.

Answer: See Appendix G.

12.3 COVALENT BONDS

LEARNING OBJECTIVE

▶ To describe the formation of a covalent bond between two nonmetal atoms by sharing valence electrons.

A covalent bond results from the sharing of electrons by two nonmetal atoms. To create an accurate picture, we can visualize shared electrons roaming about both atoms. The electrons belong to both nonmetal atoms, and each atom uses these bonding electrons to complete an octet. That is, each nonmetal atom uses shared electrons to complete its valence shell.

Now, let's see what happens during the formation of a covalent bond. As an example, consider the formation of hydrogen chloride, HCl, from a hydrogen atom and a chlorine atom. During bond formation, the hydrogen atom shares its one valence electron with the chlorine atom and its seven valence electrons. The additional electron gives the chlorine atom eight electrons in its valence shell, and thus fulfills the octet rule.

In the same process, the chlorine atom shares one of its valence electrons with the hydrogen atom. The additional electron gives the hydrogen atom two electrons in its valence shell. The hydrogen atom is thus similar to an atom of the noble gas helium, and is therefore stable. In this process, both the hydrogen atom and the chlorine atom become stable by sharing an electron pair and forming a covalent bond.

Bond Length

To understand bond formation more clearly, try to visualize the valence shells of the two atoms overlapping each other. In a molecule of HCl, the valence shells of the two atoms overlap as the $1s$ energy sublevel of the hydrogen atom mixes with the $3p$ sublevel of the chlorine atom. This mixing of sublevels draws the two nuclei closer together. The radius of the hydrogen atom is 0.037 nm, and that of the chlorine atom is 0.099 nm. If the two atoms were simply next to each another, the distance from the hydrogen nucleus to the chlorine nucleus would be $(0.037 + 0.099)$ nm or 0.136 nm. But experiments reveal that the distance between the two nuclei is actually 0.127 nm. Thus, the shells overlap, as shown in Figure 12.8. The distance between the two nuclei is called the **bond length**.

▶ Figure 12.8 **Formation of a Covalent Bond** The sharing of an electron pair by a hydrogen atom and a chlorine atom produces a covalent bond. The two atoms are held together in a molecule of HCl. The bond length (0.127 nm) is less than the sum of the two atomic radii (0.037 + 0.099 = 0.136 nm).

H atom	Cl atom	HCl molecule
atomic radius	atomic radius	bond length = 0.127 nm
r_1 = 0.037 nm	r_2 = 0.099 nm	$r_1 + r_2$ = 0.136 nm

Bond Energy

Energy is released when two ions are attracted to one another and form an ionic bond. For example, the attraction of Na^+ and Cl^- to form NaCl releases heat energy. Similarly, energy is released when two atoms are attracted and form a covalent bond. When hydrogen and chlorine atoms form an HCl molecule, heat energy is released.

$$H(g) + Cl(g) \longrightarrow HCl(g) + heat$$

Conversely, energy is necessary to break an H—Cl bond. The amount of energy required to break a covalent bond between two atoms is referred to as the **bond energy**. The amount of energy necessary to break the H—Cl bond is identical to the amount of heat released when H and Cl form a bond in the creation of a hydrogen chloride molecule.

$$HCl(g) + heat \longrightarrow H(g) + Cl(g)$$

The following example exercise summarizes the characteristics associated with the formation of a covalent bond.

Example Exercise 12.4 Characteristics of Covalent Bonds

Which of the following statements are true regarding a covalent bond between a hydrogen atom and an oxygen atom in an H_2O molecule?

(a) Valence electrons are shared by hydrogen and oxygen atoms.
(b) The H—O bond length is less than the sum of the two atomic radii.
(c) Breaking the bond between H—O requires energy.

Solution
All of the previous statements regarding a covalent bond in a molecule are true.

(a) Valence electrons are shared by the two nonmetal atoms.
(b) The bond length is less than the sum of the two atomic radii.
(c) The breaking of a covalent bond requires energy.

Practice Exercise
Which of the following statements are true regarding a covalent bond between a hydrogen atom and a sulfur atom in an H_2S molecule?

(a) Valence electrons are transferred from hydrogen to sulfur.
(b) The H—S bond length equals the sum of the two atomic radii.
(c) Forming a bond between H—S requires energy.

Answers:
(a) False, valence electrons are shared by hydrogen and sulfur.
(b) False, the bond length is less than the sum of the two atomic radii.
(c) False, the forming of a covalent bond releases energy.

Concept Exercise
Which of the following statements are true regarding the formation of a covalent bond between two nonmetal atoms?

(a) Bonding electrons are shared between two nonmetal atoms.
(b) The bond length is less than the sum of the two atomic radii.
(c) The bond energy is the energy required to break a covalent bond.

Answer: See Appendix G.

Note Energy is always released when two *atoms* form a covalent bond. However, energy is required to form an H—I bond from *molecules* of H_2 and I_2. Realize that energy is required to break H—H and I—I bonds in order to form H—I bonds. The formation of HI is an *endothermic* reaction because more energy is required in breaking H—H and I—I bonds than is released in forming H—I bonds.

12.4 ELECTRON DOT FORMULAS OF MOLECULES

LEARNING OBJECTIVES

▸ To draw the electron dot formula for a molecule.

▸ To draw the structural formula for a molecule.

In Section 5.8, we drew the electron dot formula for an atom of a representative element. We found the element in the periodic table and noted its group number to predict the number of valence electrons. For example, in the second period, we found that Li has one valence electron (Group IA/1), Be has 2 (Group IIA/2), B has 3 (Group IIIA/13), C has 4 (Group IVA/14), N has 5 (Group VA/15), O has 6 (Group VIA/16), F has 7 (Group VIIA/17), and the noble gas Ne has 8 (Group VIIIA/18). We represented each valence electron by a dot surrounding the symbol for the element.

Now, we will draw the **electron dot formula** (also called a *Lewis structure*) for a molecule. An electron dot formula shows the valence electrons that form bonds between atoms. These electron pairs shared by atoms are called **bonding electrons**. Other electron pairs that simply complete the octet around each atom are called **nonbonding electrons**, or *lone pairs*.

Guidelines for Drawing Electron Dot Formulas of Molecules[†]

1. Calculate the total number of valence electrons by adding all the valence electrons for each atom in the molecule. The total must be an even number to obey the octet rule. If the total is an odd number, check your calculations.
2. Divide the total number of valence electrons by 2 to find the number of electron pairs in the molecule.
3. Surround the central atom with four electron pairs. Use the remaining electron pairs to complete an octet around each of the other atoms. (Hydrogen is the sole exception as it requires only one electron pair.)
4. If there are not enough electron pairs to provide an octet for each atom, move a nonbonding electron pair between two atoms that already share an electron pair.

[†]When two or more atoms are bonded to a central atom, it is often difficult to recognize the central atom. Thus, this textbook will indicate the central atom in bold to aid in writing electron dot formulas for molecules.

Electron Dot Formula for Water, H_2O

To learn how to draw electron dot formulas for molecules, we will draw the electron dot formula for water, H_2O. The total number of valence electrons in the molecule is one for each hydrogen atom and six for the oxygen atom. Thus, the total number of electrons is $2(1 e-) + 6 e- = 8 e-$. The number of electron pairs is 4 ($8/2 = 4$).

In the formula H_2O, oxygen is the central atom and is indicated in bold. We place the four electron pairs around the oxygen to provide the necessary octet.

▲ **Water, H_2O**

We then place the two hydrogen atoms in any of the four electron pair positions.

two nonbonding electron pairs

two bonding electron pairs

Notice that there are two bonding and two nonbonding electron pairs. However, bonding and nonbonding electrons are identical, and the four electron pairs move about the molecule. Thus, bonding and nonbonding valence electrons spread over the entire molecule and are said to be *delocalized*.

To simplify, we represent each pair of bonding electrons by a single dash, which is called a **single bond**. The resulting structure is referred to as the **structural formula** of the molecule. In a structural formula the nonbonding electrons are usually shown, but their inclusion is optional.

$$H-\ddot{\ddot{O}}:$$
$$|$$
$$H$$

Electron Dot Formula for Sulfur Trioxide, SO₃

Now we'll try a more difficult example. Let's draw the electron dot formula for sulfur trioxide, **SO₃**. Sulfur is the central atom in the molecule and is indicated in bold. Sulfur and oxygen each have six valence electrons, so the total number of valence electrons in the molecule is $6\,e- + 3(6\,e-) = 24\,e-$. The number of electron pairs is 12 ($24/2 = 12$).

Because sulfur is the central atom, we can begin by placing four electron pairs around the sulfur and then attaching the three oxygen atoms. That gives us

$$O:\overset{..}{\underset{..}{S}}:O$$
$$O$$

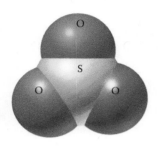

▲ Sulfur Trioxide, SO₃

We started with 12 electron pairs, and so we have eight pairs remaining. We place the remaining pairs around the oxygen atoms to complete each octet.

$$:\overset{..}{\underset{..}{O}}:\overset{..}{\underset{..}{S}}:\overset{..}{\underset{..}{O}}:$$
$$:\overset{}{\underset{..}{O}}$$

Notice that the bottom oxygen atom does not have an octet; it has only three electron pairs. According to the guidelines, we can move a nonbonding electron pair from the S atom so as to provide two bonding electron pairs between the sulfur and the oxygen atoms.

$$:\overset{..}{\underset{..}{O}}:S:\overset{..}{\underset{..}{O}}:$$
$$:\overset{..}{\underset{..}{O}}$$

The two shared electron pairs constitute a **double bond**. All four electrons in the double bond are shared by the S and the O atoms. Therefore, the sulfur atom still has an octet and the bottom oxygen atom has gained two electrons to complete its octet. The structural formula for SO₃ has one double bond and two single bonds. We represent the double bond by a double dash and the single bond by a single dash.

$$:\overset{..}{\underset{..}{O}}-S-\overset{..}{\underset{..}{O}}:$$
$$||$$
$$\underset{..}{O}:$$

We can draw the structural formula for an SO₃ molecule with the double bond between any of the oxygen atoms. Experimentally, the double bond is found to be shared by each of the three oxygen atoms. This phenomenon is known as *resonance*, and we can draw three resonance structures for an SO₃ molecule.

$$\begin{array}{ccc} O{=}S{-}O & O{-}S{-}O & O{-}S{=}O \\ | & || & | \\ O & O & O \end{array}$$

Although these structures may appear to be different, all three formulas are identical. If we were to construct the molecule using models, we could easily verify this statement. Each molecular model can be rotated and shown to be identical to the other two.

Electron Dot Formula for Hydrogen Cyanide, HCN

Let's draw the electron dot formula for hydrogen cyanide, HCN. Carbon is the central atom in the molecule and is indicated in bold. The total number of valence electrons in the molecule is $1\,e- + 4\,e- + 5\,e- = 10\,e-$. The number of electron pairs is $5\,(10/2 = 5)$. Because carbon is the central atom, we begin by placing four electron pairs around the carbon and attaching the hydrogen and nitrogen atoms.

▲ Hydrogen Cyanide, HCN

$$H:\overset{..}{\underset{..}{C}}:N$$

We started with five electron pairs, and there is only one pair remaining. The hydrogen atom has its two required electrons, so we place the remaining pair next to the nitrogen atom.

$$H:\overset{..}{\underset{..}{C}}:N:$$

The nitrogen atom now has four electrons, which is $4\,e-$ less than an octet. According to the guidelines, we can move nonbonding electron pairs between the C and the N atoms. For example,

$$H:\underset{..}{C}::N:$$

The nitrogen atom has only six electrons. If we move the other nonbonding electron pair from the carbon atom, we have

$$H:C:::N:$$

The three electron pairs produce a **triple bond**. All six electrons in the triple bond are shared by the C and the N atoms. Therefore, both the carbon atom and the nitrogen atom have obtained an octet. A triple bond is indicated by a triple dash. The structural formula for HCN is therefore written as

$$H-C\equiv N:$$

The following example exercises further illustrate how to draw electron dot and structural formulas of molecules.

Example Exercise 12.5 Electron Dot Formulas—Single Bonds

Draw the electron dot formula and the structural formula for a chloroform molecule, $CHCl_3$.

Solution
Carbon is the central atom in the chloroform molecule and is indicated in bold. The total number of valence electrons is $4\,e- + 1\,e- + 3(7\,e-) = 26\,e-$. The number of electron pairs is $13\,(26/2 = 13)$. We begin by placing four electron pairs around the carbon and adding one H and three Cl atoms.

▲ Chloroform, $CHCl_3$

$$\begin{array}{c} H \\ .. \\ Cl:\overset{..}{\underset{..}{C}}:Cl \\ .. \\ Cl \end{array}$$

We have 13 electron pairs minus the four pairs we used for the carbon. Because 9 electron pairs remain, let's place three pairs around each chlorine.

$$ \overset{\displaystyle H}{\underset{\displaystyle :\overset{..}{\underset{..}{Cl}}:}{:\overset{..}{\underset{..}{Cl}}:\overset{..}{\underset{..}{C}}:\overset{..}{\underset{..}{Cl}}:} } $$

Each atom is surrounded by an octet of electrons, except hydrogen, which has two. This is the correct electron dot formula. In the corresponding structural formula we replace each bonding electron pair by a single dash. The structural formula is

$$ \overset{\displaystyle H}{\underset{\displaystyle |}{}} $$
$$:\overset{..}{\underset{..}{Cl}}-\overset{\displaystyle |}{C}-\overset{..}{\underset{..}{Cl}}: $$
$$ \underset{\displaystyle :\overset{}{\underset{..}{Cl}}:}{|} $$

Note that the structural formula is free to rotate. We could have also written the hydrogen atom below or at the side of the carbon atom.

Practice Exercise
Draw the electron dot formula and the structural formula for a molecule of **SiHClBrI**.

Answers:

$$ \overset{\displaystyle H}{:\overset{..}{I}:\overset{..}{Si}:\overset{..}{\underset{..}{Cl}}:} \qquad \overset{\displaystyle H}{\underset{..}{:\overset{..}{I}-\overset{|}{Si}-\overset{..}{\underset{..}{Cl}}:}} $$
$$:\overset{}{\underset{..}{Br}}: \qquad\qquad :\overset{}{\underset{..}{Br}}: $$

Concept Exercise
Draw the electron dot formula for H_2S. How many nonbonding electron pairs are in a hydrogen sulfide molecule?

Answer: See Appendix G.

▲ Carbon Dioxide, CO_2

> **Example Exercise 12.6** Electron Dot Formulas—Double Bonds

Draw the electron dot formula and the structural formula for a carbon dioxide molecule, CO_2.

Solution
Carbon is the central atom in the carbon dioxide molecule, as indicated in bold. The total number of valence electrons is $4\,e- + 2(6\,e-) = 16\,e-$. The number of electron pairs is $8\ (16/2 = 8)$. We begin by placing four electron pairs around the carbon and adding the two O atoms.

$$ O:\overset{..}{\underset{..}{C}}:O $$

The number of remaining electron pairs is $8 - 4 = 4$ pairs. We can add 2 pairs to each oxygen.

$$ \overset{..}{\underset{..}{O}}:\overset{..}{\underset{..}{C}}:\overset{..}{\underset{..}{O}} $$

Each oxygen atom shares six electrons, two less than an octet. We can use the nonbonding electron pairs around carbon to complete the octet around each oxygen. We move one pair to the oxygen on the left, and the other pair to the oxygen on the right to complete the octet around each oxygen. Each carbon–oxygen bond shares two electron pairs.

$$\ddot{O}::C::\ddot{O}$$

Now the octet rule is satisfied for each atom. This is the correct electron dot formula. There are two electron pairs between each oxygen and carbon. Thus, there are two double bonds in the carbon dioxide molecule. In the structural formula each double bond is indicated by a double dash.

$$:\ddot{O}=C=\ddot{O}:$$

Practice Exercise

Draw the electron dot formula and the structural formula for a molecule of SiO_2.

Answers:

$$:\ddot{O}::Si::\ddot{O}: \quad :\ddot{O}=Si=\ddot{O}:$$

Concept Exercise

Draw the electron dot formula for SO_2. How many nonbonding electron pairs are in a sulfur dioxide molecule?

Answer: See Appendix G.

Note Writing electron dot formulas is a trial-and-error procedure that involves the use of valence electron pairs to satisfy the octet rule. However, there are common exceptions to the octet rule that are beyond the scope of this introduction to bonding. For example, in BeF_2 there are only four electrons around the **Be** atom, and in BF_3 there are only six electrons around the **B** atom. Moreover, there are exceptions that violate the octet rule by exceeding eight electrons. For example, in PF_5 there are 10 electrons around the **P** atom; and in SF_6 there are 12 electrons around the **S** atom.

12.5 ELECTRON DOT FORMULAS OF POLYATOMIC IONS

So far in our discussion of ions, we have considered only single atoms that have gained or lost electrons. This type of simple ion having a positive or negative charge is called a **monoatomic ion**. An ion can also contain two or more atoms that bears an overall charge; this type of ion is called a **polyatomic ion**. Some common polyatomic ions are the ammonium ion, NH_4^+, found in fertilizer; the hydroxide ion, OH^-, found in household products like drain and oven cleaner; and the hydrogen carbonate ion, HCO_3^-, found in baking soda.

In Section 12.4 we learned to draw the electron dot formula for molecules. Now, we can draw the electron dot formula for polyatomic ions. The following directions for ions are similar to the previous guidelines for molecules.

LEARNING OBJECTIVES

▶ To draw the electron dot formula for a polyatomic ion.

▶ To draw the structural formula for a polyatomic ion.

Guidelines for Drawing Electron Dot Formulas of Polyatomic Ions[†]

1. Calculate the valence electrons by adding the valence electrons for each atom in the polyatomic ion. If the ion is negatively charged, add electrons—equal to the charge—to the number of valence electrons. If the ion is positively charged, subtract electrons—equal to the charge—from the number of valence electrons. In each case, the result will be the total number of valence electrons.
2. Divide the total number of valence electrons and charges by two to find the number of electron pairs in the polyatomic ion.
3. Surround the central atom with four electron pairs. Use the remaining electron pairs to complete an octet around each of the other atoms. (Hydrogen is the sole exception, as H requires only one electron pair.)
4. If there are not enough electron pairs to provide an octet for each atom, move a nonbonding electron pair between two atoms that already share an electron pair.

[†]When two or more atoms are bonded to a central atom, it is often difficult to recognize the central atom. Thus, this textbook will indicate the central atom in bold to aid in writing electron dot formulas for polyatomic ions.

Electron Dot Formula for the Ammonium Ion, NH_4^+

We can draw the electron dot formula for the ammonium ion, NH_4^+, as follows. The total number of valence electrons in this positive polyatomic ion is $5\,e- + 4(1\,e-) - 1\,e- = 8\,e-$. (Note that we must subtract 1 e−, because the ion has a 1+ charge.) The number of electron pairs is 4 ($8/2 = 4$). In the formula NH_4^+, nitrogen is the central atom. We place the four electron pairs around the nitrogen atom to provide the necessary octet.

$$\left[\begin{array}{c} \text{H} \\ \text{H} :\!\overset{\displaystyle ..}{\underset{\displaystyle ..}{\text{N}}}\!: \text{H} \\ \text{H} \end{array} \right]^+$$

Notice that the electron dot formula is written correctly for the ammonium ion. The nitrogen atom has an octet, and each hydrogen atom shares two electrons.

Now, let's simplify the electron dot formula and draw the structural formula of this polyatomic ion. We represent each bonding pair of electrons by a single dash and draw the structural formula for the ammonium ion as follows:

$$\left[\begin{array}{c} \text{H} \\ | \\ \text{H} - \text{N} - \text{H} \\ | \\ \text{H} \end{array} \right]^+$$

The usual way to draw structural formulas of polyatomic ions is to enclose them in brackets. The overall charge on the polyatomic ion is indicated outside the brackets. Placing the charge outside the brackets emphasizes that the positive charge is distributed over the entire ion.

Electron Dot Formula for the Chlorate Ion, ClO_3^-

Now, let's draw the electron dot formula for the chlorate ion, ClO_3^-. The total number of valence electrons for this negative ion is $7\,e- + 3(6\,e-) + 1\,e- = 26\,e-$. (Note that we must add 1 e−, because the ion has a 1− charge.) The number of electron pairs is 13 ($26/2 = 13$). Because chlorine is the central atom, we begin by placing four electron pairs around the Cl atom and then add the three O atoms.

$$\text{O} :\!\overset{\displaystyle ..}{\underset{\displaystyle ..}{\text{Cl}}}\!: \text{O}$$
$$\text{O}$$

We started with 13 electron pairs and placed four pairs around the central atom. We place the remaining 9 electron pairs around the oxygen atoms to complete each octet.

$$\left[\ddot{\underset{..}{O}} : \ddot{Cl} : \ddot{\underset{..}{O}} : \right]^{-}$$
$$:\ddot{\underset{..}{O}}:$$

In the structural formula, each bonding electron pair is represented by a single dash. Thus, we can show the structural formula for ClO_3^- as follows:

$$\left[:\ddot{\underset{..}{O}} - \ddot{Cl} - \ddot{\underset{..}{O}}: \right]^{-}$$
$$| $$
$$:\ddot{\underset{..}{O}}:$$

Electron Dot Formula for the Carbonate Ion, CO_3^{2-}

Let's try a more difficult example and draw the electron dot formula for the carbonate ion, CO_3^{2-}. The total number of valence electrons in this polyatomic ion is $4\,e- + 3(6\,e-) + 2\,e-$ (because the ion has a 2- charge) $= 24\,e-$. The total number of electron pairs is 12 ($24/2 = 12$). Carbon is the central atom, so we begin by placing four pairs of electrons around the C atom and then add three O atoms. We have

$$O : \ddot{C} : O$$
$$\underset{..}{O}$$

We started with 12 electron pairs, and so we have 8 pairs remaining. We place the remaining pairs around the oxygen atoms to give octets as follows:

$$:\ddot{\underset{..}{O}} : \ddot{C} : \ddot{\underset{..}{O}} :$$
$$:\ddot{\underset{..}{O}}$$

Notice that the bottom oxygen atom does not have an octet; it has only three electron pairs. According to our guidelines, we can move a nonbonding electron pair. Let's shift the nonbonding pair between the C and the O atoms.

$$\left[:\ddot{\underset{..}{O}} : \ddot{C} : \ddot{\underset{..}{O}} : \right]^{2-}$$
$$:\ddot{\underset{..}{O}}$$

The two electron pairs constitute a double bond. All four electrons in the double bond are shared by the C and the O atoms. Therefore, the central carbon atom has an octet and the oxygen atom has gained two electrons to complete its octet.

However, the double bond can form between any one of the three oxygen atoms. We use brackets to convey the idea that valence electrons are free to move about the entire polyatomic ion. Consequently, there appear to be three different structural formulas for the carbonate ion.

$$\left[O = C - O \right]^{2-} \qquad \left[O - C - O \right]^{2-} \qquad \left[O - C = O \right]^{2-}$$
$$| \qquad\qquad\quad || \qquad\qquad\quad |$$
$$O \qquad\qquad\qquad O \qquad\qquad\qquad O$$

Although the structures for the carbonate ion appear to be different, they are all equivalent. No matter how we represent CO_3^{2-}, the structural formula has one double bond and two single bonds. Thus, we can draw three resonance structures for the carbonate ion. The following example exercise further illustrates how to draw electron dot and structural formulas for polyatomic ions.

Example Exercise 12.7 Electron Dot Formulas of Polyatomic Ions

Draw the electron dot formula and the structural formula for the sulfate ion, SO_4^{2-}.

Solution

The total number of valence electrons is the sum of each atom plus 2 for the negative charge: $6\,e- + 4(6\,e-) + 2\,e- = 32\,e-$. The number of electron pairs is 16 ($32/2 = 16$). We begin by placing four electron pairs around the central sulfur atom and attaching the four oxygen atoms as follows:

$$
\begin{array}{c}
O \\
O:S:O \\
O
\end{array}
$$

We have 12 remaining electron pairs, and so we place 3 electron pairs around each oxygen atom.

$$
\left[\ddot{\underset{\cdot\cdot}{O}} \; :\ddot{\underset{\cdot\cdot}{O}}:S:\ddot{\underset{\cdot\cdot}{O}}: \; \ddot{\underset{\cdot\cdot}{O}} \right]^{2-}
$$

Notice that each atom is surrounded by an octet of electrons. This is the correct electron dot formula. In the structural formula each bonding electron pair is replaced by a single dash. The structural formula is

$$
\left[\begin{array}{c} :\ddot{O}: \\ | \\ :\ddot{O}-S-\ddot{O}: \\ | \\ :\ddot{O}: \end{array} \right]^{2-}
$$

Practice Exercise

Draw the electron dot formula and the structural formula for the nitrite ion, NO_2^-.

Answers:

$$
\left[:\ddot{\underset{\cdot\cdot}{O}}:N::\ddot{O}: \right]^- \qquad \left[:\ddot{\underset{\cdot\cdot}{O}}-\ddot{N}=\ddot{O}: \right]^-
$$

Concept Exercise

Draw the electron dot formula for the polyatomic sulfite ion, SO_3^{2-}. How many nonbonding electron pairs are in a sulfite ion?

Answer: See Appendix G.

LEARNING OBJECTIVES

▸ To state the electronegativity trends in the periodic table.

▸ To calculate the electronegativity difference in a polar covalent bond.

▸ To apply delta notation (δ^+ and δ^-) to a polar bond.

12.6 POLAR COVALENT BONDS

Covalent bonds result from the sharing of valence electrons. To this point we have assumed that electrons are shared equally in a covalent bond. What about a covalent bond in which the two atoms do not share electrons equally? In many instances one of the two atoms holds the electron pair more tightly. When the electrons are drawn more closely to one of the atoms, the bond is said to be polarized. This type of bond is called a *polar covalent bond*, or simply a **polar bond**.

Electronegativity Trends

Each element has an innate ability to attract valence electrons. This ability is related to the nearness of the valence shell to the nucleus. It is also related to the magnitude of the positive charge in the nucleus. The ability of an atom to attract electrons in a chemical bond is referred to as its **electronegativity**. Atoms of elements that strongly attract bonding electrons are said to be highly electronegative.

Linus Pauling, an American chemist, devised a method for measuring the electronegativity values for each of the elements. He assigned carbon a value of 2.5 and then determined the ability of other elements to attract bonding electrons relative to carbon. He found that fluorine is the most electronegative element. It has a value of 4.0 compared to carbon. Other highly electronegative elements are oxygen, 3.5; nitrogen, 3.0; and chlorine, 3.0. The most electronegative elements are the nonmetals on the far right of the periodic table. Figure 12.9 shows selected elements in the periodic table and their Pauling electronegativity value.

▲ Figure 12.9 **Electronegativity Values for the Elements** The Pauling electronegativity value for an element is shown below the symbol. In general, electronegativity increases across a period and up a group.

Note the electronegativity trends in Figure 12.9. First, the elements generally become more electronegative from *left to right* in the periodic table. Second, elements become more electronegative from *bottom to top* within a group.

We can see that the horizontal trend is consistent with the chemical properties of elements. That is, nonmetals react by gaining electrons, and metals react by losing electrons. The vertical trend follows the trend in nonmetallic character. As an example, examine Group VA/15. We see that Bi is a metal, Sb and As are semimetals, and P and N are nonmetals. Therefore, the trend in electronegativity increases corresponding to the trend in nonmetallic character. That is, nonmetals are more electronegative than semimetals, which in turn are more electronegative than metals.

The following example exercise illustrates the prediction of electronegativity values from the general trends in the periodic table.

> ## Example Exercise 12.8 Electronegativity Predictions
>
> Predict which element in each of the following pairs is more electronegative according to the general electronegativity trends in the periodic table:
>
> (a) N or O   (b) Br or Se
> (c) F or Cl   (d) Si or C
>
> ### Solution
> According to the trends in the periodic table, elements that lie to the right in a series or at the top of a group are more electronegative.
>
> (a) O is more electronegative than N.
> (b) Br is more electronegative than Se.
> (c) F is more electronegative than Cl.
> (d) C is more electronegative than Si.
>
> ### Practice Exercise
> Predict which element in each of the following pairs is more electronegative according to the general trends in the periodic table:
>
> (a) H or Cl   (b) Br or I
> (c) P or S   (d) As or Sb
>
> ### Answers:
> (a) Cl   (b) Br
> (c) S   (d) As
>
> ### Concept Exercise
> State the general trends in the periodic table for increasing electronegativity.
>
> **Answer:** See Appendix G.

$\delta^+ \ \delta^-$

H—F

H—Cl

H—Br

H—I

▲ **Hydrogen Halides** The two atoms in each hydrogen halide molecule are joined by a polar covalent bond owing to the different electronegativity value of each halogen.

Delta Notation for Polar Bonds

In Section 12.1, we introduced the covalent bond. In Figure 12.9, we see that the electronegativity value of H is 2.1 and of Cl is 3.0. Because there is a difference in electronegativity between the two elements (3.0 − 2.1 = 0.9), the bond in a H—Cl molecule is polar. Moreover, Cl is the more electronegative element, so the bonding electron pair is attracted toward the Cl atom and away from the H atom. The Cl atom thus becomes slightly negatively charged, whereas the H atom becomes slightly positively charged.

We can indicate a polar bond with a special symbol, the Greek letter delta (δ). We indicate the atom having a partially negative charge by the symbol δ^-. Similarly, we indicate the atom having a partially positive charge by the symbol δ^+. These symbols, δ^- and δ^+, are referred to as **delta notation**. We can apply delta notation to illustrate the polar bond in a HCl molecule as follows:

$$\delta^+ \ \text{H—Cl} \ \delta^-$$

CHEMISTRY CONNECTION   Linus Pauling

Q. For which of his many accomplishments was Linus Pauling awarded the Nobel Prize in chemistry?

Linus Pauling (1901–1994) is regarded by many as the most influential chemist of the twentieth century. Pauling was born in Portland, Oregon, to a family of modest means. His father died when Linus was quite young, and he had to take on a series of menial jobs to help support the family. At age 16, he enrolled at Oregon State University where he received a bachelor's degree in chemical engineering. There he met his wife

and acknowledged inspiration, Ava Helen Miller, while teaching a chemistry class to home economics students.

Pauling decided on the California Institute of Technology for graduate school. In 1925, he received a Ph.D. and following graduation, was awarded a Guggenheim fellowship to study in Europe. In 1927, he returned to Caltech as a professor of chemistry and remained there for most of his career. Pauling received immediate recognition and was described by his department chairman in the following words:

> Were all the rest of the chemistry department wiped away except Pauling, it would still be one of the most important departments of chemistry in the world.

Among his many accomplishments, Linus Pauling invented the concept of electronegativity and provided an ingenious method for calculating the electronegativity values of elements. One of his most brilliant achievements was an explanation for the unusual stability of the benzene molecule, C_6H_6, which was discussed in Section 8.9. His most celebrated work was investigating the shapes of proteins. He found that their structures resembled a helix and further established the relationship between abnormal molecular structure and genetic disease. His work in this area earned him the 1954 Nobel Prize in chemistry.

In the 1960s, Pauling focused his energies on banning aboveground testing of nuclear weapons and pointed out the potential dangers of radiation. He spoke passionately against war and encouraged global disarmament. For his efforts, Pauling was awarded the 1962 Nobel Peace Prize. In the 1970s, he stirred controversy when he publicly advocated massive doses of vitamin C to combat the common cold. In addition to

two Nobel Prizes, Linus Pauling received numerous medals and awards, accepted honorary memberships in several scientific societies, published more than 400 research papers, and wrote the classic textbook *The Nature of the Chemical Bond.*

▲ **Linus Pauling (1901–1994)**

A: Linus Pauling won the 1954 Nobel Prize in chemistry for his pioneering work on the structure of proteins.

Because the chlorine atom is more electronegative, it draws the electron pair away from the hydrogen atom. As a result, the hydrogen atom becomes slightly positively charged. The following example exercise illustrates the application of delta notation.

Example Exercise 12.9 Delta Notation for Polar Bonds

Calculate the electronegativity difference and apply delta notation to the bond between carbon and oxygen, C—O.

Solution

From Figure 12.9, we find that the electronegativity value of C is 2.5 and of O is 3.5. By convention, we always subtract the lesser value from the greater. The difference between the two elements is $3.5 - 2.5 = 1.0$. The result shows that the C—O bond is slightly polarized.

Because O is the more electronegative element, the bonding electron pair is drawn away from the C atom and toward the O atom. The O atom thus becomes slightly negatively charged, whereas the C atom becomes slightly positively charged. Applying the delta convention, we have

$$\delta^+ \text{C}\text{—}\text{O} \, \delta^-$$

Practice Exercise

From the trends in the periodic table, apply delta notation and label each atom in the following polar covalent bonds:

(a) N—O

(b) Br—F

Answers:

(a) δ^+ N—O δ^-

(b) δ^+ Br—F δ^-

Concept Exercise

Refer to the electronegativity values in Figure 12.9 and predict which of the following bonds is most polar: H—N, H—O, or H—F.

Answer: See Appendix G.

Note Delta convention indicates partially negative and partially positive atoms in a molecule. However, polar bonds in molecules differ from ionic bonds in formula units. Ionic bonds are formed between negative anions and positive cations. An electronegativity difference between two atoms that is greater than 1.8 indicates an ionic bond. For example, NaCl has an electronegativity difference of 2.1 (3.0 − 0.9) and it is clearly an example of an ionic bond.

LEARNING OBJECTIVES

▶ To describe and identify a nonpolar covalent bond.

▶ To identify seven elements that occur naturally as diatomic molecules: H_2, N_2, O_2, F_2, Cl_2, Br_2, I_2.

12.7 NONPOLAR COVALENT BONDS

In Section 12.6, we learned that polar bonds result from the unequal sharing of bonding electrons. In a polar bond, one of the two atoms has a greater tendency to attract electrons. The atom having the greater electronegativity attracts the bonded electron pair more strongly and has a partial negative charge.

But what about a covalent bond in which each atom has the same or similar electronegativity? To answer this question, let's begin by reexamining the Pauling electronegativity values in Figure 12.9. We see that electronegativity increases across a period and up a group. Notice, however, that several elements have the same Pauling electronegativity value. For example, N and Cl have a value of 3.0, and C, S, and I all have a value of 2.5.

How then would we describe an S—I bond? The electronegativity of each atom is the same, so the bond is not polarized. A covalent bond between two atoms with the same electronegativity is referred to as a nonpolar covalent bond, or simply a **nonpolar bond**. The following example exercise illustrates the classification of polar and nonpolar bonds.

> **Example Exercise 12.10** Polar versus Nonpolar Bonds
>
> Classify each of the following as a polar or a nonpolar bond:
> (a) Cl—Cl (b) Cl—N
> (c) Cl—Br (d) Cl—H
>
> *Solution*
> From Figure 12.9 we find the following electronegativity values: Cl = 3.0, N = 3.0, Br = 2.8, and H = 2.1.
> (a) The Cl—Cl bond (3.0 − 3.0 = 0) is *nonpolar*.
> (b) The Cl—N bond (3.0 − 3.0 = 0) is *nonpolar*.
> (c) The Cl—Br bond (3.0 − 2.8 = 0.2) is slightly *polar*.
> (d) The Cl—H bond (3.0 − 2.1 = 0.9) is *polar*.
>
> **Practice Exercise**
> Classify each of the following as a polar or a nonpolar bond:
> (a) C—C (b) C—O
> (c) C—S (d) C—H
>
> **Answers:**
>
> (a) nonpolar (b) polar
> (c) nonpolar (d) slightly polar
>
> **Concept Exercise**
> Refer to the electronegativity values in Figure 12.9 and predict which of the following bonds is least polar: C—N, C—O, or C—I.
>
> **Answer:** See Appendix G.

Diatomic Nonpolar Molecules

A **diatomic molecule** consists of two nonmetal atoms joined by a covalent bond. The simplest example of a nonpolar bond is found between two identical atoms. For example, oxygen occurs naturally as a gas and contains O_2 molecules. Even though oxygen is quite electronegative, the bond in an O_2 molecule is nonpolar. This is because each oxygen atom attracts the electron pair with the same force.

In Section 5.3, we briefly studied the elements in Group VIIA/17. Recall that, collectively, these elements are called *halogens*. The halogens (F, Cl, Br, and I) are a family and have similar properties. All four elements occur naturally as diatomic molecules: F_2, Cl_2, Br_2, and I_2. Elemental fluorine is a yellowish-green gas, chlorine is a greenish-yellow gas, bromine is a reddish-brown liquid, and iodine is a dark-violet crystalline solid.

Seven elements exist naturally as diatomic molecules: H_2, N_2, O_2, F_2, Cl_2, Br_2, and I_2. Although each molecule is distinctly different, each exhibits a nonpolar covalent bond. For our discussion, we will classify a bond as nonpolar when there is no electronegativity difference between the two bonded atoms. In practice, a bond between two atoms having an electronegativity difference of 0.5 or less is usually considered a nonpolar bond.

F—F

Cl—Cl

Br—Br

I—I

▲ **Halogens** The two atoms in each halogen molecule are joined by a nonpolar covalent bond.

12.8 COORDINATE COVALENT BONDS

LEARNING OBJECTIVE

▶ To describe and identify a coordinate covalent bond.

We have described a covalent bond as an electron pair that is shared by two nonmetal atoms. Furthermore, each nonmetal atom is surrounded by nonbonding electron pairs to complete its octet.

Now, let's consider a special case of sharing electrons. An atom such as oxygen (six valence electrons) can attain an octet by sharing a nonbonding electron pair on another atom. A covalent bond resulting from one atom donating an electron pair to another atom is called a **coordinate covalent bond**. A good example of a coordinate covalent bond is found in a molecule of ozone, O_3. Here, an oxygen molecule donates a nonbonding electron pair to an oxygen atom to produce ozone.

$$:\!\ddot{O}::\!\ddot{O}: \; + \; \ddot{O}: \; \longrightarrow \; :\!\ddot{O}::\!\ddot{O}:\!\ddot{O}:$$

nonbonding electron pair   *coordinate covalent bond*

We can identify a coordinate covalent bond as follows. First, we draw the electron dot formula for the given molecule. If we can remove an atom and still have an octet around the remaining atoms, we know that the atom was joined by a coordinate covalent bond. The following example exercise further illustrates coordinate covalent bonds.

Example Exercise 12.11 Coordinate Covalent Bonds

Burning yellow sulfur powder produces sulfur dioxide, SO_2. Sulfur dioxide is a colorless gas with a suffocating odor. It is used to kill insect larvae and produces the odor released when a match is ignited. Draw the electron dot formula for SO_2. Then show the formation of a coordinate covalent bond in SO_3.

Solution

The total number of valence electrons in one molecule of SO_2 is $6\,e- + 2(6\,e-) = 18\,e-$. By trial and error, we find that the electron dot formula for SO_2 has a double bond. Because the sulfur atom has a nonbonding electron pair, it can bond to an additional oxygen atom. A diagram of the formation of the coordinate covalent bond is as follows:

$$:\overset{..}{O}:S: \; + \; \overset{..}{O}: \; \longrightarrow \; :\overset{..}{O}:S:\overset{..}{O}:$$

nonbonding electron pair   coordinate covalent bond

Practice Exercise

A nitrogen molecule can form a coordinate covalent bond with an oxygen atom to give nitrous oxide, N_2O. Draw the electron dot formula for a nitrogen molecule and attach an oxygen atom.

Answers:

(a) $:N:::N:$ (b) $:N:::N:\overset{..}{\underset{..}{O}}:$

Concept Exercise

Draw the electron dot formula for HClO and determine if the molecule contains a coordinate covalent bond.

Answer: See Appendix G.

▶ To describe hydrogen bond attraction between two molecules.

12.9 HYDROGEN BONDS

When a molecule has a polar covalent bond, it has a region that is positively charged, and a region that is negatively charged. This usually produces a molecule that has a positive end and a negative end. We can visualize this type of molecule as being similar to a miniature magnet. Like two magnets that are attracted to each other, two polar molecules are attracted to each other.

This attraction between two molecules can be significant, but is much less than the attraction between two atoms in a covalent bond. The bond length between molecules is considerably longer than the bond length between atoms in a polar bond. The most common example of this type of attraction is found between water molecules.

Recall that the bonds between H–O in water are highly polar because of the large electronegativity difference between the two elements. Thus, in a water molecule the oxygen atom is partially negative, and each hydrogen atom is partially positive. As a result, a H atom in one molecule of water is attracted to the nonbonding electron pair of the oxygen atom in another molecule of water. This intermolecular attraction between H and O in different molecules is referred to as a **hydrogen bond**.

Moreover, a hydrogen bond can result from the attraction of any two polar molecules having a hydrogen atom bonded to a highly electronegative atom (O, N, or F). Another example of hydrogen bonding occurs between ammonia molecules, NH_3. That is, the partially positive H atom in one ammonia molecule is attracted to the nonbonding electron pair of the electronegative nitrogen atom in a second molecule of ammonia.

Hydrogen bonds are especially important in living organisms where they are responsible for maintaining the structure of biochemical molecules (see Chapter 20). In large, complex biochemical molecules, hydrogen bonds are formed between H atoms and an electronegative atom (O or N) in the same molecule. In proteins, this can produce a single-stranded helix, whereas in DNA, hydrogen bonds are responsible for the double-stranded helix.

Hydrogen bonds

▲ **Hydrogen Bonding** This diagram shows hydrogen bonds between water molecules.

12.10 SHAPES OF MOLECULES

LEARNING OBJECTIVES

▸ To determine the shape of a molecule by applying VSEPR theory.

▸ To explain how a molecule with polar bonds can be nonpolar.

In the 1950s, a simple theory was proposed to explain the shapes of molecules. This theory is an extension of electron dot formulas in which pairs of electrons surround a central atom. In essence, the theory states that the electron pairs surrounding an atom tend to repel each other and that the shape of the molecule is the result of this electron pair repulsion. This model is referred to as the **valence shell electron pair repulsion (VSEPR,** pronounced "vesper") theory. The VSEPR model portrays bonding and nonbonding electron pairs as occupying specific positions around the central atom in a molecule.

The VSEPR theory uses the term **electron pair geometry** to indicate the arrangement of bonding and nonbonding electron pairs around the central atom. VSEPR theory uses the term *molecular geometry*, or **molecular shape**, to indicate the arrangement of atoms around the central atom as a result of electron pair repulsion. The angle formed by any two atoms bonded to the central atom is referred to as the **bond angle**.

Tetrahedral Molecules

Let's apply VSEPR theory to a methane molecule, CH_4, which has four pairs of bonding electrons. Electron pairs repel each other, so they try to get away from each other. The result is that in a molecule of CH_4, the central **C** atom is surrounded by four electron pairs that are repelled to the four corners of a three-dimensional figure called a *tetrahedron*. Each electron pair is bonded to a hydrogen atom, and so the shape of the molecule is said to be *tetrahedral*. Moreover, according to VSEPR theory, any molecule with four electron pairs around the central atom has a tetrahedral electron pair geometry.

▲ The electron pair geometry in methane, CH_4, is *tetrahedral*.

▲ The molecular shape of CH_4 is *tetrahedral*; the bond angle is 109.5°.

Trigonal Pyramidal Molecules

In a molecule of ammonia, NH_3, the central **N** atom is surrounded by three bonding electron pairs and one nonbonding electron pair. The electron pair geometry is once again tetrahedral, so ammonia should theoretically have bond angles of 109.5°. Experimentally, the bond angle in NH_3 is found to be 107°.

VSEPR theory explains the smaller bond angle by suggesting that the nonbonding electron pair exerts a stronger repelling force than the bonding pairs. Hence, the hydrogen atoms are pushed closer together, that is, from 109.5° to 107°. The molecular shape of NH_3 is said to be *trigonal pyramidal*.

▲ The electron pair geometry in ammonia, NH_3, is *tetrahedral*.

▲ The molecular shape of NH_3 is *trigonal pyramidal*; the bond angle is 107°.

Bent Molecules

In a molecule of water, H_2O, the central **O** atom is surrounded by two bonding electron pairs and two nonbonding electron pairs. Because the electron pair geometry is tetrahedral, the predicted bond angle between the two hydrogen atoms is 109.5°. The experimentally measured bond angle in H_2O is only 104.5°. As in the preceding example, it is proposed that the nonbonding electrons in water exert a greater repelling force than the bonding pairs. The resulting bond angle is smaller, allowing more space for the unshared electron pairs. The molecular shape of H_2O is said to be *bent* or V-shaped.

▲ The electron pair geometry in water, H_2O, is *tetrahedral*.

▲ The molecular shape of H_2O is *bent*; the bond angle is 104.5°.

Linear Molecules

In a molecule of carbon dioxide, CO_2, the central **C** atom is bonded to each O atom by two bonding electron pairs; that is, there is a double bond to each O atom (O=C=O). The four pairs of electrons are on opposite sides of the **C** atom, so the three atoms lie in a straight line. The electron pair geometry in CO_2 is said to be linear, and the predicted bond angle between the two oxygen atoms is 180°. Similarly, the molecular shape is said to be *linear*.

▲ The electron pair geometry in carbon dioxide, CO_2, is *linear*.

▲ The molecular shape of CO_2 is *linear*; the bond angle is 180°.

Trigonal Planar Molecules

In a molecule of formaldehyde, CH_2O, the central **C** atom is bonded to the O atom by a double bond (**C**=O), and to each H atom by a single bond. The bonding electron pairs repel one another, so the three atoms are found at the corners of a triangle. The electron pair geometry in CH_2O is said to be trigonal planar, and the predicted bond angle between the atoms is 120°. Similarly, the molecular shape is said to be *trigonal planar*.

▲ The electron pair geometry in formaldehyde, CH_2O, is *trigonal planar*.

▲ The molecular shape of CH_2O is *trigonal planar*; the bond angle is 120°.

We can summarize the information obtained from VSEPR theory about these types of molecules, as shown in Table 12.1.

TABLE 12.1 SUMMARY OF VSEPR THEORY

BONDING/NONBONDING ELECTRON PAIRS	ELECTRON PAIR GEOMETRY	MOLECULAR SHAPE	BOND ANGLE	EXAMPLE MOLECULE
4 / 0	tetrahedral	tetrahedral	109.5°	CH_4
3 / 1	tetrahedral	trigonal pyramidal	107°	NH_3
2 / 2	tetrahedral	bent	104.5°	H_2O
4 / 0	linear	linear	180°	CO_2
4 / 0	trigonal planar	trigonal planar	120°	CH_2O

Nonpolar Molecules with Polar Bonds

Why is carbon tetrachloride, CCl_4, a nonpolar molecule even though it has polar bonds? Recall that a chlorine atom is more electronegative than a carbon atom; hence, the C—Cl bond is polar. Furthermore, there are four C—Cl polar bonds in a CCl_4 molecule.

To explain why a CCl_4 molecule is nonpolar, we can apply VSEPR theory. There are four bonding electron pairs in CCl_4; thus, the electron pair geometry and the molecular shape are both tetrahedral. We illustrate the CCl_4 molecule as having four chlorine atoms at the corners of a tetrahedron.

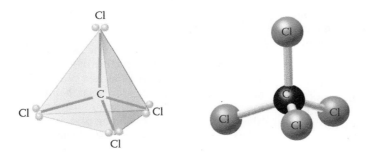

Note that each chlorine atom exerts equal attractive forces in four opposing directions. Thus, the attractions exerted by the four polar bonds cancel each other. The net effect of the polar bonds is zero, and overall, the molecule is considered nonpolar. We can illustrate that the CCl_4 molecule is nonpolar as follows:

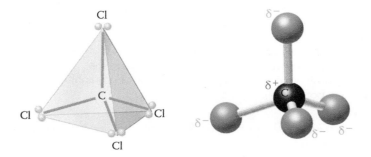

Consequently, a molecule may contain polar bonds and yet be nonpolar. In carbon dioxide, CO_2, there are two polar bonds. An O=C=O molecule is nonpolar because the more electronegative oxygen atoms pull equally in opposite directions.

On the other hand, formaldehyde, H_2C=O, is a polar molecule. The reason that formaldehyde is polar is that the H_2C=O molecule has only one oxygen atom and has a flat, triangular shape. The oxygen atom pulls electrons away from the central carbon atom and the two hydrogen atoms have little effect.

CRITICAL THINKING   Diamond versus Graphite

Q: How is it possible that a natural diamond and the graphite in a pencil are both examples of pure carbon?

▲ **Diamond—Tetrahedral Structure**

weight in becoming a finished diamond. Moreover, a misdirected blow by a diamond cutter can shatter the stone into small shards.

Diamond is a crystalline solid containing carbon atoms arranged in a three-dimensional network. Carbon atoms are bonded in a repeating tetrahedral structure as shown in the illustration. The more extensive the repeating network, the larger the actual diamond.

▲ **Graphite—Planar Structure**

Diamonds have been prized for centuries owing to their clarity and fiery sparkle. Diamonds originate deep within Earth, where they are formed under conditions of extreme heat and pressure. A diamond is the hardest known substance; its melting point is above 3500 °C, and it is inert to corrosive chemicals.

The hardness and crystalline structure of a diamond enables a rough stone to be cut so as to give numerous tiny facets. On average, an uncut stone loses 50% of its original

Like diamond, graphite is also a crystalline solid composed exclusively of carbon atoms. Unlike diamond, graphite is a soft substance that we know as the dark gray "lead" in an ordinary pencil. The structure of graphite consists of fused hexagon rings, each containing six carbon atoms. Unlike diamond, graphite is arranged in a flat, two-dimensional crystalline network. The lubricating property of graphite is due to "sheets" of carbons rings sliding past one another.

Diamonds can be synthesized from graphite by mimicking the conditions under which natural diamonds are formed. A sample of graphite is placed in a hydraulic press and converted to diamond in a few hours at high temperature and pressure. Typically, synthetic diamonds are only a few millimeters in size and are too flawed to be used as gemstones. However, synthetic diamonds are valuable industrially for use in coating drill bits and cutting tools.

◀ **Diamond and Graphite** A synthetic diamond made from powdered graphite is shown alongside the graphite in the tip of a pencil. Diamond and graphite are both examples of crystalline carbon.

A: Although diamond and graphite are both composed of pure carbon, the structure of diamond is a repeating tetrahedron, whereas the structure of graphite is a repeating hexagon.

Summary

LEARNING OBJECTIVES

LEARNING OBJECTIVES	SEC	EXERCISES
To explain how valence electrons create a chemical bond.	12.1	Exercises 1–4
To predict whether a bond is ionic or covalent.	12.1	Exercises 5–10
To describe the formation of an ionic bond between a metal atom and a nonmetal atom.	12.2	Exercises 11–28
To describe the formation of a covalent bond between two nonmetal atoms by sharing valence electrons.	12.3	Exercises 29–32
To draw the electron dot formula for a molecule.	12.4	Exercises 33–38
To draw the structural formula for a molecule.	12.4	Exercises 33–38
To draw the electron dot formula for a polyatomic ion.	12.5	Exercises 39–44
To draw the structural formula for a polyatomic ion.	12.5	Exercises 39–44
To state the electronegativity trends in the periodic table.	12.6	Exercises 45–50
To calculate the electronegativity difference in a polar covalent bond.	12.6	Exercises 51–52
To apply delta notation ($\delta+$ and $\delta-$) to a polar bond.	12.6	Exercises 53–54
To describe and identify a nonpolar covalent bond.	12.7	Exercises 55–56
To identify seven elements that occur naturally as diatomic molecules: H_2, N_2, O_2, F_2, Cl_2, Br_2, I_2.	12.7	Exercises 57–58
To describe and identify a coordinate covalent bond.	12.8	Exercises 59–66
To describe hydrogen bond attraction between two molecules.	12.9	Exercises 67–70
To determine the shape of a molecule by applying VSEPR theory.	12.10	Exercises 71–76
To explain how a molecule with polar bonds can be nonpolar.	12.10	Exercises 77–78

Section 12.1 G. N. Lewis first described the **chemical bond** when he proposed that **valence electrons** in different atoms interact in such a way that each atom completes its valence shell. Because eight electrons are found in the valence shells of noble gas atoms, the Lewis theory became known as the *rule of eight*, or more commonly, the **octet rule**.

The simplest representative particle in a substance held together by ionic bonds is a **formula unit**. When a metal atom loses valence electrons as a nonmetal atom gains electrons, an **ionic bond** results. The simplest representative particle held together by covalent bonds is a **molecule**. When valence electrons are shared by two nonmetal atoms, a **covalent bond** results.

Section 12.2 While forming ions, metal atoms lose valence electrons and are often left with a noble gas structure. Non-metal atoms gain electrons to complete their valence shells. In the process of forming ions, the radii of metal atoms become smaller while the radii of nonmetal atoms become larger. The formation of ionic bonds between metal and nonmetal ions always releases heat energy.

Section 12.3 In the formation of covalent bonds, the outer valence shells of two nonmetal atoms overlap and share electrons. Each of the atoms in the bond shares the number of electrons necessary to complete their individual octets. The **bond length** between the two atoms is always less than the sum of their atomic radii. When atoms of different elements bond, energy is always released. The amount of energy released during the formation of a bond is exactly equal to the

amount of energy required to break that bond. The amount of energy required to break a covalent bond between two atoms is called the **bond energy**.

Section 12.4 To write an **electron dot formula**, we first calculate the total number of valence electrons from all of the atoms in the molecule. We then divide the valence electron total by two to find the number of electron pairs. The electron pairs are placed around the central atom and then the remaining atoms in the molecule so as to provide octets. One pair of electrons shared by two atoms is a **single bond**. A molecule can also contain two or three electron pairs between two atoms. These bonds are referred to as a **double bond** and a **triple bond**, respectively.

Double and triple bonds result from an insufficient number of valence electrons around an atom in a molecule. To provide an octet, it may be necessary to move **nonbonding electrons** between two atoms; these electrons then become **bonding electrons**. In the **structural formula** of a molecule, a single bond is shown as a dash, a double bond as two dashes, and a triple bond as three dashes.

Section 12.5 An ionic bond can be formed by the attraction between a simple **monoatomic ion** and a complex **polyatomic ion**. Ammonium chloride, NH_4Cl, and cupric sulfate, $CuSO_4$, each contain a polyatomic ion. To draw the electron dot formula for a polyatomic ion, we must find the total number of valence electrons for each atom and then add or subtract the number of electrons equal to its ionic charge. For the ammonium cation, NH_4^+, the total number of valence electrons is 8 (9 e− minus 1 e−). For the sulfate ion, $SO_4{}^{2-}$, the total number of valence electrons is 32 e− (30 e− plus 2 e−).

Section 12.6 If one atom in a bond attracts electrons more strongly than the other, that atom is said to have a higher **electronegativity**. A **polar bond** results when one of the bonded atoms has a greater attraction for the electron pair. We can indicate a polar bond using **delta notation**: the more electronegative atom is labeled δ^- and the less electronegative atom is labeled δ^+.

Section 12.7 If each atom in a bond has an equal attraction for bonding electrons, the bond is said to be a **nonpolar bond**. A nonpolar bond always occurs in a **diatomic molecule** having two identical atoms: the bonds in naturally occurring H_2, N_2, O_2, F_2, Cl_2, Br_2, and I_2 are nonpolar bonds.

Section 12.8 A **coordinate covalent bond** is a special type of covalent bond and is formed when one atom donates an electron pair to another atom. A simple illustration of a coordinate covalent bond occurs when the chlorine atom in HCl donates an electron pair to an oxygen atom to give HClO.

Section 12.9 A **hydrogen bond** usually refers to the attraction between a hydrogen atom in one molecule, and a nonbonding electron pair on a highly electronegative atom (O or N) in a second molecule. For example, this attraction occurs between water molecules, when the partially positive H atom in one molecule attracts the unshared electron pair on the electronegative O atom in another molecule.

Section 12.10 After writing the electron dot formula for a molecule, we can draw its shape. That is, we can predict the shape of a molecule by applying valence shell electron pair repulsion (VSEPR) theory. According to **VSEPR theory**, bonding and nonbonding electron pairs surround the central atom. The arrangement of electron pairs around the central atom is termed **electron pair geometry**, and the arrangement of atoms is termed **molecular shape**. The angle formed by two atoms bonded to the central atom is referred to as the **bond angle**.

If there are four electron pairs around the central atom, they are located at the corners of a three-dimensional figure called a *tetrahedron*. Examples of molecules having four electron pairs around the central atom include methane, CH_4, ammonia, NH_3, and water, H_2O. In each of these examples, the electron pair geometry is said to be *tetrahedral*.

Key Terms *Answers to Key Terms are in Appendix H.*

Select the key term that corresponds to each of the following definitions.

_____ 1. the attraction between positive and negative ions, or two nonmetal atoms

_____ 2. the electrons in the outermost *s* and *p* sublevels of an atom that undergo reaction and form chemical bonds

_____ 3. the statement that an atom tends to bond in such a way so as to acquire eight valence electrons

_____ 4. a bond resulting from the attraction between a positively charged cation and a negatively charged anion

_____ 5. a bond resulting from the sharing of one or more pairs of valence electrons between two nonmetal atoms

_____ 6. the simplest representative particle in a substance held together by ionic bonds

_____ 7. the simplest representative particle in a substance held together by covalent bonds

_____ 8. the distance between the nuclei of two atoms joined by a covalent bond

_____ 9. the amount of energy required to break a covalent bond between two atoms

_____ 10. the valence electrons in a molecule that are shared

_____ 11. the valence electrons in a molecule that are not shared

_____ 12. a diagram of a molecule that shows the chemical symbol of each atom and a dot representing each bonding and nonbonding electron

_____ 13. a diagram of a molecule that shows the chemical symbol of each atom and a dash representing each pair of bonding electrons

_____ 14. a bond composed of one electron pair shared by two atoms

_____ 15. a bond composed of two electron pairs shared by two atoms

_____ 16. a bond composed of three electron pairs shared by two atoms

_____ 17. a single atom that bears a negative or positive charge as the result of gaining or losing valence electrons

(a) bond angle (*Sec. 12.10*)
(b) bond energy (*Sec. 12.3*)
(c) bond length (*Sec. 12.3*)
(d) bonding electrons (*Sec. 12.4*)
(e) chemical bond (*Sec. 12.1*)
(f) coordinate covalent bond (*Sec. 12.8*)
(g) covalent bond (*Sec. 12.1*)
(h) delta (δ) notation (*Sec. 12.6*)
(i) diatomic molecule (*Sec. 12.7*)
(j) double bond (*Sec. 12.4*)
(k) electron dot formula (*Sec. 12.4*)
(l) electron pair geometry (*Sec. 12.10*)
(m) electronegativity (*Sec. 12.6*)
(n) formula unit (*Sec. 12.1*)
(o) hydrogen bond (*Sec. 12.9*)
(p) ionic bond (*Sec. 12.1*)
(q) molecular shape (*Sec. 12.10*)
(r) molecule (*Sec. 12.1*)
(s) monoatomic ion (*Sec. 12.5*)
(t) nonbonding electrons (*Sec. 12.4*)

_____ **18.** a group of atoms held together by covalent bonds and having an overall positive or negative charge

_____ **19.** the ability of an atom to attract a shared pair of electrons

_____ **20.** a method of indicating a partial positive and a partial negative charge in a chemical bond

_____ **21.** a bond in which a pair of electrons is shared unequally

_____ **22.** a bond in which a pair of electrons is shared equally

_____ **23.** a molecule composed of two nonmetal atoms held together by a covalent bond

_____ **24.** a bond in which an electron pair is shared but both electrons have been donated by a single atom

_____ **25.** the attraction between a H atom bonded to O or N, and a nonbonding electron pair on an electronegative atom in another molecule

_____ **26.** a model that explains the shapes of molecules as a result of electron pairs about the central atom repelling each other

_____ **27.** the geometric shape formed by bonding and nonbonding electron pairs about the central atom in a molecule

_____ **28.** the geometric shape formed by atoms bonded to the central atom in a molecule

_____ **29.** the angle formed by two atoms attached to the central atom in a molecule

(u) nonpolar bond (_Sec. 12.7_)

(v) octet rule (_Sec. 12.1_)

(w) polar bond (_Sec. 12.6_)

(x) polyatomic ion (_Sec. 12.5_)

(y) single bond (_Sec. 12.4_)

(z) structural formula (_Sec. 12.4_)

(aa) triple bond (_Sec. 12.4_)

(bb) valence electrons (_Sec. 12.1_)

(cc) VSEPR theory (_Sec. 12.10_)

Exercises _Answers to odd-numbered Exercises are in Appendix I._

The Chemical Bond Concept (Sec. 12.1)

1. State the number of valence electrons for a lithium atom and a chlorine atom.

2. State the number of valence electrons for a hydrogen atom and a bromine atom.

3. State the number of valence electrons for a lithium ion and an chloride ion in an ionic bond.

4. State the number of valence electrons for a hydrogen atom and a bromine atom in a covalent bond.

5. Predict whether each of the following is held together by ionic or covalent bonds:
   (a) aluminum chloride, $AlCl_3$ **(b)** water, H_2O
   (c) sulfur trioxide, SO_3 **(d)** iron(II) sulfate, $FeSO_4$

6. Predict whether each of the following is held together by ionic or covalent bonds:
   (a) zinc bromide, $ZnBr_2$ **(b)** carbon dioxide, CO_2
   (c) iodine heptafluoride, IF_7 **(d)** lead(II) sulfate, $PbSO_4$

7. State whether the representative particle in each of the following substances is a formula unit or a molecule:
   (a) acetic acid, $HC_2H_3O_2$ **(b)** chlorine dioxide, ClO_2
   (c) sodium chlorate, $NaClO_3$ **(d)** titanium(IV) oxide, TiO_2

8. State whether the representative particle in each of the following substances is a formula unit or a molecule:
   (a) methanol, CH_3OH **(b)** cobaltous chloride, $CoCl_2$
   (c) acetone, CH_3COCH_3 **(d)** stannous carbonate, $SnCO_3$

9. State whether the representative particle in each of the following substances is an atom, a formula unit, or a molecule:
   (a) propane, C_3H_8 **(b)** platinum, Pt
   (c) hematite, Fe_2O_3 **(d)** sulfur, S_8

10. State whether the representative particle in each of the following substances is an atom, a formula unit, or a molecule:
    (a) xenon, Xe   **(b)** phosphorus, P_4
    (c) xenon trioxide, XeO_3 **(d)** magnetite, Fe_3O_4

Ionic Bonds (Sec. 12.2)

11. Use the periodic table to predict an ionic charge for each of the following metal ions:
    (a) Na ion   **(b)** Ba ion
    (c) Ga ion   **(d)** Sn ion

12. Use the periodic table to predict an ionic charge for each of the following metal ions:
    (a) Li ion   **(b)** Sr ion
    (c) Al ion   **(d)** Pb ion

13. Use the periodic table to predict the ionic charge for each of the following nonmetal ions:
    (a) F ion   **(b)** Br ion
    (c) Se ion   **(d)** N ion

14. Use the periodic table to predict the ionic charge for each of the following nonmetal ions:
    (a) Cl ion   **(b)** I ion
    (c) S ion   **(d)** P ion

15. Write out the electron configuration for each of the following metal ions:
    (a) Li^+ **(b)** Al^{3+}
    (c) Ca^{2+} **(d)** Mg^{2+}

16. Write out the electron configuration for each of the following metal ions:
    (a) Sc^{3+} **(b)** K^+
    (c) Ti^{4+} **(d)** Ba^{2+}

17. Write out the electron configuration for each of the following nonmetal ions:
    (a) Cl^- **(b)** I^-
    (c) S^{2-} **(d)** P^{3-}

18. Write out the electron configuration for each of the following nonmetal ions:
    (a) Br^-
    (b) O^{2-}
    (c) Se^{2-}
    (d) N^{3-}

19. Refer to the periodic table and state the noble gas with an electron configuration identical to each of the following ions:
    (a) S^{2-}
    (b) Cl^-
    (c) K^+
    (d) Ca^{2+}

20. Refer to the periodic table and state the noble gas with an electron configuration identical to each of the following ions:
    (a) Se^{2-}
    (b) Br^-
    (c) Rb^+
    (d) Sr^{2+}

21. Which noble gas is isoelectronic with each of the following metal ions?
    (a) Li^+
    (b) Al^{3+}
    (c) Ca^{2+}
    (d) Mg^{2+}

22. Which noble gas is isoelectronic with each of the following metal ions?
    (a) Sc^{3+}
    (b) K^+
    (c) Ti^{4+}
    (d) Ba^{2+}

23. Which noble gas is isoelectronic with each of the following nonmetal ions?
    (a) Cl^-
    (b) I^-
    (c) S^{2-}
    (d) P^{3-}

24. Which noble gas is isoelectronic with each of the following nonmetal ions?
    (a) Br^-
    (b) O^{2-}
    (c) Se^{2-}
    (d) N^{3-}

25. In each of the following pairs, which has the larger radius?
    (a) Li atom or Li ion
    (b) Mg atom or Mg ion
    (c) F atom or F ion
    (d) O atom or O ion

26. In each of the following pairs, which has the larger radius?
    (a) Al atom or Al ion
    (b) Pb atom or Pb ion
    (c) Se atom or Se ion
    (d) N atom or N ion

27. Which of the following statements are true regarding an ionic bond between cobalt and sulfur in a CoS formula unit?
    (a) Cobalt and sulfide ions bond by electrostatic attraction.
    (b) Cobalt atoms gain electrons and sulfur atoms lose electrons.
    (c) The ionic radius of a cobalt ion is greater than its atomic radius.
    (d) Breaking an ionic bond between cobalt and sulfur requires energy.

28. Which of the following statements are true regarding an ionic bond between aluminum and nitrogen in an AlN formula unit?
    (a) Aluminum and nitride ions bond by covalent attraction.
    (b) Aluminum atoms lose electrons and nitrogen atoms gain electrons.
    (c) The ionic radius of an aluminum ion is less than its atomic radius.
    (d) Breaking an ionic bond between aluminum and nitrogen releases energy.

Covalent Bonds (Sec. 12.3)

29. Which of the following is less?
    (a) the sum of the H and Cl atomic radii, or the bond length in H—Cl
    (b) the sum of the O and O atomic radii, or the bond length in O=O

30. Which of the following is less?
    (a) the sum of the H and Br atomic radii, or the bond length in H—Br
    (b) the sum of the S and O atomic radii, or the bond length in S=O

31. Which of the following statements are true regarding a covalent bond between nitrogen and oxygen atoms in a nitric oxide, NO, molecule?
    (a) Valence electrons are shared between nitrogen and oxygen atoms.
    (b) Bonding electrons are found only between the bonded atoms.
    (c) The bond length is greater than the sum of the two atomic radii.
    (d) Energy is required to break a covalent bond.

32. Which of the following statements are true regarding a covalent bond between carbon and oxygen atoms in a carbon monoxide, CO, molecule?
    (a) Valence electrons are transferred from carbon to oxygen atoms.
    (b) Bonding electrons are distributed over the entire CO molecule.
    (c) The bond length is less than the sum of the two atomic radii.
    (d) Energy is released when a covalent bond is broken.

Electron Dot Formulas of Molecules (Sec. 12.4)

33. Write the electron dot formula and draw the structural formula for each of the following molecules. (*The central atom is indicated in* **bold**.)
    (a) H_2
    (b) F_2
    (c) H**Br**
    (d) **N**H_3

34. Write the electron dot formula and draw the structural formula for each of the following molecules:
    (a) Cl_2
    (b) O_2
    (c) HI
    (d) PH_3

35. Write the electron dot formula and draw the structural formula for each of the following molecules:
    (a) HONO
    (b) SO_2
    (c) C_2H_4
    (d) C_2H_2

36. Write the electron dot formula and draw the structural formula for each of the following molecules:
    (a) N_2
    (b) PI_3
    (c) CS_2
    (d) HOCl

37. Write the electron dot formula and draw the structural formula for each of the following molecules:
    (a) CH_4
    (b) OF_2
    (c) H_2O_2
    (d) NF_3

38. Write the electron dot formula and draw the structural formula for each of the following molecules:
    (a) CCl_4
    (b) $HONO_2$
    (c) CH_3OH
    (d) HOCN

Electron Dot Formulas of Polyatomic Ions (Sec. 12.5)

39. Write the electron dot formula and draw the structural formula for each of the following polyatomic ions. (*Central atoms are indicated in* **bold**.)
    (a) BrO^-
    (b) BrO_2^-
    (c) BrO_3^-
    (d) BrO_4^-

40. Write the electron dot formula and draw the structural formula for each of the following polyatomic ions:
(a) IO^- (b) IO_2^-
(c) IO_3^- (d) IO_4^-

41. Write the electron dot formula and draw the structural formula for each of the following polyatomic ions:
(a) SO_4^{2-} (b) HSO_4^-
(c) SO_3^{2-} (d) HSO_3^-

42. Write the electron dot formula and draw the structural formula for each of the following polyatomic ions:
(a) PO_4^{3-} (b) HPO_4^{2-}
(c) PO_3^{3-} (d) HPO_3^{2-}

43. Write the electron dot formula and draw the structural formula for each of the following polyatomic ions:
(a) H_3O^+ (b) OH^-
(c) HS^- (d) CN^-

44. Write the electron dot formula and draw the structural formula for each of the following polyatomic ions:
(a) PH_4^+ (b) SeO_3^{2-}
(c) CO_3^{2-} (d) BO_3^{3-}

Polar Covalent Bonds (Sec. 12.6)

45. What is the general trend in electronegativity within a group of elements in the periodic table?

46. What is the general trend in electronegativity within a period of elements in the periodic table?

47. Which elements are more electronegative: metals or nonmetals?

48. Which elements are more electronegative: semimetals or nonmetals?

49. Predict which element in each of the following pairs is more electronegative according to the general trends in the periodic table:
(a) Br or Cl   (b) O or S
(c) Se or As   (d) N or F

50. Predict which element in each of the following pairs is more electronegative according to the general trends in the periodic table:
(a) Se or Br   (b) C or B
(c) Te or S   (d) Ba or Be

51. Refer to the values in Figure 12.9 and calculate the electronegativity difference in each of the following bonds:
(a) Br—Cl   (b) Br—F
(c) I—Cl   (d) I—Br

52. Refer to the values in Figure 12.9 and calculate the electronegativity difference in each of the following bonds:
(a) H—Cl   (b) H—Br
(c) N—O   (d) C—O

53. Refer to Figure 12.9 and label each atom in the following polar covalent bonds using delta notation (δ^+ and δ^-):
(a) H—S   (b) O—S
(c) N—F   (d) S—Cl

54. Refer to Figure 12.9 and label each atom in the following polar covalent bonds using delta notation:
(a) C—H   (b) Se—O
(c) P—I   (d) H—Br

Nonpolar Covalent Bonds (Sec. 12.7)

55. Refer to Figure 12.9 and indicate which of the following are nonpolar covalent bonds:
(a) Cl—Cl   (b) Cl—N
(c) N—H   (d) H—P

56. Refer to Figure 12.9 and indicate which of the following are nonpolar covalent bonds:
(a) I—C   (b) C—S
(c) S—H   (d) H—Br

57. Which of the following elements occur naturally as diatomic molecules: H, N, Cl, Br, Ar?

58. Which of the following elements occur naturally as diatomic molecules: He, O, F, I, Ne?

Coordinate Covalent Bonds (Sec. 12.8)

59. An oxygen atom can bond to a hydrogen bromide molecule to give HBrO. Draw the electron dot formula for **HBrO** and label a coordinate covalent bond.

60. An oxygen atom can bond to a hydrogen iodide molecule to give HIO. Draw the electron dot formula for **HIO** and label a coordinate covalent bond.

61. An oxygen atom can bond to a HBrO molecule to give HBrO₂. Draw the electron dot formula for **HBrO$_2$** and label a coordinate covalent bond.

62. An oxygen atom can bond to a HIO molecule to give HIO₂. Draw the electron dot formula for **HIO$_2$** and label a coordinate covalent bond.

63. A hydrogen ion can bond to an ammonia molecule, NH_3, forming NH_4^+. Draw the electron dot formula for **NH$_4^+$** and label a coordinate covalent bond.

64. A hydrogen ion can bond to a phosphine molecule, PH_3, forming PH_4^+. Draw the electron dot formula for **PH$_4^+$** and label a coordinate covalent bond.

65. A nitrite ion, NO_2^-, can bond to an oxygen atom to form the nitrate ion. Draw the electron dot formula for **NO$_3^-$** and label a coordinate covalent bond.

66. A phosphite ion, PO_3^{3-}, can bond to an oxygen atom to form the phosphate ion. Draw the electron dot formula for **PO$_4^{3-}$** and label a coordinate covalent bond.

Hydrogen Bonds (Sec. 12.9)

67. Diagram and label the hydrogen bond between two molecules of ammonia, NH_3.

68. Diagram and label the hydrogen bond between two molecules of hydrogen fluoride, HF.

69. Which is greater, the energy to break a hydrogen bond or a polar covalent bond?

70. Which is longer, the length of a hydrogen bond or a polar covalent bond?

Shapes of Molecules (Sec. 12.10)

71. Predict the electron pair geometry, the molecular shape, and the bond angle for a silane molecule, **SiH$_4$**, using VSEPR theory.

72. Predict the electron pair geometry, the molecular shape, and the bond angle for a carbon tetrabromide molecule, **CBr$_4$**, using VSEPR theory.

73. Predict the electron pair geometry, the molecular shape, and the bond angle for a nitrogen triiodide molecule, **NI$_3$**, using VSEPR theory.

74. Predict the electron pair geometry, the molecular shape, and the bond angle for a phosphine molecule, **PH$_3$**, using VSEPR theory.

75. Predict the electron pair geometry, the molecular shape, and the bond angle for a hydrogen sulfide molecule, H_2S, using VSEPR theory.

76. Predict the electron pair geometry, the molecular shape, and the bond angle for a dichlorine monoxide molecule, Cl_2O, using VSEPR theory.

77. Apply VSEPR theory to explain why **CO_2** is a nonpolar molecule even though it has two polar bonds.

78. Apply VSEPR theory to explain why **CF_4** is a nonpolar molecule even though it has four polar bonds.

General Exercises

79. State whether the representative particle in each of the following substances is an atom, a molecule, or a formula unit:
    (a) uranium, U
    (b) fluorine, F_2
    (c) uranium hexafluoride, UF_6
    (d) hydrogen fluoride, HF

80. State whether the representative particle in each of the following substances is an atom, a molecule, or a formula unit:
    (a) plutonium, Pu
    (b) oxygen, O_2
    (c) plutonium(III) oxide, Pu_2O_3
    (d) hydrogen peroxide, H_2O_2

81. Write formula units by combining the cations and anions in each of the following pairs:
    (a) Sr^{2+} and As^{3-} (b) Ra^{2+} and O^{2-}
    (c) Al^{3+} and CO_3^{2-} (d) Cd^{2+} and OH^-

82. Write formula units by combining the cations and anions in each of the following pairs:
    (a) Sc^{3+} and N^{3-} (b) Ti^{4+} and O^{2-}
    (c) NH_4^+ and CO_3^{2-} (d) Hg_2^{2+} and PO_4^{3-}

83. Explain why the radius of a sodium ion (0.095 nm) is about half that of a sodium atom (0.186 nm).

84. Explain why the radius of a chloride ion (0.181 nm) is about twice that of a chlorine atom (0.099 nm).

85. Refer to the values in Figure 12.9 and calculate the electronegativity difference in a B—Cl bond.

86. Refer to the values in Figure 12.9 and calculate the electronegativity difference in a Sb—Cl bond.

87. Refer to the values in Figure 12.9 and calculate the electronegativity difference in a H—P bond.

88. Refer to the values in Figure 12.9 and calculate the electronegativity difference in a S—I bond.

89. Label the polar Ge—Cl bond using delta notation (δ^+ and δ^-).

90. Label the polar As—Cl bond using delta notation (δ^+ and δ^-).

91. Write the electron dot formula and draw the structural formula for silane, **SiH_4**, whose central atom is a semimetal.

92. Write the electron dot formula and draw the structural formula for stibine, **SbH_3**, whose central atom is a semimetal.

93. Write the electron dot formula and draw the structural formula for the arsenate ion, **AsO_3^{3-}**, whose central atom is a semimetal.

94. Write the electron dot formula and draw the structural formula for the silicate ion, **SiO_3^{2-}**, whose central atom is a semimetal.

95. Predict the electron pair geometry, the molecular shape, and the bond angle for a carbon disulfide molecule, **CS_2**, using VSEPR theory.

96. Predict the electron pair geometry, the molecular shape, and the bond angle for a silicon dioxide molecule, **SiO_2**, using VSEPR theory.

97. Predict the electron pair geometry, the molecular shape, and the bond angle for a phosgene molecule, **CCl_2O**, using VSEPR theory.

98. Predict the electron pair geometry, the molecular shape, and the bond angle for a carbonate ion, **CO_3^{2-}**, using VSEPR theory.

Challenge Exercises

99. Xenon dioxide is a slightly stable molecule that contains a noble gas. Write the electron dot formula and draw the structural formula for **XeO_2**.

100. Xenon trioxide is a slightly stable molecule that contains a noble gas. Write the electron dot formula and draw the structural formula for **XeO_3**.

Online Exercises

Research each of the following using an Internet search engine (e.g., Google.com or Yahoo.com) and cite your URL reference.

101. In an ice crystal, how many hydrogen bonds exist between each water molecule and the surrounding water molecules?

102. In addition to water and ammonia, what small diatomic molecule forms strong hydrogen bonds?

103. In a DNA molecule, the double helix is held together by hydrogen bonds. How many hydrogen bonds are between a guanine (G) base and a cytosine (C) base in DNA?

104. In a DNA molecule, the double helix is held together by hydrogen bonds. How many hydrogen bonds are between an adenine (A) base and a thymine (T) base in DNA?

12 Chapter Self-Test

Answers to Self-Test are in Appendix J.

1. Predict which of the following has a covalent bond. (Sec. 12.1)
   (a) CaO   (b) CoO
   (c) CO   (d) all of the above
   (e) none of the above

2. Which of the following statements is true regarding an ionic bond between calcium and oxygen in a CaO formula unit? (Sec. 12.2)
   (a) Calcium atoms lose electrons and oxygen atoms gain electrons.
   (b) The ionic radius of a calcium ion is less than its atomic radius.
   (c) Forming an ionic bond between Ca^{2+} and O^{2-} releases energy.
   (d) all of the above
   (e) none of the above

3. Which of the following statements is true regarding a covalent bond between hydrogen and oxygen atoms in an H_2O molecule? (Sec. 12.3)
   (a) Bonding electrons are stationary between the H and O atoms.
   (b) The bond length is greater than the sum of the two atomic radii.
   (c) Forming a bond between H and O atoms requires energy.
   (d) all of the above
   (e) none of the above

4. Draw the electron dot formula for hydrogen peroxide, H_2O_2. How many nonbonding electron pairs are in a hydrogen peroxide molecule? (Sec. 12.4)
   (a) 1   (b) 2
   (c) 3   (d) 4
   (e) none of the above

5. Draw the electron dot formula for the carbonate ion, $CO_3{}^{2-}$. How many nonbonding electron pairs are in a carbonate ion? (Sec. 12.5)
   (a) 4   (b) 8
   (c) 12   (d) 24
   (e) none of the above

6. Which of the following shows a general increasing trend for electronegativity in the periodic table? (Sec. 12.6)
   (a) up a group of metals
   (b) up a group of nonmetals
   (c) across a series of metals from left to right
   (d) across a series of nonmetals from left to right
   (e) all of the above

7. Given the values for H (2.1) and F (4.0), calculate the electronegativity difference in a hydrogen fluoride bond, HF. (Sec. 12.7)
   (a) −1.9   (b) −6.1
   (c) 1.9   (d) 6.1
   (e) none of the above

8. Chlorine has an electronegativity value of 3.0. Given the electronegativity of C, N, O, and P (2.5, 3.0, and 3.5, respectively), which of the following molecules has nonpolar bonds? (Sec. 12.8)
   (a) CCl_4 (b) NCl_3
   (c) Cl_2O (d) all of the above
   (e) none of the above

9. What is the electron pair geometry for a molecule of H_2S? (Sec. 12.9)
   (a) bent   (b) linear
   (c) tetrahedral   (d) trigonal pyramidal
   (e) none of the above

10. What is the molecular shape for a molecule of H_2S? (*Sec.* 12.10)
    (a) bent   (b) linear
    (c) tetrahedral   (d) trigonal pyramidal
    (e) none of the above

Key Concepts

11. Classify each of the following diagrams as illustrating a substance composed of atoms, formula units, or molecules:

(a)

(b)

(c)

12. Based on electronegativity trends in the periodic table, which of the following molecules is most polar: HF, HCl, HBr, or HI?

13. Given a H_2O molecule, how many additional H_2O molecules can attach directly to the given water molecule by hydrogen bonds?

Critical Thinking

15. "Acid rain" originates with the sulfur dioxide produced from coal-burning plants. Draw the structural formulas for two resonance structures of SO_2. Given that the bond energy of a double bond is greater than a single bond, predict the stronger bond in an SO_2 molecule.

14. Using VSEPR theory, predict the electron pair geometry and molecular shape for a chloroform molecule, $CHCl_3$.

16. Using VSEPR theory, contrast the molecular shape of a water molecule, H_2O, with that of a hydronium ion, H_3O^+.

17. Using VSEPR theory, contrast the molecular shape of an ammonia molecule, NH_3, with that of an ammonium ion, NH_4^+.

Acids and Bases

Iodine in the Environment Iodine is a violet solid that undergoes sublimation (outer test tube) to give a purple vapor; and undergoes deposition (inner test tube) to give solid iodine crystals. Elemental iodine, I_2, is not found in the environment, but iodide salts are common in ocean kelp and algae. Potassium iodide is added to table salt as a source of iodine, which is required by the thyroid gland. Iodine deficiency is common in developing countries, which can lead to anemia and mental retardation.

"Many of life's failures are people who did not realize how close they were to success when they gave up."
Thomas Alva Edison, Inventor and Scientist (1847–1931)

Acids and bases play an important role in our lives. The proper acidity of our blood and other body fluids is vital to our well-being and is carefully controlled by an elaborate buffering system. Many of the foods we eat are acidic. For instance, oranges and lemons contain citric acid, and vinegar is a solution of acetic acid. Vitamin C is ascorbic acid, and aspirin is acetylsalicylic acid. We add muriatic acid to our swimming pools and sulfuric acid to our car batteries.

Acids and bases neutralize each other. Baking soda and milk of magnesia are basic. Antacid tablets contain basic substances such as carbonates, bicarbonates, and hydroxides for neutralizing an acidic, upset stomach. We use a dilute solution of basic ammonia to clean floors and a concentrated solution of sodium hydroxide to clean drains and ovens.

14.1 PROPERTIES OF ACIDS AND BASES

An *acid* is any substance that releases hydrogen ions, H^+, in water. This property of acids allows us to test for acidity. In the laboratory we can determine if a solution is acidic using a strip of litmus paper. Litmus paper turns red in the presence of hydrogen ions. Therefore, if we put a piece of litmus paper in a solution and the paper turns red, we know the solution is an acid. For example, litmus paper in lemon juice turns red because lemon juice is acidic.

Litmus paper is made from a plant pigment that is sensitive to changes in acid concentration. The colors of many plants are affected by the acidity of the soil in which they are grown. For example, the color of an orchid can vary from pale lavender to deep purple depending upon the acidity of the soil. The color of a rose fades from red to pink when the rose is placed in an acid solution.

Acids have their own special properties. One property is that they have a sour taste. The tart taste of a lemon, an apple, or vinegar shows us that these are acidic foods. The taste buds that are sensitive to acids are located along the edge of our tongue, which is why we roll our tongue when we taste something that is sour.

A *base* is any substance that releases hydroxide ions, OH^-, in water. Bases also have special properties. For instance, they feel slippery or soapy to the touch and have a bitter taste. The bitter taste of milk of magnesia shows us that it is a basic substance. The taste buds that are sensitive to bases are located on the tongue toward the back of our throat, and we often react by sticking out our tongue when we taste something that is bitter.

▲ **Litmus Paper** Litmus paper dipped in a basic solution turns blue (left). Litmus paper dipped in an acidic solution turns red (right).

We can use litmus paper to determine if a solution is basic. Litmus paper turns blue in the presence of hydroxide ion, which is found in drain cleaner. Another property of acids and bases is their ability to undergo a neutralization reaction, which we studied in Section 7.11. An acid and a base react to produce a salt and water. For example, hydrochloric acid neutralizes a potassium hydroxide solution to give potassium chloride and water.

$$HCl(aq) + KOH(aq) \longrightarrow KCl(aq) + H_2O(l)$$

The properties of acids and bases are summarized in Table 14.1.

TABLE 14.1 PROPERTIES OF ACIDS AND BASES

PROPERTY	ACIDIC SOLUTIONS	BASIC SOLUTIONS
taste	sour	bitter
feel	—	slippery, soapy
litmus paper	litmus turns red	litmus turns blue
pH value	less than 7	greater than 7
neutralization reaction	react with bases to give a salt and water	react with acids to give a salt and water

pH Scale

A pH value expresses the acidity or basicity of a solution. Most solutions have a pH between 0 and 14. For example, a 1 M HCl solution has a pH of 0 (strongly acidic), and a 1 M NaOH solution has a pH of 14 (strongly basic). A pH of 7 is considered neutral; pure distilled water has a pH of 7.

On the pH scale, acidic solutions have a pH less than 7. As the acidity increases, the pH value *decreases*. A solution having a pH of 3 is more acidic than a solution with a pH of 4. Basic solutions have a pH greater than 7. As the basicity increases, the pH value *increases*. A solution having a pH of 11 is more basic than a solution with a pH of 10.

A solution can be classified as strongly acidic, weakly acidic, neutral, weakly basic, or strongly basic on the basis of pH. A strongly acidic solution has a pH between 0 and 2. A weakly acidic solution has a pH between 2 and 7. A weakly basic solution has a pH between 7 and 12. A strongly basic solution has a pH between 12 and 14. Figure 14.1 illustrates some common substances and their approximate pH.

▲ **pH Test Strip** The indicator test strip paper uses universal indicator to test for pH. The test strip shown indicates a base at pH 10.

Acidic/Basic	pH	Example Solution
Strongly acidic	0 1	1 M HCl Stomach acid (1–3)
Weakly acidic	2 3 4 5 6	Lemon juice Vinegar, wine Grapes, orange juice Normal rain, coffee Milk, pH-balanced shampoo
Neutral	7	Pure water
Weakly basic	8 9 10 11 12	Eggs, seawater Baking soda, antacids Milk of magnesia, soap Household ammonia Liquid bleach
Strongly basic	13 14	Drain cleaner 1 M NaOH

◀ Figure 14.1 **The pH Scale** Note that solutions may be strongly acidic (pH ~1), weakly acidic (pH ~4), neutral (pH ~7), weakly basic (pH ~10), or strongly basic (pH ~14).

The following example exercise illustrates the acid–base strength of a few common solutions:

Example Exercise 14.1 The pH Scale

Indicate whether each of the following solutions is considered strongly acidic, weakly acidic, neutral, weakly basic, or strongly basic:

(a) stomach acid, pH 1.5   (b) oven cleaner, pH 13.5
(c) orange juice, pH 4.5   (d) deionized water, pH 7.0
(e) eggs, pH 7.5   (f) carbonated soda, pH 4.0

Solution
Refer to the guidelines in Figure 14.1 to classify each solution.

(a) Gastric juice has a pH between 0 and 2. It is *strongly acidic.*
(b) Oven cleaner has a pH of 13.5. It is *strongly basic.*
(c) Orange juice has a pH between 2 and 7. It is *weakly acidic.*
(d) Deionized water has a pH of 7.0 and is *neutral.*
(e) Eggs have a pH of 7.5 and are *weakly basic.*
(f) Carbonated soda has a pH of 4.0 and is *weakly acidic.*

▲ **Lemons Are Sour** Lemons, limes, oranges, and grapefruit contain citric acid, which is sour.

Practice Exercise

Indicate whether each of the following properties corresponds to an acid or to a base:

(a) sour taste

(b) slippery feel

(c) turns litmus paper red

(d) pH greater than 7

Answers: (a) acid (b) base (c) acid (d) base

Concept Exercise

Which of the following has the highest acidity: pH 1, pH 5, or pH 9?

Answer: See Appendix G.

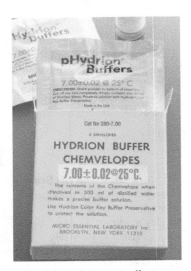

▲ **Buffer Solutions** Buffer solutions can be prepared by dissolving a buffer tablet in distilled water. Standard buffer envelopes are available for a wide range of pH values.

Buffers

Controlling acidity is important in the manufacture of food, paper, and chemicals. In agriculture, controlling the pH of the soil is necessary to obtain good crop yields. A **buffer** is a solution that resists changes and controls the pH when an acid or a base is added. A buffer solution functions by consuming excess hydrogen ions or hydroxide ions, and thereby maintains its pH.

A buffer solution is composed of an aqueous weak acid and one of its salts, for example, citric acid and sodium citrate. If we add acid to a solution, the citrate ion combines with excess hydrogen ions to form citric acid. Conversely, if we add base to a solution, citric acid neutralizes excess hydroxide ions to form a citrate salt. If the amount of acid or base added to a buffer solution is relatively small compared to the amount of buffer, there is very little change in pH.

Other examples of buffers include hydrogen carbonate ions and carbonate ions, which are present in seawater and help to preserve the pH near 8. A similar buffer system helps to control the pH of blood, which must be maintained in a very narrow range near a pH of 7.4.

LEARNING OBJECTIVES

▸ To identify an Arrhenius acid and base.

▸ To classify a strong or weak acid and base given the degree of ionization.

▸ To indicate the acid and base that react to produce a given salt.

14.2 ARRHENIUS ACIDS AND BASES

In 1884, the Swedish chemist Svante Arrhenius suggested the first definitions for an acid and a base. He proposed that an acid is a substance that ionizes in water to produce hydrogen ions. Conversely, he proposed that a base is a substance that dissociates in water to release hydroxide ions. These simple concepts define an **Arrhenius acid** and **Arrhenius base**.

Ionization versus Dissociation

Acids and bases have varying strengths. The strength of an Arrhenius acid is measured by the degree of ionization in solution. **Ionization** is the process by which molecules of a polar compound ionize to form cations and anions. Thus, a molecule of hydrochloric acid, HCl, ionizes into H^+ and Cl^-.

The strength of an Arrhenius base is measured by the degree of dissociation in the solution. **Dissociation** is the process whereby already existing ions of an ionic compound simply separate. Thus, a formula unit of sodium hydroxide, NaOH, dissociates into Na^+ and OH^-.

Strong and Weak Arrhenius Acids

An acid is considered either strong or weak depending on how much it ionizes in water. According to the Arrhenius definition, a strong acid ionizes extensively to release hydrogen ions in solution. Hydrochloric acid is considered a strong acid because it ionizes nearly 100%. Hydrofluoric acid is a weak acid because it is only slightly ionized, about 1%. Table 14.2 lists some common Arrhenius acids.

TABLE 14.2 COMMON ARRHENIUS ACIDS

AQUEOUS ACID	PERCENT IONIZATION	ACID STRENGTH
hydrochloric acid, $HCl(aq)$	~100%	strong
nitric acid, $HNO_3(aq)$	~100%	strong
sulfuric acid, $H_2SO_4(aq)$	~100%	strong
acetic acid, $HC_2H_3O_2(aq)$	slightly	weak
carbonic acid, $H_2CO_3(aq)$	slightly	weak
hydrofluoric acid, $HF(aq)$	slightly	weak
phosphoric acid, $H_3PO_4(aq)$	slightly	weak

All Arrhenius acids have a hydrogen atom attached to an acid molecule by a polar bond. Most acids are weak ternary oxyacids in which the H atom is attached to an O atom. When the acid molecule ionizes, it breaks this bond. In an aqueous solution, polar water molecules help the acid ionize by pulling the hydrogen ion away from the acid molecule. We can show the ionization for hydrochloric acid, HCl, and acetic acid, $HC_2H_3O_2$, as follows:

$$HCl(aq) + H_2O(l) \longrightarrow H_3O^+(aq) + Cl^-(aq) \qquad (\sim100\%)$$

$$HC_2H_3O_2(aq) + H_2O(l) \longrightarrow H_3O^+(aq) + C_2H_3O_2^-(aq) \quad (\sim1\%)$$

Although chemists often refer to acids as solutions containing hydrogen ions, the actual species is H_3O^+. The **hydronium ion**, H_3O^+, results from a hydrogen ion attaching to a nonbonding electron pair on a water molecule. For simplicity, we will usually refer to a hydrogen ion in aqueous solution as $H^+(aq)$.

▲ **Hydrofluoric Acid, HF** Although aqueous HF is a weak acid, it attacks glass. This design was created by coating glass with wax and then removing wax from the pattern areas. The glass was dipped into hydrofluoric acid, which etched the design.

Strong and Weak Arrhenius Bases

Recall that a base is considered either strong or weak depending on how much of it dissociates. According to the Arrhenius definition, a strong base dissociates extensively to release hydroxide ions in solution. Sodium hydroxide is a strong base and dissociates nearly 100% in an aqueous solution. A weak base dissociates very little to release few hydroxide ions in solution. Ammonium hydroxide is a weak base because it provides relatively few hydroxide ions in solution. Table 14.3 lists some common Arrhenius bases.

TABLE 14.3 COMMON ARRHENIUS BASES

AQUEOUS BASE	PERCENT DISSOCIATION	BASE STRENGTH
barium hydroxide, $Ba(OH)_2(aq)$	~100%	strong
calcium hydroxide, $Ca(OH)_2(aq)$	~100%	strong
lithium hydroxide, $LiOH(aq)$	~100%	strong
potassium hydroxide, $KOH(aq)$	~100%	strong
sodium hydroxide, $NaOH(aq)$	~100%	strong
ammonium hydroxide, $NH_4OH(aq)$*	slightly	weak

*Ammonium hydroxide is prepared by dissolving ammonia gas in water. It is referred to as an *aqueous ammonia solution*, $NH_3(aq)$, or as *ammonia water*, $NH_3 \cdot H_2O$. The name *ammonium hydroxide* is somewhat misleading since there is no evidence for ammonium hydroxide molecules in a solution. For simplicity, however, we will refer to an ammonia solution as *ammonium hydroxide*, $NH_4OH(aq)$.

▲ **Ammonium Hydroxide, NH_4OH** Ammonia gas dissolved in water is commonly referred to as an *ammonium hydroxide solution*.

When we dissolve sodium hydroxide in water, we obtain aqueous NaOH. In the dissolving process, NaOH dissociates into aqueous sodium ions and aqueous hydroxide ions. Aqueous ammonium hydroxide, NH_4OH, is a weak base and provides relatively few hydroxide ions in solution. We can show this process for the two Arrhenius bases as follows:

$$NaOH(aq) \longrightarrow Na^+(aq) + OH^-(aq) \quad (\sim 100\%)$$

$$NH_4OH(aq) \longrightarrow NH_4^+(aq) + OH^-(aq) \quad (\sim 1\%)$$

The following example exercise illustrates the classification of acid–base strength based on the ability to donate ions in solution.

Example Exercise 14.2 Strong and Weak Acids

Classify each of the following solutions as a strong or a weak Arrhenius acid given the degree of ionization:

(a) perchloric acid, $HClO_4(aq)$ $\sim 100\%$
(b) hypochlorous acid, $HClO(aq)$ $\sim 1\%$

Solution

To classify an aqueous solution as a strong or a weak acid we must know the amount of ionization.

(a) Perchloric acid is extensively ionized and is considered a *strong acid*.
    An aqueous solution is primarily $H^+(aq)$ and $ClO_4^-(aq)$.
(b) Hypochlorous acid is slightly ionized and is considered a *weak acid*.
    An aqueous solution contains primarily molecules of HClO.

Practice Exercise

Classify each of the following solutions as a strong or a weak Arrhenius base given the degree of dissociation:

(a) magnesium hydroxide, $Mg(OH)_2(aq)$ $\sim 1\%$
(b) strontium hydroxide, $Sr(OH)_2(aq)$ $\sim 100\%$

Answers: (a) weak base   (b) strong base

Concept Exercise

Which of the following is a strong Arrhenius acid: $HNO_3(aq)$, $H_2CO_3(aq)$, $H_3PO_4(aq)$?

Answer: See Appendix G.

Neutralization Reactions

An acid neutralizes a base to give a **salt** and water. For example, hydrochloric acid reacts with sodium hydroxide to give the salt sodium chloride and water. The equation for the reaction is

$$HCl(aq) + NaOH(aq) \longrightarrow NaCl(aq) + H_2O(l)$$

This reaction produces the aqueous salt NaCl. Different acids give other salts. When we completely neutralize sulfuric acid using aqueous sodium hydroxide, for example, we obtain sodium sulfate. The equation is

$$H_2SO_4(aq) + 2\,NaOH(aq) \longrightarrow Na_2SO_4(aq) + 2\,H_2O(l)$$

The hydrogen ions from an acid are neutralized by the hydroxide ions from a base. The hydrogen ions and hydroxide ions combine to form water. Note from the preceding neutralization reaction that Na_2SO_4 is the salt produced.

We can identify the Arrhenius acid and base that produce any given salt because each salt is composed of the cation from the reacting base and the anion from the acid. As an example, we can predict the neutralization reaction that produces the salt potassium acetate, $KC_2H_3O_2$. Since the salt contains potassium, the neutralized base must be potassium hydroxide, KOH. The acetate ion came from acetic acid, $HC_2H_3O_2$. The equation for the reaction is

$$HC_2H_3O_2(aq) + KOH(aq) \longrightarrow KC_2H_3O_2(aq) + H_2O(l)$$

▲ **Stomach Antacid** Milk of Magnesia, $Mg(OH)_2$, is a weak base that can neutralize excess stomach acid.

The following example exercise further illustrates the neutralization of acids and bases to give a salt and water.

Example Exercise 14.3 Neutralization Reactions

Determine the acid and base that produce each of the following salts. Write a balanced equation for the neutralization reaction:

(a) lithium fluoride, $LiF(aq)$ (b) calcium sulfate, $CaSO_4(aq)$

Solution

(a) The salt LiF is produced from the neutralization of the base LiOH and the acid HF. The equation for the reaction is

$$HF(aq) + LiOH(aq) \longrightarrow LiF(aq) + H_2O(l)$$

(b) The salt $CaSO_4$ is produced from the neutralization of the base $Ca(OH)_2$ and the acid H_2SO_4. The equation for the reaction is

$$H_2SO_4(aq) + Ca(OH)_2(aq) \longrightarrow CaSO_4(aq) + 2 H_2O(l)$$

Practice Exercise

Determine the acid and base that produce each of the following salts. Write a balanced equation for the neutralization reaction.

(a) potassium iodide, $KI(aq)$ (b) barium nitrate, $Ba(NO_3)_2(aq)$

Answers:

(a) HI is the acid and KOH is the base:

$$HI(aq) + KOH(aq) \longrightarrow KI(aq) + H_2O(l)$$

(b) HNO_3 is the acid and $Ba(OH)_2$ is the base:

$$2 HNO_3(aq) + Ba(OH)_2(aq) \longrightarrow Ba(NO_3)_2(aq) + 2 H_2O(l)$$

Concept Exercise

Which acid and base undergo neutralization to give sodium acetate, $NaC_2H_3O_2$?

Answer: See Appendix G.

CHEMISTRY CONNECTION Svante Arrhenius

Q: What grade was Arrhenius awarded for his brilliant Ph.D. dissertation on the theory of ionic solutions?

Svante Arrhenius (1859–1927) was a child genius who taught himself to read by age three. After graduating from high school at the top of his class, he enrolled at the University of Uppsala in his native Sweden. He majored in chemistry and did research on the passage of electricity through aqueous solutions.

At 22, Arrhenius began his doctoral study in Stockholm. For his graduate thesis, he continued to pursue his interest in the behavior of solutions. In particular, he found it puzzling that sodium chloride solutions conducted electricity, whereas sugar solutions did not. After carefully considering his observations, Arrhenius boldly proposed that a solution of sodium chloride conducts an electric current because it separates into charged particles in solution. Sugar does not conduct electricity because it does not form charged particles in solution.

Arrhenius also noted that the freezing point of water was lowered twice as much for a salt solution as it was for a sugar solution. He explained that when salt dissolves in solution, NaCl separates into sodium ions and chloride ions. When sugar dissolves in solution, it remains as molecules.

▲ Svante August Arrhenius (1859–1927)

Arrhenius was aware, however, that there were difficulties with the concept of charged ions in solution. At the time, the scientific community considered atoms to be indivisible, electrically neutral particles.

In 1884, Arrhenius defended his Ph.D. dissertation on the theory of ionic solutions. After a grueling four-hour defense, he was awarded the lowest possible passing grade. The dissertation committee simply was not ready to accept the idea of ions in solution.

Arrhenius' career stagnated for almost a decade, and his ideas found little support. The ionic theory was eventually championed by Wilhelm Ostwald (1853–1932), a noted German chemist, who invited Arrhenius to work with him. Gradually, evidence accumulated that supported the concept of ions. Most notably, the discovery of the electron in 1897 proved the existence of charged subatomic particles.

After the ionic theory gained credibility, Arrhenius was offered a professorship at the University of Stockholm. In 1899, he published the classic paper "On the Dissociation of Substances in Aqueous Solutions." In 1903, after struggling for 20 years to establish his ideas, Arrhenius was awarded the Nobel Prize in chemistry for his ionic theory of solutions.

A: Arrhenius received the lowest possible passing grade; the examining committee simply did not believe in the ionic theory of solutions.

LEARNING OBJECTIVE

▶ To identify a Brønsted–Lowry acid and base in a neutralization reaction.

14.3 BRØNSTED–LOWRY ACIDS AND BASES

In 1923 the Danish chemist Johannes Brønsted (1879–1947) and the English chemist Thomas Lowry (1874–1936) independently proposed broader definitions than those of Arrhenius for an acid and a base. Whereas Arrhenius defined an acid as a substance that donates a hydrogen ion in water, Brønsted and Lowry defined an acid as a substance that donates a hydrogen ion to any other substance. Since a hydrogen ion is a single proton, a **Brønsted–Lowry acid** is also referred to as a **proton donor**.

Recall the Arrhenius definition of a base as a hydroxide ion donor in water. We know that hydroxide ions neutralize hydrogen ions to form water. There are, however, many substances that neutralize hydrogen ions in addition to hydroxide ions. Brønsted and Lowry proposed that a base is any substance that accepts a hydrogen ion. Thus, a **Brønsted–Lowry base** is a **proton acceptor**.

Although the Brønsted–Lowry definitions of an acid and a base are a bit different from the Arrhenius definitions, an acid and a base still neutralize each other. The following reactions illustrate the neutralization of a Brønsted–Lowry base by hydrochloric acid:

$$HCl(aq) + NaOH(aq) \longrightarrow NaCl(aq) + H_2O(l)$$
$$HCl(aq) + NH_3(aq) \longrightarrow NH_4Cl(aq)$$
$$HCl(aq) + H_2O(l) \longrightarrow H_3O^+(aq) + Cl^-(aq)$$

In the first equation, aqueous NaOH accepts a proton. Therefore, according to the Brønsted–Lowry definition, it is a base. In the second equation, aqueous NH_3 accepts a proton. It is also a base. As the third equation shows, even water can act as a Brønsted–Lowry base because it can accept a hydrogen ion.

Unlike Arrhenius acids and bases that are defined by hydrogen ions or hydroxide ions dissolved in water, Brønsted–Lowry acids and bases depend on a particular reaction. For example, aqueous $NaHCO_3$ can act as a *base* by accepting a proton. But in a different reaction, aqueous $NaHCO_3$ can act as an *acid* by donating a proton. The following examples illustrate $NaHCO_3$ acting as both an acid and a base:

$$HCl(aq) + NaHCO_3(aq) \longrightarrow NaCl(aq) + H_2CO_3(aq)$$
$$NaOH(aq) + NaHCO_3(aq) \longrightarrow Na_2CO_3(aq) + H_2O(l)$$

In the first reaction, $NaHCO_3$ accepts a proton from HCl and therefore acts as a Brønsted–Lowry base. In the second reaction, $NaHCO_3$ donates a proton to NaOH and therefore acts as a Brønsted–Lowry acid. A substance that is capable of both accepting and donating a proton is said to be **amphiprotic**. According to the Brønsted–Lowry theory, water is amphiprotic. That is, H_2O can act as an acid and donate a proton;

H_2O can also act as a base and accept a proton to become the hydronium ion, H_3O^+. We can show the amphiprotic nature of water as follows:

$$H_2O(l) \quad + \quad H_2O(l) \quad \longrightarrow \quad H_3O^+(aq) + OH^-(aq)$$

proton donor   proton acceptor
acid   base

14.4 ACID–BASE INDICATORS

LEARNING OBJECTIVES

▶ To state the color of a solution with a given pH and a drop of phenolphthalein, methyl red, or bromthymol blue indicator.

We mentioned in Section 14.1 that litmus paper can be used to show whether a solution is acidic or basic. In addition, other paper test strips are available that indicate the pH of a solution. These test strips are permeated with substances that change color depending on the pH of the test solution. These strips contain substances extracted from plants. Some of the plant extracts come from grape juice, red cabbage, and flower petals such as those of roses, violets, and orchids.

A substance that is sensitive to a change in pH by exhibiting a different color is referred to as an **acid–base indicator**. Figure 14.2 illustrates the range in color of these indicators. Table 14.4 summarizes the pH range for each indicator.

▲ Figure 14.2 **pH and Acid–Base Indicator Color** The color of three acid–base indicators at different pH values. Methyl red (left) changes from red to yellow at pH 5. Bromthymol blue (middle) changes from yellow to blue at pH 7. Phenolphthalein (right) changes from colorless to pink at pH 9.

TABLE 14.4 ACID–BASE INDICATORS

INDICATOR	COLOR CHANGE	COLOR
methyl red	pH ~5	below pH 5, red above pH 5, yellow
bromthymol blue	pH ~7	below pH 7, yellow above pH 7, blue
phenolphthalein	pH ~9	below pH 9, colorless above pH 9, pink

If a solution has a pH above 5, the indicator methyl red is yellow. If a solution has a pH below 5, the indicator is red. At a pH of 5, methyl red appears orange because it contains both the yellow and red forms of the indicator.

If a solution has a pH of 9 or above, the indicator phenolphthalein is pink. If a solution has a pH below 9, the indicator is colorless. Although there are many acid–base indicators available in the laboratory, phenolphthalein is the only common indicator that changes to colorless. This practical consideration and ease of observation makes phenolphthalein the indicator of choice for many applications.

The following example exercise illustrates the relationship of the color of an acid–base indicator and the pH of a given solution.

<hr>

Example Exercise 14.4 Acid–Base Indicators

State the color of the acid–base indicator in each of the following solutions:

(a) A solution at pH 3 contains a drop of methyl red.
(b) A solution at pH 8 contains a drop of bromthymol blue.
(c) A solution at pH 11 contains a drop of phenolphthalein.

Solution

Refer to Table 14.4 to determine the color of each solution.

(a) A pH 3 solution containing methyl red indicator is *red*.
(b) A pH 8 solution containing bromthymol blue indicator is *blue*.
(c) A pH 11 solution containing phenolphthalein indicator is *pink*.

Practice Exercise

State the pH at which each of the following acid–base indicators changes color:

(a) methyl red
(b) bromthymol blue
(c) phenolphthalein

Answers: (a) 5   (b) 7   (c) 9

Concept Exercise

Which common acid–base indicator is colorless in acidic and neutral solutions?

Answer: See Appendix G.

<hr>

LEARNING OBJECTIVES

▸ To perform calculations given acid–base titration data.

▸ To express the molarity of a solution as a mass percent concentration.

14.5 ACID–BASE TITRATIONS

Vinegar tastes sour because it contains acetic acid. To find the molar concentration of acetic acid in vinegar we analyze the vinegar sample using a base solution of known concentration. In the laboratory, we can analyze acetic acid by a titration method. We use this **titration** process to deliver a measured volume of solution. To analyze the acetic acid in a vinegar sample we can titrate a sample by delivering a measured volume of sodium hydroxide solution. We can use phenolphthalein as an indicator to signal when we have neutralized all the acetic acid.

After the acetic acid is neutralized, an extra drop of NaOH increases the pH dramatically and the phenolphthalein indicator changes from colorless to pink. When the indicator changes color, we stop adding NaOH base and cease the titration. This turning point in the titration is the **endpoint**. Figure 14.3 illustrates the experimental procedure.

Consider the following titration of a vinegar sample for acetic acid. A 10.0-mL sample of vinegar containing acetic acid requires 37.55 mL of 0.223 *M* NaOH. The balanced equation for the reaction is

$$HC_2H_3O_2(aq) + NaOH(aq) \longrightarrow NaC_2H_3O_2(aq) + H_2O(l)$$

This is a solution stoichiometry problem (Section 13.11). To find the molarity of the acetic acid, we must first find the moles of NaOH. The volume of NaOH is 37.55 mL, and the molar concentration is 0.223 *M*. The molarity of the NaOH can be written as the unit factor 0.223 mol NaOH/1000 mL solution.

$$37.55 \text{ mL solution} \times \frac{0.223 \text{ mol NaOH}}{1000 \text{ mL solution}} = 0.00837 \text{ mol NaOH}$$

Next, we find the moles of acetic acid in the acid solution. From the balanced equation we see that 1 mol of NaOH base neutralizes 1 mol of $HC_2H_3O_2$.

$$0.00837 \text{ mol NaOH} \times \frac{1 \text{ mol } HC_2H_3O_2}{1 \text{ mol NaOH}} = 0.00837 \text{ mol } HC_2H_3O_2$$

▲ Figure 14.3 **Titration of Acetic Acid with Sodium Hydroxide**
(a) The flask contains a sample of acetic acid and a drop of phenolphthalein indicator.
(b) The buret delivers a measured volume of sodium hydroxide solution into the flask.
(c) The titration is complete when the solution attains a permanent pink color.

Finally, we can calculate the molarity of the acetic acid. The volume of the $HC_2H_3O_2$ solution is 10.0 mL.

$$\frac{0.00837 \text{ mol } HC_2H_3O_2}{10.0 \text{ mL solution}} \times \frac{1000 \text{ mL solution}}{1 \text{ L solution}} = \frac{0.837 \text{ mol } HC_2H_3O_2}{1 \text{ L solution}}$$

$$= 0.837 \ M \ HC_2H_3O_2$$

Now let's express the molar concentration of the acetic acid as a mass percent (m/m %) concentration. Given that the density of the vinegar is 1.01 g/mL and that the molar mass of acetic acid is 60.06 g/mol, we can proceed as follows:

$$\frac{0.837 \text{ mol } HC_2H_3O_2}{1000 \text{ mL solution}} \times \frac{60.06 \text{ g } HC_2H_3O_2}{1 \text{ mol } HC_2H_3O_2} \times \frac{1 \text{ mL solution}}{1.01 \text{ g solution}} \times 100\%$$

$$= \frac{0.0498 \text{ g } HC_2H_3O_2}{1 \text{ g solution}} \times 100\% = 4.98\% \ HC_2H_3O_2$$

Therefore, the concentration of acetic acid in the vinegar solution is 0.837 M, which is equivalent to 4.98% $HC_2H_3O_2$. Typically, the label on a bottle of vinegar reads "diluted in water to 5% acidity."

Titrations can also be performed on basic solutions in the same way, but an acid is added from the buret instead of a base. We can calculate the concentration of ammonia in a household cleaning solution by titrating a sample. The following example exercise illustrates the analysis of an ammonia solution.

Example Exercise 14.5 Acid–Base Titration of Ammonia

If 25.30 mL of 0.277 M HCl is used to titrate 10.0 mL of aqueous ammonia to a methyl red endpoint, what is the molarity of the ammonia? When we write aqueous ammonia as NH_4OH, the balanced equation is

$$HCl(aq) + NH_4OH(aq) \longrightarrow NH_4Cl(aq) + H_2O(l)$$

Solution
To calculate the molarity of the NH_4OH, we must find the moles of NH_4OH. From the balanced equation, we see that 1 mol of HCl neutralizes 1 mol of NH_4OH. Since the

acid solution is 0.277 M HCl, we have the unit factor 0.277 mol HCl/1000 mL solution.

$$25.30 \text{ mL solution} \times \frac{0.277 \text{ mol HCl}}{1000 \text{ mL solution}} \times \frac{1 \text{ mol NH}_4\text{OH}}{1 \text{ mol HCl}} = 0.00701 \text{ mol NH}_4\text{OH}$$

We can summarize the conversion as follows:

We obtain the molar concentration by dividing the moles of NH_4OH by the volume of aqueous ammonia titrated, 10.0 mL.

$$\frac{0.00701 \text{ mol NH}_4\text{OH}}{10.0 \text{ mL solution}} \times \frac{1000 \text{ mL solution}}{1 \text{ L solution}} = \frac{0.701 \text{ mol NH}_4\text{OH}}{1 \text{ L solution}}$$

$$= 0.701 \ M \ NH_4OH$$

Practice Exercise

If 38.30 mL of 0.250 M NaOH is used to titrate 25.0 mL of phosphoric acid, what is the molarity of the acid? The balanced equation is

$$H_3PO_4(aq) + 3\,NaOH(aq) \longrightarrow Na_3PO_4(aq) + 3\,H_2O(l)$$

Answer: 0.128 M

Concept Exercise

Which of the following describes the titration of $H_3PO_4(aq)$ with $NaOH(aq)$: strong acid with strong base, strong acid with weak base, or weak acid with strong base?

Answer: See Appendix G.

Let's try another type of problem and find the volume of base required to neutralize an acid. For example, we can find the volume of base needed to neutralize sulfuric acid in a battery acid sample. The following example exercise illustrates the analysis of battery acid by a titration method.

Example Exercise 14.6 Acid–Base Titration of Battery Acid

A 10.0-mL sample of 0.555 M battery acid, H_2SO_4, is titrated with 0.223 M NaOH. What volume of sodium hydroxide is required for the titration?

$$H_2SO_4(aq) + 2\,NaOH(aq) \longrightarrow Na_2SO_4(aq) + 2\,H_2O(l)$$

Solution

Step 1: The unit asked for in the answer is mL NaOH.

Step 2: The given value is 10.0 mL H_2SO_4.

Step 3: We apply unit conversion factors to cancel units. In this example, we use the molar concentration of an acid (0.555 mol H_2SO_4 per 1000 mL H_2SO_4) and the molar concentration of a base (0.223 mol NaOH per 1000 mL NaOH) as unit factors. From the balanced equation, we see that 1 mol H_2SO_4 = 2 mol NaOH.

$$10.0 \text{ mL solution} \times \frac{0.555 \text{ mol H}_2\text{SO}_4}{1000 \text{ mL solution}} \times \frac{2 \text{ mol NaOH}}{1 \text{ mol H}_2\text{SO}_4} \times \frac{1000 \text{ mL NaOH}}{0.223 \text{ mol NaOH}} = 49.8 \text{ mL NaOH}$$

We can summarize the overall solution as follows:

Practice Exercise

A 25.0-mL sample of hydrochloric acid is titrated with 0.125 *M* Ba(OH)$_2$. If 50.0 mL of barium hydroxide is required for the titration, what is the molar concentration of the acid? The balanced equation for the reaction is

$$2 \, HCl(aq) + Ba(OH)_2(aq) \longrightarrow BaCl_2(aq) + 2 \, H_2O(l)$$

Answer: 0.500 *M* HCl

Concept Exercise

Which of the following describes the titration of HCl(*aq*) with Ba(OH)$_2$(*aq*): strong acid with strong base, strong acid with weak base, or weak acid with strong base?

Answer: See Appendix G.

14.6 ACID–BASE STANDARDIZATION

A **standard solution** is a solution in which the concentration is known precisely, that is, three or four significant digits. For example, the concentration of NaOH used in the acetic acid titration was 0.223 *M*.

Chemists use standard solutions to repetitively analyze substances. For instance, a chemist may use a standard solution to analyze the neutralizing capacity of antacid tablets, or the tartness of soft drink flavors. Standard solutions are routinely used in the chemical industry to assure quality. Chemical samples are randomly selected and analyzed using a standard solution. This procedure is referred to as *quality control* (QC) or *quality assurance* (QA).

To standardize a solution of acid, chemists use a weighed quantity of a solid base. To standardize hydrochloric acid, for example, we can use solid sodium carbonate, Na$_2$CO$_3$. Let's find the molarity of hydrochloric acid if 25.50 mL of HCl solution is required to neutralize 0.375 g of Na$_2$CO$_3$. The balanced equation for the reaction of Na$_2$CO$_3$ dissolved in water is

$$2 \, HCl(aq) + Na_2CO_3(aq) \longrightarrow 2 \, NaCl(aq) + H_2O(l) + CO_2(g)$$

To calculate the molarity of the hydrochloric acid, we first find the number of moles of HCl. From the balanced equation we note that 2 mol of HCl react with 1 mol of Na$_2$CO$_3$ (105.99 g/mol).

$$0.375 \text{ g Na}_2\text{CO}_3 \times \frac{1 \text{ mol Na}_2\text{CO}_3}{105.99 \text{ g Na}_2\text{CO}_3} \times \frac{2 \text{ mol HCl}}{1 \text{ mol Na}_2\text{CO}_3} = 0.00708 \text{ mol HCl}$$

To obtain the molarity of the acid, we divide the moles of HCl by the 25.50 mL of HCl required to neutralize the sodium carbonate.

$$\frac{0.00708 \text{ mol HCl}}{25.50 \text{ mL solution}} \times \frac{1000 \text{ mL solution}}{1 \text{ L solution}} = \frac{0.277 \text{ mol HCl}}{1 \text{ L solution}}$$

$$= 0.277 \, M \text{ HCl}$$

To standardize a solution of base, chemists can use a weighed quantity of a solid acid. For example, we can use crystals of oxalic acid, H$_2$C$_2$O$_4$, to standardize aqueous sodium hydroxide. We first dissolve a weighed sample of H$_2$C$_2$O$_4$ in water and then neutralize it with a measured volume of a base. The following example exercise illustrates how to determine the concentration of a standard NaOH solution.

Example Exercise 14.7 Acid–Base Standardization of a Base

What is the molarity of a sodium hydroxide solution if 32.15 mL of NaOH is required to neutralize 0.424 g of oxalic acid, $H_2C_2O_4$ (90.04 g/mol)?

$$H_2C_2O_4(aq) + 2\,NaOH(aq) \longrightarrow Na_2C_2O_4(aq) + 2\,H_2O(l)$$

Solution

To calculate the molarity of the NaOH, we find the number of moles of $H_2C_2O_4$. The mass of $H_2C_2O_4$ to be neutralized is 0.424 g, and the molar mass is 90.04 g/mol. From the balanced equation we see that 2 mol of NaOH reacts with 1 mol of $H_2C_2O_4$.

$$0.424 \text{ g } H_2C_2O_4 \times \frac{1 \text{ mol } H_2C_2O_4}{90.04 \text{ g } H_2C_2O_4} \times \frac{2 \text{ mol NaOH}}{1 \text{ mol } H_2C_2O_4} = 0.00942 \text{ mol NaOH}$$

We can summarize the conversion as follows:

We can obtain the molar concentration of the base from the moles of NaOH divided by the volume of base required to neutralize the oxalic acid.

$$\frac{0.00942 \text{ mol NaOH}}{32.15 \text{ mL solution}} \times \frac{1000 \text{ mL solution}}{1 \text{ L solution}} = \frac{0.293 \text{ mol NaOH}}{1 \text{ L solution}}$$

$$= 0.293 \; M \text{ NaOH}$$

Practice Exercise

If an unknown sample of oxalic acid, $H_2C_2O_4$, is neutralized by 33.50 mL of 0.293 M NaOH, what is the mass of the sample? Refer to the previous balanced chemical equation for the neutralization of oxalic acid with sodium hydroxide.

Answer: 0.442 g $H_2C_2O_4$

Concept Exercise

What color is the phenolphthalein indicator at the endpoint of the titration of oxalic acid with sodium hydroxide?

Answer: See Appendix G.

Molar Mass of a Solid Acid or Solid Base

One application of a standard solution is to identify a crystalline solid acid by determining its molar mass. For example, using a standard base solution, we could identify an unknown solid acid as citric acid by determining its molar mass. We begin by dissolving crystals of the solid acid in water and then neutralizing the acid using a standard base solution. Given the mass of solid acid and the volume of standard base, we can calculate the molar mass of the acid.

The following example exercise illustrates the determination of molar mass for citric acid.

Example Exercise 14.8 Molar Mass of an Acid

Citric acid, abbreviated H_3Cit, gives a soft drink its tart taste. If 36.10 mL of 0.293 M NaOH neutralizes a 0.677-g sample of citric acid, what is the molar mass of citric acid? The balanced equation for the reaction is

$$H_3Cit(aq) + 3\,NaOH(aq) \longrightarrow Na_3Cit(aq) + 3\,H_2O(l)$$

Solution

The given volume of NaOH solution is 36.10 mL. Since the molar concentration is 0.293 *M*, we write the unit factor as 0.293 mol NaOH/1000 mL solution.

$$36.10 \text{ mL solution} \times \frac{0.293 \text{ mol NaOH}}{1000 \text{ mL solution}} = 0.0106 \text{ mol NaOH}$$

From the balanced chemical equation, we see that 3 mol of NaOH reacts with 1 mol of H_3Cit. Thus, the number of moles of citric acid is

$$0.0106 \text{ mol NaOH} \times \frac{1 \text{ mol } H_3\text{Cit}}{3 \text{ mol NaOH}} = 0.00353 \text{ mol } H_3\text{Cit}$$

We can summarize the conversion as follows:

Since the molar mass is defined as grams per mole, we have

$$\frac{0.677 \text{ g } H_3\text{Cit}}{0.00353 \text{ mol } H_3\text{Cit}} = 192 \text{ g/mol}$$

From titration data, we calculated the molar mass of citric acid as 192 g/mol. Given that the chemical formula of citric acid is $H_3C_6H_5O_7$, we can verify the molar mass by adding the atomic masses to obtain 192.14 g/mol.

Practice Exercise

Benzoic acid is a common food preservative, and its molecular formula is $HC_7H_5O_2$. If 22.55 mL of 0.293 *M* NaOH neutralizes a 0.806-g sample of benzoic acid, what is the molar mass of the acid? The balanced equation for the reaction is

$$HC_7H_5O_2(aq) + NaOH(aq) \longrightarrow NaC_7H_5O_2(aq) + H_2O(l)$$

Answer: 122 g/mol

Concept Exercise

What color is the phenolphthalein indicator at the endpoint of the titration of benzoic acid with sodium hydroxide?

Answer: See Appendix G.

14.7 IONIZATION OF WATER

We know that metals are good conductors of electricity. What would happen if we tested the electrical conductivity of a key? We can predict that the key conducts electricity because it is made of metal. In Figure 14.4a, we see that the key completes the circuit in the conductivity apparatus and that the bulb lights up. The explanation is as follows. Electricity is defined as the flow of electrons. Recall from the electron sea model described in Section 11.5 that the valence electrons in metals are free to flow. An electric current can push electrons from one atom to another. Thus, electricity flows from one end of the metal key to the other as electrons move from atom to atom.

LEARNING OBJECTIVES

▶ To relate the ionization constant of water to the molar hydrogen ion and hydroxide ion concentrations.

▶ To calculate the molar hydroxide ion concentration given the molar hydrogen ion concentration.

► Figure 14.4 **Conductivity Apparatus** (a) Metals are good conductors of electricity. A metal key completes the electrical circuit and the light bulb shows a bright light. (b) Pure water is a very poor conductor. It does, however, very weakly conduct electricity and the light bulb shows a dim light.

(a) Strong conductor

(b) Weak conductor

▲ Figure 14.5 **Ionization of Water** Pure water ionizes to give a few hydrogen ions and hydroxide ions. Water is a very weak conductor of electricity because only 1 molecule in about 500,000,000 forms ions.

What happens when we test the electrical conductivity of pure water? In Figure 14.4b, we see that pure water is a very poor conductor of electricity. Evidence suggests that it is difficult to push electrons from one water molecule to another. How then do we explain the observation that some electricity flows in pure water? We explain this observation by suggesting that there are ions present in pure water.

Arrhenius found that salt solutions are good conductors of electricity. He correctly concluded that *ions* in the solution are responsible for electrical conductivity. Since water is a very poor conductor, we can conclude that only a few ions are present in pure water (Figure 14.5).

We know that water molecules in the liquid state are free to move about and collide with one another. Although it happens only rarely, on occasion two water molecules collide with sufficient energy for their bonds to break apart. This bond breaking produces a hydronium ion, H_3O^+, and a hydroxide ion, OH^-. Moreover, this occurrence is a dynamic process. While some molecules are breaking apart, other ions are combining to form water molecules. At any given moment, only 1 water molecule in 500 million molecules is ionized. Apparently, however, these few ions in water are sufficient to conduct a very weak electric current. The chemical equation for the collision reaction is

$$H_2O(l) + H_2O(l) \longrightarrow \underset{\text{hydronium ion}}{H_3O^+(aq)} + \underset{\text{hydroxide ion}}{OH^-(aq)}$$

Alternatively, we can simplify the reaction by writing the ionization of water as

$$H_2O(l) \longrightarrow \underset{\text{hydrogen ion}}{H^+(aq)} + \underset{\text{hydroxide ion}}{OH^-(aq)}$$

The concentration of hydrogen ions in pure water is 1.0×10^{-7} mol/L at 25 °C. If we know the concentration of hydrogen ions, we also know the concentration of hydroxide ions. Since the ionization of water gives one H^+ and one OH^- for each molecule of water that ionizes, the two concentrations are equal. Therefore, the concentration of OH^- must also be 1.0×10^{-7} mol/L at 25 °C. Moreover, the molar concentration of H^+ multiplied by the molar concentration of OH^- equals a constant. This product is called the **ionization constant of water** (symbol K_w).

Let's calculate the value of K_w at 25 °C. For convenience, we use brackets to symbolize molar concentration. Hence, $[H^+]$ is the symbol for the molar concentration of hydrogen ions. We calculate a value for K_w as follows:

If $\qquad\qquad\qquad [H^+] = 1.0 \times 10^{-7}$

then $\qquad\qquad\qquad [OH^-] = 1.0 \times 10^{-7}$

and $\qquad\qquad\qquad [H^+][OH^-] = (1.0 \times 10^{-7})(1.0 \times 10^{-7})$

Since we add exponents when multiplying exponential numbers, we have

$$[H^+][OH^-] = 1.0 \times 10^{-14}$$
$$K_w = 1.0 \times 10^{-14} \, (\text{at } 25\,°C)$$

Notice that $[H^+]$ and $[OH^-]$ are inversely proportional. That is, if $[H^+]$ increases, $[OH^-]$ decreases, so that the constant K_w remains the same.

We should emphasize that water is neutral even though it contains small amounts of both H^+ and OH^-. Moreover, every aqueous solution has hydrogen ions and hydroxide ions. Even a hydrochloric acid solution contains H^+ and OH^-. Although an aqueous HCl solution has a high concentration of H^+, it has a few OH^- as well. In every aqueous solution, the product of $[H^+]$ and $[OH^-]$ is equal to the ionization constant of water.

$$[H^+][OH^-] = 1.0 \times 10^{-14}$$

If an aqueous HCl solution is 0.1 M, we can calculate its hydroxide ion concentration.

$$[0.1][OH^-] = 1.0 \times 10^{-14}$$

and

$$[OH^-] = 1.0 \times 10^{-13}$$

Although $[OH^-]$ is only 0.000 000 000 0001 M, the hydrochloric acid solution contains a trace of hydroxide ion!

To summarize, in an acidic aqueous solution the $[H^+]$ is greater than $[OH^-]$. In a basic aqueous solution, $[H^+]$ is less than $[OH^-]$. In a neutral aqueous solution, $[H^+]$ is equal to $[OH^-]$. Example Exercise 14.9 illustrates the concept of hydrogen and hydroxide ions in aqueous solutions.

Example Exercise 14.9 The Ionization Constant, K_w

Given the following hydrogen ion concentrations in an aqueous solution at 25 °C, what is the molar concentration of hydroxide ion?

(a) $[H^+] = 1.4 \times 10^{-6}$ 　　　　(b) $[H^+] = 5.2 \times 10^{-11}$

Solution
From the ionization constant of water, we know that $[H^+][OH^-] = 1.0 \times 10^{-14}$.

(a) If the $[H^+]$ is 1.4×10^{-6}, we can calculate $[OH^-]$ as follows:

$$K_w = [H^+][OH^-] = 1.0 \times 10^{-14}$$
$$1.4 \times 10^{-6}[OH^-] = 1.0 \times 10^{-14}$$

Dividing both sides of the equation by 1.4×10^{-6}, we have

$$[OH^-] = 7.1 \times 10^{-9}$$

(b) If the $[H^+]$ is 5.2×10^{-11}, we can calculate $[OH^-]$ as follows:

$$K_w = [H^+][OH^-] = 1.0 \times 10^{-14}$$
$$5.2 \times 10^{-11}[OH^-] = 1.0 \times 10^{-14}$$

Dividing both sides of the equation by 5.2×10^{-11}, we have

$$[OH^-] = 1.9 \times 10^{-4}$$

Practice Exercise
Given the following hydroxide ion concentrations in an aqueous solution, what is the molar concentration of hydrogen ion?

(a) $[OH^-] = 7.5 \times 10^{-4}$ 　　　　(b) $[OH^-] = 2.1 \times 10^{-10}$

Answers: (a) $[H^+] = 1.3 \times 10^{-11}$ (b) $[H^+] = 4.8 \times 10^{-5}$

Concept Exercise
Explain why distilled water is neutral even though it contains hydrogen ions and hydroxide ions.

Answer: See Appendix G.

LEARNING OBJECTIVE

▶ To relate pH and molar hydrogen ion concentration.

14.8 THE pH CONCEPT

In Section 14.1, we introduced the term *pH*. Recall that pure water is neutral and has a pH of 7. We also know that an acid has a pH of less than 7. As the pH value *decreases*, the solution becomes more acidic. Thus, a pH of 3 is more acidic than a pH of 4. As the pH value *increases*, the solution becomes more basic. Thus, a pH of 11 is more basic than a pH of 10.

▶ **Digital pH Meter** The digital pH meter measures the hydrogen ion concentration in the beaker with the glass electrode (shown). Pure boiled water has a hydrogen ion concentration of $1.0 \times 10^{-7} M$, which corresponds to a pH of 7.00.

Converting from [H⁺] to pH

In an aqueous solution, the hydrogen ion concentration can vary from more than 1 M to less than 0.000 000 000 000 01 M. The pH scale is a convenient way to express this broad range of hydrogen ion concentrations. The pH scale expresses the molar hydrogen ion concentration, $[H^+]$, as a power of 10.

In other words, the pH scale uses powers of 10 to express the amount of acid in a solution. A solution with a pH of 3 is 10 times more acidic than a solution with a pH of 4. Conversely, a solution with a pH of 11 is 10 times less acidic than a solution with a pH of 10. In mathematical terms, the **pH** is the negative logarithm (log) of the molar hydrogen ion concentration.

$$pH = -\log[H^+]$$

For example, if the molar hydrogen ion concentration, $[H^+]$, is 0.1 M, then

$$pH = -\log 0.1$$

We do not need to understand logarithms to solve pH problems. All we need to know is that if we express the hydrogen ion concentration as a power of 10, the exponent equals the logarithm. Similarly, you may be familiar with the Richter scale, which expresses the severity of an earthquake. The Richter scale is a logarithmic scale and an earthquake of magnitude 6 is 10 times more severe than an earthquake of magnitude 5.

We can write 0.1 M hydrogen ion concentration as a power of 10 (that is, 10^{-1}) and find the pH as follows:

$$pH = -\log 10^{-1}$$
$$= -(-1) = 1$$

Thus, the pH of a solution with a hydrogen ion concentration of 0.1 M is 1.

The following example exercises provide practice in finding the pH of an aqueous solution given the molar hydrogen ion concentration.

Example Exercise 14.10 Converting [H⁺] to pH

Calculate the pH of the following solutions given the molar hydrogen ion concentration:
(a) vinegar, $[H^+] = 0.001\ M$ 　　　　(b) antacid, $[H^+] = 0.000\ 000\ 001\ M$

Solution

(a) The pH of vinegar is equal to $-\log[H^+]$.

$$pH = -\log 0.001 = -\log 10^{-3}$$
$$= -(-3) \quad = 3$$

The sour taste of vinegar indicates that an acid is present. The acid in vinegar is acetic acid, $HC_2H_3O_2$ and the pH is approximately 3.

(b) The pH of the antacid is equal to $-\log[H^+]$.

$$pH = -\log 0.000\ 000\ 001 = -\log 10^{-9}$$
$$= -(-9) \quad = 9$$

Practice Exercise

Calculate the pH for apple juice if the molar hydrogen ion concentration is 0.0001 *M*.

Answer: pH = 4

Concept Exercise

Classify apple juice as weakly acidic, neutral, or weakly basic given a pH of 4.

Answer: See Appendix G.

▲ **Vinegar** Acetic acid is found in vinegar, which gives it a sour taste.

Converting from pH to [H⁺]

We can calculate the hydrogen ion concentration given the pH of a solution. Let's re-arrange the definition of pH to express the molar hydrogen ion concentration. The $[H^+]$ is equal to 10 raised to a negative pH value. That is,

$$[H^+] = 10^{-pH}$$

If milk has a pH of 6, then the $[H^+]$ can be expressed as

$$[H^+] = 10^{-6} = 0.000\ 001\ M$$

Example Exercise 14.11 further illustrates the conversion of a given pH to a molar hydrogen ion concentration.

Example Exercise 14.11 Converting pH to [H⁺]

Calculate the molar hydrogen ion concentration given the pH of the following solutions:
(a) lemon juice, pH 2 　　　　(b) tomato juice, pH 5

Solution

(a) The hydrogen concentration of lemon juice is equal to 10 raised to the negative value of the pH. Since the pH is 2,

$$[H^+] = 10^{-pH}$$
$$= 10^{-2} = 0.01\ M$$

(b) If the pH of tomato juice is 5, $[H^+]$ is expressed as

$$[H^+] = 10^{-pH}$$
$$= 10^{-5} = 0.000\ 01\ M$$

Notice that lemon juice and tomato juice differ by three pH units. Thus, lemon juice is 1000 times more acidic than tomato juice.

▲ **Lemon Juice** Citric acid is found in lemon juice, which gives it a sour taste.

Practice Exercise

Calculate the hydrogen ion concentration for milk of magnesia if the pH is 10.

Answer: $[H^+] = 0.000\ 000\ 000\ 1\ M\ (1 \times 10^{-10}\ M)$

Concept Exercise

Classify milk of magnesia as weakly acidic, neutral, or weakly basic given a pH of 10.

Answer: See Appendix G.

LEARNING OBJECTIVE

▶ To calculate pH values and molar hydrogen ion concentrations.

14.9 ADVANCED pH CALCULATIONS

We defined pH as an exponential way of expressing the hydrogen ion concentration, but we considered only whole-number pH values. Many chemical reactions, however, must be carefully controlled to a fraction of a pH unit. Biochemical reactions, for example, are extremely sensitive to small pH changes. In fact, the pH of our blood must be maintained within the narrow range of 7.3–7.5. There is an elaborate buffering system that accomplishes this task, which involves carbonates, phosphates, and proteins.

Converting from $[H^+]$ to pH

Recall the mathematical definition of pH. That is, pH is the negative logarithm of the molar hydrogen ion concentration.

$$pH = -\log[H^+]$$

Suppose we wish to express the pH of a solution having a hydrogen ion concentration of 0.00015 M. The pH expression is

$$pH = -\log 0.00015$$
$$= -\log 1.5 \times 10^{-4}$$

We can easily obtain the logarithm for a number using a scientific calculator. If we enter 1.5×10^{-4} and touch the log key, the display shows -3.82. Since pH is the negative logarithm, we must change the sign to 3.82.

$$pH = -(-3.82)$$
$$= 3.82$$

Note that the number of significant digits in the given value equals the number of decimal places in the log expression. In this example, there are two significant digits and two decimal places in the log value. Example Exercise 14.12 provides practice in finding the pH of an aqueous solution given the molar hydrogen ion concentration.

Example Exercise 14.12 Converting $[H^+]$ to pH

Calculate the pH of the following solutions given the molar hydrogen ion concentration:
(a) stomach acid, $[H^+] = 0.020\ M$ (b) blood, $[H^+] = 0.000\ 000\ 048\ M$

Solution

(a) We can calculate the pH of stomach acid as follows:

$$pH = -\log 0.020$$
$$= -(-1.70)$$
$$= 1.70$$

The pH of stomach acid ranges from 1 to 3; hence, this sample is normal.

(b) We can calculate the pH of blood as follows:

$$pH = -\log 0.000\,000\,048$$
$$= -\log 4.8 \times 10^{-8}$$
$$= -(-7.32)$$
$$= 7.32$$

The pH of blood ranges from 7.3 to 7.5; hence, this sample is normal.

Practice Exercise
Calculate the pH of grape juice if the hydrogen ion concentration is 0.000 089 M.

Answer: pH = 4.05

Concept Exercise
Classify grape juice as weakly acidic, neutral, or weakly basic given a pH of 4.05.

Answer: See Appendix G.

▲ **Grape Juice** Tartaric acid is found in grape juice, which gives it a mild sour taste.

Converting from pH to $[H^+]$

Previously, we expressed $[H^+]$ by raising 10 to the negative pH value.

$$[H^+] = 10^{-pH}$$

If orange juice has a pH of 2.75, then $[H^+]$ can be expressed as

$$[H^+] = 10^{-2.75}$$

To find the number that corresponds to the fractional exponent, we obtain the inverse logarithm using a scientific calculator. If we enter -2.75 and touch the inverse log key, the display shows 0.0018, or 1.8×10^{-3}.

$$[H^+] = 10^{-2.75} = 0.0018\,M$$

The following example exercise provides further practice in converting a given pH to a molar hydrogen ion concentration.

Example Exercise 14.13 Converting pH to $[H^+]$

Calculate the molar hydrogen ion concentration given the pH of the following solutions:
(a) acid rain, pH 3.68   (b) seawater, pH 7.85

Solution

(a) If acid rain has a pH of 3.68, we can find the $[H^+]$ as follows:

$$[H^+] = 10^{-3.68}$$

Using the inverse log key on a scientific calculator, we have

$$[H^+] = 2.1 \times 10^{-4}$$
$$= 0.000\,21\,M$$

(b) If seawater has a pH of 7.85, we can find the $[H^+]$ as follows:

$$[H^+] = 10^{-7.85}$$
$$= 1.4 \times 10^{-8}$$
$$= 0.000\,000\,014\,M$$

Practice Exercise Calculate the hydrogen ion concentration in wine if the pH is 3.25.

Answer: $[H^+] = 0.000\,56\,M$ ($5.6 \times 10^{-4}\,M$).

Concept Exercise Classify wine as weakly acidic, neutral, or weakly basic given a pH of 3.25.

Answer: See Appendix G.

CRITICAL THINKING Acid Rain

Q: What acids are found in "acid rain"

Compare a 1935 photograph of a statue of George Washington with a current photograph. The striking difference is attributed to acid rain, which attacks limestone by reacting with the calcium carbonate in the statue.

The English chemist Robert Smith coined the term *acid rain* after studying the rainfall in London. He found that the air, heavily polluted from coal burning, produced rain that was abnormally acidic. The term *acid rain* has persisted and today usually refers to rain having a pH 5 or below.

The gases that most contribute to acid rain are oxides of sulfur and nitrogen. Sulfur dioxide and sulfur trioxide in the atmosphere are released mainly by industrial steel plants and electric power plants. These plants burn low-grade coal, which has a high sulfur content. Most of the oxides of nitrogen are emitted from automobiles. When oxides of sulfur and nitrogen are released into the air, they dissolve in atmospheric water vapor. Subsequently, the rain that falls is composed of sulfuric acid and nitric acid raindrops.

Normal rain and acid rain are both acidic, but their pH values are different. Normal rain has a pH of about 5.5. It is slightly acidic because carbon dioxide in the atmosphere dissolves in raindrops to form a dilute solution of carbonic acid. Severe acid rain can be a hundred times more acidic than normal rain, and an unhealthy pH of 2.8 has been recorded. In the northeastern United States, rainfall with a pH of 4 has been blamed on sulfur oxides released from the burning of coal (see map below).

Acid rain is a global problem, and countries all over the world are attempting to reduce it. One way is to reduce the emission of environmental pollutants. Canada has begun a program to reduce its sulfur dioxide emissions. The United States, Japan, and Germany are using high-grade coal to reduce their emissions. Ultimately, the problem of acid rain may be minimized by alternative energy sources. For instance, hydroelectric power and solar power are potential sources of energy that do not pollute the atmosphere.

◀ **Acid Rain** The photograph on the left shows a limestone statue of George Washington in 1935. The recent photograph on the right shows the effect of acid rain, which attacks the statue by dissolving away calcium carbonate in the marble.

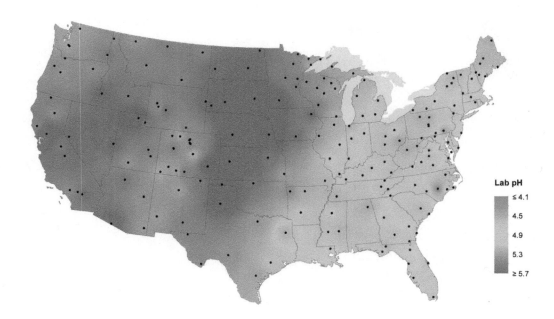

Lab pH

≤ 4.1
4.5
4.9
5.3
≥ 5.7

A: Acid rain contains carbonic acid from burning fossil fuels, nitric acid from automobile emissions, and sulfuric acid from burning low-grade coal.

14.10 STRONG AND WEAK ELECTROLYTES

Water is a weak conductor of electricity because it is very slightly ionized. In the laboratory, we can use a conductivity apparatus to determine whether a substance in an aqueous solution is a strong or a weak conductor of electricity. If an aqueous solution is a good conductor, it is called a **strong electrolyte**. If an aqueous solution is a poor conductor, it is called a **weak electrolyte**.

We can test the electrical conductivity of hydrochloric acid and acetic acid using the apparatus in Figure 14.6. From the observations, we can conclude that hydrochloric acid is highly ionized because it is a strong electrolyte. Acetic acid is only slightly ionized because it is a weak electrolyte. Similar experiments using the conductivity apparatus demonstrate the electrolyte behavior of aqueous solutions.

Degree of Ionization in an Aqueous Solution

We can measure the degree of ionization by testing the conductivity of aqueous solutions. Strong electrolytes are highly ionized. Strong electrolytes include strong acids, strong bases, and soluble ionic compounds. Soluble ionic compounds dissolve by dissociating into ions.

Weak electrolytes are slightly ionized. They include weak acids, weak bases, and slightly soluble ionic compounds. Although an ionic compound may be classified as insoluble, it is actually very slightly soluble. A sufficient amount of the insoluble ionic compound dissolves in a solution to act as a weak electrolyte. Table 14.5 lists examples of strong and weak electrolytes.

(a) Strong electrolyte

TABLE 14.5 STRONG ELECTROLYTES AND WEAK ELECTROLYTES

STRONG ELECTROLYTES	WEAK ELECTROLYTES
Strong Acids—	*Weak Acids—*
hydrochloric acid, HCl(*aq*)	hydrofluoric acid, HF(*aq*)
nitric acid, HNO_3(*aq*)	nitrous acid, HNO_2(*aq*)
sulfuric acid, H_2SO_4(*aq*)	sulfurous acid, H_2SO_3(*aq*)
perchloric acid, $HClO_4$(*aq*)	acetic acid, $HC_2H_3O_2$(*aq*)
	carbonic acid, H_2CO_3(*aq*)
	phosphoric acid, H_3PO_4(*aq*)
Strong Bases—	*Weak Bases—*
sodium hydroxide, NaOH(*aq*)	ammonium hydroxide, NH_4OH(*aq*)
potassium hydroxide, KOH(*aq*)	insoluble hydroxides such as
lithium hydroxide, LiOH(*aq*)	$Mg(OH)_2$(*s*), $Al(OH)_3$(*s*), $Fe(OH)_3$(*s*)
calcium hydroxide, $Ca(OH)_2$(*aq*)	
strontium hydroxide, $Sr(OH)_2$(*aq*)	
barium hydroxide, $Ba(OH)_2$(*aq*)	
Soluble Salts—	*Insoluble Salts*—*
sodium chloride, NaCl(*aq*)	silver chloride, AgCl(*s*)
potassium carbonate, K_2CO_3(*aq*)	calcium carbonate, $CaCO_3$(*s*)
zinc sulfate, $ZnSO_4$(*aq*)	barium sulfate, $BaSO_4$(*s*)

*Insoluble salts are very slightly soluble in water and dissociate into a sufficient number of ions to give a very weak electrolyte solution.

(b) Weak electrolyte

▲ **Figure 14.6 Conductivity of Aqueous Solutions** (a) An aqueous solution of hydrochloric acid is a strong electrolyte, and the bulb glows brightly. (b) An aqueous solution of acetic acid is a weak electrolyte, and the bulb glows dimly.

We can determine the degree of ionization in a solution from conductivity testing experiments. That is, we can distinguish between a highly ionized strong electrolyte and a slightly ionized weak electrolyte. Strong electrolytes ionize nearly completely in an aqueous solution. For example, sodium chloride and calcium chloride dissociate into ions as follows:

$$NaCl(aq) \longrightarrow Na^+(aq) + Cl^-(aq)$$

$$CaCl_2(aq) \longrightarrow Ca^{2+}(aq) + 2\,Cl^-(aq)$$

We can estimate the amount of ionization in an aqueous solution given the electrolyte strength. That is, the number of ions in solution is proportional to the conductivity. Strong electrolytes are highly ionized, and so we write their formulas in the ionized form. Weak electrolytes are only slightly ionized, and so we write their formulas in the nonionized form. The nonionized formula is sometimes referred to as the *molecular formula*. This is not quite accurate since ionic compounds exist as formula units, not molecules. The following example exercise illustrates how to write formulas for electrolytes in an aqueous solution.

Example Exercise 14.14 Strong and Weak Electrolytes

Write the ionized or nonionized formula for each of the following aqueous solutions given the electrolyte strength:

(a) $HNO_3(aq)$, strong   (b) $NH_4OH(aq)$, weak   (c) $K_2CO_3(aq)$, strong

Solution

(a) A nitric acid solution is a strong electrolyte and therefore is highly ionized. It is written in the ionized form as $H^+(aq)$ and $NO_3^-(aq)$.

(b) An ammonium hydroxide solution is a weak electrolyte and therefore is slightly ionized. It is written in the nonionized form as $NH_4OH(aq)$.

(c) A potassium carbonate solution is a strong electrolyte and therefore is highly ionized. It is written as $2\,K^+(aq)$ and $CO_3^{2-}(aq)$.

Practice Exercise

Write the ionized or nonionized formula for each of the following aqueous solutions given the electrolyte strength:

(a) $HF(aq)$, weak   (b) $Ba(OH)_2(aq)$, strong   (c) $CaCO_3(s)$, weak

Answers: (a) $HF(aq)$ (b) $Ba^{2+}(aq)$ and $2\,OH^-(aq)$ (c) $CaCO_3(s)$

Concept Exercise

When the weak acid $HF(aq)$ neutralizes the weak base $NH_4OH(aq)$, will a conductivity apparatus glow brightly or dimly?

Answer: See Appendix G.

▲ **Nitric Acid, HNO₃** Nitric acid is a strong electrolyte, which is nearly 100% ionized in an aqueous solution.

▲ **Hydrofluoric Acid, HF** Hydrofluoric acid is a weak electrolyte, which is less than 1% ionized in an aqueous solution.

Note In these examples, we considered aqueous solutions to be either strong or weak electrolytes. However, some liquids are nonelectrolytes. That is, they do not conduct electricity. Examples include organic liquids such as alcohol, ether, and acetone.

14.11 NET IONIC EQUATIONS

LEARNING OBJECTIVES

▶ To state the procedure for writing a net ionic equation.

▶ To write net ionic equations for given chemical reactions.

In Section 14.10 we learned how to write ionized formulas for strong electrolytes and nonionized formulas for weak electrolytes. The concept of ionization allows us to portray ionic solutions more accurately. That is, we can now write chemical equations by showing strong electrolytes in the ionized form.

Let's consider the neutralization reaction of hydrochloric acid and sodium hydroxide. The nonionized equation for the reaction is

$$HCl(aq) + NaOH(aq) \longrightarrow NaCl(aq) + H_2O(l)$$

By writing the ionized formula for the strong acid, strong base, and soluble salt, we can describe the reaction more accurately. Each substance in the **total ionic equation** is written as it primarily exists in the solution. Table 14.5 shows highly ionized substances. Strong electrolytes include HCl, NaOH, and NaCl. Thus, the equation is

$$H^+(aq) + Cl^-(aq) + Na^+(aq) + OH^-(aq) \longrightarrow Na^+(aq) + Cl^-(aq) + H_2O(l)$$

Note that $Na^+(aq)$ and $Cl^-(aq)$ appear on both sides of the equation. These ions are called **spectator ions**. They are in the solution but do not participate in the reaction. We can simplify the total ionic equation by eliminating spectator ions. The resulting **net ionic equation** shows only the substances undergoing reaction. The net ionic equation for the preceding reaction is

$$H^+(aq) + OH^-(aq) \longrightarrow H_2O(l)$$

▲ **Hydrochloric Acid, HCl**
Hydrochloric acid is a strong acid, which is nearly 100% ionized in an aqueous solution.

▲ **Sodium Hydroxide, NaOH**
Sodium hydroxide is a strong base, which is nearly 100% dissociated in an aqueous solution.

▲ **Sodium Chloride, NaCl**
Sodium chloride is a soluble salt, which is nearly 100% dissociated in an aqueous solution.

Note that we do not show the actual acid and base that were neutralized. This net ionic equation indicates that a strong acid and a strong base reacted to give water. In fact, the net ionic equation is identical for all strong acid and strong base reactions that yield a soluble salt.

Let's state a general procedure to be used when we write net ionic equations. Keep in mind that the net ionic equation gives us a good picture of substances undergoing reaction. That is, the net ionic equation helps us focus on only those substances that are undergoing reaction.

General Guidelines for Writing Net Ionic Equations

1. Complete and balance the nonionized chemical equation.
2. Convert the nonionized equation to a total ionic equation. Write strong electrolytes in the ionized form and weak electrolytes in the nonionized form. Write water and dissolved gases in the nonionized form. Refer to Table 7.2 to determine if a compound is soluble or insoluble.
3. Cancel spectator ions to obtain the net ionic equation.
   (a) If canceling spectator ions eliminates all species, there is no reaction.
   (b) If the coefficients can be simplified, do so to have the simplest whole number relationship.
4. Check ($\sqrt{}$) each ion or atom on both sides of the equation. The total charge (positive or negative) on the reactants side of the equation must equal the total charge on the products side of the equation.

The following example exercises illustrate the procedure for writing balanced net ionic equations.

Example Exercise 14.15 Net Ionic Equations for Neutralization Reactions

Write a net ionic equation for the reaction between nitric acid and aqueous potassium hydrogen carbonate.

$$HNO_3(aq) + KHCO_3(aq) \longrightarrow KNO_3(aq) + H_2O(l) + CO_2(g)$$

Solution

Step 1: We verify that the chemical equation is balanced. In this case, the coefficients are all 1 and the equation is balanced.

Step 2: We determine which species are highly ionized. From Table 14.5, we find that HNO_3 is a strong electrolyte. From Table 7.2, we find that $KHCO_3$ and KNO_3 are soluble strong electrolytes; H_2O and CO_2 are weak electrolytes. The total ionic equation is

$$H^+(aq) + NO_3^-(aq) + K^+(aq) + HCO_3^-(aq) \longrightarrow K^+(aq) + NO_3^-(aq) + H_2O(l) + CO_2(g)$$

Step 3: We obtain the net ionic equation by eliminating the spectator ions. In this example, K^+ and NO_3^- are in the aqueous solution, but do not participate in the reaction. The net ionic equation is

$$H^+(aq) + HCO_3^-(aq) \longrightarrow H_2O(l) + CO_2(g)$$

Step 4: We check to verify that the net ionic equation is balanced. The equation is balanced because (a) the number of atoms of each element is the same on each side and (b) the total charge on both sides is identical. In this case the net charge is zero.

Practice Exercise

Write a net ionic equation for the reaction between aqueous solutions of nitric acid and barium hydroxide.

$$2\,HNO_3(aq) + Ba(OH)_2(aq) \longrightarrow Ba(NO_3)_2(aq) + 2\,H_2O(l)$$

Answer: In this example, nitrate and barium are spectator ions and cancel.

$$H^+(aq) + OH^-(aq) \longrightarrow H_2O(l)$$

Concept Exercise

When the strong acid $HNO_3(aq)$ neutralizes the strong base $Ba(OH)_2(aq)$, will a conductivity apparatus glow brightly or dimly?

Answer: See Appendix G.

Example Exercise 14.16 Net Ionic Equations for Precipitation Reactions

Write a net ionic equation for the reaction between aqueous solutions of silver nitrate and aluminum chloride.

$$AgNO_3(aq) + AlCl_3(aq) \longrightarrow AgCl(s) + Al(NO_3)_3(aq)$$

Solution

Step 1: We balance the chemical equation as follows:

$$3\,AgNO_3(aq) + AlCl_3(aq) \longrightarrow 3\,AgCl(s) + Al(NO_3)_3(aq)$$

Step 2: We determine which of the species are strong electrolytes. From Table 7.2, we find that all the compounds are soluble except AgCl. Thus, AgCl is weakly ionized, and the total ionic equation is written as

$$3\,Ag^+(aq) + 3\,NO_3^-(aq) + Al^{3+}(aq) + 3\,Cl^-(aq) \longrightarrow 3\,AgCl(s) + Al^{3+}(aq) + 3\,NO_3^-(aq)$$

Step 3: We cancel spectator ions. In this example, Al^{3+} and NO_3^- do not participate in the reaction.

$$3\,Ag^+(aq) + 3\,Cl^-(aq) \longrightarrow 3\,AgCl(s)$$

Step 4: We verify that the equation is balanced. Note that each species has a coefficient of 3 in this equation. Thus, after simplifying, the net ionic equation is written as

$$Ag^+(aq) + Cl^-(aq) \longrightarrow AgCl(s)$$

Practice Exercise

Write a net ionic equation for the reaction between aqueous solutions of lithium sulfate and magnesium nitrate.

$$Li_2SO_4(aq) + Mg(NO_3)_2(aq) \longrightarrow MgSO_4(aq) + 2\,LiNO_3(aq)$$

Answer: $Li_2SO_4(aq) + Mg(NO_3)_2(aq) \longrightarrow$ no reaction

Concept Exercise

When the two strong electrolytes, $AgNO_3(aq)$ and $AlCl_3(aq)$, react to give insoluble $AgCl(s)$, will a conductivity apparatus glow brightly or dimly?

Answer: See Appendix G.

▲ **Silver Nitrate, AgNO₃** Silver nitrate is a soluble salt, which is nearly 100% dissociated in an aqueous solution.

▲ **Aluminum Chloride, AlCl₃** Aluminum chloride is a soluble salt, which is nearly 100% dissociated in an aqueous solution.

▲ **Silver Chloride, AgCl** Silver chloride is an insoluble salt, which is less than 1% dissociated in an aqueous solution.

Summary

LEARNING OBJECTIVES	SEC	EXERCISES
To list the general properties of acids and bases.	14.1	Exercises 1–2
To classify a solution of given pH as one of the following: strongly acidic, weakly acidic, neutral, weakly basic, or strongly basic.	14.1	Exercises 3–4
To identify an Arrhenius acid and base.	14.2	Exercises 5–8
To classify an acid and base as strong or weak given the degree of ionization.	14.2	Exercises 9–10
To indicate the acid and base that react to produce a given salt.	14.2	Exercises 11–14
To identify a Brønsted–Lowry acid and base in a neutralization reaction.	14.3	Exercises 15–20
To state the color of a solution with a given pH and a drop of phenolphthalein, methyl red, or bromthymol blue indicator.	14.4	Exercises 21–26
To perform calculations given acid–base titration data.	14.5	Exercises 27–32
To express the molarity of a solution as a mass percent concentration.	14.5	Exercises 33–34
To understand the concept of a standard acid or base solution.	14.6	Exercises 35–36
To perform calculations that involve standardization of an acid or base.	14.6	Exercises 35–42
To relate the ionization constant of water to the molar hydrogen ion and hydroxide ion concentrations.	14.7	Exercises 43–44
To calculate the molar hydroxide ion concentration given the molar hydrogen ion concentration.	14.7	Exercises 45–48
To relate pH and molar hydrogen ion concentration.	14.8	Exercises 49–52
To calculate pH values and molar hydrogen ion concentrations.	14.9	Exercises 53–60
To state the electrical conductivity of strong and weak electrolytes.	14.10	Exercises 61–66
To portray strong and weak electrolytes as ionized or nonionized.	14.10	Exercises 67–70
To state the procedure for writing a net ionic equation.	14.11	Exercises 71–72
To write net ionic equations for given chemical reactions.	14.11	Exercises 73–76

Section 14.1 The properties of an acid include having a sour taste, turning litmus paper red, having a pH less than 7, and the ability to neutralize a base. The properties of a base include having a bitter taste, being slippery to the touch, turning litmus paper blue, and having a pH greater than 7. A solution that resists changes in pH when an acid or a base is added is referred to as a **buffer**.

Section 14.2 An **Arrhenius acid** is a substance that undergoes **ionization** in water to give hydrogen ions. Hydrochloric acid is a strong acid because it ionizes extensively. Acetic acid is a weak acid because it does not ionize extensively. A hydrogen ion attaches to a water molecule in solution to form a **hydronium ion**. An **Arrhenius base** is a substance that undergoes **dissociation** in water to give hydroxide ions. A **salt** is obtained from the reaction of an acid and a base. Barium nitrate, $Ba(NO_3)_2$, is obtained from the neutralization of barium hydroxide and nitric acid.

Section 14.3 A **Brønsted–Lowry acid** is a **proton donor** and a **Brønsted–Lowry base** is a **proton acceptor**. A substance capable of either donating or accepting a proton in an acid–base reaction is said to be **amphiprotic**.

Section 14.4 We can use litmus paper to indicate if a solution is acidic or basic. In the laboratory, we can use an **acid–base indicator**. Three of the most common indicators are methyl red, bromthymol blue, and phenolphthalein. Methyl red changes color at a pH of 5, bromthymol blue changes at a pH of 7, and phenolphthalein at a pH of 9.

Section 14.5 A **titration** is a laboratory procedure for analyzing the amount of acid or base present in a solution. A measured volume of acid or base solution is delivered with a buret into a flask containing a known amount of sample. An indicator is used to signal the neutralization point in the titration. When the **endpoint** is reached, the indicator changes color, and the titration is stopped.

Section 14.6 The concentration of a **standard solution** is known accurately to at least three significant digits. Standard solutions are used to analyze the amount of acid or base in a given sample. For example, a chemist can determine the concentration of acetic acid in vinegar or the amount of baking soda in an antacid tablet.

Section 14.7 On the basis of conductivity experiments, pure water is found to be a very weak electrolyte. Water ionizes to give only a few hydrogen and hydroxide ions. $[H^+]$ and $[OH^-]$ are equal, and both have a value of 1×10^{-7}. The **ionization constant of water**, K_w, is 1×10^{-14} at 25 °C. In every aqueous solution, there is always a small number of both H^+ and OH^-.

Section 14.8 The **pH** of a solution expresses $[H^+]$ on an exponential scale. That is, a solution of pH 1 is 10 times more acidic than a solution of pH 2. To calculate the pH of a solution, we express $[H^+]$ as a power of 10 and change the sign of the exponent. For example, if $[H^+]$ is 10^{-2} M, the pH is 2. Conversely, to find $[H^+]$ given the pH, we raise 10 to the negative pH. For example, if the pH is 3, $[H^+]$ is 10^{-3} M, that is, 0.001 M.

Section 14.9 To calculate the pH of solutions whose hydrogen ion concentrations are not whole-number powers of 10, we find the negative logarithm values using a scientific calculator. That is, the pH is equal to $-\log[H^+]$. Conversely, to calculate the hydrogen ion concentration that corresponds to a given pH, we find the inverse logarithm of $-$pH using a calculator.

Section 14.10 A strong acid, a strong base, and a soluble ionic compound are each an example of a **strong electrolyte**. Therefore, these solutions are highly ionized. Hydrochloric acid is a strong acid and is written as $H^+(aq)$ and $Cl^-(aq)$. Sodium chloride is soluble in water and is represented as $Na^+(aq)$ and $Cl^-(aq)$. A weak acid, a weak base, and a slightly soluble ionic compound are each an example of a **weak electrolyte**. Therefore, these solutions are slightly ionized. Acetic acid is a weak acid and is written as $HC_2H_3O_2(aq)$. The slightly soluble ionic compound silver chloride is written as $AgCl(s)$.

Section 14.11 A **net ionic equation** portrays a solution reaction more accurately. The first step is to balance the chemical equation. Second, write a **total ionic equation** for the reaction. Strong electrolytes are written as ions in solution and weak electrolytes as nonionized. Third, cancel **spectator ions** that are identical on both sides of the equation. Verify the net ionic equation is balanced correctly and simplify the coefficients when possible.

PROBLEM-SOLVING ORGANIZER

TOPIC	PROCEDURE	EXAMPLE
Acid–Base Titrations Sec. 14.5	1. Write down the unit asked for in the answer. 2. Write down the related given value. 3. Apply unit factors to convert the given unit to the unit in the answer.	If 10.00 mL of 0.100 M sulfuric acid neutralizes 15.50 mL of KOH, what is the molarity of the base? Given: $H_2SO_4(aq) + 2KOH(aq) \longrightarrow K_2SO_4(aq) + 2H_2O(l)$ $10.00 \text{ mL solution} \times \dfrac{0.100 \text{ mol } H_2SO_4}{1000 \text{ mL solution}} \times \dfrac{2 \text{ mol KOH}}{1 \text{ mol } H_2SO_4}$ $= 0.00200 \text{ mol KOH}$ $\dfrac{0.00200 \text{ mol KOH}}{15.50 \text{ mL solution}} \times \dfrac{1000 \text{ mL solution}}{1 \text{ L solution}} = 0.129 \ M \text{ KOH}$
Acid–Base Standardization Sec. 14.6	1. Write down the unit asked for in the answer. 2. Write down the related given value. 3. Apply unit factors to convert the given unit to the unit in the answer.	If 15.50 mL of KOH neutralizes 0.995 g of KHP (204.23 g/mol), $KHC_8H_4O_4$, what is the molarity of the base? Given: $KHP(aq) + KOH(aq) \longrightarrow K_2P(aq) + H_2O(l)$ $0.995 \text{ g KHP} \times \dfrac{1 \text{ mol KHP}}{204.23 \text{ g KHP}} \times \dfrac{1 \text{ mol KOH}}{1 \text{ mol KHP}}$ $= 0.00487 \text{ mol KOH}$ $\dfrac{0.0487 \text{ mol KOH}}{15.50 \text{ mL solution}} \times \dfrac{1000 \text{ mL solution}}{1 \text{ L solution}} = 0.314 \ M \text{ KOH}$
Ionization of Water Sec. 14.7	Solve for $[H^+]$ or $[OH^-]$ in an aqueous solution using the ionization of water equation. $K_w = [H^+][OH^-]$	If $[H^+]$ is 0.0015 M in an aqueous solution, what is the hydroxide ion concentration? $[H^+][OH^-] = 1.0 \times 10^{-14}$ $[0.0015][OH^-] = 1.0 \times 10^{-14}$ $[OH^-] = 6.7 \times 10^{-12}$
The pH Concept Sec. 14.8	Convert from $[H^+]$ to pH using the following equation: $pH = -\log[H^+]$	If $[H^+]$ in an acid is 0.001 M, what is the pH? $pH = -\log[10^{-3}] = -(-3)$ $= 3$
Advanced pH Calculations Sec. 14.9	Convert from pH to $[H^+]$ using the following equation: $[H^+] = 10^{-pH}$	If the pH of an acid is 3.20, what is the $[H^+]$? $[H^+] = 10^{-3.20} = 0.00063 \ M$

Key Terms   *Answers to Key Terms are in Appendix H.*

Select the key term that corresponds to each of the following definitions.

_____ **1.** a solution that resists changes in pH when an acid or a base is added

_____ **2.** a substance that releases hydrogen ions when dissolved in water

_____ **3.** a substance that releases hydroxide ions when dissolved in water

_____ **4.** the process of a polar compound dissolving in water and forming positive and negative ions

_____ **5.** the process of an ionic compound dissolving in water and separating into positive and negative ions

_____ **6.** the ion that best represents the hydrogen ion in an aqueous solution

_____ **7.** a product obtained from a neutralization reaction in addition to water

_____ **8.** a substance that donates a proton in an acid–base reaction

_____ **9.** a substance that accepts a proton in an acid–base reaction

_____ **10.** a synonym for hydrogen ion donor

_____ **11.** a synonym for hydrogen ion acceptor

_____ **12.** a substance capable of either donating or accepting a proton in an acid–base reaction

_____ **13.** a chemical substance that changes color according to the pH of the solution

_____ **14.** a procedure for delivering a measured volume of solution using a buret

_____ **15.** the stage in a titration when the indicator changes color

_____ **16.** a solution whose concentration has been established precisely

_____ **17.** a constant that equals the product of the molar hydrogen ion concentration and the molar hydroxide ion concentration

_____ **18.** the molar hydrogen ion concentration expressed on an exponential scale

_____ **19.** an aqueous solution that is a good conductor of electricity

_____ **20.** an aqueous solution that is a poor conductor of electricity

_____ **21.** a chemical equation that shows ionized substances in solution as ions and slightly ionized substances as nonionized

_____ **22.** ions in an aqueous solution that do not participate in a reaction, and do not appear in the net ionic equation

_____ **23.** a chemical equation that results from canceling spectator ions in a total ionic equation

(a) acid–base indicator (*Sec. 14.4*)

(b) amphiprotic (*Sec. 14.3*)

(c) Arrhenius acid (*Sec. 14.2*)

(d) Arrhenius base (*Sec. 14.2*)

(e) Brønsted–Lowry acid (*Sec. 14.3*)

(f) Brønsted–Lowry base (*Sec. 14.3*)

(g) buffer (*Sec. 14.1*)

(h) dissociation (*Sec. 14.2*)

(i) endpoint (*Sec. 14.5*)

(j) hydronium ion (H_3O^-) (*Sec. 14.2*)

(k) ionization (*Sec. 14.2*)

(l) ionization constant of water (K_w) (*Sec. 14.7*)

(m) net ionic equation (*Sec. 14.11*)

(n) pH (*Sec. 14.8*)

(o) proton acceptor (*Sec. 14.3*)

(p) proton donor (*Sec. 14.3*)

(q) salt (*Sec. 14.2*)

(r) spectator ions (*Sec. 14.11*)

(s) standard solution (*Sec. 14.6*)

(t) strong electrolyte (*Sec. 14.10*)

(u) titration (*Sec. 14.5*)

(v) total ionic equation (*Sec. 14.11*)

(w) weak electrolyte (*Sec. 14.10*)

Exercises   *Answers to odd-numbered Exercises are in Appendix I.*

Properties of Acids and Bases (Sec. 14.1)

1. Which of the following is a general property of an acidic solution?
   (a) tastes sour   **(b)** turns litmus paper red
   (c) pH less than 7   **(d)** neutralizes a base

2. Which of the following is a general property of a basic solution?
   (a) tastes bitter   **(b)** turns litmus paper blue
   (c) pH greater than 7   **(d)** feels slippery

3. Classify the following aqueous solutions as strongly acidic, weakly acidic, neutral, weakly basic, or strongly basic:
   (a) stomach acid, pH 1.5   **(b)** vinegar, pH 3.2
   (c) shampoo, pH 7.0   **(d)** ammonia, pH 11.1

4. Classify the following aqueous solutions as strongly acidic, weakly acidic, neutral, weakly basic, or strongly basic:
   (a) battery acid, pH 0   **(b)** lime juice, pH 2.7
   (c) distilled water, pH 7.0 **(d)** drain cleaner, pH 13.5

▲ **Common Acids** Methyl red indicator is added to beakers of lime juice, vinegar, and club soda. The color of the indicator shows a different pH in each beaker.

Arrhenius Acids and Bases (Sec. 14.2)

5. Classify each of the following Arrhenius acids as strong or weak given the degree of ionization:
   (a) acetic acid, $HC_2H_3O_2(aq)$, ~1%
   (b) carbonic acid, $H_2CO_3(aq)$, ~1%
   (c) chlorous acid, $HClO_2(aq)$, ~1%
   (d) chloric acid, $HClO_3(aq)$, ~100%

6. Classify each of the following Arrhenius bases as strong or weak given the degree of ionization:
   (a) lithium hydroxide, $LiOH(aq)$, ~100%
   (b) calcium hydroxide, $Ca(OH)_2(aq)$, ~100%
   (c) barium hydroxide, $Ba(OH)_2(aq)$, ~100%
   (d) ammonium hydroxide, $NH_4OH(aq)$, ~1%

7. Classify each of the following as an Arrhenius acid, an Arrhenius base, or a salt:
   (a) $HNO_3(aq)$ (b) $KNO_3(aq)$
   (c) $KOH(aq)$ (d) $K_2CO_3(aq)$

8. Classify each of the following as an Arrhenius acid, an Arrhenius base, or a salt:
   (a) $H_2SO_4(aq)$ (b) $CaSO_4(aq)$
   (c) $Ca(OH)_2(aq)$ (d) $CaCO_3(aq)$

9. Identify the Arrhenius acid and Arrhenius base in each of the following neutralization reactions:
   (a) $HI(aq) + NaOH(aq) \longrightarrow NaI(aq) + H_2O(l)$
   (b) $HC_2H_3O_2(aq) + LiOH(aq) \longrightarrow LiC_2H_3O_2(aq) + H_2O(l)$

10. Identify the Arrhenius acid and Arrhenius base in each of the following neutralization reactions:
    (a) $2\,HClO_3(aq) + Ba(OH)_2(aq) \longrightarrow$
    $$Ba(ClO_3)_2(aq) + 2\,H_2O(l)$$
    (b) $H_2SO_4(aq) + 2\,KOH(aq) \longrightarrow K_2SO_4(aq) + 2\,H_2O(l)$

11. Determine the acid and base that were neutralized to produce each of the following salts:
    (a) sodium fluoride, $NaF(aq)$
    (b) magnesium iodide, $MgI_2(aq)$
    (c) calcium nitrate, $Ca(NO_3)_2(aq)$
    (d) lithium carbonate, $Li_2CO_3(aq)$

12. Determine the acid and base that were neutralized to produce each of the following salts:
    (a) potassium bromide, $KBr(aq)$
    (b) barium chloride, $BaCl_2(aq)$
    (c) cobalt(II) sulfate, $CoSO_4(aq)$
    (d) sodium phosphate, $Na_3PO_4(aq)$

13. Complete and balance the following neutralization reactions:
    (a) $HNO_3(aq) + Ca(OH)_2(aq) \longrightarrow$
    (b) $H_2CO_3(aq) + Ba(OH)_2(aq) \longrightarrow$

14. Complete and balance the following neutralization reactions:
    (a) $HC_2H_3O_2(aq) + Sr(OH)_2(aq) \longrightarrow$
    (b) $H_2SO_4(aq) + NH_4OH(aq) \longrightarrow$

Brønsted–Lowry Acids and Bases (Sec. 14.3)

15. Identify the Brønsted–Lowry acid and base in each of the following neutralization reactions:
    (a) $HC_2H_3O_2(aq) + LiOH(aq) \longrightarrow LiC_2H_3O_2(aq) + H_2O(l)$
    (b) $2\,NH_3(aq) + H_2SO_4(aq) \longrightarrow (NH_4)_2SO_4(aq)$

16. Identify the Brønsted–Lowry acid and base in each of the following neutralization reactions:
    (a) $2\,HClO_4(aq) + K_2CO_3(aq) \longrightarrow$
    $$2\,KClO_4(aq) + H_2O(l) + CO_2(g)$$
    (b) $NaCN(aq) + HBr(aq) \longrightarrow NaBr(aq) + HCN(aq)$

17. Identify the Brønsted–Lowry acid and base in each of the following neutralization reactions:
    (a) $HI(aq) + H_2O(l) \longrightarrow H_3O^+(aq) + I^-(aq)$
    (b) $HC_2H_3O_2(aq) + HS^-(aq) \longrightarrow H_2S(aq) + C_2H_3O_2^-(aq)$

18. Identify the Brønsted–Lowry acid and base in each of the following neutralization reactions:
    (a) $HCO_3^-(aq) + OH^-(aq) \longrightarrow CO_3^{2-}(aq) + H_2O(l)$
    (b) $NO_2^-(aq) + HClO_4(aq) \longrightarrow HNO_2(aq) + ClO_4^-(aq)$

19. Complete and balance the following Brønsted–Lowry neutralization reactions:
    (a) $HF(aq) + NaHS(aq) \longrightarrow$
    (b) $HNO_2(aq) + NaC_2H_3O_2(aq) \longrightarrow$

20. Complete and balance the following Brønsted–Lowry neutralization reactions:
    (a) $H_3O^+(aq) + SO_4^{2-}(aq) \longrightarrow$
    (b) $H_2PO_4^-(aq) + NH_3(aq) \longrightarrow$

Acid–Base Indicators (Sec. 14.4)

21. Given the following pH values for solutions containing a drop of methyl red indicator, state the color of each solution:
    (a) pH 3   (b) pH 7

22. What is the color of methyl red indicator in a solution of pH 5?

23. Given the following pH values for solutions containing a drop of bromthymol blue indicator, state the color of each solution:
    (a) pH 5   (b) pH 9

24. What is the color of bromthymol blue indicator in a solution of pH 7?

25. Given the following pH values for solutions containing a drop of phenolphthalein indicator, state the color of each solution:
    (a) pH 6   (b) pH 12

26. What is the color of phenolphthalein indicator in deionized water?

◀ **Natural Indicator** A rose contains a natural acid–base indicator. After the indicator is extracted from the dark-red rose (left beaker), the rose petals are a pale pink (right beaker).

Acid–Base Titrations (Sec. 14.5)

27. If the titration of a 10.0-mL sample of sulfuric acid requires 28.15 mL of 0.100 M sodium hydroxide, what is the molarity of the acid?

$$H_2SO_4(aq) + 2\,NaOH(aq) \longrightarrow Na_2SO_4(aq) + 2\,H_2O(l)$$

28. If the titration of a 25.0-mL sample of acetic acid requires 34.45 mL of 0.100 M calcium hydroxide, what is the molarity of the acid?

$$2\,HC_2H_3O_2(aq) + Ca(OH)_2(aq) \longrightarrow$$
$$Ca(C_2H_3O_2)_2(aq) + 2H_2O(l)$$

29. If 34.45 mL of 0.210 M NaOH neutralizes 50.0 mL of phosphoric acid, what is the molarity of the acid?

$$H_3PO_4(aq) + 3\,NaOH(aq) \longrightarrow Na_3PO_4(aq) + 3\,H_2O(l)$$

30. If 29.50 mL of 0.175 M nitric acid neutralizes 50.0 mL of ammonium hydroxide, what is the molarity of the base?

$$HNO_3(aq) + NH_4OH(aq) \longrightarrow NH_4NO_3(aq) + H_2O(l)$$

31. How many milliliters of 0.100 M potassium hydroxide are required to completely neutralize 10.0 mL of 0.165 M H_2SO_3?

$$H_2SO_3(aq) + 2\,KOH(aq) \longrightarrow K_2SO_3(aq) + 2\,H_2O(l)$$

32. How many milliliters of 0.100 M barium hydroxide are required to completely neutralize 10.0 mL of 0.225 M HNO_2?

$$2\,HNO_2(aq) + Ba(OH)_2(aq) \longrightarrow Ba(NO_2)_2(aq) + 2\,H_2O(l)$$

33. Given the molarity and density for each of the following acidic solutions, calculate the mass/mass percent concentration:
    (a) 6.00 M HCl($d = 1.10\,g/mL$)
    (b) 1.00 M $HC_2H_3O_2$($d = 1.01\,g/mL$)
    (c) 0.500 M HNO_3($d = 1.01\,g/mL$)
    (d) 3.00 M H_2SO_4($d = 1.18\,g/mL$)

34. Given the molarity and density for each of the following basic solutions, calculate the mass/mass percent concentration:
    (a) 3.00 M NaOH($d = 1.12\,g/mL$)
    (b) 0.500 M KOH($d = 1.02\,g/mL$)
    (c) 6.00 M NH_3($d = 0.954\,g/mL$)
    (d) 1.00 M Na_2CO_3($d = 1.10\,g/mL$)

Acid–Base Standardization (Sec. 14.6)

35. What is the molarity of standard sulfuric acid if 27.75 mL of H_2SO_4 neutralizes 1.000 g of sodium hydrogen carbonate?

$$H_2SO_4(aq) + 2\,NaHCO_3(aq) \longrightarrow \\ Na_2SO_4(aq) + 2\,H_2O(l) + 2\,CO_2(g)$$

36. What is the molarity of standard nitric acid if 33.25 mL of HNO_3 neutralizes 0.500 g of sodium carbonate?

$$2\,HNO_3(aq) + Na_2CO_3(aq) \longrightarrow \\ NaNO_3(aq) + H_2O(l) + CO_2(g)$$

37. What is the molarity of hydrochloric acid if 40.95 mL of HCl is required to neutralize 0.550 g of sodium oxalate, $Na_2C_2O_4$?

$$2\,HCl(aq) + Na_2C_2O_4(aq) \longrightarrow H_2C_2O_4(aq) + 2\,NaCl(aq)$$

38. What is the molarity of sodium hydroxide if 28.85 mL of NaOH is required to neutralize 0.506 g of oxalic acid, $H_2C_2O_4$?

$$H_2C_2O_4(aq) + NaOH(aq) \longrightarrow NaHC_2O_4(aq) + H_2O(l)$$

39. What volume of 0.479 M lithium hydroxide is required to neutralize 0.627 g of oxalic acid, $H_2C_2O_4$?

$$H_2C_2O_4(aq) + 2\,LiOH(aq) \longrightarrow Li_2C_2O_4(aq) + 2\,H_2O(l)$$

40. What volume of 0.167 M barium hydroxide is required to neutralize 1.655 g of potassium hydrogen phthalate, $KHC_8H_4O_4$(204.23 g/mol)?

$$2\,KHC_8H_4O_4(aq) + Ba(OH)_2(aq) \longrightarrow \\ BaK_2(C_8H_4O_4)_2(aq) + 2\,H_2O(l)$$

41. Ascorbic acid, abbreviated HAsc, is the chemical name for vitamin C. If 30.95 mL of 0.176 M NaOH neutralizes 0.959 g of acid, what is the molar mass of vitamin C?

$$HAsc(aq) + NaOH(aq) \longrightarrow NaAsc(aq) + H_2O(l)$$

42. Tartaric acid, abbreviated H_2Tart, gives grapes a sour taste. If 28.15 mL of 0.295 M NaOH neutralizes 0.623 g of acid, what is the molar mass of tartaric acid?

$$H_2Tart(aq) + 2\,NaOH(aq) \longrightarrow Na_2Tart(aq) + 2\,H_2O(l)$$

Ionization of Water (Sec. 14.7)

43. Indicate each of the following for the ionization of pure water:
    (a) the simplified ionization equation
    (b) the ionization constant equation, K_w
    (c) the ionization constant at 25 °C

44. Indicate each of the following for the ionization of pure water:
    (a) the molecular collision equation
    (b) the molar hydrogen ion concentration at 25 °C
    (c) the molar hydroxide ion concentration at 25 °C

45. Given the molar concentration of hydrogen ion, calculate the concentration of hydroxide ion:
    (a) $[H^+] = 0.025$ (b) $[H^+] = 0.000\,017$

46. Given the molar concentration of hydrogen ion, calculate the concentration of hydroxide ion:
    (a) $[H^+] = 6.2 \times 10^{-7}$ (b) $[H^+] = 4.6 \times 10^{-12}$

47. Given the molar concentration of hydroxide ion, calculate the concentration of hydrogen ion:
    (a) $[OH^-] = 0.0016$ (b) $[OH^-] = 0.000\,29$

48. Given the molar concentration of hydroxide ion, calculate the concentration of hydrogen ion:
    (a) $[OH^-] = 8.8 \times 10^{-8}$ (b) $[OH^-] = 4.6 \times 10^{-13}$

The pH Concept (Sec. 14.8)

49. Calculate the pH of each of the following given the molar hydrogen ion concentration:
    (a) soft drink, $[H^+] = 0.001\,M$
    (b) coffee, $[H^+] = 0.000\,01\,M$

50. Calculate the pH of each of the following given the molar hydrogen ion concentration:
    (a) egg white, $[H^+] = 0.000\,000\,01\,M$
    (b) sour milk, $[H^+] = 0.000\,001\,M$

51. Calculate the molar hydrogen ion concentration of each of the following given the pH:
    (a) shampoo, pH 6   (b) pH-balanced shampoo, pH 8

52. Calculate the molar hydrogen ion concentration of each of the following given the pH:
    (a) phosphate detergent, pH 9
    (b) nonphosphate detergent, pH 11

Advanced pH Calculations (Sec. 14.9)

53. Calculate the pH of each of the following given the molar hydrogen ion concentration:
    (a) milk, $[H^+] = 0.000\,000\,30\,M$
    (b) eggs, $[H^+] = 0.000\,000\,016\,M$

54. Calculate the pH of each of the following given the molar hydrogen ion concentration:
    (a) carrots, $[H^+] = 0.000\,007\,9\,M$
    (b) peas, $[H^+] = 0.000\,000\,39\,M$

55. Calculate the molar hydrogen ion concentration of each of the following biological solutions given the pH:
    (a) gastric juice, pH = 1.80
    (b) urine, pH = 4.75

56. Calculate the molar hydrogen ion concentration of each of the following biological solutions given the pH:
    (a) saliva, pH = 6.55   (b) blood, pH = 7.50

57. Calculate the pH of each of the following given the molar hydroxide ion concentration:
    (a) $[OH^-] = 0.11\ M$ (b) $[OH^-] = 0.000\ 55\ M$

58. Calculate the pH of each of the following given the molar hydroxide ion concentration:
    (a) $[OH^-] = 0.000\ 031\ M$
    (b) $[OH^-] = 0.000\ 000\ 000\ 66\ M$

59. Calculate the molar hydroxide ion concentration of each of the following solutions given the pH:
    (a) pH = 0.90   (b) pH = 1.62

60. Calculate the molar hydroxide ion concentration of each of the following solutions given the pH:
    (a) pH = 4.55   (b) pH = 5.20

Strong and Weak Electrolytes (Sec. 14.10)

61. State whether each of the following substances in an aqueous solution is highly ionized or slightly ionized:
    (a) strong acids
    (b) strong bases
    (c) soluble ionic compounds

62. State whether each of the following substances in an aqueous solution is highly ionized or slightly ionized:
    (a) weak acids
    (b) weak bases
    (c) slightly soluble ionic compounds

63. Classify each of the following acids as a strong or weak electrolyte:
    (a) $HF(aq)$ (b) $HCl(aq)$
    (c) $HNO_3(aq)$ (d) $HNO_2(aq)$

64. Classify each of the following bases as a strong or weak electrolyte:
    (a) $KOH(aq)$ (b) $NH_4OH(aq)$
    (c) $Sr(OH)_2(aq)$ (d) $Al(OH)_3(s)$

65. Classify each of the following aqueous solutions as a strong or weak electrolyte:
    (a) $ZnCO_3(s)$ (b) $Sr(NO_3)_2(aq)$
    (c) $K_2SO_4(aq)$ (d) $PbI_2(s)$

66. Classify each of the following aqueous solutions as a strong or weak electrolyte:
    (a) $Fe(C_2H_3O_2)_3(aq)$ (b) $AlPO_4(s)$
    (c) $Ag_2CrO_4(s)$ (d) $CdSO_4(aq)$

67. Write the following acids in either the ionized or the nonionized form to best represent an aqueous solution:
    (a) $HF(aq)$ (b) $HBr(aq)$
    (c) $HNO_3(aq)$ (d) $HNO_2(aq)$

68. Write the following bases in either the ionized or the nonionized form to best represent an aqueous solution:
    (a) $NaOH(aq)$ (b) $NH_4OH(aq)$
    (c) $Ba(OH)_2(aq)$ (d) $Al(OH)_3(s)$

69. Write the following salts in either the ionized or the nonionized form to best represent an aqueous solution:
    (a) $AgF(aq)$ (b) $AgI(s)$
    (c) $Hg_2Cl_2(s)$ (d) $NiCl_2(aq)$

70. Write the following salts in either the ionized or the nonionized form to best represent an aqueous solution:
    (a) $AlPO_4(s)$ (b) $Co(C_2H_3O_2)_3(aq)$
    (c) $MnSO_4(aq)$ (d) $PbSO_4(s)$

Net Ionic Equations (Sec. 14.11)

71. List the four steps for writing a balanced net ionic equation.

72. What term describes ions in a total ionic equation that do not react?

73. Write a balanced net ionic equation for each of the following acid–base reactions. Refer to Table 14.5 and Appendix D for electrolyte information.
    (a) $HCl(aq) + KOH(aq) \longrightarrow KCl(aq) + H_2O(l)$
    (b) $HC_2H_3O_2(aq) + Ca(OH)_2(aq) \longrightarrow$
    $Ca(C_2H_3O_2)_2(aq) + H_2O(l)$

74. Write a balanced net ionic equation for each of the following acid–base reactions. Refer to Table 14.5 and Appendix D for electrolyte information.
    (a) $HF(aq) + Li_2CO_3(aq) \longrightarrow LiF(aq) + H_2O(l) + CO_2(g)$
    (b) $H_2SO_4(aq) + Ba(OH)_2(aq) \longrightarrow BaSO_4(s) + H_2O(l)$

75. Write a balanced net ionic equation for each of the following solution reactions. Refer to Table 14.5 and Appendix D for electrolyte information.
    (a) $AgNO_3(aq) + KI(aq) \longrightarrow AgI(s) + KNO_3(aq)$
    (b) $BaCl_2(aq) + K_2CrO_4(aq) \longrightarrow BaCrO_4(s) + KCl(aq)$

76. Write a balanced net ionic equation for each of the following solution reactions. Refer to Table 14.5 and Appendix D for electrolyte information.
    (a) $Zn(NO_3)_2(aq) + NaOH(aq) \longrightarrow$
    $Zn(OH)_2(s) + NaNO_3(aq)$
    (b) $MgSO_4(aq) + NH_4OH(aq) \longrightarrow$
    $Mg(OH)_2(s) + (NH_4)_2SO_4(aq)$

General Exercises

77. A drop of methyl red indicator and a drop of phenolphthalein are both added to a beaker of distilled water. What is the resulting color of the water?

78. A drop of bromthymol blue indicator and a drop of phenolphthalein are both added to a beaker of distilled water. What is the resulting color of the water?

79. The acid–base indicator methyl orange changes color from pH 3.2 to pH 4.4. It appears red in strongly acidic solutions and yellow in basic solutions. Predict the color of the indicator in a solution having a pH of 3.8.

80. The acid–base indicator bromcresol green changes color from pH 3.8 to pH 5.4. It appears yellow in strongly acidic solutions and blue in basic solutions. Predict the color of the indicator in a solution having a pH of 4.6.

81. Identify an amphiprotic substance given the following reactions:

    $HCl(aq) + NaH_2PO_4(aq) \longrightarrow H_3PO_4(aq) + NaCl(aq)$
    $NaOH(aq) + NaH_2PO_4(aq) \longrightarrow Na_2HPO_4(aq) + H_2O(l)$

82. Identify an amphiprotic substance given the following reactions:

    $HCl(aq) + H_2O(l) \longrightarrow H_3O^+(aq) + Cl^-(aq)$
    $NH_2^-(aq) + H_2O(l) \longrightarrow NH_3(aq) + OH^-(aq)$

83. What is the pH of a 0.50 M HCl solution?

84. What is the pH of a 0.50 M NaOH solution?

85. In 1 mL of water there are 3×10^{22} molecules of H_2O. How many hydrogen ions are in 1 mL of water? (*Hint:* In 1 billion water molecules, 2 are ionized.)

86. In 10 mL of water there are 3×10^{23} molecules of H_2O. How many hydroxide ions are in 10 mL of water? (*Hint:* In 1 billion water molecules, 2 are ionized.)

87. Write the net ionic equation for the reaction of the weak electrolytes acetic acid and ammonium hydroxide.

88. Write the net ionic equation for the reaction of the strong electrolytes nitric acid and potassium hydroxide.

Challenge Exercises

89. Alanine, abbreviated HAla, is an amino acid in protein. If 21.05 mL of 0.145 M NaOH neutralizes 0.272 g HAla, what is the molar mass of the amino acid?

90. Cream of tartar, abbreviated KHTart, is used in baking. If 42.10 mL of 0.100 KOH neutralizes 0.791 g KHTart, what is the molar mass of cream of tartar?

Online Exercises

http://www

Research each of the following using an Internet search engine (e.g., Google.com or Yahoo.com) and cite your URL reference.

91. Why is *acid rain* harmful to humans and what are the health problems?

92. Why is *acid rain* harmful to trees and how does it destroy forests?

14

Chapter Self-Test Answers to Self-Test are in Appendix J.

1. Which of the following is a general property of a basic solution? (Sec. 14.1)
(a) tastes bitter
(b) feels slippery
(c) turns litmus paper blue
(d) pH greater than 7
(e) all of the above

2. Which of the following is a weak Arrhenius acid? (Sec. 14.2)
(a) HCl(aq) (~100% ionized)
(b) $HNO_3(aq)$ (~100% ionized)
(c) $HC_2H_3O_2(aq)$ (~1% ionized)
(d) all of the above
(e) none of the above

3. In the following reaction, which reactant is a Brønsted–Lowry base? (Sec. 14.3)

$$HCl(aq) + KHS(aq) \longrightarrow KCl(aq) + H_2S(aq)$$

(a) HCl
(b) KHS
(c) KCl
(d) H_2S
(e) none of the above

4. What is the color of phenolphthalein indicator at pH 7? (Sec. 14.4)
(a) red
(b) blue
(c) pink
(d) colorless
(e) none of the above

5. If 25.0 mL of 0.100 M HCl is titrated with 0.150 M Ba(OH)$_2$, what volume of barium hydroxide is required to neutralize the acid? (Sec. 14.5)

$$2\,HCl(aq) + Ba(OH)_2(aq) \longrightarrow BaCl_2(aq) + 2\,H_2O(l)$$

(a) 8.33 mL
(b) 16.7 mL
(c) 18.8 mL
(d) 33.3 mL
(e) 37.5 mL

6. What is the molarity of a hydrochloric acid solution if 20.00 mL of HCl is required to neutralize 0.424 g of sodium carbonate (105.99 g/mol)? (Sec. 14.6)

$$2\,HCl(aq) + Na_2CO_3(aq) \longrightarrow 2\,NaCl(aq) + H_2O(l) + CO_2(g)$$

(a) 0.100 M
(b) 0.200 M
(c) 0.300 M
(d) 0.400 M
(e) 0.500 M

7. Given an aqueous solution in which the $[H^+] = 2.5 \times 10^{-7}$, what is the molar hydroxide ion concentration? (Sec. 14.7)
(a) $[OH^-] = 2.5 \times 10^{-7}\,M$
(b) $[OH^-] = 2.5 \times 10^{-8}\,M$
(c) $[OH^-] = 4.0 \times 10^{-6}\,M$
(d) $[OH^-] = 4.0 \times 10^{-7}\,M$
(e) $[OH^-] = 4.0 \times 10^{-8}\,M$

8. What is the hydrogen ion concentration in a urine sample that registers a pH of 4 on a strip of pH paper? (Sec. 14.8)
(a) 0.001 M
(b) 0.004 M
(c) 0.0001 M
(d) 0.0004 M
(e) 0.00001 M

9. What is the hydrogen ion concentration in a blood sample that registers a pH of 7.30 using a pH meter? (Sec. 14.9)
(a) 0.000 000 020 M
(b) 0.000 000 050 M
(c) 0.000 000 20 M
(d) 0.000 000 50 M
(e) 0.000 073 M

10. If a drain cleaner solution is a strong electrolyte, which of the following must be true? (Sec. 14.10)
(a) Drain cleaner is highly reactive.
(b) Drain cleaner is slightly reactive.
(c) Drain cleaner is highly ionized.
(d) Drain cleaner is slightly ionized.
(e) none of the above

11. Nitric acid is a strong acid, sodium hydroxide is a strong base, and sodium nitrate is a soluble salt. Which of the following is the net ionic equation for the reaction? (Sec. 14.11)

$$HNO_3(aq) + NaOH(aq) \longrightarrow NaNO_3(aq) + H_2O(l)$$

(a) $H^+(aq) + OH^-(aq) \longrightarrow H_2O(l)$
(b) $NO_3^-(aq) + Na^+(aq) \longrightarrow NaNO_3(s)$
(c) $H^+(aq) + NaOH(aq) \longrightarrow Na^+(aq) + H_2O(l)$
(d) $HNO_3(aq) + OH^-(aq) \longrightarrow NO_3^-(aq) + H_2O(l)$
(e) none of the above

Key Concepts

12. What must be done first before applying unit analysis to solve an acid–base titration problem?

(a) Beaker X

13. Beakers X and Y contain either nitric acid or nitrous acid. Based on the conductivity test shown, which beaker contains HNO_3? Which contains HNO_2?

(b) Beaker Y

Critical Thinking

14. The smell of fish is due to a basic organic compound related to ammonia. What common kitchen chemical can be used to neutralize an unpleasant fish odor?

15. What color is the solution in a test tube that contains 10 mL of acid, 1 drop of phenolphthalein, and 1 drop of bromthymol blue indicator?

16. Examine the following illustrations of HCl and HF ionizing in solution. At the molecular level, explain why HCl is more highly ionized than HF.

(a) HCl highly ionized

(b) HF slightly ionized

CHAPTER

18

Nuclear Chemistry

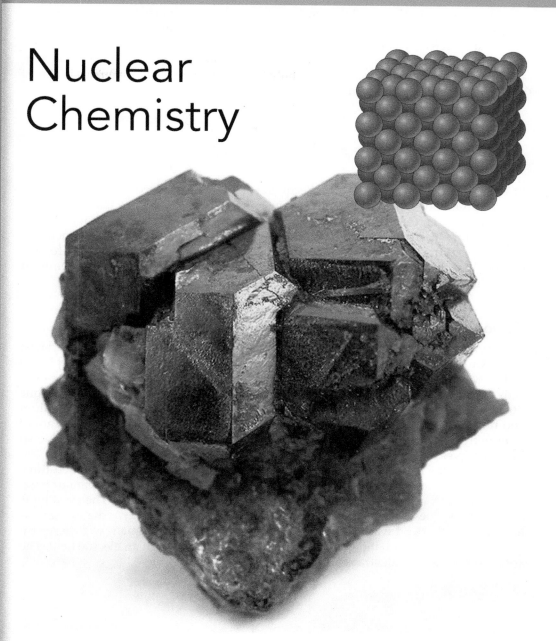

Uranium in the Environment Pitchblende (shown) is a mixture of uranium oxides and occurs naturally in the environment; the richest deposits are in Kazakhstan, Canada, and Australia. Uranium ore is refined into yellowcake, which is a concentrated form of uranium oxides. Yellowcake can be converted to uranium hexafluoride for use in nuclear reactors.

"I am among those who think that science has great beauty."
Marie Curie, Polish/French Physicist (1867–1934)

The energy requirements of industrial nations and the rapid consumption of non-renewable fossil fuels have created a need to develop additional energy sources. To compensate for declining oil and natural gas resources, there is great interest in developing alternative energy sources. Nuclear energy is one possibility. The energy released from the splitting of atomic nuclei, most notably uranium nuclei, is called *nuclear fission energy*, or simply, *nuclear energy*. Although the United States has enough uranium to meet its nuclear energy needs through the middle of this century, the threat of nuclear accident and the disposal of radioactive waste are problems of great public concern.

Approximately 15% of all the world's electrical power comes from nuclear power plants. Interestingly, the United States generates the most nuclear energy, and about 20% of its electricity comes from nuclear power plants. In England, Germany, and Japan, the percentage is somewhat less than the United States. In China the percentage of electricity from nuclear power is only 1%, but in France the percentage is almost 80%, and in regions of Eastern Europe it is even higher.

18.1 NATURAL RADIOACTIVITY

In 1896, the French physicist Henri Becquerel (1852–1908) noticed a fogged image on an unexposed photographic plate he had just removed from its heavy black protective paper. Moreover, the image was that of a uranium-containing crystal that had been resting on the paper wrapping around the photographic plate. Becquerel concluded that the uranium crystal had given off high-energy radiation to produce the fogged image. After further experiments, he discovered that the uranium crystal emitted small charged particles in addition to high-energy radiation.

▲ **Marie Curie** In 1903, Marie Curie shared the Nobel Prize in physics with her husband Pierre and Henri Becquerel. In 1911, she won an unshared Nobel Prize in chemistry.

Radioactive Decay of Unstable Atoms

The rays Becquerel discovered were of immediate interest to the French physicist Pierre Curie (1859–1906) and his soon-to-be wife, Marie Sklodowska (1867–1934). In fact, it was Marie who coined the name **radioactivity** for Becquerel's rays. A radioactive element decays by emitting particles and/or energy from an unstable atomic nucleus. In 1898, the Curies discovered two other radioactive elements, polonium and radium. However, it took 4 years of meticulous labor to isolate a single gram of radium from 8 tons of uranium ore. In 1903, Pierre and Marie Curie shared the Nobel Prize in Physics with Becquerel for their work with radioactivity.

By 1903, the British physicist Ernest Rutherford had identified and named three different types of radioactivity. One type, an alpha ray, consists of a stream of positive particles. A second type, a beta ray, consists of negative particles. The third type, a gamma ray, does not consist of particles, but rather is high-energy radiation similar to X-rays. Rutherford was able to separate alpha, beta, and gamma rays experimentally by passing the radiation from a radioactive sample through an electric field. The apparatus he used is illustrated in Figure 18.1.

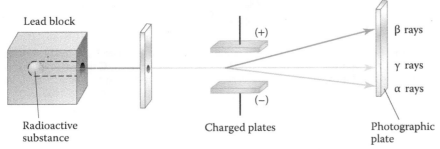

▲ Figure 18.1 **Separation of Alpha, Beta, and Gamma Rays** Notice that the alpha ray is deflected toward the negative electrode, and the beta ray toward the positive electrode. This indicates that the alpha ray is positively charged and the beta ray is negatively charged. The gamma ray is not affected because it has no charge.

▲ **Penetrating Power of Radiation** Alpha particles are stopped by the skin, whereas beta particles can penetrate about a centimeter. Gamma rays easily pass through the human body.

After studying the radiation from unstable atoms, Rutherford eventually identified alpha particles as helium nuclei. That is, an **alpha particle** (α) is identical to a helium nucleus containing two protons and two neutrons. He found that a **beta particle** (β) is identical to an electron. A **gamma ray** (γ) is a powerful type of nuclear radiation that has neither mass nor charge. Table 18.1 lists the properties of alpha, beta, and gamma radiation.

TABLE 18.1 PROPERTIES OF NUCLEAR RADIATION

RADIATION	IDENTITY	APPROXIMATE VELOCITY*	SHIELDING REQUIRED	PENETRATING POWER
alpha, α	helium nucleus	$\leq 10\%$ c	paper, clothing	low, stopped by the skin
beta, β	electron	$\leq 90\%$ c	30 cm wood, aluminum foil	medium, ~1 cm of flesh
gamma, γ	high-energy radiation	100% c	10 cm lead, 30 cm concrete	high, passes through body

*The letter **c** is the symbol for the velocity of light, 3×10^8 m/s.

LEARNING OBJECTIVES

▸ To illustrate the following types of radiation using atomic notation: alpha, beta, gamma, positron, neutron, and proton.

▸ To write balanced nuclear equations involving natural radioactivity.

18.2 NUCLEAR EQUATIONS

In Section 4.4, we introduced the atomic notation used to indicate the composition of an atomic nucleus. In atomic notation, the symbol for the element is preceded by a subscript and superscript. The subscript indicates the number of protons (atomic number). The superscript indicates the number of protons and neutrons (mass number). In the following example, the **atomic number** (symbol Z) appears as a subscript, and the **mass number** (symbol A) appears as a superscript.

mass number (p$^+$ and n^0) $\longrightarrow$ $_Z^A\text{Sy}$ — symbol of the element

atomic number (p$^+$) $\longrightarrow$

In this chapter, we will use the term **nuclide** when referring to the nucleus of a specific atom. For example, the nucleus of strontium-90 is a radioactive nuclide that contains a total of 90 protons and neutrons. From the periodic table, we find that strontium has an atomic number of 38. Thus, the atomic notation for strontium-90 is

$$_{38}^{90}\text{Sr}$$

If we subtract the atomic number from the mass number ($90 - 38 = 52$), we find that strontium-90 has 52 neutrons in addition to 38 protons. Although strontium-90 is radioactive, other strontium nuclides are not. For example, Sr-86, Sr-87, and Sr-88 are stable. Thus, we conclude that the number of neutrons can affect the stability of a Sr nucleus and perhaps the nuclides of other elements. Nuclear equations represent changes in nuclides due to radioactivity, and just like chemical equations they need to be balanced. Unlike chemical changes that involve valence electrons, nuclear reactions involve atomic nuclei.

Balancing Nuclear Equations

A **nuclear reaction** involves a high-energy change in an atomic nucleus. For example, a uranium-238 nucleus changes into a thorium-231 nucleus by releasing a helium-4 particle, and a great deal of energy.

$$_{92}^{235}\text{U} \longrightarrow {}_{90}^{231}\text{Th} + {}_2^4\text{He}$$

To write a balanced **nuclear equation**, we must account for all atomic numbers and mass numbers. That is, the sums of the atomic numbers for reactants and products must be equal. Similarly, the sums of the mass numbers for reactants and products must be equal. The guidelines for balancing a nuclear equation are as follows.

General Guidelines for Balancing a Nuclear Equation

1. The sum of the atomic numbers (subscripts) on the left side of the equation must equal the sum of the atomic numbers on the right side.

   sum of atomic numbers   =   sum of atomic numbers
   for reactants   for products

2. The sum of the mass numbers (superscripts) on the left side of the equation must equal the sum of the mass numbers on the right side.

   sum of mass numbers   =   sum of mass numbers
   for reactants   for products

3. After completing the equation by writing all the nuclear particles in atomic notation, a coefficient may be necessary to balance the following:
   (a) atomic numbers of reactants and products
   (b) mass numbers of reactants and products

To balance the atomic numbers and mass numbers in a nuclear equation, we must be able to write the atomic notation for each particle in the reaction. Table 18.2 lists some common particles involved in nuclear reactions.

TABLE 18.2 PARTICLES IN NUCLEAR REACTIONS

PARTICLE	NOTATION	MASS	CHARGE
alpha, α	$^{4}_{2}\text{He}$	~4 amu	2+
beta, β^{-}	$^{0}_{-1}\text{e}$	~0 amu	1−
gamma*, γ	$^{0}_{0}\gamma$	0 amu	0
positron, β^{+}	$^{0}_{+1}\text{e}$	~0 amu	1+
neutron, n^{0}	$^{1}_{0}\text{n}$	~1 amu	0
proton, p^{+}	$^{1}_{1}\text{H}$	~1 amu	1+

*Unlike particle radiation, a gamma ray is radiant energy and has no mass.

Alpha Particle Emission

Let's write a balanced nuclear equation for the radioactive decay of radium-226 by alpha emission. We can write the decay process using symbols as follows:

$$^{226}_{88}\text{Ra} \longrightarrow {}^{A}_{Z}\text{X} + {}^{4}_{2}\text{He} \ (\alpha \text{ particle})$$

To balance the number of protons, the atomic number (represented by Z) of X the unknown element must be 86 (88 = 86 + 2). Therefore, we can write

$$^{226}_{88}\text{Ra} \longrightarrow {}^{A}_{86}\text{X} + {}^{4}_{2}\text{He}$$

When we refer to the periodic table, we find that element 86 is radon, Rn. Thus,

$$^{226}_{88}\text{Ra} \longrightarrow {}^{A}_{86}\text{Rn} + {}^{4}_{2}\text{He}$$

To balance the number of protons and neutrons, the mass number of X (represented by A) must be 222 (226 = 222 + 4). The balanced equation is

$$^{226}_{88}\text{Ra} \longrightarrow {}^{222}_{86}\text{Rn} + {}^{4}_{2}\text{He}$$

▲ **Natural Radioactivity**
Before the hazards of radiation exposure were fully understood, radioactive radium was used on the face of a watch. Radiation from the radium causes the watch to glow in the dark.

Beta Particle Emission

Unlike radium-226 that decays by alpha emission, radium-228 decays by beta emission. In beta emission, a neutron essentially decays into a proton and releases an electron. We can write this decay process in symbols as follows:

$$^{228}_{88}\text{Ra} \longrightarrow {}^{A}_{Z}\text{X} + {}^{0}_{-1}\text{e} \ (\beta^{-}\text{particle})$$

To balance the number of protons, the atomic number of X must be 89 (88 = 89 − 1). Since nuclide X has an atomic number of 89, the periodic table shows us that the element is actinium, Ac. The equation is

$$^{228}_{88}\text{Ra} \longrightarrow {}^{A}_{89}\text{Ac} + {}^{0}_{-1}\text{e}$$

To balance the mass numbers for reactants and products, the A value for the Ac nuclide must be 228 since a beta particle has a mass number of zero (228 = 228 + 0). The balanced equation for the reaction is

$$^{228}_{88}\text{Ra} \longrightarrow {}^{228}_{89}\text{Ac} + {}^{0}_{-1}\text{e}$$

Note that beta emission increases the atomic number by 1, thus producing the next higher atomic number element in the periodic table. The net result is that one neutron in the radium-228 nucleus decays into a proton as it releases an electron.

Gamma Ray Emission

Now let's try a more complex example. Uranium-233 decays by releasing both alpha particles and gamma rays. We can write the decay process as follows:

$$^{233}_{92}\text{U} \longrightarrow {}^{A}_{Z}\text{X} + {}^{4}_{2}\text{He} + {}^{0}_{0}\gamma \ (\gamma \ \text{ray})$$

To balance subscripts, the atomic number of X must be 90 (92 = 90 + 2 + 0). Since nuclide X has an atomic number of 90, we see from the periodic table that the element is thorium, Th. The equation is

$$^{233}_{92}\text{U} \longrightarrow {}^{A}_{90}\text{Th} + {}^{4}_{2}\text{He} + {}^{0}_{0}\gamma$$

To balance the mass numbers for reactants and products, the A value for the Th nuclide must be 229 (233 = 229 + 4 + 0). The balanced equation for the reaction is

$$^{233}_{92}\text{U} \longrightarrow {}^{229}_{90}\text{Th} + {}^{4}_{2}\text{He} + {}^{0}_{0}\gamma$$

Note that the atomic number and mass number of a gamma ray are zero and have no effect on the equation. The gamma ray is included, however, to indicate that high-energy radiation is emitted during the decay process.

Positron Particle Emission

In 1932, a new particle was discovered. Its mass is identical to that of an electron, but its charge is 1+ rather than 1−. The newly discovered particle was given the name **positron** (β^+), for positive electron. When positrons strike electrons, they immediately annihilate each other. A collision between a positron and an electron causes mutual destruction and the release of two gamma rays.

Scientists have studied and cataloged the types of emission from radioactive nuclides. Sodium-22 emits positrons and is used in medicine to diagnose small lesions in the brain. The nuclear equation for the decay of Na-22 is as follows:

$$^{22}_{11}\text{Na} \longrightarrow {}^{A}_{Z}\text{X} + {}^{0}_{+1}\text{e} \ (\text{positron})$$

To balance the atomic numbers of reactants and products in this reaction, the atomic number of X must be 10 (11 = 10 + 1). Referring to the periodic table, we see that the atomic number 10 corresponds to neon, Ne. The equation is

$$^{22}_{11}\text{Na} \longrightarrow {}^{A}_{10}\text{Ne} + {}^{0}_{+1}\text{e}$$

To balance the mass numbers of reactants and products, the mass number of Ne must be 22 since a positron has a mass number of zero (22 = 22 + 0). The balanced equation for the reaction is

$$^{22}_{11}\text{Na} \longrightarrow {}^{22}_{10}\text{Ne} + {}^{0}_{+1}\text{e}$$

Note that positron emission decreases the atomic number by 1, thus producing the next lower element in the periodic table. The net result is that one proton in the Na-22 nucleus decays into a neutron while releasing a positron.

Electron Capture

A few large, unstable nuclides decay by a process called **electron capture** (**EC**). In this process, a heavy, positively charged nucleus strongly attracts an electron that lies close to the nucleus. If the attraction is sufficient, the negatively charged electron is captured by the nucleus and converts a positive proton to a neutral neutron. Since the number of protons is less, the atomic number decreases by one and a different element is formed. Consider a lead-205 nuclide that captures an electron as follows:

$$^{205}_{82}Pb + {}^{0}_{-1}e \longrightarrow {}^{A}_{Z}X$$

To balance the atomic numbers, the atomic number of X must be 81 ($82 - 1 = 81$). From the periodic table we see that element 81 is thallium, Tl. Since the mass number of an electron is 0, the mass number does not change ($205 + 0 = 205$). The balanced equation for the reaction is

$$^{205}_{82}Pb + {}^{0}_{-1}e \longrightarrow {}^{205}_{81}Tl$$

The following example exercise further illustrates how to write balanced nuclear equations for radioactively decaying nuclides.

Example Exercise 18.1 Writing Nuclear Equations for Natural Radiation

Write a balanced nuclear equation for each of the following radioactive decay reactions.

(a) Radon-222 decays by alpha and gamma emission.

(b) Barium-133 decays by electron capture.

Solution

To write a balanced nuclear equation we must have

1. equal sums of atomic numbers for reactants and products
2. equal sums of mass numbers for reactants and products

(a) We can write the equation for the decay of radon-222 by alpha and gamma emission as follows:

$$^{222}_{86}Rn \longrightarrow {}^{218}_{84}Po + {}^{4}_{2}He + {}^{0}_{0}\gamma$$

Since the sums of the atomic numbers (86) and mass numbers (222) are the same for reactants and products, the equation is balanced.

(b) We can write the balanced nuclear equation for the decay of barium-133 by electron capture as follows:

$$^{133}_{56}Ba + {}^{0}_{-1}e \longrightarrow {}^{133}_{55}Cs$$

Since the sums of the atomic numbers (55) and mass numbers (133) are the same for reactants and products, the equation is balanced.

Practice Exercise

Identify nuclide X in the following nuclear reactions that represents the radioactive decay product from (a) beta emission and (b) positron emission.

(a) $^{99}_{43}Tc \longrightarrow {}^{A}_{Z}X + {}^{0}_{-1}e$

(b) $^{30}_{15}P \longrightarrow {}^{A}_{Z}X + {}^{0}_{+1}e$

Answers: (a) $^{99}_{44}Ru$ (b) $^{30}_{14}Si$

Concept Exercise

Which type of natural radiation corresponds to each of the following descriptions?

(a) stopped by human skin and requires heavy cloth shielding
(b) penetrates human skin and requires aluminum shielding
(c) passes through the body and requires lead shielding

Answer: See Appendix G.

18.3 RADIOACTIVE DECAY SERIES

In Section 18.2, we discussed the radioactive decay of unstable nuclides. During this process, unstable nuclides stabilize by emitting radiation. Many nuclides become stable by emitting radiation in a single step. Heavy nuclides, such as uranium-238, must go through a series of decay steps to reach a nuclide that is stable. This stepwise disintegration of a radioactive nuclide until a stable nucleus is reached is called a **radioactive decay series**.

Natural Decay Series

The decay series for three naturally occurring radioactive nuclides have been studied extensively by physicists and chemists. They are uranium-238, uranium-235, and thorium-232. Each of these radioactive nuclides decays into a stable isotope of lead in a series of steps.

$$U\text{-}238 \longrightarrow \longrightarrow \longrightarrow Pb\text{-}206$$
$$U\text{-}235 \longrightarrow \longrightarrow \longrightarrow Pb\text{-}207$$
$$Th\text{-}232 \longrightarrow \longrightarrow \longrightarrow Pb\text{-}208$$

We use the term **parent–daughter nuclides** to describe a decaying parent nucleus and the resulting daughter nucleus. Although we have not shown the number of steps necessary to reach a stable nuclide, the actual sequence has been determined for each nuclide. In the case of uranium-238, 14 decay steps are required to become stable. Uranium-235 requires 11 steps, and thorium-232 requires 10 steps.

The first step in the radioactive decay of uranium-238 is the emission of an alpha particle to give thorium-234.

$$\underset{\text{parent nuclide}}{^{238}_{92}U} \longrightarrow \underset{\text{daughter product}}{^{234}_{90}Th} + \underset{\text{alpha particle}}{^{4}_{2}He}$$

The second step is the radioactive decay of Th-234 into Pa-234 by the emission of a beta particle.

$$^{234}_{90}Th \longrightarrow {^{234}_{91}Pa} + {^{0}_{-1}e}$$

The third step in the series is the decay of Pa-234 by beta emission. Several more steps in the decay series are required before a stable nuclide, Pb-206, is reached. Figure 18.2

▶ **Figure 18.2 Radioactive Decay Series for Uranium-238** Uranium-238 requires 14 decay steps before reaching a stable nuclide. Notice that several radioactive nuclides of Po, Pb, and Bi are unstable and decay. Only Pb-206, which ends the series, is stable.

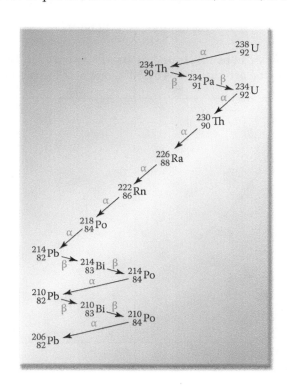

illustrates the entire decay series for uranium-238. Notice that the atomic number *decreases* by 2 after each α emission ($_2^4$He), whereas the atomic number *increases* by 1 for each β emission ($_{-1}^0$e).

Note When we examine the periodic table, we see that a mass number in parentheses, rather than an atomic mass, is listed for all the elements following bismuth. This indicates that there are no stable nuclides of any elements higher in atomic number than bismuth. All the elements beyond atomic number 83 are unstable and therefore undergo spontaneous radioactive decay.

18.4 RADIOACTIVE HALF-LIFE

In 1908, Hans Geiger, while working for Rutherford, developed an instrument for measuring radiation. Geiger filled a tube with a gas that ionizes when struck by radiation. The ionized gas particles allow passage of a pulse of electricity that can be converted to an audio signal heard as a click. Each click of a *Geiger counter* indicates an emission from the radioactive sample (Figure 18.3). A digital counter registers the number of clicks, providing a measure of the number of atomic nuclei undergoing radioactive decay. The number of nuclei that disintegrate in a given period of time is called the **activity** of the sample.

Half-Life of a Radioactive Sample

Scientists have observed that the level of radioactivity for all radioactive samples decreases with time. If we begin, for example, with a sample that has an activity of 1000 disintegrations per minute (dpm), after a given period of time the radioactivity will drop to 500 dpm, which is half the original level. Moreover, after the same period of time, the activity will drop from 500 dpm to 250 dpm.

The amount of time required for the activity of a sample to decrease by half is called the **half-life** (symbol $t_{1/2}$). If the half-life of a sample is 4 hours, it requires 4 hours for the activity to drop by half. That is, it takes 4 hours for each of the following half-life changes: 1000 to 500 dpm, 500 to 250 dpm, and 250 to 125 dpm. Since three half-lives are required for the activity to drop from 1000 to 125 dpm, the total time required is

$$3\,t_{1/2} \times \frac{4\,\text{hours}}{1\,t_{1/2}} = 12\,\text{hours}$$

The decrease in activity can be illustrated by the decay curve in Figure 18.4. The curve shows that each time the activity drops by 50%, one half-life has elapsed.

LEARNING OBJECTIVES

▶ To understand the concept of half-life for a radioactive sample.

▶ To relate the amount of radioactive sample, and its radioactivity, to a given half-life.

▲ Figure 18.3 **Geiger Counter** A Geiger counter gives a "click" each time a radioactive nucleus decays and releases a particle.

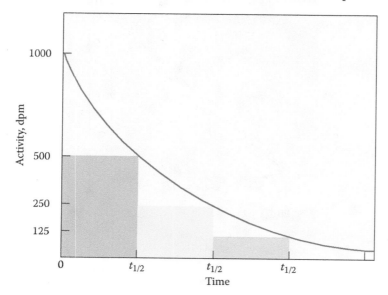

◀ Figure 18.4 **Decay Curve and Half-Life** The time required for the activity of a radioactive sample to decrease from 1000 to 500 dpm is one half-life. Notice that it requires the same amount of time, one half-life, for the activity to drop from 500 to 250 dpm.

Radioactive Waste

Disposing of radioactive waste material is a major concern because dangerous levels of radioactivity can persist for thousands of years. For example, the radioactive fuel from a plutonium-239 nuclear reactor emits high levels of radioactivity long after it is too weak to run a nuclear reactor. Let's find out how long it takes for the radioactivity of plutonium-239 waste to decrease from 20,000 to 625 dpm.

The half-life of Pu-239 is 24,000 years. By definition, we know that the activity of a radioactive sample drops by one-half after each half-life. We can list the activity of the sample corresponding to the elapsed time.

ACTIVITY	ELAPSED TIME	ELAPSED TIME
20,000 dpm	—	0
10,000 dpm	$1\ t_{1/2}$	24,000 y
5000 dpm	$2\ t_{1/2}$	48,000 y
2500 dpm	$3\ t_{1/2}$	72,000 y
1250 dpm	$4\ t_{1/2}$	96,000 y
625 dpm	$5\ t_{1/2}$	120,000 y

We see that it takes five half-lives for the radioactivity of plutonium to drop from 20,000 to 625 dpm. Given that the half-life is 24,000 years, we can calculate the amount of time required for the radiation to drop to 625 dpm. The equation is

$$5\ t_{1/2} \times \frac{24{,}000\ \text{y}}{1\ t_{1/2}} = 120{,}000\ \text{y}$$

The activity of a sample is proportional to the number of radioactive nuclei, and thus to the mass of the sample. The time required for radioactive substances to decay to a safe level varies according to the nuclide. When debating the use of nuclear energy, we must consider the problem of radioactive waste disposal and its potential effect on the environment for thousands of years.

Example Exercise 18.2 | Half-Life of a Radioactive Nuclide

Iodine-131, in a sodium iodide tablet, is used to measure the activity of the thyroid gland. If a tablet initially contains 88 mg of I-131, what is the mass of the nuclide that remains after 24 days? The half-life of I-131 is 8 days.

Solution

This problem asks us to find the mass of I-131 remaining after 24 days. Let's begin by determining the number of half-lives that elapse. One half-life equals 8 days. Thus,

$$24\ \text{days} \times \frac{1\ t_{1/2}}{8\ \text{days}} = 3\ t_{1/2}$$

To calculate the mass of I-131 remaining after three half-lives, we decrease the mass of I-131 by one-half for each half-life. We can proceed as follows.

$$88\ \text{mg I-131} \times \frac{1}{2} \times \frac{1}{2} \times \frac{1}{2} = \text{mg I-131}$$

$$= 11\ \text{mg I-131}$$

Practice Exercise

Iodine-128, in a potassium iodide solution, is used to treat a thyroid condition. If the initial activity is 10,000 dpm and the activity drops to 1250 dpm after 75 minutes, what is the half-life of I-128?

Answer: $t_{1/2} = 25$ minutes

Concept Exercise

When 500 mg of technetium-99 is administered for medical diagnosis, how much of the radionuclide remains after 24 hours? ($t_{1/2} = 6$ hours)

Answer: See Appendix G.

▲ **Thyroid Scan** Physicians use radioactive iodine-131 as a diagnostic tool to assess activity of the thyroid gland, which regulates metabolism.

18.5 APPLICATIONS OF RADIONUCLIDES

LEARNING OBJECTIVES

▸ To describe the radiocarbon dating method.

▸ To describe the uranium–lead dating method.

▸ To state applications of selected radionuclides.

A nuclide that is unstable is called a **radionuclide**. Different radionuclides decay by emitting different types of radiation. These different types of radioactive emission have many applications in agriculture, industry, medicine, and research.

Radiocarbon Dating

Carbon occurs naturally as two stable nuclides, carbon-12 and carbon-13. It also occurs as an unstable nuclide, carbon-14, which decays by beta emission. The fact that carbon-14 is unstable allows its half-life to be used to estimate the age of any substance containing carbon. Scientists date objects by measuring the level of carbon-14 radioactivity in a sample. This process is called *carbon-14 dating,* or *radiocarbon dating.*

Among other things, radiocarbon dating has been used to establish the age of human remains that may be thousands of years old, the age of artifacts such as ancient wooden bowls, and the age of carbon dioxide gas from the atmosphere that has been trapped for thousands of years in glacial ice. This technique is considered reliable up to 50,000 years. Older objects usually emit too little radiation for accurate measurement.

Carbon-14 is continuously produced in Earth's upper atmosphere. The process begins when cosmic rays strike molecules and scatter high-energy neutrons. These neutrons in turn collide with nitrogen in the atmosphere. These collisions produce carbon-14 and protons. The nuclear equation is as follows:

$$^{14}_{7}\text{N} + ^{1}_{0}\text{n} \longrightarrow ^{14}_{6}\text{C} + ^{1}_{1}\text{H}$$

Carbon-14 atoms in the atmosphere combine with oxygen molecules to give radioactive CO_2. This carbon dioxide is then incorporated into plant life through the process of photosynthesis. The food chain begins with plants and continues through animals and eventually humans. A substance that contains carbon-14 emits beta radiation according to the following nuclear equation:

$$^{14}_{6}\text{C} \longrightarrow ^{14}_{7}\text{N} + ^{0}_{-1}\text{e}$$

In a living plant or animal, the radiation from radiocarbon is 15.3 dpm per gram of carbon. When a plant or animal dies, it ceases to intake carbon-14, and the radiation level begins to decrease. After one half-life has elapsed, the activity declines to about 7.7 dpm. The half-life of carbon-14 is 5730 years. Therefore, if a radioactive sample has an activity of 7.7 dpm, its estimated age is 5730 years.

When a piece of wood was found on Mt. Ararat in eastern Turkey it was proposed that the wood might be from Noah's Ark. The wood sample underwent carbon-14 dating and gave an activity of 12.5 dpm per gram of carbon. This activity corresponds to that of a sample about 1000 years old. Thus, using radiocarbon dating, scientists concluded that the wood was not part of Noah's Ark.

When the Dead Sea Scrolls were found, radiocarbon dating was used to verify their authenticity. Actually, it was the linen wrapping around the Old Testament writings that gave a dating value of 2000 years. This value corresponds to a time that is consistent with biblical texts. It was this evidence from radiocarbon dating that led scholars to believe that the Dead Sea Scrolls are authentic writings.

In a similar fashion, Stonehenge in England was dated using charcoal from various campsites. The charcoal samples gave an activity of 9.5 dpm per gram of carbon, which corresponds to a sample about 3800 years old. Thus, the Stonehenge site is believed to have been active in about 1800 B.C. Figure 18.5 illustrates radiocarbon dating.

◀ Figure 18.5 **Radiocarbon Dating** The activity of carbon-14 in living tissue is about 15.3 dpm. When tissue expires, it continues to decay radioactively, but the tissue no longer incorporates carbon-14. After 5730 years, half the carbon-14 nuclides in the sample have decayed and the activity is about 7.7 dpm.

The accuracy of radiocarbon dating depends on a fundamental assumption: *the amount of carbon-14 in the atmosphere has remained constant for the last 50,000 years.* If this assumption is not true, radiocarbon dating is not valid.

Uranium–Lead Dating

Naturally occurring uranium-238 radioactively decays to lead-206 in a series of 14 steps. The half-life for the overall process is 4.5 billion years. We can indicate the net reaction according to the following equation:

$$^{238}_{92}\text{U} \longrightarrow {}^{206}_{82}\text{Pb} + 8\,{}^{4}_{2}\text{He} + 6\,{}^{0}_{-1}\text{e}$$

The ratio of uranium-238 to lead-206 in uranium samples provides an estimate of the age of very old geological events. For example, a meteorite that fell in Mexico is found to have a uranium-238/lead-206 ratio of 1:1. A ratio of 1:1 corresponds to a single half-life. Thus, the meteorite is about 4.5 billion years old.

The uranium–lead dating technique has also been used to estimate the age of Earth and of lunar rock samples collected during the *Apollo* missions to the Moon. Uranium–lead dating indicates that Earth and the Moon are about the same age. Thus, scientists have evidence for the theory that the Moon may have originally been part of Earth and broke away while Earth was in an early molten stage.

Agricultural Applications of Radionuclides

Pesticides like DDT can effectively control insects, but they often persist in the environment for a long time. Some of these pesticides are toxic to animals and humans. As an alternative, insect populations can be controlled using radiation. Gamma rays from a radionuclide such as cobalt-60 have been employed to sterilize male insects. When large numbers of sterilized males are released in an infested area, they mate with the females, but fertilization does not occur. The insect population is thus reduced and effectively controlled. A decrease in the insect population results in an increase in agricultural harvests.

Gamma irradiation of processed food destroys microorganisms. For example, cobalt-60 irradiation of pork destroys the parasite that causes trichinosis; irradiation of chicken destroys the bacteria that cause salmonella. Irradiation of other foods can extend shelf life without the use of preservatives.

▲ Irradiation of Food
Gamma irradiation destroys microorganisms in food and extends freshness. All the strawberries shown were picked at the same time; however, the strawberries on the left were irradiated.

Medical Applications

Today, more than 100 radionuclides are available for medical diagnoses and treatments. An interesting example is plutonium-238, which decays by gamma emission. The gamma rays are used to power pacemakers in patients with irregular heartbeats. The radionuclide is sealed in a stainless steel case and implanted in the chest of the patient. The radiation from a plutonium-238 source can power a pacemaker for up to 10 years before it needs to be replaced.

CRITICAL THINKING Nuclear Medicine

Q: Which radionuclide emits gamma rays that are used for radiation therapy on tumors in cancer patients?

The term *nuclear medicine* refers to the use of radionuclides for medical purposes. For example, iodine-131 is used to measure the activity of the thyroid gland, which requires iodine to regulate metabolism. Patients diagnosed as having a thyroid condition are given an iodine-131 tablet, and after 24 hours a radiation scan is performed. The amount of radiation detected at the base of the throat, where the thyroid is located, is an indication of thyroid activity. Iodine-131 can also be used in veterinary medicine for the diagnosis of hyperthyroidism in cats.

Xenon-133 is used to diagnose respiratory problems. A patient inhales air containing the radionuclide. Both oxygen and xenon-133 are taken up by healthy lung tissue. As the chest is scanned for radiation, healthy areas of the lungs are revealed. An area where respiration is impaired is indicated by less radiation.

Iron-59 is used to diagnose anemia, a condition marked by a low red blood cell count. Red blood cells contain hemoglobin, which in turn contains iron atoms. A patient is given iron-59, and the radionuclide bonds to the hemoglobin. When the patient is checked for radiation, a scan reveals radioactive hemoglobin, providing an indirect count of red blood cells.

Brain tumors can be diagnosed using technetium-99, which concentrates in brain tissue. When a patient is given technetium-99, rapidly dividing cancer cells incorporate more of the radionuclide than normal cells. A scan shows radiation hot spots that can help locate the tumor. After locating the tumor, a cobalt-60 source of gamma radiation is focused on the tumor, which destroys the cancer cells and a small portion of the surrounding healthy tissue.

Breast cancer can be treated with iridium-192. A hypodermic needle is first injected into the tumor, followed by insertion of an iridium-192 bead through the needle. The needle is then withdrawn, and gamma rays from the radionuclide destroy the tumor. However, similar to radiation therapy, the gamma rays destroy some healthy tissue at the periphery of the tumor.

Although there is public concern about the use of radioactive substances, nuclear medicine is considered safe. In fact, diagnoses and treatments involving medical radionuclides save or prolong thousands of lives each year.

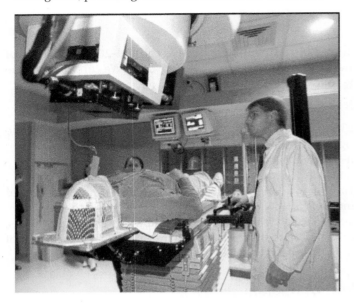

◀ **Radiation Therapy** A cancer patient receiving radiation therapy for a brain tumor.

A: Cobalt-60 is radioactive and emits gamma rays for radiation therapy treatment that destroys tumors in cancer patients.

18.6 INDUCED RADIOACTIVITY

LEARNING OBJECTIVE

▶ To write balanced nuclear equations involving induced radioactivity.

When a nuclide is bombarded with an atomic particle, the nuclide is converted to a different element. That is, a nuclear reaction occurs. Causing a nuclear reaction by particle bombardment is termed *induced radioactivity*. The conversion of one element to another by an induced nuclear reaction is called **transmutation**.

In 1919, Ernest Rutherford discovered the first transmutation reaction. When he bombarded nitrogen-14 with alpha particles, he detected the release of a proton, $^{1}_{1}H$. After careful analysis, he concluded that oxygen had also been produced. The equation for the transmutation is

$$^{14}_{7}N + ^{4}_{2}He \longrightarrow ^{17}_{8}O + ^{1}_{1}H$$

In 1932, James Chadwick, a student of Rutherford's, fired alpha particles at a sheet of beryllium metal. He found that some of the beryllium was changed to carbon and that a neutral particle was released. Chadwick called the neutral particle a neutron. Interestingly, Rutherford had predicted a neutral particle two decades earlier; however, at that time the neutron was too elusive to be confirmed experimentally. The equation for the transmutation is

$$^{9}_{4}Be + ^{4}_{2}He \longrightarrow ^{12}_{6}C + ^{1}_{0}n$$

Synthesis of New Elements

After the discovery of the neutron, it was proposed that a neutral particle could easily invade another nucleus. In 1940, this proposal proved correct, as uranium was transmuted into a new element. The new element was named neptunium for the planet Neptune. (Neptune lies just beyond Uranus, the planet for which uranium is named.) The equation for the synthesis of neptunium is

$$^{238}_{92}U + ^{1}_{0}n \longrightarrow ^{239}_{93}Np + ^{0}_{-1}e$$

▲ UC Berkeley Cyclotron
The cyclotron was invented at the University of California, Berkeley, and was used to create neptunium, plutonium, and other heavy elements.

The elements beyond uranium in the periodic table do not occur naturally. Rather, they have been created in the laboratory. These transuranium elements are synthesized by accelerating a projectile particle to a high velocity and firing it at a heavy nuclide that serves as a target nucleus. One instrument used to accelerate particles to sufficient energy to overcome the repulsion of the target nucleus is a *cyclotron*. Most of the elements beyond uranium have been synthesized using the cyclotron at the University of California at Berkeley. In fact, element 103 is named lawrencium (Lr) for the Berkeley physicist who invented the cyclotron, Ernest O. Lawrence.

Another instrument for accelerating particles is the *linear accelerator*. Linear accelerators and cyclotrons are sometimes referred to as "atom smashers" because they send high-velocity particles smashing into a target nucleus. The linear accelerator at Stanford University was completed in 1966, and is the longest in the world. It is capable of accelerating projectile particles to velocities approaching the speed of light (Figure 18.6).

▲ Figure 18.6 Stanford Linear Accelerator The Stanford linear accelerator is operated by Stanford University and is located near the campus. It is about two miles long and is the longest linear accelerator in the world.

In 1964 Soviet physicists claimed a successful synthesis of element 104. They named the element kurchatovium (Ku) in honor of their team leader, Igor Kurchatov. They used a linear accelerator to send a neon-22 projectile smashing into a plutonium target nucleus. Although the half-life of the new element was only 0.3 s, the Russians proposed the following reaction:

$$^{242}_{94}\text{Pu} + ^{22}_{10}\text{Ne} \longrightarrow ^{260}_{104}\text{Ku} + ^{1}_{0}\text{n}$$

Notice that the mass numbers in the equation are not balanced. The total of the reactant superscripts is 264 (242 + 22), but the total of the product superscripts is only 261 (260 + 1). To balance the equation, we must use 4 neutrons. The balanced nuclear equation is

$$^{242}_{94}\text{Pu} + ^{22}_{10}\text{Ne} \longrightarrow ^{260}_{104}\text{Ku} + 4^{1}_{0}\text{n}$$

When the Americans tried to confirm the Russian experiment, they were unsuccessful, which cast doubt on the credibility of element 104. In 1969, however, scientists at the University of California at Berkeley reported a different nuclide of element 104 that has a half-life of 5 s. The Berkeley group named the element rutherfordium (Rf) in honor of Ernest Rutherford. They induced the reaction by firing a carbon-12 projectile at a californium target nucleus.

$$^{249}_{98}\text{Cf} + ^{12}_{6}\text{C} \longrightarrow ^{257}_{104}\text{Rf} + ^{1}_{0}\text{n}$$

When we check the equation, we find that the atomic numbers are balanced but the mass numbers are not. The superscript total is 261 on the left side, but only 258 on the right side. To balance the equation, we place the coefficient 4 before the neutrons. The balanced nuclear equation is

$$^{249}_{98}\text{Cf} + ^{12}_{6}\text{C} \longrightarrow ^{257}_{104}\text{Rf} + 4^{1}_{0}\text{n}$$

The following example exercise provides additional practice in writing balanced nuclear equations for the synthesis of new elements.

Example Exercise 18.3 Writing Nuclear Equations for Induced Radiation

Write a balanced nuclear equation for the following nuclear reaction induced by an iron nuclide.

$$\text{Bi-209} + \text{Fe–?} \longrightarrow \text{Mt-266} + 1 \text{ neutron}$$

Solution

To write a nuclear equation, we must balance atomic numbers and mass numbers. Let's begin by writing the equation using atomic notation. We obtain the atomic number of each nuclide from the periodic table.

$$^{209}_{83}\text{Bi} + ^{?}_{26}\text{Fe} \longrightarrow ^{266}_{109}\text{Mt} + ^{1}_{0}\text{n}$$

We see that the sum of the atomic numbers is 109 on both sides of the equation. Since the sum of the mass numbers on the right side is 267, the sum on the left side must be 267. Thus, the mass number for Fe must be 58 (209 + 58 = 267). The balanced nuclear equation is

$$^{209}_{83}\text{Bi} + ^{58}_{26}\text{Fe} \longrightarrow ^{266}_{109}\text{Mt} + ^{1}_{0}\text{n}$$

Practice Exercise

Write a balanced nuclear equation for the following nuclear synthesis reaction.

$$\text{Cf-249} + \text{O-18} \longrightarrow \text{Sg–?} + 4 \text{ neutrons}$$

Answer:

$$^{249}_{98}\text{Cf} + ^{18}_{8}\text{O} \longrightarrow ^{263}_{106}\text{Sg} + 4^{1}_{0}\text{n}$$

Concept Exercise

In 1994, physicists in Darmstadt, Germany, synthesized element 110. If Ds-269 and a neutron were produced by firing a projectile into Pb-208, what was the projectile nuclide?

Answer: See Appendix G.

18.7 NUCLEAR FISSION

Spontaneous **nuclear fission** is the process whereby a heavy nucleus, such as uranium-235, splits into lighter nuclei while releasing energy. Many heavy nuclei are unstable and decay by spontaneous nuclear fission. For example, californium-252 can split apart spontaneously into lighter nuclei as follows:

$$^{252}_{98}\text{Cf} \longrightarrow ^{142}_{56}\text{Ba} + ^{106}_{42}\text{Mo} + 4^{1}_{0}\text{n} + \text{energy}$$

There are only a few nuclides that can be made to undergo fission, for example, uranium-235, uranium-233, and plutonium-239. The fission process is induced by a slow-moving neutron. When the neutron strikes a heavy nucleus and is captured, the resulting nucleus becomes unstable. The unstable nucleus then decays by splitting into lighter nuclei and releasing a few neutrons. The fission of uranium-235 can occur as follows:

$$^{1}_{0}\text{n} + ^{235}_{92}\text{U} \longrightarrow ^{137}_{52}\text{Te} + ^{97}_{40}\text{Zr} + 2^{1}_{0}\text{n} + \text{energy}$$

LEARNING OBJECTIVES

▶ To describe the process in a nuclear fission reaction.

▶ To write a nuclear equation for a given fission reaction.

After uranium-235 is struck by a neutron, the resulting unstable nucleus can undergo fission in a number of ways, one of which is depicted in Figure 18.7. As an analogy, a glass jar can split apart in various ways after being shot by a pellet. For example, uranium-235 can give the following nuclei as products:

$$_{0}^{1}n + _{92}^{235}U \longrightarrow _{56}^{142}Ba + _{36}^{91}Kr + 3\,_{0}^{1}n + \text{energy}$$

▲ Figure 18.7 **Nuclear Fission** A slow-moving neutron collides with a uranium-235 nucleus to form uranium-236. The resulting nucleus is unstable and splits into two lighter nuclei, releasing a few neutrons. In addition to particles, the fission reaction releases a huge burst of energy.

Nuclear Chain Reaction

The process of nuclear fission is analogous to a single domino knocking over three dominos, which in turn can ultimately topple an entire row of dominos. For each nucleus that undergoes fission, two or three neutrons are usually released. The emitted neutrons can cause additional fission reactions. In turn, the neutrons released from these fission reactions can initiate more fission reactions. If the fission process continues to repeat itself and is self-sustaining, it is called a **chain reaction**. We can indicate the growth in the number of neutrons in a chain reaction of uranium-235 as follows:

$$1\,_{0}^{1}n \longrightarrow 3\,_{0}^{1}n \longrightarrow 9\,_{0}^{1}n \longrightarrow 27\,_{0}^{1}n$$

We can illustrate a chain reaction as shown in Figure 18.8. Starting with a single uranium-235 nucleus and 1 neutron, the chain reaction quickly escalates to give fission products and 9 neutrons.

▶ Figure 18.8 **Nuclear Chain Reaction** A single neutron can cause the fission of a uranium-235 nucleus that releases three neutrons. In turn, the three emitted neutrons can cause three additional nuclei to fission with the release of three neutrons each (nine total), and so on.

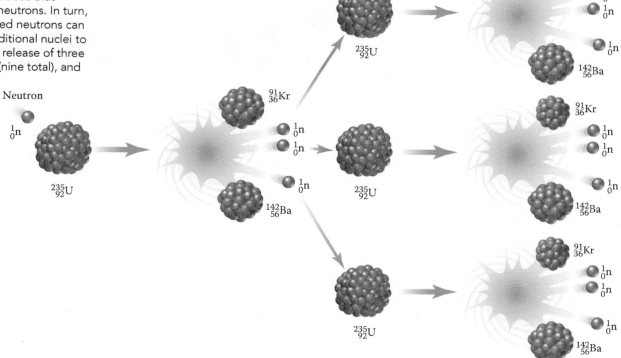

CHEMISTRY CONNECTION Nuclear Power Plant

Q: What fissionable radionuclides can be used in the fuel rods of a nuclear reactor?

Nuclear energy is an attractive source of energy because of its enormous potential compared to that of energy from ordinary reactions. For example, the fission of 1 g of uranium-235 produces about 12 million times more energy than the combustion of 1 g of gasoline!

A nuclear power plant generates electrical energy by a nuclear chain reaction. Nuclear fission occurs in the *reactor core*, which contains cylindrical metal *fuel rods*. Each fuel rod is filled with a fissionable nuclide, such as uranium-235, plutonium-239, or uranium-233. The fuel rods are separated by *control rods* made of boron or cadmium. These rods absorb neutrons and thus regulate the rate of fission. When the control rods are raised, more of the fuel rods are exposed, and the fission rate increases. When the control rods are lowered, more neutrons are absorbed and the rate slows, thus preventing the reactor core from overheating.

A liquid *coolant* such as water circulates through the reactor core to absorb heat. If the coolant is D_2O, the reactor is called a "heavy water" reactor. If the coolant is ordinary H_2O, the reactor is called a "light water" reactor. The coolant also serves to slow neutrons released from nuclear fission. Slower neutrons are more easily captured by the fissionable nuclides in the fuel rods. Since the coolant affects the rate of capture, it acts as a *moderator* for the fission reaction.

In a nuclear power plant, the nuclear reactor is housed in a concrete building to lessen the chance of an accidental release of radiation into the environment. When the fuel rods are exhausted, they are still highly radioactive and must be stored safely. Many nuclear power plants have on-site underwater vaults for temporary storage. Later, the fuel rods are recycled and the nuclear fuel recovered.

▲ **Nuclear Reactor Core** Notice the control rods inserted between the fuel rods. Lowering the control rods slows the chain reaction by absorbing neutrons released by the fuel rods.

▲ **Nuclear Power Plant** The Diablo Canyon power plant in southern California generates electricity using nuclear energy.

A: The fissionable radionuclides that are used for fuel in nuclear reactors are U-235, Pu-239, and U-233.

For a chain reaction to occur, there must be a fairly large mass of fissionable nuclide. Recall that atoms are mostly empty space. If the mass is too small, fission neutrons simply pass through the fissionable substance without striking a nucleus and causing it to fission. The minimum mass of fissionable nuclide required to sustain a chain reaction is called the **critical mass**. The critical mass depends on the purity of the sample and other factors, but for uranium-235 the critical mass is about 50 kg.

In 1939, nuclear fission was discovered in Germany. The possibility for a sustained chain reaction was experimentally confirmed three years later. In 1942, the Italian physicist Enrico Fermi directed an international group of scientists who carried out the first self-sustaining nuclear chain reaction. This landmark event took place on a converted squash court beneath the University of Chicago and is commemorated by a plaque at the university (Figure 18.9).

ON DECEMBER 2, 1942
MAN ACHIEVED HERE
THE FIRST SELF-SUSTAINING CHAIN REACTION
AND THEREBY INITIATED THE
CONTROLLED RELEASE OF NUCLEAR ENERGY

▲ Figure 18.9 **Commemoration Plaque** This large plaque at the University of Chicago signifies the ushering in of the nuclear age.

Uranium-235 Enrichment

Naturally occurring uranium is only 0.7% fissionable uranium-235. Most of the uranium, 99.3%, is nonfissionable uranium-238. To obtain a chain reaction, it is necessary to enrich the natural mixture with the fissionable nuclide. That is, the mixture must be enriched from 0.7% to about 3% uranium-235. The enrichment process is started by reacting uranium with fluorine gas to give gaseous uranium hexafluoride.

$$^{235}U(s) + 3\,F_2(g) \longrightarrow\ ^{235}UF_6(g)$$
$$^{238}U(s) + 3\,F_2(g) \longrightarrow\ ^{238}UF_6(g)$$

The nuclides $^{235}UF_6$ and $^{238}UF_6$ are too similar to separate chemically. However, the two gaseous nuclides can be separated physically. The lighter nuclide, $^{235}UF_6$, diffuses slightly faster than the heavier nuclide $^{238}UF_6$. When the first fraction that diffuses through the tube is collected, it is richer in the faster-diffusing nuclide, $^{235}UF_6$. The collected uranium fraction is then reduced to the element, which is enriched in the nuclide uranium-235.

18.8 NUCLEAR FUSION

LEARNING OBJECTIVES

▶ To describe the process of nuclear fusion using deuterium and tritium.

▶ To write a nuclear equation for a given fusion reaction.

Nuclear fusion is the process of combining two light nuclei into a heavier nucleus. It is more difficult to initiate a fusion reaction than a fission reaction, but a fusion reaction releases more energy than a comparable fission reaction. In addition, nuclear fusion is a cleaner process than fission because it produces very little radioactive waste.

The Sun is a huge nuclear fusion reactor operating at millions of degrees. The Sun is made up of 73% hydrogen, 26% helium, and only 1% of all other elements. Three of the fusion reactions thought to occur on the Sun are

$$^1_1H + ^1_1H \longrightarrow\ ^2_1H + ^0_{+1}e + energy$$
$$^2_1H + ^1_1H \longrightarrow\ ^3_2He + energy$$
$$^3_2He + ^1_1H \longrightarrow\ ^4_2He + ^0_{+1}e + energy$$

Extreme temperatures, greater than 10,000,000 °C, are needed to overcome the strong repulsive forces of the positively charged nuclei. Experimentally, a powerful laser beam is used to generate the necessary heat to initiate nuclear fusion. A major practical problem is how to confine a reaction that takes place at millions of degrees. Since ordinary materials vaporize at this temperature, a strong magnetic field is used to confine the fusion reaction. Thus, nuclear fusion is said to occur in a "magnetic bottle."

Nuclear fusion has been achieved in research fusion reactors on a limited scale (Figure 18.10). To date, continuous nuclear fusion has not been achieved, and no commercial fusion reactors are in operation. If the technology obstacles can be overcome, the fusion of two deuterium nuclei could be used to supply the world with electrical energy.

Deuterium, ^2_1H, is the nuclide of hydrogen that contains one proton and one neutron. Deuterium is available from the sea in the form of heavy water molecules, D_2O (Section 4.5). It is estimated that more energy is potentially available from the deuterium in one cubic mile of seawater than from all the current petroleum reserves in the world. A typical fusion reaction of deuterium is as follows:

$$^2_1 H + {}^2_1 H \longrightarrow {}^4_2 He + energy$$

◀ Figure 18.10 **Fusion Re-actor** A nuclear fusion reactor is essentially a large "magnetic bottle" that contains small nuclei heated to millions of degrees by a powerful pulse laser.

Another promising nuclear fusion reaction involves deuterium and tritium. **Tritium**, $^3_1 H$, is the nuclide of hydrogen that contains one proton and two neutrons. Here again, the fusion of nuclei requires temperatures above 10,000,000 °C and is initiated by a powerful laser. A typical fusion reaction of deuterium and tritium produces an alpha particle and a neutron, while releasing a huge amount of energy.

$$^3_1 H + {}^2_1 H \longrightarrow {}^4_2 He + {}^1_0 n + energy$$

Summary

LEARNING OBJECTIVES	SEC	EXERCISES
To state the properties of alpha, beta, and gamma radiation.	18.1	Exercises 1–6
To illustrate the following types of radiation using atomic notation: alpha, beta, gamma, positron, neutron, and proton.	18.2	Exercises 7–8
To write balanced nuclear equations involving natural radioactivity.	18.2	Exercises 9–12
To identify products in the decay series for uranium-238 given the radiation emitted.	18.3	Exercises 13–14
To identify products in the decay series for uranium-235 given the radiation emitted.	18.3	Exercises 15–16
To identify products in the decay series for thorium-232 given the radiation emitted.	18.3	Exercises 17–20
To understand the concept of half-life for a radioactive sample.	18.4	Exercises 21–24
To relate the amount of radioactive sample, and its radioactivity, to a given half-life.	18.4	Exercises 25–32
To describe the radiocarbon dating method.	18.5	Exercise 33
To describe the uranium–lead dating method.	18.5	Exercise 34
To state applications of selected radionuclides.	18.5	Exercises 35–42
To write balanced nuclear equations involving induced radioactivity.	18.6	Exercises 43–54
To describe the process in a nuclear fission reaction.	18.7	Exercises 55–58
To write a nuclear equation for a given fission reaction.	18.7	Exercises 59–64
To describe the process of nuclear fusion using deuterium and tritium.	18.8	Exercises 65–66
To write a nuclear equation for a given fusion reaction.	18.8	Exercises 67–70

Section 18.1 An unstable atomic nucleus disintegrates naturally by emitting **radioactivity** in the form of alpha, beta, or gamma radiation. An **alpha particle** (α) has a positive charge and is identical to a helium-4 nucleus. A **beta particle** (β) has a negative charge and is identical to an electron. A **gamma ray** (γ) is a powerful type of nuclear radiation that has neither mass nor charge.

Section 18.2 The composition of a nucleus is indicated using atomic notation, where the **atomic number** of the element is indicated by a subscript and the **mass number** by a superscript. In this chapter, we have used the term **nuclide** to refer to the nucleus of an atom with a specific composition of protons and neutrons.

A **nuclear reaction** involves a change in a nucleus, for example, **electron capture** or **positron** emission. A **nuclear equation** represents the nuclear change using atomic notation for each particle. To balance a nuclear equation, two criteria are necessary: (1) the sums of the atomic numbers must be the same on each side of the equation, and (2) the sums of the mass numbers must be equal for reactants and products.

Section 18.3 If a nuclide disintegrates through the emission of radiation in more than one step, the overall process is called a **radioactive decay series**. The decaying nucleus is referred to as the parent nuclide, and the resulting nucleus is the daughter nuclide. Together, they are referred to as **parent–daughter nuclides**. In nature, uranium-235, uranium-238, and thorium-232 decay naturally in a series of steps. Each of these nuclides continues to decay in a series of steps until a stable nuclide of lead is produced.

Section 18.4 We can keep track of the number of decaying nuclei in a sample using a Geiger counter. The **activity** of the sample refers to the number of unstable nuclei that decay in a given period of time. The activity of a sample decreases with time because there are fewer nuclei to decay. However, the time required for 50% of the radioactive nuclei to decay is constant and is called the **half-life**. After each half-life, only 50% of the radioactive nuclei remain.

Section 18.5 Scientists have found important applications for a broad selection of radioactive nuclides. **Radionuclides** are available for dating objects, for improving agricultural harvests, and for providing energy. In addition, there is a long and growing list of radionuclides that are used for medical diagnosis and treatment.

Section 18.6 Scientists can induce radioactivity by firing light, accelerated nuclides at heavy nuclei. In the event that the atomic number changes and the new nucleus corresponds to a different element, the change is called a **transmutation** reaction. With particle accelerators, it is possible to cause hundreds of nuclear reactions. A particle accelerator, such as a *cyclotron* or a *linear accelerator*, accelerates a projectile nuclide and sends it crashing into a target nucleus. This technique is called "atom smashing" and has created hundreds of synthetic nuclides.

Section 18.7 A neutron striking an unstable nucleus can induce **nuclear fission**; that is, the nucleus can split into two or more particles while releasing energy. The three most important nuclides that undergo fission are uranium-235, plutonium-239, and uranium-233. When a nucleus fissions, two or three neutrons are usually released. These neutrons can in turn cause a second and a third nuclear fission. If a single neutron initiates continuous fission, the process is called a **chain reaction**. For a chain reaction to occur, there must be a sufficient amount of fissionable nuclide. The minimum size of sample that can support a chain reaction is called the **critical mass**.

Section 18.8 The process of combining two light nuclei into a single nucleus is called **nuclear fusion**. In the interior of the Sun at temperatures above 10,000,000 °C, there is continuous nuclear fusion. In the laboratory, scientists have had limited success and to date have not been able to create continuous nuclear fusion. One promising fusion reaction is that involving two **deuterium**, $^2_1$H, nuclei. Another possibility is the fusion of deuterium and **tritium**, $^3_1$H, nuclei. The technological problems are considerable because the fusion process requires temperatures of millions of degrees. However, nuclear fusion does not produce radioactive waste and is therefore an attractive possibility as a future energy source.

Key Terms *Answers to Key Terms are in Appendix H.*

Select the key term that corresponds to each of the following definitions.

_____ **1.** the emission of particles or energy from an unstable nucleus

_____ **2.** nuclear radiation identical to a helium-4 nucleus

_____ **3.** nuclear radiation identical to an electron

_____ **4.** nuclear radiation that has neither mass nor charge

_____ **5.** the value that indicates the number of protons in a nucleus

_____ **6.** the value that indicates the number of protons and neutrons in a nucleus

_____ **7.** an atom with a specific number of protons and neutrons

_____ **8.** a high-energy change involving the atomic nucleus

_____ **9.** a shorthand representation using atomic notation to describe a nuclear reaction

_____ **10.** nuclear radiation identical in mass but opposite in charge to that of an electron

_____ **11.** a nuclear reaction in which a heavy nuclide attracts one of its inner core electrons into the nucleus

_____ **12.** the stepwise disintegration of a radioactive nucleus until a stable nuclide is reached

_____ **13.** the relationship of a decaying nuclide and the resulting nuclide that is produced

_____ **14.** the number of radioactive nuclei in a sample that disintegrate in a given period of time, for example, 500 dpm

_____ **15.** the amount of time required for 50% of the radioactive nuclei in a given sample to decay

_____ **16.** an atom whose nucleus is unstable and decays radioactively

_____ **17.** the conversion of one element to another by a nuclear reaction

_____ **18.** a nuclear reaction in which a nucleus splits into two or more lighter nuclei

_____ **19.** a fission reaction in which the neutrons released initiate a second reaction, which in turn initiate a third reaction, and so on

_____ **20.** the minimum mass of a fissionable nuclide necessary to sustain a chain reaction

_____ **21.** a nuclear reaction in which two light nuclei combine into a single nucleus

_____ **22.** the nuclide of hydrogen having one neutron

_____ **23.** the nuclide of hydrogen having two neutrons

(a) activity (*Sec. 18.4*)

(b) alpha particle (α) (*Sec. 18.1*)

(c) atomic number (Z) (*Sec. 18.2*)

(d) beta particle (β^-) (*Sec. 18.1*)

(e) chain reaction (*Sec. 18.7*)

(f) critical mass (*Sec. 18.7*)

(g) deuterium (*Sec. 18.8*)

(h) electron capture (EC) (*Sec. 18.2*)

(i) gamma ray (γ)(*Sec. 18.1*)

(j) half-life ($t_{1/2}$)(*Sec. 18.4*)

(k) mass number (A) (*Sec. 18.2*)

(l) nuclear equation (*Sec. 18.2*)

(m) nuclear fission (*Sec. 18.7*)

(n) nuclear fusion (*Sec. 18.8*)

(o) nuclear reaction (*Sec. 18.2*)

(p) nuclide (*Sec. 18.2*)

(q) parent–daughter nuclides (*Sec. 18.3*)

(r) positron (β^+)(*Sec. 18.2*)

(s) radioactive decay series (*Sec. 18.3*)

(t) radioactivity (*Sec. 18.1*)

(u) radionuclide (*Sec. 18.5*)

(v) transmutation (*Sec. 18.6*)

(w) tritium (*Sec. 18.8*)

Exercises *Answers to odd-numbered Exercises are in Appendix I.*

Natural Radioactivity (Sec. 18.1)

1. Which type of radiation cannot penetrate human skin and requires heavy paper or clothing as minimum protective shielding?

2. Which type of radiation is a helium nucleus and is deflected toward the negative electrode as it passes between electrically charged plates?

3. Which type of radiation can penetrate about 1 cm of human flesh and requires wood or aluminum as minimum protective shielding?

4. Which type of radiation is identical to an electron and is deflected toward the positive electrode as it passes between electrically charged plates?

5. Which type of radiation can pass through the human body and requires thick lead or concrete as minimum protective shielding?

6. Which type of radiation is powerful radiant energy that is *not* deflected as it passes between electrically charged plates?

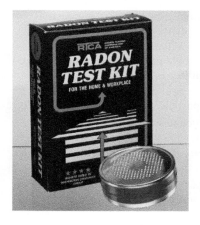

◀ **Radon Test Kit** Earth releases radioactive radon gas that may collect beneath a home. Although the gas is only present in trace amounts, it may accumulate in basements and areas with minimal ventilation and pose a health hazard.

Nuclear Equations (Sec. 18.2)

7. What is the approximate mass for each of the following?
   (a) alpha particle   (b) beta particle
   (c) gamma ray   (d) positron
   (e) neutron   (f) proton

8. What is the relative charge for each of the following?
   (a) α (b) β^- (c) γ (d) β^+ (e) n^0 (f) p^+

9. Write an equation for each of the following natural radioactive decay processes:
   (a) W-160 decays by alpha emission
   (b) P-32 decays by beta emission
   (c) Co-55 decays by positron emission
   (d) Ti-44 decays by electron capture

10. Write an equation for each of the following natural radioactive decay processes:
    (a) U-238 decays by alpha emission
    (b) Al-28 decays by beta emission
    (c) O-15 decays by positron emission
    (d) Fe-55 decays by electron capture

11. Identify X, an unknown radioactive nuclide, given the following information:
    (a) Nuclide X decays by alpha emission to give ^{218}Ra.
    (b) Nuclide X decays by beta emission to give ^{56}Fe.
    (c) Nuclide X decays by positron emission to give ^{19}F.
    (d) Nuclide X decays by electron capture to give ^{37}Cl.

12. Identify X, an unknown radioactive nuclide, given the following information:
    (a) Nuclide X decays by alpha emission to give ^{217}Rn.
    (b) Nuclide X decays by beta emission to give ^{43}Ca.
    (c) Nuclide X decays by positron emission to give ^{73}Br.
    (d) Nuclide X decays by electron capture to give ^{133}Cs.

Radioactive Decay Series (Sec. 18.3)

13. The uranium-238 decay series begins with the emission of an alpha particle. The daughter product emits a beta particle to give which nuclide?

14. In the final step of the uranium-238 disintegration series, the parent nuclide decays into lead-206 and an alpha particle. Identify the parent nuclide.

15. The uranium-235 decay series begins with the emission of an alpha particle. The daughter product emits a beta particle to give which nuclide?

16. In the final step of the uranium-235 disintegration series, the parent nuclide decays into lead-207 and a beta particle. Identify the parent nuclide.

17. Supply each of the following emission particles in the 10-step decay series for radioactive thorium-232.

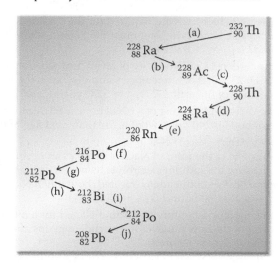

18. Supply each of the following decaying nuclides in the 11-step decay series for radioactive neptunium-237.

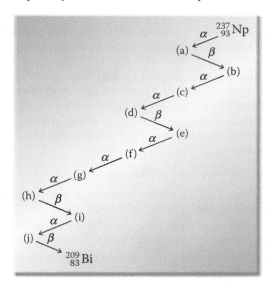

19. Plutonium-241 decays in a series of 13 steps, beginning with the emission of a beta particle, followed by an alpha particle, followed by another alpha particle. Identify the radionuclide produced in Step 3 of the Pu-241 series.

20. Plutonium-241 decays in a series of 13 steps. In Step 11, bismuth-213 emits a beta particle, followed by an alpha particle, and ending with a beta particle. Identify the radionuclide produced in Step 13 of the Pu-241 series.

Radioactive Half-Life (Sec. 18.4)

21. What percentage of U-238 radionuclides in a sample remain after two half-lives?

22. What percentage of U-238 radionuclides in a sample remain after three half-lives?

23. A nuclear reactor produces spent Pu-239 fuel rods that are highly radioactive after they no longer support fission. If 15 half-lives are required for the nuclide to reach a safe level, how long must the rods be stored? ($t_{1/2} = 24{,}400$ years)

24. A nuclear fission reactor produces Sr-90 radioactive waste. If 20 half-lives are required for the nuclide to reach a safe level, how long must the nuclear waste be stored? ($t_{1/2} = 28.8$ years)

25. If the carbon-14 radioactivity of an ancient wooden artifact is 6.25% that of a reference sample, what is the estimated age of the artifact? ($t_{1/2} = 5730$ years)

26. If the carbon-14 reading of a fossil bone is 60 dpm, and a recent bone is 240 dpm, what is the estimated age of the fossil? ($t_{1/2} = 5730$ years)

27. Sodium-24 in the form of NaCl is given as an injection to measure the sodium electrolyte balance. If 80 mg of the medical radionuclide is injected, how much Na-24 remains after 60 hours? ($t_{1/2} = 15$ hours)

28. If 160 mg of technetium-99 is administered for a medical diagnosis, how much of the nuclide remains after 24 hours? ($t_{1/2} = 6$ hours)

29. Small beads of iridium-192 are sealed in a plastic tube and inserted through a needle into breast tumors. If an Ir-192 sample has an initial activity of 560 dpm, how much time is required for the activity to drop to 35 dpm? ($t_{1/2} = 74$ days)

30. If an iron-59 sample has an initial activity of 200 dpm, how much time is required for the activity to drop to 25 dpm? ($t_{1/2} = 45$ days)

31. The initial radioactivity of a cobalt-60 sample was 1200 dpm and after 21.2 years the activity dropped to 75 dpm. What is the half-life of the radionuclide?

32. If 2400 μg of hydrogen-3 decay to 600 μg after 24.8 years, what is the half-life of this radionuclide that is used as a chemical tracer?

Applications of Radionuclides (Sec. 18.5)

33. What radionuclide technique can be used to estimate the age of fossils up to 50,000 years old?

34. What radionuclide technique can be used to estimate the age of geological events up to a few billion years?

35. What radionuclide can be used to sterilize male insects and control pests?

36. What radionuclide can be used to irradiate food and destroy microorganisms?

37. What γ-emitting radionuclide is used to power pacemakers for heart patients?

38. What γ-emitting radionuclide can be used to diagnose and locate inactive lung tissue in the respiratory system?

39. What β-emitting radionuclide can be used to measure the activity of the thyroid gland?

40. What β-emitting radionuclide can be used to diagnose anemia by attaching to a hemoglobin molecule?

41. What γ-emitting radionuclide can be used to treat breast cancer?

42. What γ-emitting radionuclide can be used to diagnose and locate brain tumors?

Induced Radioactivity (Sec. 18.6)

43. Bombarding Br-81 with gamma rays gives a radioactive nuclide and a neutron. Identify the radionuclide.

44. Bombarding Na-23 with a proton gives a radioactive nuclide and a neutron. Identify the radionuclide.

45. Bombarding U-238 with a hydrogen-2 nucleus produces a radioactive nuclide, a beta particle, and two neutrons. Identify the radionuclide.

46. Bombarding Li-6 with a neutron produces a radioactive nuclide and an alpha particle. Identify the radionuclide.

47. Firing a hydrogen-2 nucleus at a target nucleus gives I-131 and a neutron. What is the target nuclide?

48. Firing a neutron at a target nucleus gives Mn-56 and an alpha particle. What is the target nuclide?

49. Firing an accelerated particle at a boron-10 target nucleus produces N-14 and a gamma ray. What is the projectile particle?

50. Firing an accelerated particle at a Mg-26 target nucleus produces Mg-27 and a proton. What is the projectile particle?

51. In 1967, a Russian team smashed a neon nucleus into an americium target and claimed it had synthesized a new element, X. Given the equation for the reaction, what nuclide did the team create?

$$^{243}_{95}\text{Am} + ^{22}_{10}\text{Ne} \longrightarrow ^{A}_{Z}\text{X} + 5\,^{1}_{0}\text{n}$$

52. In 1970, a group at the University of California at Berkeley fired a nitrogen nucleus into a californium target and claimed it had synthesized a new element, X. Given the equation for the reaction, what nuclide did the group create?

$$^{249}_{98}\text{Cf} + ^{15}_{7}\text{N} \longrightarrow ^{A}_{Z}\text{X} + 4\,^{1}_{0}\text{n}$$

53. In 1974, a team of Russian physicists smashed a chromium-54 nucleus into a lead-207 target. If a new element, X, and one neutron were produced from the collision, what nuclide did the team create?

54. In 1976, a team of German physicists smashed a chromium-54 nucleus into a bismuth-209 target. If a new element, X, and one neutron were produced from the collision, what nuclide did the team create?

Nuclear Fission (Sec. 18.7)

55. If a neutron causes a fission reaction that releases two neutrons, how many neutrons have been produced from the third fission step? (Assume each step in the fission process releases two neutrons.)

56. If a neutron causes a fission reaction that releases three neutrons, how many neutrons have been produced from the third fission step? (Assume each step in the fission process releases three neutrons.)

57. The fission of uranium-235 produces 2.4 neutrons per nucleus. Why is there a fractional value for the number of neutrons released?

58. Why must uranium ore be enriched in U-235 before it can be used in the fuel rods of a nuclear reactor?

59. How many neutrons are produced from the following fission reaction?

$$^{235}_{92}\text{U} + ^{1}_{0}\text{n} \longrightarrow ^{144}_{54}\text{Xe} + ^{90}_{38}\text{Sr} + ^{1}_{0}\text{n}$$

60. How many neutrons are produced from the following fission reaction?

$$^{235}_{92}U + ^{1}_{0}n \longrightarrow ^{142}_{56}Ba + ^{91}_{36}Kr + ^{1}_{0}n$$

61. How many neutrons are produced from the following fission reaction?

$$^{239}_{94}Pu + ^{1}_{0}n \longrightarrow ^{137}_{55}Cs + ^{100}_{39}Y + ^{1}_{0}n$$

62. How many neutrons are produced from the following fission reaction?

$$^{239}_{94}Pu + ^{1}_{0}n \longrightarrow ^{142}_{57}La + ^{94}_{37}Rb + ^{1}_{0}n$$

63. What nuclide undergoes nuclear fission to give barium-143, krypton-88, and three neutrons?

64. What nuclide undergoes nuclear fission to give xenon-142, strontium-90, and two neutrons?

◄ **Nuclear Fission** In a uranium-235 atomic bomb explosion, the large uranium nucleus spits (fissions) into two smaller fragments, and releases neutrons and energy.

Nuclear Fusion (Sec. 18.8)

65. The nuclear fusion of two deuterium nuclei gives a tritium nucleus, a positron, and particle X. Identify particle X.

66. The nuclear fusion of two helium-3 nuclei gives two protons and particle X. Identify particle X.

67. The nuclear fusion of a helium-3 nucleus and particle X releases an alpha particle and a positron. Identify particle X.

68. The nuclear fusion of a lithium-7 nucleus and particle X releases two alpha particles and a neutron. Identify particle X.

69. The nuclear fusion of two identical nuclides produces an alpha particle and a gamma ray. Identify the fusion nuclide.

70. The nuclear fusion of two identical nuclides produces a deuterium nucleus and a positron. Identify the fusion nuclide.

General Exercises

71. Plutonium-241 undergoes a 13-step decay series. If an alpha particle is emitted in the first step, what is the daughter product?

72. Plutonium-241 undergoes a 13-step decay series. If an alpha particle is emitted in the first step followed by a beta particle, what is the granddaughter product?

73. Nuclide X has a half-life of 23 s and decays by beta emission to produce Xe-136 and a neutron. Write a nuclear equation for the reaction.

74. Nuclide X has a half-life of 2.6 years and decays by electron capture to produce Mn-55 and a gamma ray. Write a nuclear equation for the reaction.

75. Crater Lake in Oregon was formed by volcanic explosion. If a tree charred by the explosion gave an activity of ~7.7 dpm and the half-life of C-14 is 5730 years, what is the approximate age of Crater Lake?

76. Uranium–lead dating of lunar rock samples gave a U-238 to Pb-206 ratio of ~1.0. If the half-life of U-238 is 4.5 billion years, what is the approximate age of the lunar rocks?

77. A radionuclide ionizes the air in a smoke detector, which in turn allows the flow of electricity. When smoke particles enter the detector, they disrupt the electric current and set off an alarm. What α-emitting radionuclide is used to ionize the air in a smoke detector? (*Hint:* The radionuclide decays into Np-237.)

78. A PET scan is a medical imaging technique for the circulatory system. First, a radionuclide is injected that decays by positron emission. When the positron is emitted, it strikes an electron, causing mutual annihilation and the release of two gamma rays. Write an equation for the annihilation reaction.

79. Element 99 was first synthesized by bombarding uranium-238 with neutrons. The reaction yielded Es-253 and seven beta particles. How many neutrons are necessary to balance the equation?

80. Element 100 was first synthesized by bombarding uranium-238 with neutrons. The reaction yielded Fm-255 and eight beta particles. How many neutrons are necessary to balance the equation?

81. In 1955, a single atom of a new element was synthesized using the cyclotron at the University of California at Berkeley. If Es-253 reacted with an alpha particle to release a neutron, what new nuclide was produced?

82. In the Middle Ages, alchemists attempted to transmute base metals into gold. Recently, platinum has been transmuted into gold by bombarding Pt-198 with a deuterium nucleus to give a platinum nuclide and a proton. If the platinum nuclide decays by beta emission, what nuclide results?

Challenge Exercises

83. The nuclear fission of lithium-6 by a neutron releases an alpha particle, energy, and nuclide X. Identify nuclide X.

84. The nuclear fusion of deuterium and tritium releases an alpha particle, energy, and nuclide X. Identify nuclide X.

Online Exercises

Research each of the following using an Internet search engine (e.g., Google.com or Yahoo.com) and cite your URL reference.

85. In 2012, flerovium (Fl) and livermorium (Lv) were officially named by IUPAC. Identify the longest-lived isotope of each element and its half-life.

86. In 2010, six atoms of element 117 were synthesized at the Joint Institute for Nuclear Research in Russia. Identify the target nucleus and projectile used in the reaction for the synthesis of element 117.

18 Chapter Self-Test
Answers to Self-Test are in Appendix J.

1. Which type of nuclear radiation is identical to an electron and is deflected toward the positive electrode as it passes between electrically charged plates? (Sec. 18.1)
   - **(a)** alpha
   - **(b)** beta
   - **(c)** gamma
   - **(d)** all of the above
   - **(e)** none of the above

2. What is the approximate mass and relative charge of gamma radiation? (Sec. 18.2)
   - **(a)** 4 amu and 2+
   - **(b)** 1 amu and 1+
   - **(c)** 1 amu and 0
   - **(d)** 0 amu and 0
   - **(e)** 0 amu and 1−

3. What is the name of the particle having the following notation: $_{+1}^{0}$e? (Sec. 18.2)
   - **(a)** electron
   - **(b)** neutron
   - **(c)** positron
   - **(d)** proton
   - **(e)** none of the above

4. What particle is emitted when a Ra-221 nucleus decays to Rn-217? (Sec. 18.2)
   - **(a)** alpha
   - **(b)** beta
   - **(c)** neutron
   - **(d)** positron
   - **(e)** proton

5. In the final step of the uranium-235 decay series, the parent nuclide decays to a lead-207 nuclide and a beta particle. What is the parent nuclide? (Sec. 18.3)
   - **(a)** $_{82}^{206}$Pb
   - **(b)** $_{82}^{208}$Pb
   - **(c)** $_{83}^{207}$Bi
   - **(d)** $_{81}^{207}$Tl
   - **(e)** none of the above

6. If an iron-59 sample has an initial activity of 160 dpm, how much time is required for the activity to drop to 20 dpm? ($t_{1/2}$ = 45 days) (Sec. 18.4)
   - **(a)** 45 days
   - **(b)** 90 days
   - **(c)** 135 days
   - **(d)** 180 days
   - **(e)** 210 days

7. What is the principle assumption for radiocarbon dating to be reliable? (Sec. 18.5)
   - **(a)** The amount of nitrogen-14 in the atmosphere has remained constant.
   - **(b)** The amount of carbon-14 in the atmosphere has remained constant.
   - **(c)** The number of neutrons in the atmosphere has remained constant.
   - **(d)** The number of protons in the atmosphere has remained constant.
   - **(e)** The temperature of the atmosphere has remained constant.

8. In 1934 Irene Curie (daughter of Marie and Pierre) and her husband Frederic Joliot synthesized the first radionuclide. They bombarded aluminum-27 with an alpha particle and obtained a neutron and what other radionuclide? (Sec. 18.6)
   - **(a)** phosphorus-30
   - **(b)** phosphorus-31
   - **(c)** silicon-30
   - **(d)** silicon-31
   - **(e)** none of the above

9. How many neutrons are produced from the following fission reaction? (Sec. 18.7)

$$_{92}^{235}\text{U} + _{0}^{1}\text{n} \longrightarrow _{56}^{141}\text{Ba} + _{36}^{91}\text{Kr} + _{0}^{1}\text{n}$$

   - **(a)** 1
   - **(b)** 2
   - **(c)** 3
   - **(d)** 4
   - **(e)** none of the above

10. The nuclear fusion of a helium-3 nucleus and nuclide X releases an alpha particle and a positron. What is nuclide X? (Sec. 18.8)
    - **(a)** deuterium
    - **(b)** tritium
    - **(c)** neutron
    - **(d)** positron
    - **(e)** proton

Key Concepts

11. Write a nuclear equation for each of the following natural decay reactions:
    - **(a)** U-238 decays by alpha emission
    - **(b)** U-239 decays by beta emission
    - **(c)** K-40 decays by positron emission
    - **(d)** K-40 decays by electron capture

12. A single neutron causes uranium-235 to undergo nuclear fission and release three neutrons. Assuming each of the neutrons released causes a fission that releases three more neutrons, how many neutrons are released in the second step?

13. The nuclear fusion of two protons releases a deuterium nucleus and nuclide X. Identify nuclide X.

Critical Thinking

14. Write a nuclear equation corresponding to the following illustration of radioactive decay:

$$\boxed{\begin{array}{c} 82\ p^+ \\ 128\ n^0 \end{array}} \rightarrow \boxed{\begin{array}{c} 83\ p^+ \\ 127\ n^0 \end{array}} + \bigcirc$$

15. In 2003 an international team of scientists at the Lawrence Livermore Laboratories claimed the synthesis of a new element by firing a krypton-86 nucleus into a lead-208 target. If one neutron was released from the collision, identify the new element by its nuclide.

Weights and Measures

METRIC SYSTEM EXACT EQUIVALENTS

Length:	1 meter (m)	=	100 centimeters (cm)
	1 meter (m)	=	1000 millimeters (mm)
	1 kilometer (km)	=	1000 meters (m)
Mass:	1 gram (g)	=	1000 milligrams (mg)
	1 kilogram (kg)	=	1000 grams (g)
	1 metric ton	=	1000 kilograms (kg)
Volume:	1 liter (L)	=	1000 milliliters (mL)
	1 liter (L)	=	10 deciliters (dL)
	1 milliliter (mL)	=	1 cubic centimeter (cm^3)

ENGLISH SYSTEM EXACT EQUIVALENTS

Length:	1 foot (ft)	=	12 inches (in.)
	1 mile (mi)	=	1760 yards (yd)
	1 mile (mi)	=	5280 feet (ft)
Mass:	1 pound (lb)	=	16 ounces (oz)
	1 troy pound (t lb)	=	12 troy ounces (t oz)
	1 ton	=	2000 pounds (lb)
Volume:	1 quart (qt)	=	32 fluid ounces (fl oz)
	1 quart (qt)	=	2 pints (pt)
	1 gallon (gal)	=	4 quarts (qt)

ENGLISH–METRIC APPROXIMATE EQUIVALENTS

Length:	1 inch (in.)	=	2.54 centimeters (cm)
Mass:	1 pound (lb)	=	454 grams (g)
Volume:	1 quart (qt)	=	946 milliliters (mL)
Time:	1 second (sec)	=	1.00 second (s)

TEMPERATURE EQUIVALENTS

$$\frac{9}{5}\,°C + 32 \quad = \quad °F$$

$$\frac{5}{9}\,(°F - 32) \quad = \quad °C$$

$$°C + 273 \quad = \quad K$$

ENERGY EQUIVALENTS

1 calorie (cal)	=	4.184 joules (J)
1 kilocalorie (kcal)	=	1000 calories (cal)
1 kilocalorie (kcal)	=	4.184 kilojoules (kJ)

Physical Constants

Avogadro's number	=	6.02×10^{23}
Absolute zero		
Kelvin scale	=	$0\,K$
Celsius scale	=	$-273.15\,°C$
Standard temperature and pressure (STP)		
standard temperature	=	$0\,°C$ (273 K)
standard atmospheric pressure	=	1 atm
	=	760 mm Hg (760 torr)
	=	76 cm Hg
	=	29.9 in. Hg
	=	14.7 psi
	=	101 kPa
Molar volume of a gas (STP)	=	22.4 L/mol
Ideal gas constant, R	=	$0.0821\,L \cdot atm/mol \cdot K$
Ionization constant of water, K_w	=	1.00×10^{-14}
Mass of proton	=	1.0073 amu
Mass of neutron	=	1.0087 amu
Mass of electron	=	0.00055 amu
Velocity of light	=	$3.00 \times 10^{8}\,m/s$

Activity Series for Metals

Most Active Metal:

$$Li \rightarrow Li^+ + e^-$$
$$K \rightarrow K^+ + e^-$$
$$Ba \rightarrow Ba^{2+} + 2\,e^-$$
$$Sr \rightarrow Sr^{2+} + 2\,e^-$$
$$Ca \rightarrow Ca^{2+} + 2\,e^-$$
$$Na \rightarrow Na^+ + e^-$$

(metals above react with water at 25 °C)

$$Mg \rightarrow Mg^{2+} + 2\,e^-$$
$$Al \rightarrow Al^{3+} + 3\,e^-$$
$$Mn \rightarrow Mn^{2+} + 2\,e^-$$
$$Zn \rightarrow Zn^{2+} + 2\,e^-$$
$$Cr \rightarrow Cr^{3+} + 3\,e^-$$
$$Fe \rightarrow Fe^{2+} + 2\,e^-$$
$$Cd \rightarrow Cd^{2+} + 2\,e^-$$
$$Co \rightarrow Co^{2+} + 2\,e^-$$
$$Ni \rightarrow Ni^{2+} + 2\,e^-$$
$$Sn \rightarrow Sn^{2+} + 2\,e^-$$
$$Pb \rightarrow Pb^{2+} + 2\,e^-$$

(metals above react with acid)

$$\mathbf{H_2 \rightarrow 2\,H^+ + 2\,e^-}$$

(metals below do not react with acid)

$$Cu \rightarrow Cu^{2+} + 2\,e^-$$
$$Ag \rightarrow Ag^+ + e^-$$
$$Hg \rightarrow Hg^{2+} + 2\,e^-$$

Least Active Metal: $Au \rightarrow Au^{3+} + 3\,e^-$

D

Solubility Rules for Ionic Compounds

Ionic compounds containing the following ions are generally **soluble** in water.

1. alkali metal ions and the ammonium ion, Li^+, Na^+, K^+, NH_4^+
2. acetate ion, $C_2H_3O_2^-$
3. nitrate ion, NO_3^-
4. halide ions ($X = Cl^-, Br^-, I^-$)
   (AgX, Hg_2X_2, and PbX_2 are exceptions and are *insoluble*)
5. sulfate ion, SO_4^{2-}
   ($SrSO_4$, $BaSO_4$, and $PbSO_4$ are exceptions and are *insoluble*)

Ionic compounds containing the following ions are generally **insoluble*** in water.

6. carbonate ion, CO_3^{2-}
   (see Rule 1 exceptions, which are *soluble*)
7. chromate ion, CrO_4^{2-}
   (see Rule 1 exceptions, which are *soluble*)
8. phosphate ion, PO_4^{3-}
   (see Rule 1 exceptions, which are *soluble*)
9. sulfide ion, S^{2-}
   (CaS, SrS, BaS, and Rule 1 exceptions are *soluble*)
10. hydroxide ion, OH^-
    [$Ca(OH)_2$, $Sr(OH)_2$, $Ba(OH)_2$, and Rule 1 exceptions are *soluble*]

---

* These compounds are actually slightly soluble, or very slightly soluble, in water.

Vapor Pressure of Water

TEMPERATURE (°C)	VAPOR PRESSURE (mm Hg)	TEMPERATURE (°C)	VAPOR PRESSURE (mm Hg)	TEMPERATURE (°C)	VAPOR PRESSURE (mm Hg)
0	4.6	21	18.7	35	41.2
5	6.5	22	19.8	40	55.3
10	9.2	23	21.1	45	71.9
12	10.5	24	22.4	50	92.5
14	12.0	25	23.8	55	118.0
16	13.6	26	25.2	60	149.4
17	14.5	27	26.7	70	233.7
18	15.5	28	28.4	80	355.1
19	16.5	29	30.0	90	525.8
20	17.5	30	31.8	100	760.0

Properties of Water

Density of H$_2$O:	0.99987 g/mL at 0 °C
	1.00000 g/mL at 4 °C
	0.99707 g/mL at 25 °C

Heat of fusion at 0 °C:	80.0 cal/g (335 J/g)
Heat of solidification at 0 °C:	80.0 cal/g (335 J/g)

Heat of vaporization at 100 °C:	540 cal/g (2260 J/g)
Heat of condensation at 100 °C:	540 cal/g (2260 J/g)

Specific heat of H$_2$O

ice:	0.50 cal/(g × °C) [2.1 J/(g × °C)]
water:	1.00 cal/(g × °C) [4.18 J/(g × °C)]
steam:	0.48 cal/(g × °C) [2.0 J/(g × °C)]

Ionization constant of H$_2$O

K_w: 1.00 × 10^{-14} at 25 °C

Answers to Concept Exercises

Chapter 1

1. Alchemists believed in a magic potion that had the power to heal and to transmute lead into gold.

Prerequisite Science Skills

1. No instrument is capable of an exact measurement.

2. No measurement is exact due to uncertainty.

3. No measurement has infinite significant digits because no measurement is exact.

4. The rules for significant digits do not apply to exact numbers; the rules apply only to measurements.

5. When *adding* or *subtracting* measurements, the answer is limited by the decimal place with the most uncertainty. That is, the measurement that is least certain in a set of data limits the answer.

6. When *multiplying* or *dividing* measurements, the answer is limited by the number of significant digits in the data. That is, the measurement with the least number of significant digits limits the number of digits in the answer.

7. The length 1×10^{-3} cm is less; note the negative power of 10.

8. The mass $0.000\,001$ g is less; note the extra placeholder zero.

9. The mass $0.000\,01$ g is greater; that is, 1×10^{-5} g is greater than 1×10^{-6} g.

Chapter 2

1. The basic units of the metric system are meter, gram, and liter.

2. Since 1 m equals 1000 mm exactly, there is an infinite number of significant digits in the unit equation.

3. Since 1 L = 1000 mL exactly, there is an infinite number of significant digits in the unit factor.

4. The volume of a cube 1 cm on a side ($1\ cm^3$) equals 1 mL.

5. There is an infinite number of significant digits in the unit factor $1\ g/1000\ mg$ because $1\ g = 1000\ mg$ is an exact relationship.

6. There are an infinite number of significant digits in the unit factor $1\ gal/4\ qt$ because $1\ gal = 4\ qt$ is an exact relationship.

7. There are three significant digits in the unit factor $1\ kg/2.20\ lb$ because $1\ kg = 2.20\ lb$ is not an exact relationship. The kilogram and pound come from different systems of measurement.

8. The percent of gold in the alloy is 75%; that is, pure gold is 100% minus 20% silver and 5% copper.

9. The unit factors are: $\dfrac{11.2\ g\ hydrogen}{100\ g\ water}$ and $\dfrac{100\ g\ water}{11.2\ g\ hydrogen}$.

10. The volume of a cube 10 cm on a side ($1000\ cm^3$) equals 1 L.

11. The thicknesses are all equal; that is,
$1\ mm = 0.1\ cm = 0.001\ m$.

12. A volume of 500 in.^{3} is greater than 500 cm^3 because 1 in. is greater than 1 cm.

13. The volumes are equal because $1\ mL = 1\ cm^3$.

14. Since ice floats in water, water has the greater density.

15. Since $1\ kg = 1000\ g$ and $1\ L = 1000\ mL$, the two densities are equal.

16. The temperatures are the same, but the term *degrees centigrade* is discouraged.

17. The Kelvin temperature scale is assigned a value of zero for the coldest possible temperature; thus, -100 K cannot exist.

18. If the can feels cold, heat is flowing away from your hand into the can.

Chapter 3

1. (a) solid, (b) liquid, (c) gas

2. (a) element, (b) element, (c) compound, (d) mixture

3. Calcium is a solid metal under normal conditions.

4. Bromine is a liquid nonmetal under normal conditions.

5. The molecular formula for vitamin C is $C_6H_8O_6$.

6. Nitroglycerin has a total of 20 atoms in one molecule.

7. Copper turning black when heated is an example of a chemical change.

8. An Alka–Seltzer® tablet dissolving in water and producing gas bubbles is an example of a chemical change.

9. Applying the conservation of mass law, the mass of sulfur is found by difference to be 0.252 g (1.252 g − 1.000 g).

10. As the temperature increases, the kinetic energy of air molecules increases. As kinetic energy increases, the velocity of air molecules increases.

11. Chemical, electrical, heat, light, mechanical, and nuclear are all basic forms of energy; solar energy is an example of light energy.

Chapter 4

1. Atoms of different elements have a different number of protons, and *cannot have* the same atomic number.

2. Atoms of different elements *can have* isotopes with the same mass number.

3. (a) Simple Average Mass: $\dfrac{2.00 \text{ g} + 1.00 \text{ g}}{2} = 1.50 \text{ g}$

    (b) Weighted Average Mass:

$$2.00 \text{ g} \left(\frac{75 \text{ large marbles}}{100 \text{ total marbles}} \right) + 1.00 \text{ g} \left(\frac{25 \text{ small marbles}}{100 \text{ total marbles}} \right)$$

$$= 1.50 \text{ g} + 0.25 \text{ g} = 1.75 \text{ g}$$

4. Atomic number and mass number are always whole numbers; the atomic mass is never a whole number because it is the result of a mass measurement.

5. The energy *decreases* as the wavelength increases; but the energy *increases* as frequency increases.

6. A water wave is to a drop of water, as a light wave is to a *photon*.

7. All three statements are true.

8. The theoretical number of sublevels corresponds to the energy level. Thus, the 10th energy level has 10 sublevels.

9. The sublevels are closer together and the energy difference between sublevels *decreases* moving away from the nucleus. (Refer to Figure 4.13.)

10. The atomic number of Mn is one more than Cr, so Mn has one more *d* electron in the outermost sublevel.

11. All three statements are true.

Chapter 5

1. The modern periodic law states that elements are arranged according to *increasing atomic number*.

2. The group number for each family of elements is as follows: (a) IA/1 (b) IIA/2 (c) VIIA/17 (d) VIIIA/18

3. Period 1 at the top of the periodic table represents the smallest atomic radius. Group IA/1 at the far left of the periodic table represents the most metallic character.

4. Since Li is directly above Na in the periodic table, we can apply periodic trends to estimate values for Li. The atomic radius is less (~0.15 nm), the density is less (~0.50 g/mL), and the melting point is greater (~150 °C). Refer to Table 6.2 and note the estimated values are reasonable.

5. Since Zn and Cd are in the same group, they have very similar chemical properties.

6. Since Ag is in Period 5 and Group 1B/11, the highest energy sublevel is 4*d*.

7. Since Pt is the 8th element in the 5*d* sublevel, we predict the number of 5*d* electrons is 8.

8. Representative elements have valence electrons only in the outermost *s* and *p* sublevels. Transition elements have electrons in the outermost *d* and *f* sublevels, which complicates making reliable predictions.

9. Since Mg has two valence electrons in a 3*s* sublevel, we can draw the two electrons next to each other, or separate.

$$\text{Mg} \colon \text{ which may be preferable to } \cdot \text{Mg} \cdot$$

Either formula is acceptable. However, valence electrons are not stationary and the electron dot formula is only a tool for keeping track of valence electrons.

10. The noble gases have the highest ionization energies since they have filled valence shells. The alkali metals have the lowest ionization energies since they assume a noble gas electron configuration by losing one electron.

11. Group IA/1 elements have a charge of 1+; Group IIA/2 elements have a charge of 2+, and Group VIIA/17 elements have a charge of 1−.

12. The next ion in the isoelectronic series Se^{2-}, Br^-, Kr, Rb^+, Sr^{2+} is Y^{3+}.

13. The electron configuration is simply [Rn].

Chapter 6

1. A binary acid is in an aqueous solution and is indicated by (*aq*) [e.g., HCl(*aq*)].

2. Hg^{2+} is a monoatomic cation; whereas, Hg_2^{2+} is a polyatomic cation.

3. The Stock system specifies the charge on a cation using a Roman numeral in parentheses.

4. Iodide is a monoatomic anion because it has an *–ide* suffix.

5. A monoatomic anion has an *–ide* suffix; a polyatomic anion has an *–ate* or *–ite* suffix.

6. The formula for the metal oxide is M_2O_3.

7. The formula for the metal carbonate is $M_2(CO_3)_3$.

8. The charge on an oxide ion is 2−, and there are two oxide ions. The total negative charge is 4−. Thus, the positive charge on metal M is 4+.

9. Sodium chloride is a binary ionic compound as indicated by the *–ide* suffix.

10. LiCl is a binary ionic compound because it has two elements.

11. Since potassium and sodium are in the same family, and fluorine and iodine are in the same family, the formula for potassium iodide is KI.

12. The charge on a carbonate ion is 2−. Thus, the positive charge on metal M is 2+.

13. Potassium nitrate and potassium nitrite are both ternary ionic compounds as indicated by the *–ate* and *–ite* suffixes.

14. LiClO and $LiClO_2$ are both ternary ionic compounds because they have three elements.

15. Since calcium and strontium are in the same family, the formula for strontium sulfate is $SrSO_4$.

16. P_2O_3 is a binary molecular compound and requires Greek prefixes to specify the nonmetal ratio; that is, diphosphorus trioxide. Fe_2O_3 is an ionic compound and does not use Greek prefixes; that is, iron(III) oxide.

17. Nitrogen oxide is a binary molecular compound because it contains a nonmetal and oxygen.

18. HBr(*aq*) is a binary acid named hydrobromic acid.

19. $HBrO_3$(*aq*) is a ternary oxyacid named bromic acid, similar to chloric acid, $HClO_3$(*aq*). $HBrO_2$(*aq*) is a ternary oxyacid named bromous acid, similar to chorus acid, $HClO_2$(*aq*).

Chapter 7

1. Evidence for a chemical reaction include the following: (1) a gas is produced; (2) an insoluble solid is produced in solution; (3) a permanent color change is observed; (4) an energy change is observed.

2. The nonmetals that occur naturally as diatomic molecules are H_2, N_2, O_2, F_2, Cl_2, Br_2, and I_2.

3. No, changing a subscript gives an incorrect chemical formula.

4. Writing water as HOH often makes a neutralization equation easier to balance, as it is a special type of a double replacement reaction.

5. Decomposition reactions are easily recognized as they only have one reactant, unlike other types of reactions.

6. Heating a metal and oxygen produces a metal oxide.

7. Heating a nonmetal and oxygen produces a nonmetal oxide.

8. Heating a metal and nonmetal produces an ionic compound.

9. Heating a metal hydrogen carbonate produces a metal carbonate, water, and carbon dioxide gas.

10. Heating a metal carbonate produces a metal oxide and carbon dioxide gas.

11. Heating an oxygen-containing compound often releases oxygen gas.

12. Zn and Cu metals react with aqueous $AgNO_3$ (above Ag in the activity series), but not Au.

13. The metals that react with aqueous acid (above H in the activity series) include Zn, but not Cu and Au.

14. $Pb(NO_3)_2$ is soluble in water; $PbCl_2$ and $PbCO_3$ are insoluble.

15. $AgCl(s)$ is the insoluble product.

16. $NaCl(aq)$ is the salt product.

Chapter 8

1. A platinum atom has a mass of 195.08 amu. Avogadro's number of platinum atoms has a mass of 195.08 g.

2. The number of atoms in 1.00 mol of a metallic element is 6.02×10^{23}.

3. The number of molecules is 1.00 mol of a diatomic nonmetal is 6.02×10^{23}.

4. The mass of Avogadro's number of water molecules is 18.02 g.

5. The mass of Avogadro's number of sulfur molecules is $256.56\,g$ ($8 \times 32.07\,g$).

6. The mass of Avogadro's number of ozone molecules is $48.00\,g$ ($3 \times 16.00\,g$).

7. The mass of a carbon monoxide molecule is 28.01 amu.

8. The He balloon rises because the density of helium gas is much less than air. The N_2 balloon does not rise because the density of nitrogen gas is about the same as air, which is composed of 78% N_2 and 21% O_2.

9. The volume of 1.00 mol of any gas at STP is 22.4 L.

10. The number of molecules in 1.00 mol of ozone gas is 6.02×10^{23}.

11. The mass of 1.00 mol of hydrogen gas is 2.02 g.

12. The percent oxygen is 53.3% (100.0% − 40.0% − 6.7%).

13. The empirical formula is SO_2.

14. The empirical formula is SO_3.

15. The empirical formula is HO.

Chapter 9

1. The coefficients of a balanced equation indicate the ratio of moles and volumes of gases, but *not* the masses of gas, which vary with the molar mass of each gas.

2. One unit factor is required for a mole–mole conversion problem.

3. The three types of stoichiometry problem are mass–mass, mass–volume, and volume–volume.

4. The three steps in the unit analysis method of problem solving are as follows: (1) Write down the unit asked for in the answer. (2) Write down the given value that is related to the answer. (3) Apply unit factor(s) to convert the given value to the units in the answer.

5. Three unit factors are usually required to convert the mass given to the mass in the answer.

6. The three steps in unit analysis are as follows: (1) Write down the unit in the answer. (2) Write down the given value. (3) Apply unit factor(s) to convert the given value to the answer.

7. Three unit factors are usually required to convert the mass given to the volume in the answer.

8. One unit factor is usually required to convert the volume given to the volume in the answer.

9. Each bicycle frame requires two tires for a total of six tires. Thus, only three bicycles can be assembled.

10. Zn metal is the limiting reactant.

11. S powder is the limiting reactant.

12. A percent yield greater than 100% is possible as some experimental errors lead to high results, and others to low results.

Chapter 10

1. An atmosphere is the largest unit, and the greatest gas pressure is 1 atm.

2. Increasing the volume produces a *decrease* in gas pressure because molecules are further apart and collide less frequently.

3. The gas pressure *increases* because the volume decreases, and there are more molecular collisions.

4. The volume *decreases* when the temperature cools; the air molecules move slower, and the balloon shrinks to maintain constant pressure.

5. The pressure *decreases* when the temperature cools; the air molecules move slower, and the collisions are fewer and less energetic.

6. The pressure doubles when the temperature doubles, but the pressure halves when the volume doubles. Thus, the volume does not change.

7. The partial pressure of a NO gas is found by subtracting the partial pressure of N_2 and O_2 from 2.50 atm. Thus, the partial pressure of NO is 0.50 atm.

8. No real gases are ideal; however, He behaves most like an ideal gas.

9. The proportionality constant (R) in the ideal gas law equals PV/nT.

Chapter 11

1. Since CH_3-CH_2-OH can hydrogen bond, it has a stronger intermolecular attraction than CH_3-O-CH_3.

2. Since CH_3-CH_2-OH can hydrogen bond, it has a higher boiling point than CH_3-O-CH_3.

3. A paper clip can float on water due to the surface tension between water molecules. If you disturb the paper clip, it will sink because it is more dense.

4. An *ionic crystalline solid* has a high melting point, and is a conductor of electricity only when melted. A *molecular crystalline solid* has a low melting point, and is a nonconductor of electricity.

5. Since the heat of vaporization is greater than the heat of fusion, it requires more heat to vaporize 1 g of water (540 cal) than to melt 1 g of water (80 cal).

6. The systematic names for the hydrates are calcium chloride *monohydrate*, calcium chloride *dihydrate*, and calcium chloride *hexahydrate*, respectively.

7. The hexahydrate, $CaCl_2 \cdot 6H_2O$, has the highest percentage of water.

8. The hexahydrate, $CaCl_2 \cdot 6H_2O$, has the highest water of hydration (6).

Chapter 12

1. The attraction between a metal cation and a nonmetal anion gives an *ionic bond*; the attraction between two nonmetal atoms produces a *covalent bond*.

2. Xenon is isoelectronic with both Ba^{2+} and I^-.

3. All three statements are true.

4. All three statements are true.

5. There are 2 pairs of nonbonding electrons in H_2S.

6. There are 6 pairs of nonbonding electrons in SO_2.

7. There are 10 pairs of nonbonding electrons in SO_3^{2-}.

8. The general trends for increasing electronegativity in the periodic table is from left to right in a period, and from bottom to top in a group.

9. HF has the greatest difference in electronegativity ($4.0 - 2.1 = 1.9$); thus, the bond in H—F is the most polar.

10. The bond in C—I is the least polar because there is no difference in the electronegativity of carbon and iodine ($2.5 - 2.5 = 0$).

11. The structural formula for the molecule is H—Cl—O. Since the oxygen atom can be removed with its six valence electrons, the Cl—O bond is coordinate covalent.

Chapter 13

1. Since atmospheric pressure is less at higher elevations, Lake Tahoe has less dissolved oxygen gas than Lake Havasu.

2. According to the *like dissolves like* rule, two liquids are miscible when both liquids are polar, or both liquids are nonpolar.

3. According to the *like dissolves like* rule, a solid is soluble in a liquid when the solid and liquid are both polar, or both nonpolar. An ionic compound is more soluble in a polar liquid than a nonpolar liquid.

4. Since the oxygen atom in a water molecule is partially negative, it is attracted to the positive cation in the solid solute.

5. Grinding the solute gives smaller particles with more surface area. Since solvent molecules attack the particle surface, the solute dissolves faster.

6. A hot cup of coffee can dissolve more sugar than coffee at a lower temperature.

7. By saturating a solution at a higher temperature, and allowing the solution to cool without disturbing it, the solute remains in the solution at a lower temperature and is said to be supersaturated.

8. There are six mass percent concentration unit factors; that is, three unit factors and their reciprocals.

9. There are four molar concentration unit factors; that is, two unit factors and their reciprocals.

10. Since equal volumes of $6\,M$ sulfuric acid and distilled water are added together, the concentration is halved, and the diluted acid is $3\,M$.

11. Before solving a stoichiometry problem, first write a balanced chemical equation for the reaction.

Chapter 14

1. The solution with the lowest pH (1) has the highest acidity.

2. Aqueous HNO_3 is a strong Arrhenius acid (refer to Table 14.2).

3. Aqueous $HC_2H_3O_2$ and NaOH react to give sodium acetate, $NaC_2H_3O_2$.

4. Phenolphthalein is colorless in acidic and neutral solutions (refer to Table 14.4).

5. The titration of H_3PO_4 with NaOH is the titration of a weak acid with a strong base.

6. The titration of HCl with $Ba(OH)_2$ is the titration of a strong acid with a strong base.

7. Phenolphthalein is pink at the endpoint of the titration of oxalic acid.

8. Phenolphthalein is pink at the endpoint of the titration of benzoic acid.

9. Distilled water is neutral because the concentration of hydrogen ions and hydroxide ions is equal.

10. Apple juice at pH 4 is weakly acidic.

11. Milk of magnesia at pH 10 is weakly basic.

12. Grape juice at pH 4.05 is weakly acidic.

13. Wine at pH 3.25 is weakly acidic.

14. The reaction of HF(*aq*) and NH_4OH(*aq*) produces NH_4F and H_2O; NH_4F is a soluble salt, so the conductivity apparatus will glow brightly.

15. The reaction of HNO_3(*aq*) and $Ba(OH)_2$(*aq*) produces $Ba(NO_3)_2$ and H_2O; $Ba(NO_3)_2$ is a soluble salt, so the apparatus will glow brightly.

16. The reaction of $AgNO_3$(*aq*) and $AlCl_3$(*aq*) gives AgCl and $Al(NO_3)_3$. Although AgCl is insoluble, $Al(NO_3)_3$ is soluble, so the apparatus will glow brightly.

Chapter 15

1. A mole of gas is related to: (1) mass of gas; (2) number of gaseous particles; (3) volume of a gas at STP; and (4) molar concentration of a solution.

2. A balanced chemical equation is required to solve a stoichiometry problem.

3. According to the balanced equation, the mole ratio is 2 mol H_2S to 3 mol O_2. Since the starting volumes of gas are equal, the limiting reactant is O_2. That is, 2.00 L H_2S produces 2.00 L SO_2, but 2.00 L O_2 produces only 1.33 L SO_2.

4. Since ice floats in water, 1.00 cm^3 of water weighs more than a 1.00-cm cube of ice.

5. Similar to a plant greenhouse that retains heat energy from sunlight, carbon dioxide gas in the atmosphere traps heat energy from the Sun, and contributes to global warming (see the Chemistry Connection in Section 10.1).

6. Since $pV = nRT$, $n = pV/RT$. The number of moles of gas (n) is equal to its mass divided by its molar mass (MM); that is, $n = g/MM$. Substituting g/MM for n in the ideal gas law, and rearranging, we have $MM = gRT/PV$.

7. The volume of wet hydrogen gas is greater than the same number of hydrogen molecules in a dry gas assuming the temperature and pressure are equal.

8. The beaker of water containing AgCl contains the least number of chloride ions because silver chloride is insoluble.

9. Since the molar mass of $NaHCO_3$ is less than $KHCO_3$, a 1.00-g $NaHCO_3$ tablet has more moles of bicarbonate and neutralizes more stomach acid.

Chapter 16

1. (a) At higher temperatures molecules have a greater velocity, and the collision frequency increases. As the number of collisions increases, there are more effective collisions. (b) At higher temperatures molecules have more kinetic energy, and collision energy increases. If the collisions are more energetic, more molecules have the necessary energy to react.

2. Notice that the progress of reaction (a) goes from lower to higher energy, which characterizes an endothermic reaction. The progress of reaction (b) is higher to lower, which characterizes an *exothermic reaction*.

3. *After* a reaction reaches chemical equilibrium, the concentrations of reactants and products are constant.

4. *Before* a reaction reaches chemical equilibrium, the concentration of reactants is decreasing, and the concentration of products is increasing.

5. The equilibrium constant expression is: $K_{eq} = \dfrac{[X_2Y_3]^2}{[X_2]^2[Y_2]^3}$.

6. (a) Increasing temperature for an endothermic reaction shifts the equilibrium to the right, toward the products. (b) Increasing pressure for this reaction has no effect on the equilibrium because there are the same number of reactant and product molecules.

7. The ionization constant expression is: $K_i = \dfrac{[H^+][H_2PO_4^-]}{[H_3PO_4]}$.

8. (a) Adding NH_4Cl increases the NH_4^+ concentration; thus, shifting the equilibrium to the left toward the reactants. (b) Adding NaOH increases the OH^- concentration; thus, shifting the equilibrium to the left toward the reactants.

9. The solubility product constant expression is: $K_{sp} = [Al^{3+}][OH^-]^3$.

10. (a) Adding $Ca(NO_3)_2$ increases the Ca^{2+} concentration; thus, shifting the equilibrium to the left toward the reactants. (b) Adding Na_2CO_3 increases the CO_3^{2-} concentration; thus, shifting the equilibrium to the left toward the reactants.

Chapter 17

1. (a) 0; (b) +1; (c) −1; (d) +7

2. (a) −1; (b) +1; (c) +3; (d) +5

3. oxidizing agent: HX; reducing agent: M

4. oxidizing agent: Y_2; reducing agent: X^-

5. $2\,M_2O_3(s) + 6\,X_2(g) \rightarrow 4\,MX_3(aq) + 3\,O_2(g)$

6. $2\,MnO_4^-(aq) + 5\,SO_3^{2-}(aq) + 6\,H^+(aq) \rightarrow$
$$2\,Mn^{2+}(aq) + 5\,SO_4^{2-}(aq) + 3\,H_2O(l)$$

7. $2\,MnO_4^-(aq) + 3\,SO_3^{2-}(aq) + H_2O(l) \rightarrow$
$$2\,MnO_2(s) + 3\,SO_4^{2-}(aq) + 2\,OH^-(aq)$$

8. Figure 17.4 lists Cr and Al as stronger reducing agents than $Fe^{2+}(aq)$. Thus, Cr and Al react spontaneously with $FeSO_4(aq)$; Ag and Ni are weaker and do not react.

9. $Fe(s) + Sn^{2+}(aq) \rightarrow Sn(s) + Fe^{2+}(aq)$

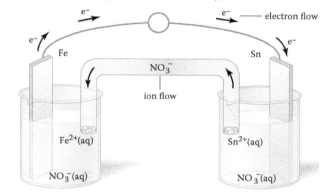

Voltaic Cell

10. $C(s) + 2\,MgCl_2(l) \rightarrow 2\,Mg(l) + CCl_4(g)$

Electrolytic Cell

Chapter 18

1. (a) alpha ray, (b) beta ray, (c) gamma ray

2. 31 mg

3. $^{208}_{82}\text{Pb} + ^{62}_{28}\text{Ni} \rightarrow ^{269}_{110}\text{Ds} + ^{1}_{0}\text{n}$

Chapter 19

1. Note that decane ($C_{10}H_{22}$) has an *–ane* suffix, and fits the general molecular formula for an alkane (C_nH_{2n+2}).

2. Note that decene ($C_{10}H_{20}$) has an *–ene* suffix, and fits the general molecular formula for an alkene (C_nH_{2n}).

3. Note that decyne ($C_{10}H_{18}$) has a *–yne* suffix, and fits the general molecular formula for an alkyne (C_nH_{2n-2}).

4. Note that decene ($C_{10}H_{20}$) and naphthalene ($C_{10}H_8$) both have an *–ene* suffix, but decene fits the general molecular formula for an alkene (C_nH_{2n}).

5. Aldehydes, ketones, carboxylic acids, esters, and amides contain a carbonyl group. Organic halides, alcohols, phenols, ethers, and amines do not.

Chapter 20

1. A spiral helix describes the *secondary* structure of a protein. The sequence of amino acids in the protein corresponds to the *primary* structure, and a twisted helix describes the *tertiary* structure.

Answers to Key Term Exercises

Chapter 1

1. j, **2.** d, **3.** k, **4.** f, **5.** l, **6.** h, **7.** a, **8.** c, **9.** i, **10.** g, **11.** b, **12.** e

Prerequisite Science Skills

1. f, **2.** a, **3.** c, **4.** g, **5.** d, **6.** m, **7.** e, **8.** l, **9.** h, **10.** j, **11.** b, **12.** i, **13.** k

Chapter 2

1. e, **2.** o, **3.** n, **4.** h, **5.** m, **6.** r, **7.** j, **8.** w, **9.** f, **10.** x, **11.** q, **12.** v, **13.** p, **14.** c, **15.** y, **16.** d, **17.** s, **18.** i, **19.** u, **20.** g, **21.** b, **22.** l, **23.** t, **24.** a, **25.** k

Chapter 3

1. z, **2.** cc, **3.** i, **4.** l, **5.** m, **6.** dd, **7.** a, **8.** h, **9.** k, **10.** b, **11.** g, **12.** t, **13.** s, **14.** j, **15.** v, **16.** bb, **17.** c, **18.** w, **19.** r, **20.** u, **21.** e, **22.** y, **23.** f, **24.** d, **25.** x, **26.** aa, **27.** n, **28.** p, **29.** o, **30.** q

Chapter 4

1. h, **2.** t, **3.** q, **4.** d, **5.** e, **6.** p, **7.** c, **8.** n, **9.** b, **10.** a, **11.** y, **12.** m, **13.** o, **14.** x, **15.** v, **16.** g, **17.** s, **18.** f, **19.** k, **20.** j, **21.** l, **22.** i, **23.** w, **24.** u, **25.** r

Chapter 5

1. r, **2.** h, **3.** q, **4.** b, **5.** c, **6.** i, **7.** p, **8.** t, **9.** u, **10.** o, **11.** a, **12.** j, **13.** s, **14.** v, **15.** f, **16.** d, **17.** w, **18.** g, **19.** k, **20.** m, **21.** l, **22.** n, **23.** e

Chapter 6

1. h, **2.** g, **3.** d, **4.** n, **5.** e, **6.** b, **7.** c, **8.** o, **9.** f, **10.** a, **11.** j, **12.** l, **13.** m, **14.** i, **15.** k, **16.** g, **17.** k

Chapter 7

1. h, **2.** o, **3.** n, **4.** d, **5.** q, **6.** g, **7.** s, **8.** r, **9.** f, **10.** l, **11.** i, **12.** v, **13.** j, **14.** k, **15.** u, **16.** m, **17.** p, **18.** c, **19.** b, **20.** a, **21.** e, **22.** t

Chapter 8

1. a, **2.** g, **3.** e, **4.** f, **5.** j, **6.** b, **7.** d, **8.** i, **9.** c, **10.** h

Chapter 9

1. j, **2.** b, **3.** d, **4.** h, **5.** m, **6.** f, **7.** g, **8.** o, **9.** i, **10.** l, **11.** c, **12.** e, **13.** a, **14.** n, **15.** k

Chapter 10

1. k, **2.** v, **3.** b, **4.** d, **5.** u, **6.** c, **7.** p, **8.** i, **9.** e, **10.** f, **11.** l, **12.** g, **13.** t, **14.** w, **15.** h, **16.** r, **17.** x, **18.** q, **19.** m, **20.** s, **21.** j, **22.** a, **23.** o, **24.** n

Chapter 11

1. g, **2.** f, **3.** n, **4.** x, **5.** b, **6.** y, **7.** w, **8.** d, **9.** o, **10.** r, **11.** q, **12.** v, **13.** k, **14.** l, **15.** c, **16.** s, **17.** i, **18.** p, **19.** t, **20.** m, **21.** a, **22.** z, **23.** j, **24.** u, **25.** e, **26.** h

Chapter 12

1. e, **2.** bb, **3.** v, **4.** p, **5.** g, **6.** n, **7.** r, **8.** c, **9.** b, **10.** d, **11.** t, **12.** k, **13.** z, **14.** y, **15.** j, **16.** aa, **17.** s, **18.** x, **19.** m, **20.** h, **21.** w, **22.** u, **23.** i, **24.** f, **25.** o, **26.** cc, **27.** l, **28.** q, **29.** a

Chapter 13

1. c, **2.** n, **3.** p, **4.** o, **5.** b, **6.** i, **7.** k, **8.** j, **9.** e, **10.** g, **11.** d, **12.** q, **13.** a, **14.** s, **15.** m, **16.** l, **17.** t, **18.** r, **19.** f, **20.** h

Chapter 14

1. g, **2.** c, **3.** d, **4.** k, **5.** h, **6.** j, **7.** q, **8.** e, **9.** f, **10.** p, **11.** o, **12.** b, **13.** a, **14.** u, **15.** i, **16.** s, **17.** l, **18.** n, **19.** t, **20.** w, **21.** v, **22.** r, **23.** m

Chapter 15

1. e, **2.** l, **3.** a, **4.** b, **5.** r, **6.** p, **7.** q, **8.** c, **9.** g, **10.** t, **11.** s, **12.** k, **13.** v, **14.** m, **15.** f, **16.** j, **17.** d, **18.** u, **19.** i, **20.** h, **21.** n, **22.** o

Chapter 16

1. d, **2.** e, **3.** f, **4.** o, **5.** r, **6.** a, **7.** h, **8.** b, **9.** p, **10.** n, **11.** c, **12.** l, **13.** g, **14.** j, **15.** i, **16.** m, **17.** k, **18.** q

Chapter 17

1. l, **2.** n, **3.** k, **4.** p, **5.** m, **6.** o, **7.** j, **8.** q, **9.** f, **10.** e, **11.** i, **12.** r, **13.** s, **14.** g, **15.** h, **16.** a, **17.** c, **18.** b, **19.** d

Chapter 18

1. t, **2.** b, **3.** d, **4.** i, **5.** c, **6.** k, **7.** p, **8.** o, **9.** l, **10.** r, **11.** h, **12.** s, **13.** q, **14.** a, **15.** j, **16.** u, **17.** v, **18.** m, **19.** e, **20.** f, **21.** n, **22.** g, **23.** w

Chapter 19

1. s, **2.** n, **3.** v, **4.** x, **5.** g, **6.** b, **7.** c, **8.** e, **9.** u, **10.** r, **11.** f, **12.** w, **13.** q, **14.** d, **15.** h, **16.** t, **17.** l, **18.** a, **19.** k, **20.** o, **21.** m, **22.** i, **23.** p, **24.** j

Chapter 20

1. b, **2.** t, **3.** c, **4.** j, **5.** m, **6.** a, **7.** p, **8.** d, **9.** r, **10.** f, **11.** k, **12.** l, **13.** e, **14.** s, **15.** i, **16.** h, **17.** y, **18.** g, **19.** o, **20.** v, **21.** q, **22.** z, **23.** w, **24.** n, **25.** u, **26.** x

Answers to Odd-Numbered Exercises

Chapter 1

1. water

3. air, earth, fire, water, and ether

5. Robert Boyle

7. Analyze the data and propose a tentative hypothesis.

9. A hypothesis is an initial proposal that is tentative, whereas a theory is a proposal that has been tested extensively.

11. (b) and (d)

13. Antoine Lavoisier

15. agriculture, medicine, and the pharmaceutical, electronics, paper, construction, transportation, and petrochemical industries

17. A solution to the nine–dot problem with only one straight line is to use a *very wide* line; the unconscious assumption regards the thickness of the line.

19. Stare at the point where the blocks intersect. "Flip" the image to view the blocks stacking upward, or downward.

21. The BSN degree typically requires three years of nursing school to earn a diploma and the AARN requires two years. To apply to either program, it is necessary to complete prerequisite chemistry and biology classes.

Prerequisite Science Skills

1. (a) length; (b) mass; (c) volume; (d) time

3. (a) 2.0 cm; (d) 2.5 cm

5. (d) 25.000 g

7. (b) 25.0 mL; (c) 25.5 mL

9. (a) 1; (b) 2; (c) 3; (d) 4

11. (a) 2; (b) 3; (c) 1; (d) 4

13. (a) 1; (b) 2; (c) 3; (d) 1

15. (a) 20.2; (b) 0.205; (c) 2060; (d) 0.207

17. (a) 1.45×10^1; (b) 1.46×10^2; (c) 1.51×10^{-3}; (d) 1.50×10^{-4}

19. (a) 1.3 g; (b) 23.1 g

21. (a) 67 g; (b) 13.01 g

23. (a) $7.67 \, cm^2$; (b) $10.1 \, cm^2$; (c) $28 \, cm^2$; (d) $400 \, cm^2$

25. (a) 2.57 cm; (b) 66 cm; (c) $6.846 \, cm^2$; (d) $6.86 \, cm^2$

27. (a) 10^3; (b) $(1/10)^3$ or 10^{-3}

29. (a) 2^3; (b) $(1/2)^3$ or 2^{-3}

31. (a) 1×10^9; (b) 1×10^{-8}

33. (a) 1000; (b) 0.000 000 1

35. (a) 10; (b) 0.1

37. (a) 8.0916×10^7; (b) 1.5×10^{-8}; (c) 3.356×10^{14}; (d) 9.27×10^{-13}

39. 2.69×10^{22} argon atoms

41. 0.000 000 000 000 000 000 000 033 5 g/neon atom

43. 10.00 mL (± 0.01 mL)

45. 1.86×10^5 miles per second

47. 258.1 g

49. (a) 3.52×10^6; (b) 1.91×10^{-6}

51. 3.3475×10^{-24} g

53. 2.00×10^2 lb

55. 22 kilograms

Chapter 2

1. (a) meter; (b) gram; (c) liter; and (d) second

3. (a) Tm; (b) Gg; (c) nL; (d) ps

5. (a) length, (b) mass, (c) volume, and (d) time

7. (a) tera (T); (b) giga (G); (c) milli (m); (d) micro (μ)

9. (a) terameter; (b) gigagram; (c) milliliter; (d) microsecond

11. (a) 1×10^{12} m = 1 Tm; (b) 1×10^9 g = 1 Gg; (c) 1 L = 1×10^3 mL; (d) 1 s = $1 \times 10^6 \, \mu$s

13. (a) $\dfrac{1 \times 10^{12} \, m}{1 \, Tm}$ and $\dfrac{1 \, Tm}{1 \times 10^{12} \, m}$

    (b) $\dfrac{1 \times 10^9 \, g}{1 \, Gg}$ and $\dfrac{1 \, Gg}{1 \times 10^9 \, g}$

    (c) $\dfrac{1 \, L}{1 \times 10^3 \, mL}$ and $\dfrac{1 \times 10^3 \, mL}{1 \, L}$

    (d) $\dfrac{1 \, s}{1 \times 10^6 \, \mu s}$ and $\dfrac{1 \times 10^6 \, \mu s}{1 \, s}$

15. (a) 5.00×10^{-3} km; (b) 5.00×10^2 cg; (c) 50.0 dL; (d) 5.00×10^9 ns

17. (a) 6.50×10^6 Mm; (b) 6.50×10^8 kg; (c) 6.50×10^{-2} dL; (d) 0.650 ps

19. (a) 2.54 cm = 1 in.; (b) 454 g = 1 lb; (c) 946 mL = 1 qt (d); 1.00 s = 1 sec

21. (a) 9.8 in.; (b) 0.055 lb; (c) 2,370 mL; (d) 2.50 s

23. (a) 1.8 m; (b) 79.5 kg; (c) 0.473 L; (d) 0.273 ds

25. 54 mi/gal

27. 4.91 g copper

29. 40.5% of solution is ethanol

31. 56.3 g water

33. 94.99% copper

35. $6.25 \, cm^3$

37. 0.825 cm

39. (a) 1000 mL; (b) $1000 \, cm^3$

41. 45.8 in.^{3}

43. 2.5 mL

45. 62.5 mL

47. (a) float; (b) sink

49. (a) rise; (b) drop

51. 1.00 g/mL

53. (a) 170 g; (b) 120 g

55. (a) 10.9 g; (b) 3.98 g

57. (a) 0.788 g/mL; (b) 0.714 g/mL

59. (a) 32 °F; (b) 0 °C; (c) 273 K

61. (a) 38 °C; (b) −137 °C

63. (a) 768 K; (b) 88 K

65. −252 °C, 21 K

67. Temperature is a measure of the *average* kinetic energy and heat is a measure of the *total* kinetic energy.

69. Gold is the best conductor of heat per gram. (Note: Silver is the best conductor of heat per mole.)

71. 1900 kJ

73. 1.5 × 10^6 MB

75. 320 DVDs

77. (a) exact relationship (metric-metric); (b) not exact (English-metric); (c) exact relationship (metric-metric); (b) not exact (English-metric)

79. 35,000 μs; 3.5 × 10^4 μs

81. 5.87 × 10^{12} mi

83. 435 m^2

85. 1500-meter race is shorter than a mile

87. 7690 tablets

89. 5.0 g/mL

91. 0.801

93. 62.4 lb/ft^3

95. 1.36 × 10^4 kg/m^3

97. *meter:* platinum/iridium, H-shaped, metal bar
    kilogram: platinum/iridium, solid, metal cylinder

Chapter 3

1. gaseous state

3. liquid state

5. solid state

7. (a) melting; (b) vaporizing

9. (a) heating; (b) cooling

11. heating

13. (a) element; (b) element; (c) compound; (d) mixture

15. (a) element; (b) heterogeneous mixture; (c) compound; (d) homogeneous mixture

17. (a) Sr; (b) Xe; (c) O; (d) Zn; (e) F; (f) Na; (g) Cu; (h) Ni

19. (a) phosphorus; (b) sulfur; (c) krypton; (d) iron; (e) antimony; (f) nitrogen; (g) platinum; (h) silver

21. (a) 1; (b) 5; (c) 13; (d) 22; (e) 33; (f) 38; (g) 50; (h) 83

23. (a) metal; (b) nonmetal; (c) metal; (d) nonmetal

25. (a) metal; (b) nonmetal; (c) nonmetal; (d) metal

27. (a) nonmetal; (b) metal; (c) nonmetal; (d) metal

29. (a) semimetal; (b) metal; (c) metal; (d) metal

31. (a) gas; (b) solid; (c) gas ; (d) solid

33. (a) gas; (b) solid; (c) gas; (d) liquid

35. (a) 12 carbon atoms; 17 hydrogen atoms; 4 nitrogen atoms; 1 oxygen atom; 1 sulfur atom
    (b) 17 carbon atoms; 20 hydrogen atoms; 4 nitrogen atoms; 6 oxygen atoms

37. (a) $C_{20}H_{30}O$; (b) $C_{31}H_{46}O_2$

39. (a) 56 atoms; (b) 167 atoms

41. The mass ratio of the elements in water is constant: 1:8.

43. (a) physical; (b) physical; (c) physical; (d) chemical

45. (a) physical; (b) chemical; (c) chemical; (d) physical

47. (a) chemical; (b) physical; (c) physical; (d) physical

49. (a) chemical; (b) physical; (c) physical; (d) chemical

51. (a) chemical; (b) physical; (c) physical; (d) chemical

53. (a) physical; (b) chemical; (c) physical; (d) physical

55. (a) physical; (b) chemical; (c) physical; (d) chemical

57. (a) chemical; (b) physical; (c) chemical; (d) physical

59. 7.77 g iron phosphide

61. 0.055 g oxygen gas

63. gaseous state

65. increase

67. the motion of helium atoms will *increase*

69. 1500 kcal

71. 807 cal

73. 48.0 kcal

75. (a) chemical → heat; (b) heat → mechanical; (c) mechanical → mechanical; (d) mechanical → electrical

77. (a) heat → mechanical; (b) mechanical → mechanical; (c) mechanical → mechanical; (d) mechanical → electrical

79. A pre-1982 penny is an alloy, thus a homogeneous mixture.

81. homogeneous mixture

83. germanium

85. oxygen, silicon, and aluminum

87. (a) 47; (b) 82; (c) 50; (d) 79

89. 3250 cal

91. The mass of products is slightly less corresponding to the energy released.

93. E = energy, m = mass, c = speed of light

95. physical change

97. Scheele (1772); Priestley (1774)

99. −297 °F, −183 °C, 90 K

Chapter 4

1. (a) Atoms are indestructible proved to be invalid (*fission*).
   (b) Atoms of the same element are identical proved to be invalid (*isotopes*).

3. law of conservation of mass, law of definite proportion (i.e., definite composition)

5. electrons

7. electron (e^-)

9. electron (-1)

11. Electrons are found outside the nucleus.

13. 1×10^{-13} cm

15. -1 and $+1$

17. (a) $10\,n^0$; (b) $22\,n^0$; (c) $44\,n^0$; (d) $77\,n^0$

19. (a) $0\,n^0$; (b) $7\,n^0$; (c) $32\,n^0$; (d) $74\,n^0$

21.

Atomic Notation	Atomic Number	Mass Number	Number of Protons	Number of Neutrons	Number of Electrons
$^{11}_{5}B$	5	11	5	6	5
$^{15}_{7}N$	7	15	7	8	7
$^{40}_{20}Ca$	20	40	20	20	20
$^{200}_{80}Hg$	80	200	80	120	80

23. (a)

4n^0
3p^+ } 3e^-

(b)

7n^0
6p^+ } 6e^-

(c)

8n^0
8p^+ } 8e^-

(d)

10n^0
10p^+ } 10e^-

25. The atomic number refers to the number of protons in the nucleus; whereas, the mass number refers to the number of protons *and* neutrons.

27. The carbon-12 reference isotope is exactly 12 amu.

29. 22.99 amu

31. 19.00 amu

33. 6.941 amu

35. 55.85 amu

37. red light

39. red light

41. red light

43. 550 nm

45. photon

47. (a) continuous; (b) quantized

49. (a) continuous; (b) quantized

51.

nucleus (p^+ and $n°$)

e^- energy levels

53. $5 \rightarrow 2$

55. blue-green line

57. ultraviolet energy

59. red line

61. (a) 1; (b) 1

63. (a) ultraviolet; (b) red; (c) infrared

65. lines in the emission spectrum of hydrogen

67. (a) 1 sublevel; (b) 2 sublevels; (c) 3 sublevels; (d) 4 sublevels

69. (a) $2\,e^-$; (b) $6\,e^-$; (c) $10\,e^-$; (d) $14\,e^-$

71. $8\,e^-$

73. $3d$ sublevel

75. (a) $1s^2$;

(b) $1s^2\,2s^2$;

(c) $1s^2\,2s^2\,2p^6\,3s^2\,3p^6\,4s^2\,3d^7$;

(d) $1s^2\,2s^2\,2p^6\,3s^2\,3p^6\,4s^2\,3d^{10}\,4p^6\,5s^2\,4d^{10}$

77. (a) Li; (b) Si; (c) Ti; (d) Sr

79. (a)

1s

(b)

2p_x

(c)

3p_y

(d)

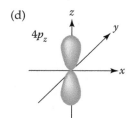

4p_z

81. (a) $3s$; (b) $3px$; (c) equal; (d) equal

83. (a) $5s$; (b) $4p$

85. (a) $2\,e^-$; (b) $2\,e^-$; (c) $2\,e^-$; (d) $2\,e^-$

87. 106.9 amu

89. no stable isotope

91. (a) ultraviolet; (b) infrared

93. Br-81

95. If one of the copper $4s$ electrons drops into the $3d$ sublevel, energy level 3 is completely filled ($3s$, $3p$, and $3d$)), and thus the atom is more stable.

97. copper

99. purple

Chapter 5

1. Helium was not discovered until 1895 (see Figure 3.7).

3. Radium was not discovered until 1898 (see Figure 3.7).

5. increasing atomic mass

7. Co and Ni

9. groups or families

11. representative elements

13. the lanthanides

15. inner transition elements

17. metals

19. Po and At

21. (a) IA/1; (b) IIA/2; (c) VIIA/17; (d) VIIIA/18

23. (a) 1; (b) 13; (c) 15; (d) 17; (e) 11; (f) 3; (g) 5; (h) 7

25. (a) Sb; (b) Ba; (c) Zr; (d) He

27. (a) Mg; (b) Br; (c) Lu; (d) Th

29. decreases

31. decreases

33. (a) Al; (b) K; (c) Ba; (d) Fe

35. (a) Na; (b) P; (c) Ca; (d) Kr

37. 0.230 nm; 1.38 g/mL; 14.5 °C

39. 0.097 nm; 3.27 g/mL; 152.2 °C

41. (a) KF; (b) CaF_2; (c) BBr_3; (d) GeI_4

43. (a) CaF_2; (b) $CaCl_2$; (c) $CaBr_2$; (d) CaI_2

45. (a) As_2O_3 and As_2O_5; (b) Sb_2O_3 and Sb_2O_5

47. s sublevels

49. d sublevels

51. $4f$ sublevel

53. (a) $1s$; (b) $3s$; (c) $4f$; (d) $4p$; (e) $5s$; (f) $2p$; (g) $5p$; (h) $6s$

55. (a) $1s^2 2s^1$

    (b) $1s^2 2s^2 2p^5$

    (c) $1s^2 2s^2 2p^6 3s^2$

    (d) $1s^2 2s^2 2p^6 3s^2 3p^3$

    (e) $1s^2 2s^2 2p^6 3s^2 3p^6 4s^2$

    (f) $1s^2 2s^2 2p^6 3s^2 3p^6 4s^2 3d^5$

    (g) $1s^2 2s^2 2p^6 3s^2 3p^6 4s^2 3d^{10} 4p^1$

    (h) $1s^2 2s^2 2p^6 3s^2 3p^6 4s^2 3d^{10} 4p^6 5s^1$

57. (a) 1; (b) 3; (c) 5; (d) 7

59. (a) 1; (b) 3; (c) 5; (d) 7; (e) 2; (f) 4; (g) 6; (h) 8

61. (a) H·   (b) ·B·

    (c) ·N̈:   (d) :F̈:

    (e) Ca·   (f) ·S̈i·

    (g) ·Ö: (h) :Är:

63. increases

65. Group IA/1

67. (a) Mg; (b) S; (c) Sn; (d) N

69. (a) Cs; (b) Ar; (c) Al; (d) I

71. (a) 1+; (b) 2+; (c) 3+; (d) 4+

73. (a) 1+; (b) 3+; (c) 2−; (d) 1−

75. (b) Ca^{2+}; (c) S^{2-}

77. (a) [Ne]

    (b) [Ar]

    (c) [Ar] $3d^6$

    (d) [Kr] $4d^2$

79. (a) [He] $2s^2 2p^6$, or [Ne]

    (b) [Ne] $3s^2 3p^6$, or [Ar]

    (c) [He] $2s^2 2p^6$, or [Ne]

    (d) [Kr] $5s^2 4d^{10} 5p^6$, or [Xe]

81. (a) Group IA; (b) Group IB; (c) Group IIIB; (d) Group IIIA

83. 0.284 nm; 2.21 g/mL; 17.9 °C

85. (a) [Kr] $5s^2$; (b) [Kr] $5s^2 4d^6$; (c) [Kr] $5s^2 4d^{10} 5p^3$; (d) [Xe] $6s^1$

87. Although H and the Group IA/1 metals each have one valence electron, in H the electron is closer to its nucleus. Because the negatively charged electron is closer to the positively charged nucleus, it requires more energy to remove the electron from hydrogen than a Group IA/1 metal.

89. scandium (Sc)

91. When an alkali metal atom loses one electron, it gains a noble gas configuration. An alkaline earth metal atom must lose two electrons to gain a noble gas configuration.

93. kurchatovium (Ku)

95. mercury

Chapter 6

1. (a) binary molecular; (b) binary ionic; (c) ternary ionic; (d) binary acid

3. (a) polyatomic cation; (b) monoatomic cation; (c) monoatomic anion; (d) polyatomic anion

5. (a) calcium ion; (b) cadmium ion; (c) cobalt(II) ion; (d) copper(II) ion

7. (a) K+; (b) Ba^{2+}; (c) Fe^{2+}; (d) Sn^{2+}

9. (a) cupric ion; (b) ferrous ion; (c) stannous ion; (d) plumbous ion

11. (a) Co^{2+}; (b) Co^{3+}

13. (a) fluoride ion; (b) chloride ion; (c) bromide ion; (d) iodide ion

15. (a) nitrate ion; (b) nitrite ion; (c) hypochlorite ion; (d) chlorite ion

17. (a) CrO_4^{2-}; (b) $Cr_2O_7^{2-}$; (c) OH^-; (d) CN^-

19. (a) $AlBr_3$; (b) CdS; (c) Mn_3P_2; (d) PbF_4

21. (a) KNO_3; (b) $(NH_4)_2Cr_2O_7$; (c) $Al_2(SO_3)_3$; (d) $Cr(ClO)_3$

23. (a) $Sr(NO_2)_2$; (b) $Zn(MnO_4)_2$; (c) $CaCrO_4$; (d) $Cr(ClO_4)_3$

25. (a) magnesium oxide; (b) zinc oxide; (c) cadmium oxide; (d) barium oxide

27. (a) cobalt(II) oxide; (b) iron(II) oxide; (c) mercury(II) oxide; (d) tin(II) oxide

29. (a) Cu_2O; (b) FeN; (c) $HgCl_2$; (d) PbS_2

31. (a) RbCl; (b) NaBr

33. (a) GaN; (b) AlAs

35. (a) lithium permanganate; (b) strontium chlorite; (c) barium carbonate; (d) ammonium dichromate

37. (a) copper(II) sulfate; (b) iron(II) chromate; (c) mercury(II) nitrite; (d) lead(II) acetate

39. (a) $Mn(C_2H_3O_2)_2$; (b) $Cu(ClO_2)_2$; (c) $Sn_3(PO_4)_2$; (d) $Fe(ClO)_3$
41. (a) Fr_2SO_4; (b) Na_2SO_3
43. (a) $Ra(ClO_3)_2$; (b) $Ba(BrO_3)_2$
45. (a) bromine monofluoride; (b) carbon tetrafluoride; (c) diiodine tetraoxide; (d) dichlorine trioxide
47. (a) N_2O_5; (b) CCl_4; (c) IBr; (d) H_2S
49. (a) hydrobromic acid; (b) hydroiodic acid
51. (a) chlorous acid; (b) phosphoric acid
53. (a) $HC_2H_3O_2(aq)$; (b) $HNO_3(aq)$
55. (a) $HIO(aq)$; (b) $HBrO(aq)$
57. (a) 0; (b) 2+; (c) 3+; (d) 0
59. SiO_3^{2-}
61.

Ions	chloride ion	sulfide ion	phosphide ion
copper(I) ion	$CuCl$ copper(I) chloride	Cu_2S copper(I) sulfide	Cu_3P copper(I) phosphide
cobalt(III) ion	$CoCl_3$ cobalt(III) chloride	Co_2S_3 cobalt(III) sulfide	CoP cobalt(III) phosphide
lead(IV) ion	$PbCl_4$ lead(IV) chloride	PbS_2 lead(IV) sulfide	Pb_3P_4 lead(IV) phosphide

63.

Ions	hydroxide ion	sulfate ion	phosphate ion
mercurous ion	$Hg_2(OH)_2$ mercurous hydroxide	Hg_2SO_4 mercurous sulfate	$(Hg_2)_3(PO_4)_2$ mercurous phosphate
ferrous ion	$Fe(OH)_2$ ferrous hydroxide	$FeSO_4$ ferrous sulfate	$Fe_3(PO_4)_2$ ferrous phosphate
stannous ion	$Sn(OH)_2$ stannous hydroxide	$SnSO_4$ stannous sulfate	$Sn_3(PO_4)_2$ stannous phosphate

65. (a) –ide; (b) –ic acid
67. (a) –ite; (b) –ous acid
69. (a) –ate; (b) –ic acid
71. (a) H_2O; (b) $NaClO$; (c) $NaOH$; (d) $NaHCO_3$
73. (a) boron trifluoride; (b) silicon tetrachloride; (c) diarsenic pentaoxide; (d) diantimony trioxide
75. TiO_2
77. $AcCl_3$
79. Shark, swordfish, mackerel, and tuna contain higher-than-normal concentrations of mercury.

Chapter 7

1. (a) chemical reaction; (b) physical change
3. (a) chemical reaction; (b) chemical reaction
5. (a) chemical reaction; (b) chemical reaction
7. $Mg(s) + Br_2(l) \rightarrow MgBr_2(s)$
9. $Zn(HCO_3)_2(s) \rightarrow ZnCO_3(s) + CO_2(g) + H_2O(g)$
11. $Cd(s) + Co(NO_3)_2(aq) \rightarrow Cd(NO_3)_2(aq) + Co(s)$
13. $LiI(aq) + AgNO_3(aq) \rightarrow AgI(s) + LiNO_3(aq)$
15. $HNO_3(aq) + NH_4OH(aq) \rightarrow NH_4NO_3(aq) + HOH(l)$
17. (a) $3\,H_2(g) + N_2(g) \rightarrow 2\,NH_3(g)$
(b) $Al_2(CO_3)_3(s) \rightarrow Al_2O_3(s) + 3\,CO_2(g)$
(c) $Sr(s) + 2\,H_2O(l) \rightarrow Sr(OH)_2(aq) + H_2(g)$
(d) $K_2SO_4(aq) + Ba(OH)_2(aq) \rightarrow BaSO_4(s) + 2\,KOH(aq)$
(e) $2\,H_3PO_4(aq) + 3\,Mn(OH)_2(s) \rightarrow Mn_3(PO_4)_2(s) + 6\,HOH(l)$
19. (a) $H_2CO_3(aq) + 2\,NH_4OH(aq) \rightarrow (NH_4)_2CO_3(aq) + 2\,HOH(l)$
(b) $Hg_2(NO_3)_2(aq) + 2\,NaBr(aq) \rightarrow Hg_2Br_2(s) + 2\,NaNO_3(aq)$
(c) $Mg(s) + 2\,HC_2H_3O_2(aq) \rightarrow Mg(C_2H_3O_2)_2(aq) + H_2(g)$
(d) $2\,LiNO_3(s) \rightarrow 2\,LiNO_2(s) + O_2(g)$
(e) $2\,Pb(s) + O_2(g) \rightarrow 2\,PbO(s)$
21. (a) combination; (b) decomposition; (c) single replacement; (d) double replacement; (e) neutralization
23. (a) neutralization; (b) double replacement; (c) single replacement; (d) decomposition; (e) combination
25. metal + oxygen gas → metal oxide
(a) $2\,Ni(s) + O_2(g) \rightarrow 2\,NiO(s)$
(b) $4\,Fe(s) + 3\,O_2(g) \rightarrow 2\,Fe_2O_3(s)$
27. (a) $2\,C(s) + O_2(g) \rightarrow 2\,CO(g)$
(b) $4\,P(s) + 5\,O_2(g) \rightarrow 2\,P_2O_5(s)$
29. (a) $2\,Cu(s) + Cl_2(g) \rightarrow 2\,CuCl(s)$
(b) $Co(s) + S(s) \rightarrow CoS(s)$
31. (a) $4\,Cr(s) + 3\,O_2(g) \rightarrow 2\,Cr_2O_3(s)$
(b) $2\,Cr(s) + N_2(g) \rightarrow 2\,CrN(s)$
33. (a) $4\,Li + O_2 \rightarrow 2\,Li_2O$
(b) $2\,Ca + O_2 \rightarrow 2\,CaO$
35. (a) $2\,Na + I_2 \rightarrow 2\,NaI$
(b) $3\,Ba + N_2 \rightarrow Ba3N_2$
37. (a) $2\,KHCO_3(s) \rightarrow K_2CO_3(s) + H_2O(g) + CO_2(g)$
(b) $Sr(HCO_3)_2(s) \rightarrow SrCO_3(s) + H_2O(g) + CO_2(g)$
39. (a) $Co_2(CO_3)_3(s) \rightarrow Co_2O_3(s) + 3\,CO_2(g)$
(b) $Sn(CO_3)_2(s) \rightarrow SnO_2(s) + 2\,CO_2(g)$
41. (a) $2\,AgHCO_3(s) \rightarrow Ag_2CO_3(s) + H_2O(g) + CO_2(g)$
(b) $Zn(HCO_3)_2(s) \rightarrow ZnCO_3(s) + H_2O(g) + CO_2(g)$
43. (a) $Ca(NO_3)_2(s) \rightarrow Ca(NO_2)_2(s) + O_2(g)$
(b) $2\,Ag_2SO_4(s) \rightarrow 2\,Ag_2SO_3(s) + O_2(g)$
45. (a) $2\,NaClO_3(s) \rightarrow 2\,NaCl(s) + 3\,O_2(g)$
(b) $Ca(NO_3)_2(s) \rightarrow Ca(NO_2)_2(s) + O_2(g)$
47. (b) Sn; (c) Co; (d) Mn
49. (b) Sn; (c) Co; (d) Mn
51. (a) Li; (c) Ca
53. (a) $Cu(s) + Al(NO_3)_3(aq) \rightarrow NR$
(b) $2\,Al(s) + 3\,Cu(NO_3)_2(aq) \rightarrow 3\,Cu(s) + 2\,Al(NO_3)_3(aq)$

55. (a) $Ni(s) + Pb(C_2H_3O_2)_2(aq) \rightarrow Pb(s) + Ni(C_2H_3O_2)_2(aq)$
    (b) $Pb(s) + Ni(C_2H_3O_2)_2(aq) \rightarrow NR$

57. (a) $Mg(s) + 2 HNO_3(aq) \rightarrow Mn(NO_3)_2(aq) + H_2(g)$
    (b) $Mn(s) + 2 HCl(aq) \rightarrow MgCl_2(s) + H_2(g)$

59. (a) $2 Li(s) + 2 H_2O(l) \rightarrow 2 LiOH(aq) + H_2(g)$
    (b) $Ba(s) + 2 H_2O(l) \rightarrow Ba(OH)_2(aq) + H_2(g)$

61. (a) $Zn(s) + Pb(NO_3)_2(aq) \rightarrow Pb(s) + Zn(NO_3)_2(aq)$
    (b) $Cd(s) + Fe(NO_3)_2(aq) \rightarrow NR$

63. (a) $Zn(s) + 2 HNO_3(aq) \rightarrow Zn(NO_3)_2(aq) + H_2(g)$
    (b) $Cd(s) + 2 HNO_3(aq) \rightarrow Cd(NO_3)_2(aq) + H_2(g)$

65. (a) $2 K(s) + 2 H_2O(l) \rightarrow 2 KOH(aq) + H_2(g)$
    (b) $Ba(s) + 2 H_2O(l) \rightarrow Ba(OH)_2(aq) + H_2(g)$

67. (a) $Al(NO_3)_3$; (b) Na_2SO_4

69. (a) insoluble; (c) insoluble; (d) insoluble

71. (a) $SnCl_2(aq) + K_2S(aq) \rightarrow SnS(s) + 2 KCl(aq)$
    (b) $Co(NO_3)_2(aq) + Na_2CrO_4(aq)$
    $\rightarrow CoCrO_4(s) + 2 NaNO_3(aq)$

73. (a) $2 AgC_2H_3O_2(aq) + SrI_2(aq)$
    $\rightarrow 2 AgI(s) + Sr(C_2H_3O_2)_2(aq)$
    (b) $FeSO_4(aq) + Ca(OH)_2(aq) \rightarrow Fe(OH)_2(s) + CaSO_4(aq)$

75. (a) $H_2CO_3(aq) + 2 LiOH(aq) \rightarrow Li_2CO_3(aq) + 2 HOH(l)$
    (b) $2 HNO_3(aq) + Ca(OH)_2(aq)$
    $\rightarrow Ca(NO_3)_2(aq) + 2 HOH(l)$

77. (a) $2 HNO_3(aq) + Ba(OH)_2(aq)$
    $\rightarrow Ba(NO_3)_2(aq) + 2 HOH(l)$
    (b) $H_2SO_4(aq) + 2 NaOH(aq) \rightarrow Na_2SO_4(aq) + 2 HOH(l)$

79. If a chemical equation is impossible to balance, it is most likely that the equation has a chemical formula with an incorrect subscript.

81. (a) $3 Fe(s) + 4 H_2O(g) \rightarrow Fe_3O_4(s) + 4 H_2(g)$
    (b) $4 FeS(s) + 7 O_2(g) \rightarrow 2 Fe_2O_3(s) + 4 SO_2(g)$

83. (a) $F_2(g) + 2 NaBr(aq) \rightarrow Br_2(l) + 2 NaF(aq)$
    (b) $Sb_2S_3(s) + 6 HCl(aq) \rightarrow 2 SbCl_3(aq) + 3 H_2S(g)$

85. (a) $CH_4(g) + 2 O_2(g) \rightarrow CO_2(g) + 2 H_2O(g)$
    (b) $C_3H_8(g) + 5 O_2(g) \rightarrow 3 CO_2(g) + 4 H_2O(g)$

87. $Fe_2O_3(l) + 3 CO(g) \rightarrow 2 Fe(l) + 3 CO_2(g)$

89. (1) $4 NH_3(g) + 5 O_2(g) \rightarrow 4 NO(g) + 6 H_2O(g)$
    (2) $2 NO(g) + O_2(g) \rightarrow 2 NO_2(g)$
    (3) $3 NO_2(g) + H_2O(l) \rightarrow 2 HNO_3(aq) + NO(g)$

Chapter 8

1. (a) 6.94 amu; (b) 47.88 amu; (c) 196.97 amu; (d) 208.98 amu

3. (a) 6.94 g; (b) 47.88 g; (c) 196.97 g; (d) 208.98 g

5. (a) 6.02×10^{23} atoms C; (b) 6.02×10^{23} molecules CH_4

7. (a) 1 mol Li; (b) 1 mol Br_2

9. (a) 6.02×10^{22} atoms Zn; (b) 1.20×10^{23} molecules Cl_2;
   (c) 1.81×10^{23} formula units $ZnCl_2$

11. (a) 0.0166 mol Mn; (b) 0.332 mol SO_3; (c) 4.98 mol $MnSO_4$

13. (a) 26.98 g/mol; (b) 28.09 g/mol; (c) 32.00 g/mol;
    (d) 256.56 g/mol

15. (a) 72.15 g/mol; (b) 136.15 g/mol; (c) 173.95 g/mol;
    (d) 357.49 g/mol

17. (a) 98.3 g Hg; (b) 0.540 g N_2; (c) 1.75 g $BaCl_2$

19. (a) 2.31×10^{22} atoms K; (b) 8.84×10^{21} molecules O_2;
    (c) 1.75×10^{21} formula units $AgClO_3$

21. (a) 1.50×10^{-23} g/atom; (b) 3.82×10^{-23} g/atom;
    (c) 9.79×10^{-23} g/atom; (d) 1.24×10^{-22} g/atom

23. 0 °C and 1 atm

25. (a) 1.78 g/L; (b) 3.17 g/L; (c) 0.717 g/L; (d) 1.34 g/L

27. (a) 32.0 g/mol; (b) 34.0 g/mol; (c) 44.1 g/mol; (d) 121 g/mol

29.

Gas	Molecules	Mass	Volume at STP
nitrogen, N_2	6.02×10^{23}	28.02 g	22.4 L
oxygen, O_2	6.02×10^{23}	32.00 g	22.4 L
nitrogen dioxide, NO_2	6.02×10^{23}	46.01 g	22.4 L

31. (a) 1.40 L He; (b) 4.04 L N_2

33. (a) 1.60 g H_2S; (b) 18.1 g N_2O_3

35. (a) 2.69×10^{21} molecules H_2;
    (b) 1.89×10^{21} molecules NH_3

37.

Gas	Molecules	Mass	Volume at STP
methane, CH_4	1.50×10^{23}	4.00 g	5.58 L
ethane, C_2H_6	1.50×10^{23}	7.50 g	5.58 L
propane, C_3H_8	1.50×10^{23}	11.0 g	5.58 L

39. The law of definite composition states that a compound always contains the same elements in the same proportion by mass. Thus, the percent hydrogen by mass in a kilogram of water is 11%.

41. 42.10% C, 6.49% H, 51.42% O

43. 40.24% C, 7.444% H, 9.388% N, 21.49% S, 21.44% O

45. 26.722% Hg, 6.125% Na, 31.999% C, 1.08% H, 21.288% Br, 12.79% O

47. SnO_2

49. CuO

51. Co_2S_3

53. $CuCl$

55. $SnBr_2$

57. C_2HCl_3

59. $C_9H_8O_4$

61. $C_6H_{16}N_2$

63. CH_3O, $C_2H_6O_2$

65. $CHCl$, $C_6H_6Cl_6$

67. C_5H_7N, $C_{10}H_{14}N_2$

69. 5-g nickel coin

71. Earth

73. Ga_2O_3

75. 2.99×10^{-23} cm^3 H_2O

77. 2.11×10^{22} atoms C

79. 11.3 g Cu_2O

81. 6.04×10^{23} atoms Cu/mol

83. 6.02×10^{23} photons

Chapter 9

1. (a) 3 mol C; (b) 2 L B
3. (a) 2.50 g C; (b) 3.00 g B
5. (a) 88.04 g → 88.04 g; (b) 92.02 g → 92.02 g
7. 2.50 mol O_2
9. 0.150 mol Cl_2 react; 0.100 mol $FeCl_3$
11. 0.500 mol C_3H_8 react; 1.50 mol CO_2
13. mass–volume problem
15. volume–volume problem
17. mass–mass problem
19. 3.39 g Ag
21. 1.24 g ZnO
23. 5.21 g $BiCl_3$
25. 6.38 g Hg
27. 1.68 g $Ca_3(PO_4)_2$
29. 262 mL CO_2
31. 1620 mL O_2
33. 0.244 g Mg
35. 0.154 g Na
37. 125 mL I_2
39. 22.5 mL N_2
41. 5.00 L O_2
43. 1750 mL Cl_2
45. 50.0 L SO_3
47. 500.0 cm^3 N_2
49. The limiting reactant is NO, which produces 1.00 mol of NO_2.
51. N_2 or O_2 are each a limiting reactant because each produces the same amount of product (10.0 mol NO).
53. The limiting reactant is H_2, which produces 5.00 mol of H_2O.
55. The limiting reactant is C_2H_6, which produces 3.00 mol of H_2O.
57. (a) Neither Co or S is a limiting reactant; the reaction produces 1.00 mol CoS. After the reaction: Co = 0.00 mol; S = 0.00 mol; CoS = 1.00 mol.
   (b) The limiting reactant is Co, which produces 2.00 mol of CoS. After the reaction: Co = 0.00 mol; S = 1.00 mol; CoS = 2.00 mol.
59. 23.0 g Fe
61. 77.6 g Fe
63. 0.742 g $MgSO_4$
65. 0.693 g H_2O
67. 90.0 mL NO_2
69. 30.0 mL N_2O_3
71. 2.50 L SO_3
73. 20.0 L Cl_2
75. 89.9%
77. 106%
79. g/mol
81. 0.929 g Cr_2O_3
83. 655 g Al

85. 0.593 L H_2S
87. 16.3 g H_2O
89. 124 L H_2
91. Venus

Chapter 10

1. (a), (b), and (d)
3. (a) 760 mm Hg; (b) 76 cm Hg
5. (a) 73.5 psi; (b) 3.80×10^2 cm Hg
7. (a) 104 kPa; (b) 783 torr
9. (a) pressure decreases; (b) pressure increases; (c) pressure increases
11. (a) pressure decreases; (b) pressure increases; (c) pressure decreases
13. Increasing the volume of a gas causes gas molecules to be further apart; thus, the molecules collide less frequently and the pressure decreases.
15.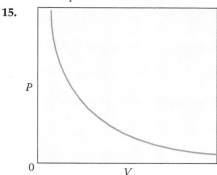
17. 3.50 atm
19. 1.19 L
21.
23. 602 mL
25. 144 °C
27.

29. 1.31 atm

31. 215 °C

33. 8.83 L

35. 1.33 L

37. 8.19 atm

39. 5190 °C

41. 756 mm Hg

43. The vapor pressure of a liquid increases as the temperature increases.

45. (a) 23.8 mm Hg; (b) 92.5 mm Hg

47. 760 mm Hg

49. 135 mm Hg

51. A gas may be collected over water in a graduated cylinder by displacing an equal volume of water (see Figure 10.11).

53. 749 mm Hg

55. Refer to Section 10.10 in the text.

57. high temperature, low pressure

59. (a) all gases are equal; (b) all gases are equal; (c) He atoms; (d) Ar atoms

61. 0 mm Hg

63. 2.45 atm

65. 2.78 mol

67. 3750 lb

69. 1030 cm H_2O

71. 2350 psi

73. 38.5 mL

75. 1.23 atm

77. CH_4 molecules

79. 3.92 g Cl_2

81. O_3 (48.0 g/mol)

83. 12.5 g/mol

85. Venus and Mars

Chapter 11

1. (a), (b), and (d) are observed properties of liquids.

3. (a) gas; (b) solid; (c) gas; (d) solid; (e) liquid; (f) gas

5. A *temporary dipole* is caused by electrons moving about in a molecule. The resulting positive and negative charges in a molecule give rise to a temporary attraction between molecules. A *permanent dipole* is caused by electrons being drawn closer to one atom than another within a molecule. The resulting positive charge in one molecule is attracted to the negative change in another molecule.

7. The vapor pressure of water is the pressure exerted by water vapor molecules when the rate of evaporation is equal to the rate of condensation.

9. The intermolecular attraction in water is strong; thus the viscosity of water is higher than other liquids with molecules the same size.

11. (a) high; (b) low; (c) low; (d) low

13. (a) C_2H_5Cl; (b) CH_3OCH_3

15. (a) CH_3COOH; (b) C_2H_5OH

17. As the temperature of a liquid increases, the vapor pressure increases.

19. (a) ~180 mm Hg; (b) ~330 mm Hg

21. 56 °C

23. (a) true; (b) true; (c) true; (d) false

25. (a) liquid; (b) liquid

27. NaCl, Cl_2, and Na

29. (a) ions; (b) molecules; (c) atoms

31. (a) metallic; (b) ionic; (c) molecular; (d) molecular

33.

35. 4.00×10^3 cal (4.00 kcal)

37. 15,400 cal (15.4 kcal)

39. 82,800 cal (82.8 kcal)

41. 28,100 cal (28.1 kcal)

43. 75,200 cal (75.2 kcal)

45. Water has an unusually *high* boiling point.

47. 104.5°

49.

$$\overset{\delta-}{O}$$
$$\underset{\substack{H \\ \delta+}}{} \quad \underset{\substack{H \\ \delta+}}{}$$

51. Water has the highest specific heat of any liquid.

53. Water is more dense than ice.

55. (a) H_2O; (b) H_2Se

57. (a) H_2O; (b) H_2Se

59. (a) increases; (b) increases; (c) increases; (d) increases

61. $2 H_2(g) + O_2(g) \rightarrow 2 H_2O(l)$

63. (a) $2 Li(s) + 2 H_2O(l) \rightarrow 2 LiOH(aq) + H_2(g)$
(b) $Na_2O(s) + H_2O(l) \rightarrow 2 NaOH(aq)$
(c) $CO_2(g) + H_2O(l) \rightarrow H_2CO_3(aq)$

65. (a) $Mg(s) + H_2O(l) \rightarrow NR$
(b) $SrO(s) + H_2O(l) \rightarrow Sr(OH)_2(aq)$
(c) $N_2O_5(g) + H_2O(l) \rightarrow 2 HNO_3(aq)$

67. (a) $2 C_3H_6(g) + 9 O_2(g) \rightarrow 6 CO_2(g) + 6 H_2O(g)$
(b) $Na_2Cr_2O_7 \cdot 2 H_2O(s) \rightarrow Na_2Cr_2O_7(s) + 2 H_2O(g)$
(c) $2 HF(aq) + Ca(OH)_2(aq) \rightarrow CaF_2(aq) + 2 HOH(l)$

69. (a) $2 C_4H_{10}(g) + 13 O_2(g) \rightarrow 8 CO_2(g) + 10 H_2O(g)$
(b) $Co(C_2H_3O_2)_2 \cdot 4 H_2O(s) \rightarrow Co(C_2H_3O_2)_2(s) + 4 H_2O(g)$
(c) $2 HNO_3(aq) + Ba(OH)_2(aq) \rightarrow Ba(NO_3)_2(aq) + 2 HOH(l)$

71. (a) magnesium sulfate heptahydrate; (b) cobalt(III) cyanide trihydrate; (c) manganese(II) sulfate monohydrate; (d) sodium dichromate dihydrate

73. (a) $Na_2CO_3 \cdot 10H_2O$; (b) $Ni(NO_3)_2 \cdot 6H_2O$; (c) $CoI_3 \cdot 8H_2O$; (d) $Cr(C_2H_3O_2)_3 \cdot H_2O$

75. (a) 40.55% H_2O; (b) 10.91% H_2O; (c) 28.28% H_2O; (d) 30.80% H_2O

77. (a) $NiCl_2 \cdot 2 H_2O$; (b) $Sr(NO_3)_2 \cdot 6 H_2O$; (c) $CrI_3 \cdot 9 H_2O$; (d) $Ca(NO_3)_2 \cdot 4 H_2O$

79. ~75%

81. (a) dispersion force; (b) dipole force; (c) hydrogen bond; (d) dipole force

83. ~80 °C

85. Sulfuric acid, H_2SO_4, has O—H bonds and molecules show strong intermolecular attraction. Thus, sulfuric acid has high surface tension, minimal surface area, and sulfuric acid "raindrops" on Saturn will be spherical.

87. 1,140,000 cal (1,140 kcal)

89. Saturn is about 100 times more massive, but Earth is about 10 times more dense.

Chapter 12

1. Li (1 valence e^-); Cl (7 valence e^-)

3. Li^+ (0 valence e^-); Cl^- (8 valence e^-)

5. (a) ionic; (b) covalent; (c) covalent; (d) ionic

7. (a) molecule; (b) molecule; (c) formula unit; (d) formula unit

9. (a) molecule; (b) atom; (c) formula unit; (d) molecule

11. (a) 1+; (b) 2+; (c) 3+; (d) 4+

13. (a) 1−; (b) 1−; (c) 2−; (d) 3−

15. (a) $1s^2$ (b) $1s^2\,2s^2\,2p^6$ (c) $1s^2\,2s^2\,2p^6\,3s^2\,3p^6$ (d) $1s^2\,2s^2\,2p^6$

17. (a) $1s^2\,2s^2\,2p^6\,3s^2\,3p^6$
(b) $1s^2\,2s^2\,2p^6\,3s^2\,3p^6\,4s^2\,3d^{10}\,4p^6\,5s^2\,4d^{10}\,5p^6$
(c) $1s^2\,2s^2\,2p^6\,3s^2\,3p^6$
(d) $1s^2\,2s^2\,2p^6\,3s^2\,3p^6$

19. (a) Ar; (b) Ar; (c) Ar; (d) Ar

21. (a) He; (b) Ne; (c) Ar; (d) Ne

23. (a) Ar; (b) Xe; (c) Ar; (d) Ar

25. (a) Li atom; (b) Mg atom; (c) F ion; (d) O ion

27. The true statements are (a) and (d).

29. (a) The bond length in H—Cl is less. (b) The bond length in O=O is less.

31. The true statements are (a) and (d).

33. (a) H:H   H—H
(b) :F̈:F̈:   :F̈—F̈:
(c) H:B̈r: H—B̈r:
(d) H   H
   H:N̈:H |
            H—N—H
                |

35. (a) H:Ö:N::Ö   H—Ö—N̈=Ö:
(b) :Ö:S̈::Ö   :Ö—S̈=Ö:
(c) H:C::C:H   H—C=C—H
      H H | |
                   H H
(d) H:C:::C:H   H—C≡C—H

37. (a) H   H
   H:C:H |
      H   H—C—H
                 |
                 H
(b) :F̈:Ö:F̈:   :F̈—Ö—F̈:
(c) H:Ö:Ö:H   H—Ö—Ö—H
(d)   :F̈:   :F̈:
   :F̈:N̈:F̈: |
            :F̈—N—F̈:

39. (a) $\left[:\ddot{B}r:\ddot{O}:\right]^-$ $\left[:\ddot{B}r—\ddot{O}:\right]^-$
(b) $\left[:\ddot{O}:\ddot{B}r:\ddot{O}:\right]^-$ $\left[:\ddot{O}—\ddot{B}r—\ddot{O}:\right]^-$
(c) $\left[:\ddot{O}:\ddot{B}r:\ddot{O}:\right]^-$ $\left[:\ddot{O}—\ddot{B}r—\ddot{O}:\right]^-$ (with :Ö: below)
(d) $\left[:\ddot{O}:\ddot{B}r:\ddot{O}:\right]^-$ $\left[:\ddot{O}—Br—\ddot{O}:\right]^-$ (with :Ö: above and below)

41. (a) $\left[:\ddot{O}:S:\ddot{O}:\right]^{2-}$ $\left[:\ddot{O}—S—\ddot{O}:\right]^{2-}$ (with :Ö: above and below)
(b) $\left[H:\ddot{O}:S:\ddot{O}:\right]^-$ $\left[H—\ddot{O}—S—\ddot{O}:\right]^-$ (with :Ö: above and below)
(c) $\left[:\ddot{O}:S:\ddot{O}:\right]^{2-}$ $\left[:\ddot{O}—S—\ddot{O}:\right]^{2-}$ (with :Ö: below)
(d) $\left[H:\ddot{O}:S:\ddot{O}:\right]^-$ $\left[H—\ddot{O}—S—\ddot{O}:\right]^-$ (with :Ö: below)

43. (a) $\left[H:\ddot{O}:H\right]^+$ $\left[H—\ddot{O}—H\right]^+$ (with H below)
(b) $\left[:\ddot{O}:H\right]^-$ $\left[:\ddot{O}—H\right]^-$
(c) $\left[H:\ddot{S}:\right]^-$ $\left[H—\ddot{S}:\right]^-$
(d) $[:C:::N:]^-$ $[:C≡N:]^-$

45. Electronegativity increases from bottom to top in the periodic table.

47. nonmetals

49. (a) Cl; (b) O; (c) Se; (d) F

51. (a) 0.2; (b) 1.2; (c) 0.5; (d) 0.3

53. (a) δ^+ H—S δ^-; (b) δ^- O—S δ^+; (c) δ^+ N—F δ^-; (d) δ^+ S—Cl δ^-

55. (a), (b), and (d)

57. H_2, N_2, Cl_2, and Br_2

59. H:Br:O:

H:Br—O:

61. H:Br:O:
:O:

H:Br—O:
:O:

63. [H
H:N:H]+
H

[H
H:N:H]+
H

65. [:O:
:O:N::O:]− [:O:
:O:N::O:]−

67. H   H
H—N:--¦--H—N:
H   H
⬆
Hydrogen bond

69. The *bond energy is much less* in a hydrogen bond than in a polar covalent bond.

71. tetrahedral, tetrahedral, 109.5°

73. tetrahedral, trigonal pyramidal, 107°

75. tetrahedral, bent, 104.5°

77. In CO_2, each of the two $C{=}O$ bonds is polar, but the oxygen atoms pull equally in opposite directions to give a nonpolar molecule. All three atoms lie in a straight line, and the molecular shape is described as *linear*.

79. (a) atom; (b) molecule; (c) formula unit; (d) molecule

81. (a) Sr_3As_2; (b) RaO; (c) $Al_2(CO_3)_3$; (d) $Cd(OH)_2$

83. The sodium ion has one less energy level ($3s$).

85. 1.0 (polar)

87. 0 (nonpolar)

89. $\delta^+ Ge{-}Cl\ \delta^-$

91. H   H
H:Si:H
H
H—Si—H
H

91. [:O:As:O:]3− [:O—As—O:]3−
:O: :O:

95. linear, linear, 180°

97. trigonal planar, trigonal planar, 120°

99. :O:Xe:O: :O—Xe—O:

101. four

103. three

Chapter 13

1. (a) decreases; (b) increases

3. 8.55 mL N_2/1 dL blood

5. 2.1 atm

7. (a) miscible; (b) immiscible

9. (a) polar; (b) nonpolar; (c) polar; (d) nonpolar

11. (a) miscible; (b) immiscible; (c) immiscible; (d) miscible

13. Add a few drops of water to the unknown liquid. If the unknown liquid is miscible with water, it is polar. If the unknown liquid is immiscible with water, it is nonpolar.

15. (a) soluble; (b) insoluble; (c) soluble

17. (a) insoluble; (b) soluble; (c) soluble; (d) insoluble

19. (a) fat soluble; (b) water soluble; (c) water soluble; (d) fat soluble

21.
$$H_2O---C_6H_{12}O_6---H_2O$$
with H_2O above and H_2O below

23. (a) structures showing $O---Li^+---O$ coordinated with water molecules, and $H---Br^---H$ coordinated with water molecules

(b) structures showing $O---Ca^{2+}---O$ coordinated with water molecules, and two $H---Cl^---H$ coordinated with water molecules

25. (1) heating the solution; (2) stirring the solution; (3) grinding the solute

27. (a) ~35 g NaCl; (b) ~35 g KCl

29. (a) ~35 g NaCl/100 g H_2O; (b) ~40 g KCl/100 g H_2O

31. (a) ~0 °C; (b) ~70 °C

33. (a) ~100 °C; (b) ~35 °C

35. (a) supersaturated; (b) saturated; (c) unsaturated

37. (a) supersaturated; (b) saturated; (c) unsaturated

39. saturated

41. (a) ~80 g LiCl; (b) ~20 g LiCl

43. (a) 1.25%; (b) 2.63%; (c) 4.00%; (d) 52.0%

45. (a) $\dfrac{1.50 \text{ g KBr}}{100 \text{ g solution}}$ and $\dfrac{100 \text{ g solution}}{1.50 \text{ g KBr}}$

$\dfrac{98.50 \text{ g } H_2O}{100 \text{ g solution}}$ and $\dfrac{100 \text{ g solution}}{98.50 \text{ g } H_2O}$

$\dfrac{1.50 \text{ g KBr}}{98.50 \text{ g } H_2O}$ and $\dfrac{98.50 \text{ g } H_2O}{1.50 \text{ g KBr}}$

(b) $\dfrac{2.50 \text{ g AlCl}_3}{100 \text{ g solution}}$ and $\dfrac{100 \text{ g solution}}{2.50 \text{ g AlCl}_3}$

$\dfrac{97.50 \text{ g } H_2O}{100 \text{ g solution}}$ and $\dfrac{100 \text{ g solution}}{97.50 \text{ g } H_2O}$

$$\frac{2.50 \text{ g AlCl}_3}{97.50 \text{ g H}_2\text{O}} \quad \text{and} \quad \frac{97.50 \text{ g H}_2\text{O}}{2.50 \text{ g AlCl}_3}$$

(c) $\dfrac{3.75 \text{ g AgNO}_3}{100 \text{ g solution}} \quad \text{and} \quad \dfrac{100 \text{ g solution}}{3.75 \text{ g AgNO}_3}$

$$\frac{96.25 \text{ g H}_2\text{O}}{100 \text{ g solution}} \quad \text{and} \quad \frac{100 \text{ g solution}}{96.25 \text{ g H}_2\text{O}}$$

$$\frac{3.75 \text{ g AgNO}_3}{96.25 \text{ g H}_2\text{O}} \quad \text{and} \quad \frac{96.25 \text{ g H}_2\text{O}}{3.75 \text{ g AgNO}_3}$$

(d) $\dfrac{4.25 \text{ g Li}_2\text{SO}_4}{100 \text{ g solution}} \quad \text{and} \quad \dfrac{100 \text{ g solution}}{4.25 \text{ g Li}_2\text{SO}_4}$

$$\frac{95.75 \text{ g H}_2\text{O}}{100 \text{ g solution}} \quad \text{and} \quad \frac{100 \text{ g solution}}{95.75 \text{ g H}_2\text{O}}$$

$$\frac{4.25 \text{ g Li}_2\text{SO}_4}{95.75 \text{ g H}_2\text{O}} \quad \text{and} \quad \frac{95.75 \text{ g H}_2\text{O}}{4.25 \text{ g Li}_2\text{SO}_4}$$

47. (a) 53.6 g solution; (b) 2.00×10^2 g solution

49. (a) 1.70 g $FeBr_2$; (b) 5.25 g Na_2CO_3

51. (a) 95.0 g H_2O; (b) 225 g H_2O

53. (a) 0.257 M NaCl; (b) 0.0510 M $K_2Cr_2O_7$; (c) 0.400 M $CaCl_2$; (d) 0.313 M Na_2SO_4

55. (a) $\dfrac{0.100 \text{ mol LiI}}{1 \text{ L solution}} \quad \text{and} \quad \dfrac{1 \text{ L solution}}{0.100 \text{ mol LiI}}$

$$\frac{0.100 \text{ mol LiI}}{1000 \text{ mL solution}} \quad \text{and} \quad \frac{1000 \text{ mL solution}}{0.100 \text{ mol LiI}}$$

(b) $\dfrac{0.100 \text{ mol NaNO}_3}{1 \text{ L solution}} \quad \text{and} \quad \dfrac{1 \text{ L solution}}{0.100 \text{ mol NaNO}_3}$

$$\frac{0.100 \text{ mol NaNO}_3}{1000 \text{ mL solution}} \quad \text{and} \quad \frac{1000 \text{ mL solution}}{0.100 \text{ mol NaNO}_3}$$

(c) $\dfrac{0.500 \text{ mol K}_2\text{CrO}_4}{1 \text{ L solution}} \quad \text{and} \quad \dfrac{1 \text{ L solution}}{0.500 \text{ mol K}_2\text{CrO}_4}$

$$\frac{0.500 \text{ mol K}_2\text{CrO}_4}{1000 \text{ mL solution}} \quad \text{and} \quad \frac{1000 \text{ mL solution}}{0.500 \text{ mol K}_2\text{CrO}_4}$$

(d) $\dfrac{0.500 \text{ mol ZnSO}_4}{1 \text{ L solution}} \quad \text{and} \quad \dfrac{1 \text{ L solution}}{0.500 \text{ mol ZnSO}_4}$

$$\frac{0.500 \text{ mol ZnSO}_4}{1000 \text{ mL solution}} \quad \text{and} \quad \frac{1000 \text{ mL solution}}{0.500 \text{ mol ZnSO}_4}$$

57. (a) 0.866 L solution; (b) 0.198 L solution; (c) 0.177 L solution; (d) 0.0800 L solution

59. (a) 73.0 g $FeCl_3$; (b) 104 g KIO_4; (c) 2.38 g $ZnSO_4$; (d) 2.69 g $Ni(NO_3)_2$

61. 0.0154 M $CaSO_4$

63. (a) 5.00%; (b) 0.291 M $C_6H_{12}O_6$

65. 0.48 M HCl

67. 0.014 L (14 mL)

69. 0.719 M $AgNO_3$; 1.88 g AgBr

71. The auditorium air contains colloidal-size particles of smoke and dust.

73. Helium gas is less soluble in blood and allows for quicker decompression.

75. 228 g SO_2

77. Although ethyl ether, $C_4H_{10}O$, contains two C—O polar bonds, it is only partially miscible in water because it has mostly nonpolar C—H bonds.

79. Water can hydrogen bond with the polar —OH in an alcohol, and draw it into solution. As the nonpolar C_xH_y– portion of the alcohol molecule increases, the alcohol becomes less soluble, and eventually immiscible with water.

81. (a) In a 40% solution, ethanol is the solute and water is the solvent. (b) In a 95% solution, water is the solute and ethanol is the solvent.

83. 0.838 M NaClO

85. (a) vitamin B-complex (B_1, B_2, B_3, B_6, B_{12}) and C

(b) vitamins A, D, E, and K

Chapter 14

1. (a), (b), (c), and (d) are general properties of an acidic solution.

3. (a) strongly acidic; (b) weakly acidic; (c) neutral; (d) weakly basic

5. (a) weak acid; (b) weak acid; (c) weak acid; (d) strong acid

7. (a) Arrhenius acid; (b) salt; (c) Arrhenius base; (d) salt

9. (a) HI(aq), NaOH(aq); (b) $HC_2H_3O_2$(aq), LiOH(aq)

11. (a) HF(aq), NaOH(aq); (b) HI(aq), $Mg(OH)_2$ (aq); (c) HNO_3(aq), $Ca(OH)_2$(aq); (d) H_2CO_3(aq), LiOH(aq)

13. (a) 2 HNO_3(aq) + $Ca(OH)_2$(aq) → $Ca(NO_3)_2$(aq) + 2 H_2O(l)

(b) H_2CO_3(aq) + $Ba(OH)_2$(aq) → $BaCO_3$(aq) + 2 H_2O(l)

15. (a) $HC_2H_3O_2$(aq), LiOH(aq); (b) H_2SO_4(aq), NH_3(aq)

17. (a) HI(aq), H_2O(l); (b) $HC_2H_3O_2$(aq), HS^-(aq)

19. (a) HF(aq) + NaHS(aq) → H_2S(aq) + NaF(aq)

(b) HNO_2(aq) + $NaC_2H_3O_2$(aq)

$$\rightarrow NaNO_2(aq) + HC_2H_3O_2(aq)$$

21. (a) red; (b) yellow

23. (a) yellow; (b) blue

25. (a) colorless; (b) pink

27. 0.141 M H_2SO_4

29. 0.0482 M H_3PO_4

31. 33.0 mL KOH

33. (a) 19.9% HCl; (b) 5.95% $HC_2H_3O_2$; (c) 3.12% HNO_3; (d) 24.9% H_2SO_4

35. 0.214 M H_2SO_4

37. 0.200 M HCl

39. 29.0 mL LiOH

41. 176 g/mol

43. (a) H_2O(l) → H^+(aq) + OH^-(aq); (b) $K_w = [H^+][OH^-]$; (c) $K_w = 1.0 \times 10^{-14}$

45. (a) $[OH^-] = 4.0 \times 10^{-13}\,M$; (b) $[OH^-] = 5.9 \times 10^{-10}\,M$

47. (a) $[H^+] = 6.3 \times 10^{-12}\,M$; (b) $[H^+] = 3.4 \times 10^{-11}\,M$

49. (a) pH = 3; (b) pH = 5

51. (a) $[H^+] = 0.000\,001\,M$; (b) $[H^+] = 0.000\,000\,01\,M$

53. (a) pH = 6.52; (b) pH = 7.80

55. (a) $[H^+] = 0.016\,M$; (b) $[H^+] = 0.000\,018\,M$

57. (a) pH = 13.04; (b) pH = 10.74

59. (a) $[OH^-] = 7.7 \times 10^{-14}\,M$; (b) $[OH^-] = 4.2 \times 10^{-13}\,M$

61. (a) highly ionized; (b) highly ionized; (c) highly ionized

63. (a) weak; (b) strong; (c) strong; (d) weak

65. (a) weak; (b) strong; (c) strong; (d) weak

67. (a) HF(aq); (b) H$^+$(aq) and Br$^-$(aq); (c) H$^+$(aq) and NO$_3^-$(aq); (d) HNO$_2$(aq)

69. (a) Ag$^+$(aq) and F$^-$(aq); (b) AgI(s); (c) Hg$_2$Cl$_2$(s); (d) Ni^{2+}(aq) and 2 Cl$^-$(aq)

71. (1) Complete and balance the nonionized equation.
(2) Convert the nonionized equation to the total ionic equation.
(3) Cancel spectator ions to obtain the net ionic equation.
(4) Check ($\sqrt{}$) each ion or atom on both sides of the equation.

73. (a) H$^+$(aq) + OH$^-$(aq) → H$_2$O(l)
(b) HC$_2$H$_3$O$_2$(aq) + OH$^-$(aq) → C$_2$H$_3$O$_2^-$(aq) + H$_2$O(l)

75. (a) Ag$^+$(aq) + I$^-$(aq) → AgI(s)
(b) Ba^{2+}(aq) + CrO$_4^{2-}$(aq) → BaCrO$_4$(s)

77. yellow

79. orange (red + yellow)

81. NaH$_2$PO$_4$

83. pH = 0.30

85. 6 × 10^{13} H$^+$

87. NH$_4$OH(aq) + HC$_2$H$_3$O$_2$(aq) →
NH$_4^+$(aq) + C$_2$H$_3$O$_2^-$(aq) + H$_2$O(l)

89. 89.2 g/mol

91. Sulfur dioxide and nitrogen dioxide are precursors to sulfuric acid and nitric acid. These acids can be harmful by breaking down skin oils that protect the body from bacterial infection. Breathing SO$_2$ and NO$_2$ can cause asthma, headaches, and eye/nose/throat irritation. In addition, SO$_2$ and NO$_2$ react with chemicals in the air to produce airborne particles that are harmful to the lungs.

Chapter 15

1. (a) unit analysis; (b) algebraic analysis

3. (a) meter (m); (b) gram (g); (c) liter (L); (d) second (s); (e) degree Celsius (°C); (f) calorie (cal)

5. (a) length; (b) mass; (c); volume; (d) time; (e) temperature; (f) heat energy

7. (a) velocity; (b) density; (c) specific heat; (d) m/m % concentration

9. (a) estimated answer: ~2 g MgO; calculated answer: 1.24 g MgO
(b) estimated answer: ~3 g Cr; calculated answer: 2.018 g Cr

11. (a)

molecules SO$_2$ → moles SO$_2$ → volume SO$_2$ (STP)

(b)

volume N$_2$ (STP) → moles N$_2$ → mass N$_2$

13. (a)

mass of reactant → moles of reactant → moles of product → mass of product

(b)

mass of reactant → moles of reactant → moles of product → volume of product

15. Refer to Figure 15.2. (a) 0.518 g HCl; (b) 0.318 L HCl; (c) 8.55 × 10^{21} molecules HCl; (d) 0.299 M HCl

17. Refer to Figure 15.2. (a) 1.12 L HF; (b) 3.01 × 10^{22} molecules HF; (c) 0.500 M HF

19. Refer to Figure 15.2. (a) 1.96 g CO$_2$; (b) 2.69 × 10^{22} molecules CO$_2$; (c) 0.0893 M H$_2$CO$_3$

21. Refer to Figure 15.2. (a) 0.826 L H$_2$S; (b) 1.26 g H$_2$S; (c) 0.0819 M H$_2$S

23. Refer to Figure 15.3. (a) 2.23 g CH$_4$; (b) 3.11 L CO$_2$

25. Refer to Figure 15.3. (a) 0.580 L H$_2$; (b) 518 mL HCl solution

27. Refer to Figure 15.3. (a) 0.719 M AgNO$_3$; (b) 1.88 g AgBr

29. (a) 91.6 g CO$_2$; (b) 46.6 L CO$_2$;
(c) 1st reaction + 2nd reaction: 33.3 g + 33.3 g = 66.6 g O$_2$

31. (a) 2500 g SO$_3$; (b) 698 L SO$_3$; (c) 1680 g H$_2$SO$_4$

33. (a) 6.30 g N$_2$; (b) 5.04 L N$_2$; (c) 5.41 g H$_2$O

35. 4.43 g NO$_2$

37. 0.622 M Ca^{2+}; 1.24 M Cl$^-$

39. 44.6 mL solution

41. 3.64 × 10^{21} molecules N$_2$O; 0.266 g N$_2$O

43. C$_6$H$_{14}$O$_6$

45. 0.683 g NaClO$_3$

47. 8,250 reams

49. (a) SO$_2$ is the limiting reactant; (b) 25.0 L SO$_3$

51. (a) H$_2$SO$_4$ is the limiting reactant; (b) 0.451 g H$_2$O

53. 3.16 × 10^9 kg seawater

55. 0.250 M Na$^+$

57. 0.784 g Na$_2$CO$_3$

59. A concept map for the software application program is:

61. Nitric acid is used in the production of fertilizers and explosives. Nitric acid is also used in the purification of metals, and in the synthesis of other chemicals.

63. A *googol* is the digit one followed by a hundred zeros, that is, 1×10^{100}. The term *googol* was popularized by the American mathematician, Edward Kasner, whose nine-year-old nephew coined the term.

Chapter 16

1. (a), (b), and (c) increase the rate of a reaction

3.

5. (a), (b), and (c) increase the rate of a reaction

7. No, a catalyst speeds up the rate of reaction, but does not affect the amount of product.

9. $PCl_5(g) + heat \rightleftharpoons PCl_3(g) + Cl_2(g)$

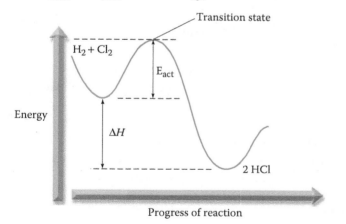

11. $H_2(g) + Cl_2(g) \rightleftharpoons 2\,HCl(g) + heat$

13. lowers E_{act}

15. The E_{act} is greater in the forward direction for an endothermic reaction.

17. (a) The rate of the forward reaction corresponds to the rate of *decrease* in the concentration of reactant(s).
(b) The rate of the forward reaction corresponds to the rate of *increase* in the concentration of product(s).

19. (b) The K_{eq} for a gaseous equilibrium does not include solid substances, which are omitted from gaseous equilibrium expressions.

21. (a) $K_{eq} = \dfrac{[C]}{[A]^2}$

(b) $K_{eq} = \dfrac{[C]^3}{[A][B]^2}$

(c) $K_{eq} = \dfrac{[C]^4[D]}{[A]^2[B]^3}$

23. no

25. (a) $K_{eq} = \dfrac{[HF]^2}{[H_2][F_2]}$

(b) $K_{eq} = \dfrac{[NO_2]^4[H_2O]^6}{[NH_3]^4[O_2]^7}$

(c) $K_{eq} = [CO_2]$

27. $K_{eq} = 1.10$

29. (a) increases; (b) decreases

31. (a) right; (b) left; (c) left; (d) right; (e) right; (f) left; (g) right; (h) left; (i) no shift; (j) no shift

33. (a) right; (b) left; (c) left; (d) right; (e) left; (f) right; (g) right; (h) left; (i) no shift; (j) no shift

35. (a) $K_i = \dfrac{[H^+][CHO_2^-]}{[HCHO_2]}$

(b) $K_i = \dfrac{[H^+][HC_2O_4^-]}{[H_2C_2O_4]}$

(c) $K_i = \dfrac{[H^+][H_2C_6H_5O_7^-]}{[H_3C_6H_5O_7]}$

37. $K_i = 4.5 \times 10^{-4}$

39. $K_i = 7.2 \times 10^{-4}$

41. (a) right; (b) left; (c) left; (d) right; (e) left; (f) left; (g) right; (h) right

43. (a) right; (b) left; (c) left; (d) right; (e) left; (f) no shift; (g) right; (h) right

45. (a) $K_{sp} = [Ag^+][I^-]$; (b) $K_{sp} = [Ag^+]^2[CrO_4^{2-}]$; (c) $K_{sp} = [Ag^+]^3[PO_4^{3-}]$

47. $K_{sp} = 5.9 \times 10^{-21}$

49. $K_{sp} = 3.4 \times 10^{-35}$

51. The calcium ion concentration in a saturated solution of $CaCO_3$ is slightly greater than in a saturated solution of CaC_2O_4.

53. (a) left; (b) left; (c) right; (d) right; (e) no shift; (f) left; (g) no shift; (h) right

55. (a) left; (b) left; (c) right; (d) right; (e) no shift; (f) left; (g) no shift; (h) right

57. A swinging pendulum represents a *dynamic, reversible process* as it is in constant motion and swings back and forth in opposite directions.

59. rate of forward reaction = rate of reverse reaction

61. $K_{eq} = 0.20$

63. (a) left; (b) right; (c) right; (d) left

65. $Zn(OH)_2$ is more soluble in acid than in water because of the following reaction:

$$Zn(OH)_2(s) + 2\,HCl(aq) \rightleftharpoons ZnCl_2(aq) + 2\,H_2O(l)$$

67. $K_{sp} = 5.3 \times 10^{-6}$

69. rate of forward reaction = rate of reverse reaction

71. Los Angeles is the smoggiest city in the United States, primarily owing to auto emissions. However, the current smog level in Los Angeles is much lower than in the 1970s, 1980s, and 1990s.

Chapter 17

1. (a) 0; (b) 0; (c) 0; (d) 0

3. (a) +3; (b) +2; (c) −3; (d) −2

5. (a) −3; (b) +4; (c) −3; (d) +5

7. (a) +4; (b) +6; (c) −2; (d) +7

9. (a) reduction; (b) reducing agent

11. (a) oxidized—Co, reduced—S;
(b) oxidized—Cd, reduced—Cl_2

13. (a) oxidizing agent—CuO; reducing agent—H_2;
(b) oxidizing agent—PbO; reducing agent—CO

15. (a) oxidized—Al, reduced—Cr^{3+};
(b) oxidized—Cl^-, reduced—F_2

17. (a) oxidizing agent—AgI; reducing agent—Cr^{2+};
(b) oxidizing agent—Hg^{2+}; reducing agent—Sn^{2+}

19. Yes, the total electron loss by oxidation must always equal the total electron gain by reduction.

21. (a) $Br_2(l) + 2\,NaI(aq) \rightarrow 2\,NaBr(aq) + I_2(s)$
(b) $2\,PbS(s) + 3\,O_2(g) \rightarrow 2\,PbO(s) + 2\,SO_2(g)$

23. (a) $2\,MnO_4^-(aq) + 10\,I^-(aq) + 16\,H^+(aq)$
$\rightarrow 2\,Mn^{2+}(aq) + 5\,I_2(s) + 8\,H_2O(l)$
(b) $Cu(s) + SO_4^{2-}(aq) + 4\,H^+(aq)$
$\rightarrow Cu^{2+}(aq) + SO_2(g) + 2\,H_2O(l)$

25. (a) $SO_2(g) + 2\,H_2O(l) \rightarrow SO_4^{2-}(aq) + 4\,H^+(aq) + 2\,e^-$
(b) $2\,BrO_3^-(aq) + 12\,H^+(aq) + 10\,e^- \rightarrow Br_2(l) + 6\,H_2O(l)$

27. (a) $ClO^-(aq) + H_2O(l) + 2\,e^- \rightarrow Cl^-(aq) + 2\,OH^-(aq)$
(b) $MnO_4^-(aq) + 2\,H_2O(l) + 3\,e^- \rightarrow MnO_2(s) + 4\,OH^-(aq)$

29. (a) $3\,Zn(s) + 2\,NO_3^-(aq) + 8\,H^+(aq)$
$\rightarrow 3\,Zn^{2+}(aq) + 2\,NO(g) + 4\,H_2O(l)$
(b) $\rightarrow 2\,Mn^{2+}(aq) + 5\,BiO_3^-(aq) + 14\,H^+(aq)$
$2\,MnO_4^-(aq) + 5\,Bi^{3+}(aq) + 7\,H_2O(l)$

31. (a) $3\,S^{2-}(aq) + 2\,MnO_4^-(aq) + 4\,H_2O(l)$
$\rightarrow 3\,S(s) + 2\,MnO_2(s) + 8\,OH^-(aq)$
(b) $Cu(s) + ClO^-(aq) + H_2O(l)$
$\rightarrow Cu^{2+}(aq) + Cl^-(aq) + 2\,OH^-(aq)$

33. $Cl_2(g) + H_2O(l) \rightarrow Cl^-(aq) + HOCl(aq) + H^+(aq)$

35. $4\,Cl_2(g) + 8\,OH^-(aq)$
$\rightarrow 2\,ClO_2^-(aq) + 6\,Cl^-(aq) + 4\,H_2O(l)$

37. (a) $Li(s)$; (b) $Mg(s)$; (c) $I^-(aq)$; (d) $Br^-(aq)$

39. (a) $F_2(g)$; (b) $Br_2(l)$; (c) $Cu^{2+}(aq)$; (d) $Mn^{2+}(aq)$

41. (a) nonspontaneous; (b) spontaneous

43. (a) spontaneous; (b) spontaneous

45. $C > B > A$

47.

$$Ni(s) + 2\,AgNO_3(aq) \rightarrow 2\,Ag(s) + Ni(NO_3)_2(aq)$$

49.

$$Ni(s) + 2\,AgNO_3(aq) \rightarrow 2\,Ag(s) + Ni(NO_3)_2(aq)$$

51. (a) $Mn(s) \rightarrow Mn^{2+}(aq) + 2\,e^-$; (b) $Fe^{2+}(aq) + 2\,e^- \rightarrow Fe(s)$;
(c) Mn anode, Cu cathode; (d) Mn anode → Fe cathode
(e) Fe half-cell → Mn half-cell

53. (a) $Mg(s) \rightarrow Mg^{2+}(aq) + 2\,e^-$; (b) $Pb^{2+}(aq) + 2\,e^- \rightarrow Pb(s)$;
(c) Mg anode, Pb cathode; (d) Mg anode → Pb cathode;
(e) Pb half-cell → Mg half-cell

55. (a) $Ni(s) \rightarrow Ni^{2+}(aq) + 2\,e^-$; (b) $Fe^{2+}(aq) + 2\,e^- \rightarrow Fe(s)$;
(c) Ni anode, Fe cathode; (d) Ni anode → Fe cathode;
(e) Fe half-cell → Ni half-cell

57. (a) $Pb(s) \rightarrow Pb^{2+}(aq) + 2\,e^-$; (b) $Zn^{2+}(aq) + 2\,e^- \rightarrow Zn(s)$;
(c) Pb anode, Zn cathode; (d) Pb anode → Zn cathode;
(e) Fe half-cell → Pb half-cell

59. (a) $2\,F^-(aq) \rightarrow F_2(g) + 2\,e^-$; (b) $Cl_2(g) + 2\,e^- \rightarrow 2\,Cl^-(aq)$;
(c) $Pt(F_2)$ anode, $Pt(Cl_2)$ cathode;
(d) $Pt(F_2)$ anode → $Pt(Cl_2)$ cathode;
(e) $Pt(F_2)$ half-cell → $Pt(Cl_2)$ half-cell

61. 2+

63. $Co(s) + Hg^{2+}(aq) \rightarrow Co^{2+}(aq) + Hg(l)$

65. $Zn(s) + 2\,H^+(aq) \rightarrow Zn^{2+}(aq) + H_2(g)$

67. $2\,Li(s) + 2\,H_2O(l) \rightarrow 2\,Li^+(aq) + 2\,OH^-(aq) + H_2(g)$

69. $3\,C_2H_5OH(aq) + 2\,Cr_2O_7^{2-}(aq) + 16\,H^+(aq)$
$\rightarrow 3\,HC_2H_3O_2(aq) + 4\,Cr^{3+}(aq) + 11\,H_2O(l)$

71. Chromium(VI) is very toxic although human blood can eliminate small amounts of chromium(VI) before it enters red blood cells. Chromium(VI) can damage the liver and kidneys, and chromium poisoning may require dialysis.

Chapter 18

1. alpha particle (α)

3. beta particle (β)

5. gamma ray (γ)

7. (a) ~4 amu; (b) ~0 amu; (c) 0 amu; (d) ~0 amu;
(e) ~1 amu; (f) ~1 amu

9. (a) $^{160}_{74}W \rightarrow ^{156}_{72}Hf + ^{4}_{2}He$; (b) $^{32}_{15}p \rightarrow ^{32}_{16}S + ^{0}_{-1}e$;
(c) $^{55}_{27}Co \rightarrow ^{55}_{26}Fe + ^{0}_{+1}e$; (d) $^{44}_{22}Ti + ^{0}_{-1}e \rightarrow ^{44}_{21}SC$

11. (a) $^{222}_{90}Th$; (b) $^{56}_{25}Mn$; (c) $^{19}_{10}Ne$; (d) $^{37}_{18}Ar$

13. $^{234}_{91}Pa$

15. $^{231}_{91}Pa$

17. (a) α; (b) β; (c) β; (d) α; (e) α; (f) α; (g) α; (h) β; (i) β; (j) α

19. $^{233}_{91}Pa$

21. 25%

23. 366,000 years

25. 22,900 years old

27. 5 mg

29. 296 days

31. 5.30 years/half-life

33. radiocarbon dating

35. cobalt-60

37. plutonium-238

39. iodine-131

41. iridium-192

43. $^{80}_{35}Br$

45. $^{238}_{94}Pu$

47. $^{130}_{52}Te$

49. $^{4}_{2}He$

51. $^{260}_{105}X$

53. $^{260}_{106}X$

55. 8 neutrons

57. The number of neutrons varies, but the *average* number is 2.4.

59. 2 neutrons

61. 3 neutrons

63. $^{233}_{92}U$

65. $^{1}_{0}n$

67. $^{1}_{1}H$

69. $^{2}_{1}H$

71. $^{237}_{92}U$

73. $^{137}_{53}I$

75. ~6000 years

77. $^{241}_{95}Am$

79. 15 neutrons

81. $^{256}_{101}Md$

83. $^{4}_{2}He$

85. The longest lived half-life for an isotope of flerovium is 2.6 s for Fl-289. The longest lived half-life for an isotope of livermorium is 18 ms for Lv-292. (An unconfirmed half-life of 53 s has been reported for Lv-293.)

Chapter 19

1. alkanes

3. alkenes and alkynes

5. alkenes

7. (b) $C_{10}H_{22}$

9. (a) propane; (b) pentane; (c) heptane; (d) nonane

11. $CH_3-CH_2-CH_2-CH_2-CH_2-CH_3$

13. $CH_3-CH_2-CH_2-Cl$ and $CH_3-CH(Cl)-CH_3$

15. (a) CH_3-; (b) CH_3CH_2-

17. (a) 2-methylpentane; (b) 4-ethyl-2-methylhexane;
(c) 2,4,4-trimethylheptane; (d) 3,4,5-trimethyloctane

19. (a) $CH_4 + 2O_2 \rightarrow CO_2 + 2H_2O$
(b) $C_3H_8 + 5O_2 \rightarrow 3CO_2 + 4H_2O$
(c) $2C_6H_{14} + 19O_2 \rightarrow 12CO_2 + 14H_2O$
(d) $2C_8H_{18} + 25O_2 \rightarrow 16CO_2 + 18H_2O$

21. (b) $C_{10}H_{20}$

23. (a) 1-butene; (b) 1-pentene; (c) 2-hexene; (d) 4-octene

25. (b) $C_{10}H_{18}$

27. (a) 2-pentyne; (b) 1-pentyne; (c) 3-hexyne; (d) 2-heptyne

29. $CH_2=CH-CH_2-CH_2-CH_3$ and
$CH_3-CH=CH-CH_2-CH_3$

31. (a) 4-methyl-2-pentene; (b) 3,5-dimethyl-2-hexene

33. (a) 4,4-dimethyl-2-heptyne; (b) 3,4,5-trimethyl-1-octyne

35. (a) $CH_2=CH_2 + 3O_2 \rightarrow 2CO_2 + 2H_2O$
(b) $CH_3-CH=CH_2 + H_2 \rightarrow CH_3-CH_2-CH_3$
(c) $CH_3-CH=CH-CH_3 + Br_2$
$\rightarrow CH_3-CHBr-CHBr-CH_3$

37.

ortho   *meta*   *para*

39. CO_2 and H_2O

41. (a) ether; (b) organic halide; (c) phenol; (d) amine

43. (a) amine; (b) organic halide; (c) ester; (d) carboxylic acid;
(e) aldehyde; (f) ether; (g) ketone; (h) amide

45. (a) "methyl iodide"; (b) "ethyl bromide"; (c) "propyl fluoride"; (d) "isopropyl chloride"

47. $CCl_2\!=\!CHCl$

49. (a) insoluble; (b) soluble

51. (a) 1-butanol; (b) 2-butanol; (c) 1-butanol; (d) 2-butanol

53. (a) phenol; (b) para-methylphenol

55. (a) "dimethyl ether"; (b) "methyl ethyl ether"; (c) "dipropyl ether"; (d) "phenyl ethyl ether"

57. "Ethyl alcohol" molecules can hydrogen bond.

59. $CH_3\!-\!CH_2\!-\!OH$ and $CH_3\!-\!O\!-\!CH_3$

61. (a) "ethylamine"; (b) "propylamine"

63. "Ethylamine" molecules can hydrogen bond.

65. (a) methanal; (b) ethanal; (c) propanal; (d) butanal

67. (a) 2-propanone; (b) 2-butanone; (c) 2-pentanone; (d) 3-pentanone

69. (a) higher boiling point; (b) higher boiling point

71.

$$CH_3CH_2\!-\!\overset{\overset{\displaystyle O}{\|}}{C}\!-\!H \quad \text{and} \quad CH_3\!-\!\overset{\overset{\displaystyle O}{\|}}{C}\!-\!CH_3$$

73. (a) methanoic acid; (b) ethanoic acid; (c) propanoic acid; (d) butanoic acid

75. (a) ethyl methanoate; (b) methyl ethanoate; (c) ethyl propanoate; (d) phenyl methanoate

77. (a) methanamide ("formamide"); (b) benzamide

79. (a) and (c)

81. propionic acid

83. (a)

(b)

85. phenyl ethanoate ("phenyl acetate")

87. methanamide ("formamide")

89. (a) saturated; (b) unsaturated

91. carboxylic acid

93. ketone

95. organic chloride, aldehyde

97. (a) $CH_3CH_2\!-\!OH$; (b) $CH_3CH_2CH_2\!-\!NH_2$

99. A fullerene is a molecule composed entirely of carbon in the shape of a sphere or tube. A spherical fullerene (C_{60}) is referred to as a "buckyball," as it resembles a soccer ball as well as the geodesic domes designed by Buckminster Fuller.

Chapter 20

1. (a) protein; (b) nucleic acid

3. (a) peptide linkage; (b) phosphate linkage

5. (a) carboxylic acid, amine, amide (b) aldehyde or ketone, alcohol (c) carboxylic acid, alcohol, ester (d) aldehyde, alcohol, amine

7. covalent amide bond

9. The primary structure of a protein refers to the amino acid sequence. The secondary structure of a protein refers to the shape of the polymer chain.

11.

13.

15. (1) Ala–Gln–Met; (2) Ala–Met–Gln; (3) Gln–Ala–Me; (4) Gln–Met–Ala; (5) Met–Ala–Gln; (6) Met–Gln–Ala

17. glutamic acid, lysine, and serine

19. In oxytocin, *isoleucine* replaces phenyl alanine and *leucine* replaces arginine.

21. The lock represents the *substrate (S)*.

23. The enzyme location that conforms to the shape of the substrate molecule is called an *active site*.

25. In Step 1, the substrate molecule binds to the active site on the enzyme.

27. An enzyme is inactive under experimental conditions where the pH or temperature is too high or too low.

29. aldehyde and alcohol groups

31. six carbon atoms

33. A monosaccharide is a simple sugar such as glucose, whereas a disaccharide has two simple sugar molecules joined by a glycoside linkage.

35. See Figure 20.9.

37. See Figure 20.11.

39. galactose and glucose

41. $C_{12}H_{22}O_{11} + H_2O \xrightarrow{H^+} C_6H_{12}O_6 + C_6H_{12}O_6$
  lactose   water   galactose glucose

43. (a) fat; (b) oil; (c) fat and oil; (d) fat and oil

45.

47. (a) palmitic acid, $CH_3\!-\!(CH_2)_{14}\!-\!COOH$;

(b) lauric acid, $CH_3\!-\!(CH_2)_{10}\!-\!COOH$;

(c) myristic acid, $CH_3\!-\!(CH_2)_{12}\!-\!COOH$

49. A triglyceride (fat, oil) has *three* fatty acids esterified to glycerol; a phospholipid has *two* fatty acids and phosphoric acid esterifed to glycerol.

51. $CH_3\!-\!(CH_2)_{24}\!-\!COO^-Na^+$ and $CH_3\!-\!(CH_2)_{29}\!-\!OH$

53.

55. deoxyribose sugar, a base, and phosphoric acid

57. adenine (A), cytosine (C), guanine (G), and thymine (T)

59. The structures are identical except deoxyribose is missing an —OH group.

61. 2 strands of nucleotides

63. 2 hydrogen bonds

65. thymine (T)

67. uracil (U)

69. long and extended

71. When a protein is denatured in aqueous acid, hydrogen bonds are broken and the molecule assumes a random shape.

73. protein

75. A, D, E, and K

77. ACG, AGC, CAG, CGA, GAC, and GCA

79. Replication is the process by which a DNA molecule synthesizes two identical molecules of DNA; whereas, transcription is the process by which a DNA molecule synthesizes two complementary single strands of RNA.

81. The first step in *replication* is for a DNA molecule to unwind by breaking the hydrogen bonds (A=T and C≡G) holding together the double helix. Next, each strand of DNA acts as a template to synthesize a complementary strand. For example, adenine (A) on the template strand codes for thymine (T) on the growing strand; cytosine (C) codes for guanine (G); guanine (G) codes for cytosine (C); and thymine (T) codes for adenine (A).

At the conclusion, each pair of template strands and complementary strands are joined by hydrogen bonds (A=T and C≡G), and the two resulting structures are exact duplicates of the original DNA molecule. Thus, two identical molecules of DNA are produced from one molecule of DNA.

83. (a) retinol (vitamin A)   ~1 mg
(b) thiamine (vitamin B_1)   ~1 mg
(c) niacin (vitamin B_3)   ~15 mg
(d) ascorbic acid (vitamin C)   ~100 mg

It should be noted that the daily requirements vary significantly depending upon a number of factors including age, gender, lifestyle, and nutrition.

Answers to Chapter Self-Tests

Chapter 1—Self-Test

1. (c); 2. (b); 3. (e)

Key Concepts

4. The image of a cube creates a dual perception. By mentally pulling the red dot, the front face of the cube appears to be down and to the right. By mentally pushing the red dot, the front face of the cube appears to be up and to the left.

Critical Thinking

5. Chemical evolution is a *scientific theory* because it is not measurable, and the relationship between elements is not expressed as a mathematical equation.

6. Biological evolution is a *scientific theory* because it is not measurable, and the relationship between species is not expressed as a mathematical equation.

Prerequisite Science Skills—Self-Test

1. (d); 2. (b); 3. (e); 4. (b); 5. (c); 6. (a); 7. (c)

Key Concepts

8. Round off the answer in the display after the final calculation. Rounding off the final answer is more accurate and convenient.

Critical Thinking

9. Note the exponent for the mass of an alpha and beta particle. Since 10^{-24} g is four powers of 10 greater than 10^{-28} g, the alpha particle is much heavier.

10. Precious metals such as silver and gold are weighed in troy ounces, whereas copper and iron are weighed in avoirdupois ounces. In the metric system, the unit of gram is constant. Thus, an ounce of gold (31.1 g) weighs more than an ounce of iron (28.4 g).

Chapter 2—Self-Test

1. (e); 2. (a); 3. (b); 4. (c); 5. (d); 6. (e); 7. (a); 8. (c); 9. (b); 10. (d)

Key Concepts

11. Fool's gold ($d = 5.00$ g/mL) sinks in water, but rests on liquid mercury. The gold nugget ($d = 18.3$ g/mL) sinks in both water and liquid mercury ($d = 13.6$ g/mL), and comes to rest at the bottom of the glass cylinder.

12. Since the absolute scale begins at zero Kelvin, the coldest possible temperature is 0 K; for comparison, 0 °F is 523 K, and 0 °C is 273 K.

Critical Thinking

13. Add a few drops of each liquid to water and observe if they sink or float. Hexane ($d = 0.70$ g/mL) is *less dense* than water ($d = 1.00$ g/mL), so it floats. Chloroform ($d = 1.5$ g/mL) is *more dense* than water, so it sinks.

14. A silver dime weighs more than a zinc penny because the silver metal in a dime coin is more dense than the zinc metal in a penny coin.

Chapter 3—Self-Test

1. (d); 2. (a); 3. (e); 4. (c); 5. (d); 6. (b); 7. (e); 8. (a); 9. (b); 10. (d)

Key Concepts

11. (a) liquid; (b) gas; (c) solid

12. (a) heterogeneous mixture; (b) compound; (c) element; (d) homogeneous mixture

13. The photo shows a mineral and illustrates a heterogeneous mixture. The model illustrates a molecule of S_8, which is an element.

14. The molecular formula for aspirin is $C_9H_8O_4$.

Critical Thinking

15. Ice floating in water is an example of a heterogeneous mixture because ice and water have different densities, and can be separated by physical methods.

16. The properties of an element (Fe) and its compounds (FeO, Fe_2O_3, $Fe(NO_3)_3$) are not related, and their physical and chemical properties are different.

17. When a playground swing is at its lowest point, the potential energy is minimum, and kinetic energy is maximum.

18. On a roller coaster ride the potential energy is greatest when the coaster is at its highest point. As the coaster travels down, it loses potential energy and gains kinetic energy. Thus, the potential energy is maximum, and the kinetic energy is minimum, when the roller coaster is at its highest point.

Chapter 4—Self-Test

1. (d); 2. (a); 3. (c); 4. (b); 5. (a); 6. (d); 7. (c); 8. (a); 9. (e); 10. (b); 11. (d)

Key Concepts

12. In the analogy "like a marble in Dallas Cowboys Stadium" the marble represents the atomic nucleus, and the stadium represents the entire atom.

13. In the analogy, the missile represents an alpha particle and the solar system represents the planets in our solar system.

14. An *electron* is to electricity, as a *photon* is to light.
15. The evidence for electrons occupying fixed energy states is an "atomic fingerprint" and the line spectrum of an element.

Critical Thinking

16. If the two isotopes, Cu-63 and Cu-65, were each 50% abundant, the atomic mass would be approximately 64 amu. Since the atomic mass of copper is 63.55, the lighter isotope, Cu-63, is more abundant.
17. No, atoms of different elements have different atomic numbers, and cannot have the same number of protons.
18. Yes, atoms of different elements can have the same mass number, and the same number of neutrons.

Chapter 5—Self-Test

1. (e); 2. (a); 3. (d); 4. (b); 5. (c); 6. (a); 7. (d); 8. (e); 9. (b); 10. (c)

Key Concepts

11. The metallic character *decreases* up a group of elements, and generally *decreases* from left to right in a period.
12. The atomic radius *decreases* up a group of elements, and generally *decreases* from left to right in a period.
13. The ionization energy *increases* up a group of elements, and generally *increases* from left to right in a period.
14. Elements in the same group react to form compounds with similar chemical formulas; for example, P and As are in Group VA/15 and react with oxygen to form P_2O_5 and As_2O_5.

Critical Thinking

15. *Yes*, ions of different elements can have the same number of electrons. For example, Na^+ and Mg^{2+} each have 10 electrons.
16. *No*, ions of different elements have a different number of protons.
17. *Yes*, ions of different elements can have the same number of neutrons. For example, O^{2-} and F^- each have isotopes with 10 neutrons (O-18 and F-19).
18. The yellow substance appears to be sulfur powder. The gray substance appears metallic, so it must be the semimetal antimony. By elimination, the orange substance must be antimony sulfide, Sb_2S_3.

Chapter 6—Self-Test

1. (c); 2. (b); 3. (a); 4. (c); 5. (b); 6. (d); 7. (a); 8. (b); 9. (d)

Key Concepts

10. NaCl is binary ionic; $NaClO_3$ is ternary ionic; HCl is binary molecular; HCl(*aq*) is a binary acid; $HClO_3$(*aq*) is a ternary oxyacid
11. NaCl is named using an *–ide* suffix; that is, sodium chlor**ide**.
12. $NaClO_3$ is named using an *–ate* suffix; that is, sodium chlo**rate**.
13. $NaClO_2$ is named using an *–ite* suffix; that is, sodium chlo**rite**.
14. HCl(*aq*) is named as a *hydro + nonmetal stem + ic* acid; that is, hydrochloric acid.
15. $HClO_3$(*aq*) is named *nonmetal stem + ic* acid; that is, chloric acid.
16. $HClO_2$(*aq*) is named *nonmetal stem + ous* acid; that is, chlorous acid.

Critical Thinking

17. Copper predictably loses two 4*s* electrons giving Cu^{2+}. Copper can also lose one 4*s* electron giving Cu^+. This ion is especially stable as the remaining 4*s* electron moves into the 3*d* sublevel, thus filling the third energy level.
18. Iron predictably loses two 4*s* electrons giving Fe^{2+}. Iron can also lose one 3*d* electron giving Fe^{3+}. This ion is especially stable as five electrons remain in the 3*d* sublevel; this half-filled 3*d* sublevel has one electron in each 3*d* orbital.
19. White chalk is made by grinding limestone into a fine powder and pressing the powder into a stick. Marble is a crystalline form of the mineral found naturally.

Chapter 7—Self-Test

1. (d); 2. (e); 3. (c); 4. (a); 5. (a); 6. (d); 7. (c); 8. (c); 9. (b); 10. (e); 11. (d)

Key Concepts

12. $4\,Fe(s) + 3\,O_2(g) \rightarrow 2\,Fe_2O_3(s)$
13. $Ca(HCO_3)_2(s) \rightarrow CaCO_3(s) + H_2O(g) + CO_2(g)$
14. $Zn(s) + Ni(NO_3)_2(aq) \rightarrow Zn(NO_3)_2(aq) + Ni(s)$
15. $HNO_3(aq) + NH_4OH(aq) \rightarrow NH_4NO_3(aq) + HOH(l)$
16. $C_2H_5OH(l) + 3\,O_2(g) \xrightarrow{spark} 2\,CO_2(g) + 3\,H_2O(g)$

Critical Thinking

17. $HCl(aq) + NaHCO_3(aq) \rightarrow NaCl(aq) + H_2O(l) + CO_2(g)$
18. $Pb(NO_3)_2(aq) + 2\,KI(aq) \rightarrow PbI_2(s) + 2\,KNO_3(aq)$

Chapter 8—Self-Test

1. (a); 2. (c); 3. (b); 4. (c); 5. (e); 6. (b); 7. (c); 8. (b); 9. (d)

Key Concepts

10. The mass is found in the periodic table. One atom of F has a mass of 19.00 amu, and Avogadro's number of atoms has a mass of 19.00 g.
11. One mole of fluorine gas, F_2, has a mass of 38.00 g, a volume of 22.4 L, and contains 6.02×10^{23} molecules.
12. Avogadro's number of steel balls has an estimated mass equal to Earth.
13. Avogadro's number of small marbles has a total volume equal to the Moon.

Critical Thinking

14. No. Ten trillion (1×10^{13}) copper atoms weigh 1×10^{-9} g, which is one-thousandth of a microgram (1×10^{-6} g).
15. A googol (1×10^{100}) of atoms is many times more than 1×10^{22}, the number of carbon atoms in a 1-carat diamond.

Chapter 9—Self-Test

1. (a); 2. (d); 3. (b); 4. (c); 5. (d); 6. (a); 7. (b); 8. (b); 9. (c)

Key Concepts

10. A balanced chemical equation is necessary before solving a stoichiometry problem.
11. Typically, *three* unit factors are required to solve a mass–mass problem.
12. Typically, *three* unit factors are required to solve a mass–volume problem.

13. Typically, only *one* unit factor is required to solve a volume–volume problem because the coefficients of the balanced equation are in the same ratio as the volumes of gaseous reactants and products.

Critical Thinking

14. The limiting reactant is gasoline; the excess reactant is oxygen.

15. (a) $2 Ag_2S$, $2 S$ (Ag is limiting reactant)

    (b) $2 Ag_2S$, $2 Ag$ (S is limiting reactant)

Chapter 10—Self-Test

1. (c); 2. (e); 3. (a); 4. (b); 5. (a); 6. (d); 7. (c); 8. (a); 9. (b); 10. (e);

11. (a)

Key Concepts

12. As the steam cools inside the capped can, it condenses to a liquid, thus reducing gaseous molecules and the pressure inside the can. The pressure outside the can is greater than inside, and atmospheric pressure crushes the can.

13. If you check tire pressure after rolling several miles, the pressure is greater because road friction has heated the tire and the air molecules inside are moving faster and colliding more frequently.

14. You would be repulsed first because H_2S (34 amu) has less molecular mass than $C_3H_6O_2$ (74 amu), so the molecules of H_2S move faster.

Critical Thinking

15. The balloon rises because the density of air inside the balloon is less than outside. Heating air in a hot-air balloon causes air molecules to move faster and escape so as to equalize pressure inside and outside the balloon.

16. If you release a helium balloon into the air, the volume of the balloon increases as it ascends because atmospheric pressure outside the balloon is less at higher elevations.

17. On a hot day the water bottle bulges because the vapor pressure of water inside the bottle increases, whereas the outside atmospheric pressure remains constant.

18. On a cold night the water bottle crushes because the vapor pressure of water inside the bottle decreases, whereas the outside atmospheric pressure remains constant.

19. At the top of the mountain the atmospheric pressure is less than the pressure inside the bottle, so the plastic bottle bulges.

Chapter 11—Self-Test

1. (a); 2. (c); 3. (d); 4. (c); 5. (b); 6. (e); 7. (c); 8. (e); 9. (a); 10. (b)

Key Concepts

11. A beehive surrounded by flying honey bees is analogous to the gaseous physical state. If honey bees move about faster in warm weather, their movement is analogous to gas molecules when a gas is heated.

12. As the water freezes to a solid, water molecules will form hydrogen bonds and the volume will expand. Thus, the cap will pop off, or the bottle will break.

Critical Thinking

13. At sea level (Miami, FL), water boils at 100 °C. At a high elevation (Denver, CO), water boils at 95 °C due to lower atmospheric pressure. Food cooks faster at higher temperatures, and eggs hard-boil faster at 100 °C than at 95 °C.

14. Water has a concave lens because there is intermolecular *attraction* between polar water molecules and glass. Mercury has a convex lens because there is *repulsion* between nonpolar mercury atoms and glass.

Chapter 12—Self-Test

1. (c); 2. (d); 3. (e); 4. (d); 5. (b); 6. (e); 7. (c); 8. (b); 9. (c); 10. (a)

Key Concepts

11. The three diagrams represent (a) atoms, (b) molecules, and (c) formula units; for example, (a) Na atoms, (b) H_2O molecules, and (c) NaCl formula units.

12. The HF molecule is most polar because F is the most electronegative element in Group VIIA/17.

13. A water molecule has two pairs of nonbonding electrons on the oxygen atom, and two hydrogen atoms. Thus, *four* H_2O molecules can attach directly to a single H_2O molecule by hydrogen bonds (see Figure 11.12).

14. The electron pair geometry of $CHCl_3$ is *tetrahedral*, and the molecular shape is *tetrahedral*.

Critical Thinking

15. The two resonance structures for sulfur dioxide are: $O{=}S{-}O$ and $O{-}S{=}O$. Due to resonance, the two bonds in an SO_2 molecule are equivalent and have the same bond energy and bond length.

16. The electron pair geometry in both H_2O and H_3O^+ is tetrahedral. However, in H_3O^+ the molecular shape is *trigonal pyramidal*, and in H_2O the molecular shape is *bent*.

17. The electron pair geometry in both NH_3 and NH_4^+ is tetrahedral. However, in NH_3 the molecular shape is *trigonal pyramidal* and in NH_4^+ the molecular shape is *tetrahedral*.

Chapter 13—Self-Test

1. (a); 2. (c); 3. (b); 4. (d); 5. (e); 6. (c); 7. (a); 8. (b); 9. (a); 10. (b);

11. (c)

Key Concepts

12. Bubbles form on the inside surface of a pan when the water is heated because water contains air and the solubility of a gas in water is less as the temperature increases.

13. Peanut butter can dissolve grease in clothing because peanut butter and grease are both nonpolar.

14. Powdered sugar has smaller solute particles than granulated sugar, and thus greater surface area to be attacked by solvent water molecules.

Critical Thinking

15. Lake Green has more dissolved oxygen gas. Lake Nuclear cools a nuclear power plant and the heat raises the temperature of the water. At a higher temperature (Lake Nuclear), the solubility of oxygen gas is less.

16. At the conceptual level, we can explain the greater solubility of NaCl versus AgCl as follows. With NaCl there is less attraction between Na^+ and Cl^- ions than the ion attraction for solvent water molecules. Conversely, with AgCl there is more attraction between Ag^+ and Cl^- ions than the ion attraction for solvent water molecules.

Chapter 14—Self-Test

1. (e); 2. (c); 3. (b); 4. (d); 5. (a); 6. (d); 7. (e); 8. (c); 9. (b); 10. (c);

11. (a)

Key Concepts

12. We must always start with a balanced equation before applying unit analysis to solve an acid–base titration problem.

13. The bright light indicates Beaker X contains a strong electrolyte such as HNO_3, which is highly ionized. The dim light indicates Beaker Y has a weak electrolyte such as HNO_2, which is slightly ionized.

Critical Thinking

14. A "fishy smell" due to a basic organic compound can be neutralized using an acid. Household vinegar contains acetic acid, which we can use to neutralize the fish odor.

15. Since phenolphthalein is colorless in acid, and bromthymol blue is yellow in acid, the color of the solution in the test tube will be yellow.

16. At the conceptual level, we can explain the higher ionization of HCl versus HF as follows. It requires less energy to break H—Cl bonds than to break H—F bonds. In addition, more energy is released by the solvent water molecules surrounding H^+ and Cl^- than H^+ and F^-.

Chapter 15—Self-Test

1. (b); 2. (c); 3. (e); 4. (c); 5. (a); 6. (b); 7. (c); 8. (d); 9. (d); 10. (a)

Key Concepts

11. The *unit analysis method* converts a given value to an unknown value by applying one or more unit factors.

12. The *algebraic method* requires rearranging variables in an equation to calculate an unknown quantity.

13. *Concept mapping* traces the relationship of chemical concepts by connected boxes.

14. *Visualization* helps to understand concepts that cannot be observed directly.

Critical Thinking

15. (a) The molar mass of a substance can be found from the periodic table. (b) The physical properties of a substance can be found online, or using a reference book, such as the *Handbook of Chemistry and Physics*.

16. The given value must have compound units, for example, g/mL.

Chapter 16—Self-Test

1. (d); 2. (c); 3. (b); 4. (a); 5. (e); 6. (b); 7. (d); 8. (e); 9. (d)

Key Concepts

10. The reaction profile shows products at a higher energy level than reactants; thus, the profile represents an endothermic reaction.

11. $K_{eq} = [O_3]^2/[O_2]^3$

12. After heating an endothermic reaction, the equilibrium shifts to the right.

13. After reducing the volume of a reaction in which products have fewer molecules than reactants, the equilibrium shifts to the right.

14. After adding a catalyst, the rate increases but there is no shift in equilibrium.

Critical Thinking

15. In a coal mine, small particles of coal dust in the air provide more surface area for reaction. In the barbecue, large briquettes have less surface area to contact oxygen in air.

16. At equilibrium, the rate of evaporation of the liquid equals the rate of condensation of the vapor.

Chapter 17—Self-Test

1. (a); 2. (b); 3. (c); 4. (d); 5. (b); 6. (e); 7. (e)

Key Concepts

8. In the redox reaction shown:

(a) $H_2O(l) + NO_2^-(aq) \rightarrow NO_3^-(aq) + 2\,H^+(aq) + 2\,e^-$

(b) $2\,e^- + 2\,H^+(aq) + H_2O_2(aq) \rightarrow 2\,H_2O(l)$

(c) $NO_2^-(aq)$

(d) $H_2O_2(aq)$

(e) $H_2O_2(aq)$

(f) $NO_2^-(aq)$

9. In the voltaic cell shown:

(a) $Mn(s) \rightarrow Mn^{2+}(aq) + 2\,e^-$

(b) $Fe^{2+}(aq) + 2\,e^- \rightarrow Fe(s)$

(c) anode: Mn; cathode: Fe

(d) Electrons flow from Mn anode to Fe cathode.

(e) SO_4^{2-} ions flow from Fe compartment to Mn compartment.

Critical Thinking

10. As a NiCad battery is *recharging*, $Ni(OH)_2$ is being *oxidized*.

11. As a NiCad battery is *discharging*, Cd is being *oxidized*.

12. Zinc metal is being *oxidized*, while silver oxide is *reduced*.

Chapter 18—Self-Test

1. (b); 2. (d); 3. (c); 4. (a); 5. (d); 6. (c); 7. (b); 8. (a); 9. (d); 10. (e)

Key Concepts

11. (a) $^{238}_{92}U \rightarrow ^{234}_{92}U + ^{4}_{2}He$

(b) $^{239}_{92}U \rightarrow ^{239}_{93}Np + ^{0}_{1}e$

(c) $^{40}_{19}K \rightarrow ^{40}_{18}Ar + ^{0}_{+1}e$

(d) $^{40}_{19}K + ^{0}_{-1}e \rightarrow ^{40}_{18}Ar$

12. $1\,n^0 \rightarrow 3\,n^0 \rightarrow 9\,n^0$

13. positron, $^{0}_{+1}e$

Critical Thinking

14. $^{210}_{82}Pb \rightarrow ^{210}_{83}Bi + ^{0}_{-1}e$

15. $^{86}_{36}Kr + ^{208}_{82}Pb \rightarrow ^{293}_{118}X + ^{1}_{0}n$ (Element 118)

Chapter 19—Self-Test

1. (a); 2. (c); 3. (b); 4. (a); 5. (e); 6. (c); 7. (b); 8. (d); 9. (e); 10. (d)

Key Concepts

11. alcohol: CH_3—CH_2—OH; ether: CH_3—O—CH_3

12. aldehyde: CH_3—CH_2—CHO; ketone: CH_3—CO—CH_3

13. carboxylic acid: CH_3—CO—OH; ester: H—CO—OCH_3

14. Thyroxine contains the following functional groups (left to right): phenol, organic halide, ether, amine, carboxylic acid.

Critical Thinking

15. (a) $CH_3-CH(CH_3)-CH_2-C(CH_3)_2-CH_3$
    (b) $CH_3-CH(OH)-CH_2-CH_3$

16. Caffeine is an *amine*; an *–ine* suffix usually denotes an amine.

17. Cholesterol is an *alcohol*; an *–ol* suffix usually denotes an alcohol.

18. Cortisone is a *ketone*; an *–one* suffix usually denotes a ketone.

Chapter 20—Self-Test

1. (a); 2. (c); 3. (c); 4. (a); 5. (b); 6. (a); 7. (e); 8. (b); 9. (d); 10. (e)

Key Concepts

15.

$$H_2N-\underset{\underset{H}{|}}{CH}-\overset{\overset{O}{\|}}{C}-NH-\underset{\underset{\underset{CH_3}{|}}{CH-CH_3}}{CH}-\overset{\overset{O}{\|}}{C}-OH$$

12. $C_{12}H_{22}O_{11} + H_2O \xrightarrow{H^+} C_6H_{12}O_6 + C_6H_{12}O_6$
    sucrose   water   glucose   fructose

13. A *lipid* is a water-insoluble fat, oil, or wax.

14. A *nucleic acid* is a polymer of a sugar, a base, and phosphoric acid.

15.

$$\text{fat} + 3\,NaOH \rightarrow \begin{array}{l} CH_2-OH + CH_3-(CH_2)_{10}-COO^-Na^+ \\ | \\ CH-OH + CH_3-(CH_2)_{14}-COO^-Na^+ \\ | \\ CH_2-OH + CH_3-(CH_2)_{16}-COO^-Na^+ \end{array}$$

The products are glycerol and soap. The soap is composed of the sodium salts of lauric acid, palmitic acid, and stearic acid.

16.

$$CH_3-(CH_2)_{34}-\overset{\overset{O}{\|}}{C}-O-(CH_2)_{35}-CH_3$$

17. During DNA replication, an adenine base will code for *thymine.*

18. During DNA transcription, an adenine base will code for *uracil.*

Critical Thinking

19. The shape of a protein that forms muscle tissue is long and extended. The shape of a protein that has a metabolic role is compact and folded.

20. (a) Nucleotide A shows the sugar deoxyribose and the base adenine; thus, nucleotide A is found in DNA.
    (b) Nucleotide B shows the sugar ribose and the base cytosine; thus, nucleotide B is found in RNA.

Glossary

A

absolute zero The theoretical temperature at which the kinetic energy of a gas is zero. *(Sec. 10.10)*

acid A substance that releases hydrogen ions (H^+) when dissolved in water. *(Sec. 7.11)*

acid–base indicator A chemical substance that changes color according to the pH of the solution. *(Sec. 14.4)*

acidic oxide See *nonmetal oxide.*

actinide series The elements with atomic numbers 90–103. *(Sec. 5.3)*

activation energy (E_{act}) The energy necessary for reactants to achieve the transition state and form products. *(Sec. 16.2)*

active metal A metal that is sufficiently active to react with water at room temperature; the active metals include Li, Na, K, Ca, Sr, and Ba. *(Sec. 7.7)*

activity The number of radioactive nuclei in a given sample that decay per unit time; for example, 500 disintegrations per minute (dpm). *(Sec. 18.4)*

activity series A relative order of metals arranged according to their ability to undergo a reaction; also called an *electromotive series. (Sec. 7.7)*

actual yield The amount of product that is experimentally obtained from given amounts of reactants. *(Sec. 9.9)*

addition reaction A chemical reaction in which an unsaturated compound adds hydrogen or a halogen. *(Sec. 19.3)*

alchemy A pseudoscience that attempted to convert a base metal, such as lead, into gold; a medieval science that sought to discover a universal cure for disease and a magic potion for immortality. *(Sec. 1.2)*

alkali metals The Group IA/1 elements, excluding hydrogen. *(Sec. 5.3)*

alkaline earth metals The Group IIA/2 elements. *(Sec. 5.3)*

alkanes A family of saturated hydrocarbon compounds. *(Sec. 19.2)*

alkenes A family of unsaturated hydrocarbon compounds having a double bond. *(Sec. 19.3)*

alkyl group (R–) The part that remains after a hydrogen atom is removed from an alkane. *(Sec. 19.2)*

alkynes A family of unsaturated hydrocarbon compounds having a triple bond. *(Sec. 19.3)*

alloy A homogeneous mixture of two or more metals. *(Sec. 3.2)*

alpha particle (α) A particle in an alpha ray that is identical to a helium-4 nucleus. *(Sec. 18.1)*

amino acid A carboxylic acid with an amine group on the alpha carbon; also referred to as an α-amino acid. *(Sec. 20.2)*

amphiprotic A substance capable of either donating or accepting a proton in an acid–base reaction. *(Sec. 14.3)*

anhydrous compound A compound that does not contain water. *(Sec. 11.10)*

anion A negatively charged ion. *(Sec. 6.1)*

anode The electrode in an electrochemical cell at which oxidation occurs. *(Sec. 17.6)*

aqueous solution (aq) A homogeneous mixture of a substance dissolved in water. *(Secs. 6.1 and 7.1)*

arenes A family of aromatic hydrocarbon compounds. *(Sec. 19.4)*

aromatic hydrocarbon A hydrocarbon compound typically containing a benzene ring. *(Sec. 19.1)*

Arrhenius acid A substance that releases hydrogen ions when dissolved in water. *(Sec. 14.2)*

Arrhenius base A substance that releases hydroxide ions when dissolved in water. *(Sec. 14.2)*

aryl group (Ar–) The part that remains after a hydrogen atom is removed from an arene. *(Sec. 19.2)*

atmospheric pressure The pressure exerted by the air molecules in Earth's atmosphere. The atmospheric pressure at sea level is 1 atm or 760 mm of Hg. *(Sec. 10.2)*

atom The smallest particle that represents an element. *(Sec. 3.3)*

atomic mass The weighted average mass of all the naturally occurring isotopes of an element. *(Sec. 4.5)*

atomic mass unit (amu) A unit of mass exactly equal to 1/12 the mass of a carbon-12 atom. *(Sec. 4.5)*

atomic notation A symbolic method for expressing the composition of an atomic nucleus; the mass number and atomic number are indicated to the left of the chemical symbol for the element. *(Sec. 4.4)*

atomic nucleus A region of very high density in the center of the atom that contains protons and neutrons. *(Sec. 4.3)*

atomic number (Z) A number that identifies a specific element. *(Sec. 3.4)* A value that indicates the number of protons in the nucleus of an atom. *(Secs. 4.4 and 18.2)*

Avogadro's number (N) The value that corresponds to the number of carbon atoms in 12.01 g of carbon; 6.02×10^{23} particles. *(Sec. 8.1)*

Avogadro's theory The principle that equal volumes of gases, at the same temperature and pressure, contain equal numbers of molecules; also referred to as *Avogadro's law* or *Avogadro's hypothesis. (Secs. 8.5, 9.1, and 10.3)*

B

barometer An instrument for measuring atmospheric pressure. *(Sec. 10.2)*

base A substance that releases hydroxide ions (OH^-) when dissolved in water. *(Sec. 7.11)*

basic oxide See *metal oxide.*

battery A general term for any electrochemical cell that produces electrical energy spontaneously. *(Sec. 17.6)*

beta particle (β) A particle in a beta ray that is identical to an electron. *(Sec. 18.1)*

binary acid A compound that contains hydrogen and a nonmetal dissolved in water. *(Sec. 6.1)*

binary ionic compound A compound that contains one metal and one nonmetal. *(Sec. 6.1)*

binary molecular compound A compound that contains two nonmetals. *(Sec. 6.1)*

biochemistry The study of chemical substances derived from plants and animals. *(Sec. 1.2)* The study of biological compounds. *(Sec. 20.1)*

Bohr atom A model of the atom that describes an electron circling the atomic nucleus in an orbit of specific energy. *(Sec. 4.8)*

boiling point (Bp) The temperature at which the vapor pressure of a liquid is equal to the atmospheric pressure. *(Sec. 11.3)*

bond angle The angle formed by two atoms bonded to the central atom in a molecule. *(Secs. 11.7 and 12.10)*

bond energy The amount of energy required to break a covalent bond between two atoms. *(Sec. 12.3)*

bond length The distance between the nuclei of two atoms that are joined by a covalent bond. *(Sec. 12.3)*

bonding electrons The valence electrons in a molecule that are shared between two atoms. *(Sec. 12.4)*

Boyle's law The statement that the pressure and the volume of a gas are inversely proportional at constant temperature; that is, $P_1V_1 = P_2V_2$. *(Sec. 10.4)*

Brønsted-Lowry acid A substance that donates a proton in an acid–base reaction. *(Sec. 14.3)*

Brønsted-Lowry base A substance that accepts a proton in an acid–base reaction. *(Sec. 14.3)*

buffer A solution that resists changes in pH when an acid or a base is added. *(Sec. 14.1)*

C

calorie (cal) The amount of heat required to raise the temperature of 1 g of water 1 °C. *(Sec. 2.10)*

carbohydrate A biological compound that contains one or more sugar molecules; a sugar is a polyhydroxy aldehyde or ketone. *(Sec. 20.1)*

carbonyl group (—C=O) The C=O group, which is present in aldehydes, ketones, carboxylic acids, esters, and amides. *(Sec. 19.5)*

carboxyl group (—COOH) The —COOH group, which is present in carboxylic acids. *(Sec. 19.10)*

catalyst A substance that speeds up a reaction without being permanently changed. *(Sec. 7.2)* A substance that allows a reaction to proceed faster by lowering the energy of activation. *(Sec. 16.2)*

cathode The electrode in an electrochemical cell at which reduction occurs. *(Sec. 17.6)*

cation A positively charged ion. *(Sec. 6.1)*

Celsius degree (°C) The basic unit of temperature in the metric system. *(Sec. 2.9)*

chain reaction A fission reaction in which the neutrons released initiate a second reaction, which in turn initiates a third reaction, and so on. *(Sec. 18.7)*

Charles's law The statement that the volume and the Kelvin temperature of a gas are directly proportional at constant pressure; that is, $V_1/T_1 = V_2/T_2$. *(Sec. 10.5)*

centimeter (cm) A common unit of length in the metric system that is equal to one-hundredth of a meter. *(PSS.1)*

chemical bond The attraction between positive and negative ions, or two nonmetal atoms. *(Sec. 12.1)*

chemical change A modification of a substance that alters its chemical composition. *(Sec. 3.7)*

chemical equation A shorthand representation using formulas and symbols to describe a chemical reaction. *(Sec. 7.2)*

chemical equilibrium A dynamic state for a reversible reaction in which the rates of the forward and reverse reactions are equal and the amounts of reactants and products are constant. *(Sec. 16.3)*

chemical formula An abbreviation for the name of a chemical compound that indicates the number of atoms of each element; for example, H_2O is the formula for water. *(Sec. 3.5)*

chemical property A characteristic of a substance that cannot be observed without changing its chemical formula. *(Sec. 3.6)*

chemical reaction The process of undergoing a chemical change. *(Sec. 7.1)*

chemical symbol An abbreviation for the name of a chemical element; for example, Cu is the symbol for copper. *(Sec. 3.3)*

chemistry The branch of science that studies the composition and properties of matter. *(Sec. 1.2)*

class of compounds A family of compounds in which all the members have the same structural feature (that is, an atom or group of atoms) and similar chemical properties. *(Sec. 19.5)*

coefficient A digit in front of a chemical formula that helps to balance an equation; a digit that helps to balance the number of atoms of each element on the left side of an equation with those on the right side of the equation. *(Sec. 7.3)*

collision theory The principle that the rate of a chemical reaction is regulated by the collision frequency, collision energy, and the orientation of molecules striking each other. *(Sec. 16.1)*

colloid A homogeneous mixture in which the diameters of the dispersed particles range from 1 to 100 nm. *(Sec. 13.3)*

combination reaction A type of reaction in which two substances produce a single compound. *(Sec. 7.4)*

combined gas law The statement that the pressure exerted by a gas is inversely proportional to its volume and directly proportional to its Kelvin temperature; that is, $P_1V_1/T_1 = P_2V_2/T_2$. *(Sec. 10.7)*

combustion reaction A chemical reaction in which a hydrocarbon reacts rapidly with oxygen (burns) to produce carbon dioxide, water, and heat. *(Sec. 19.2)*

compound A pure substance that can be broken down into two or more simpler substances by a chemical reaction. *(Sec. 3.2)*

continuous spectrum A single, broad band of radiant energy. *(Sec. 4.6)*

coordinate covalent bond A bond in which an electron pair is shared, but both electrons have been donated by a single atom. *(Sec. 12.8)*

core electrons The inner electrons in an atom, which are not available for bonding. *(Sec. 5.8)*

core notation A method of writing the electron configuration in which the inner core electrons are represented by a noble gas symbol in brackets followed by valence electrons; for example, [Ne] $3s^2$. *(Sec. 5.10)*

covalent bond A bond resulting from the sharing of one or more pairs of valence electrons between two nonmetal atoms. *(Sec. 12.1)*

critical mass The minimum mass of a fissionable nuclide necessary to sustain a continuous chain reaction. *(Sec. 18.7)*

crystalline solid A solid substance composed of ions or molecules that repeat in a regular geometric pattern. *(Sec. 11.4)*

cubic centimeter (cm³) A unit of volume occupied by a cube 1 cm on a side; 1 cm^3 is exactly equal to 1 mL. *(Sec. 2.6)*

D

Dalton's law of partial pressures The statement that the pressure exerted by a mixture of gases is equal to the sum of the individual pressures exerted by each gas; that is, $P_1 + P_2 + P_3 + \ldots = P_{total}$. *(Sec. 10.9)*

decay series See *radioactive decay series.*

decomposition reaction A type of reaction in which a single compound produces two or more substances. *(Sec. 7.4)*

degree Celsius See *Celsius degree.*

degree Fahrenheit See *Fahrenheit degree.*

deionized water Water purified by removing ions using an ion exchange method; also termed *demineralized water*. (Sec. 11.7)

delta (δ) notation A method of indicating the partial positive charge (δ^+) and the partial negative charge (δ^-) in a polar covalent bond. (Sec. 12.6)

density (d) The amount of mass in one unit volume of matter. (Sec. 2.8)

deposition A direct change of state from a gas to a solid without forming a liquid. (Sec. 3.1)

deuterium (^2_1H) The nuclide of hydrogen with one neutron in the nucleus. (Sec. 18.8)

diatomic molecule A particle composed of two nonmetal atoms. (Sec. 7.2) A molecule composed of two nonmetal atoms held together by a covalent bond. (Sec. 12.7)

dipeptide A molecule that contains two amino acids joined by an amide bond. (Sec. 20.2)

dipole A region in a molecule having partial negative charge and partial positive charge resulting from a polar bond. (Sec. 13.2)

dipole force A type of attraction between two molecules that have permanent dipoles. (Sec. 11.2)

directly proportional A relationship between two variables that have a direct relationship; for example, if one variable doubles the other doubles, or if one variable is halved the other is halved. (Sec. 10.5)

disaccharide A carbohydrate composed of two simple sugar molecules joined by a glycoside linkage. (Sec. 20.4)

dispersion force A type of attraction between two molecules that have temporary dipoles. A temporary dipole arises from the unequal distribution of charge as electrons move around a molecule; also called a *London dispersion force*. (Sec. 11.2)

dissociation The process of an ionic compound dissolving in water and separating into positive and negative ions; for example, NaOH dissolves in water to give sodium ions and hydroxide ions. (Sec. 14.2)

distilled water Water purified by boiling and collecting the condensed vapor. (Sec. 11.7)

double bond A bond composed of two electron pairs shared between two atoms. A double bond is represented by two dashes between the symbols of the two atoms. (Sec. 12.4)

double-replacement reaction A type of reaction in which two cations in different compounds exchange anions. (Sec. 7.4)

dry cell An electrochemical cell in which the anode and cathode reactions do not take place in an aqueous solution. (Sec. 17.6)

ductile The property of a metal that allows it to be drawn into a wire. (Sec. 3.4)

E

elastic collision An impact between gas molecules in which the total energy remains constant. (Sec. 10.10)

electrochemical cell A general term for an apparatus that contains two solutions with electrodes in separate compartments that are connected by a conducting wire and salt bridge. (Sec. 17.6)

electrochemistry The study of the interconversion of chemical and electrical energy from redox reactions. (Sec. 17.6)

electrolysis The chemical reaction produced by passing electricity through an aqueous solution. (Sec. 11.9) The providing of electricity to a nonspontaneous redox process to cause a reaction. (Sec. 17.7)

electrolytic cell An electrochemical cell in which a nonspontaneous redox reaction occurs as a result of the input of direct electric current. (Sec. 17.7)

electromotive series See *activity series*.

electron (e^-) A negatively charged subatomic particle having a tiny mass. (Sec. 4.2)

electron capture (EC) A nuclear reaction in which a heavy nuclide attracts one of its core electrons into the nucleus. (Sec. 18.2)

electron configuration A shorthand description of the arrangement of electrons by sublevels according to increasing energy. (Secs. 4.10 and 5.6)

electron dot formula The chemical symbol of an element surrounded by a dot representing each valence electron. (Sec. 5.8) A diagram of a molecule or polyatomic ion that shows the chemical symbol of each atom and a dot representing each bonding and nonbonding electron. An electron dot formula is also called a *Lewis structure*. (Sec. 12.4)

electron pair geometry The geometric shape formed by bonding and nonbonding electron pairs surrounding the central atom in a molecule. (Sec. 12.9)

electronegativity The ability of an atom to attract a pair of electrons in a chemical bond. (Sec. 12.6)

element A pure substance that cannot be broken down by an ordinary chemical reaction. (Sec. 3.2)

emission line spectrum Several narrow bands of radiant energy that result from excited atoms releasing energy. (Sec. 4.8)

empirical formula A chemical formula that expresses the simplest whole-number ratio of atoms of each element in a molecule, or ions in an ionic compound. (Sec. 8.8)

endothermic reaction A chemical reaction that absorbs heat energy. (Secs. 7.1 and 16.2)

endpoint The stage in a titration when the indicator changes color permanently. (Sec. 14.5)

energy level An orbit of specific energy that electrons occupy at a fixed distance from the nucleus; also referred to as a *main energy level*; designated as 1, 2, 3, 4. . . . (Sec. 4.8)

energy sublevel An electron energy level that results from splitting a main energy level; designated as s, p, d, f. . . . (Sec. 4.9)

English system A nondecimal system of measurement without any basic unit for length, mass, or volume. (Sec. 2.1)

enzyme A protein molecule that catalyzes a specific biochemical reaction. (Sec. 20.3)

equilibrium constant See *general equilibrium constant* (K_{eq}), *ionization equilibrium constant* (K_i), or *solubility product equilibrium constant* (K_{sp}).

evaporation See *vaporization*.

exact equivalent A statement that relates two values that are exactly equal; for example, 1 yd = 36 in. and 1 m = 100 cm. (Sec. 2.2)

exothermic reaction A chemical reaction that releases heat energy. (Secs. 7.1 and 16.2)

experiment A scientific procedure for collecting data and recording observations under controlled conditions. (Sec. 1.1)

exponent A number written as a superscript, indicating that a value is multiplied by itself; for example, $10^4 = 10 \times 10 \times 10 \times 10$ and $cm^3 = cm \times cm \times cm$. (PSS.6)

F

Fahrenheit degree (°F) A basic unit of temperature in the English system. (Sec. 2.9)

fat A triglyceride from an animal source that contains mostly saturated fatty acids. *(Sec. 20.5)*

fatty acid A carboxylic acid with a long hydrocarbon chain. *(Sec. 20.5)*

formula unit The simplest representative particle in a compound composed of ions. *(Sec. 6.4)* The simplest representative particle in a substance held together by ionic bonds. *(Sec. 12.1)*

frequency The number of times a light wave travels a complete cycle in one second. *(Sec. 4.6)*

functional group An atom or group of atoms that characterizes a class of compounds and contributes to their similar chemical properties. *(Sec. 19.5)*

G

galvanic cell See *voltaic cell*.

gamma ray (γ) A powerful type of nuclear radiation that has neither mass nor charge. *(Sec. 18.1)*

gas density The ratio of mass per unit volume for a gas, usually expressed in grams per liter. *(Sec. 8.5)*

gas pressure A measure of the frequency and energy of gas molecules colliding against the walls of their container. *(Sec. 10.2)*

Gay-Lussac's law The statement that the pressure and the Kelvin temperature of a gas are directly proportional at constant volume; that is, $P_1/T_1 = P_2/T_2$. *(Sec. 10.6)*

Gay-Lussac's law of combining volumes See *law of combining volumes*.

general equilibrium constant (K_{eq}) A constant that expresses the molar equilibrium concentration of each substance participating in a reversible reaction at a given temperature. *(Sec. 16.3)*

glycoside linkage An —O— bond that joins two simple sugar molecules. *(Sec. 20.4)*

gram (g) A common metric unit of mass. *(PSS.1)* The basic unit of mass in the metric system. *(Sec. 2.1)*

green chemistry A term that refers to the design of products and processes that reduce or eliminate hazardous chemical substances; also referred to as the *sustainable chemistry*. (Sec. 1.2)

group A vertical column in the periodic table; a family of elements with similar properties. *(Sec. 5.3)*

H

half-cell A portion of an electrochemical cell having a single electrode where either oxidation or reduction occurs. *(Sec. 17.6)*

half-life ($t_{1/2}$) The amount of time required for 50% of the radioactive nuclei in a given sample to decay. *(Sec. 18.4)*

half-reaction A reaction that represents either an oxidation or reduction process separately and indicates the number of electrons lost or gained. *(Sec. 17.4)*

halogens The Group VIIA/17 elements. *(Sec. 5.3)*

hard water Water that contains a variety of cations and anions such as Ca^{2+}, Mg^{2+}, Fe^{3+}, CO_3^{2-}, SO_4^{2-}, and PO_4^{3-}. *(Sec. 11.7)*

heat The flow of energy from an object at a higher temperature to an object at a lower temperature. *(Sec. 2.10)*

heat of fusion (H_{fusion}) The heat required to convert a solid to a liquid at its melting point. Conversely, the heat released when a liquid changes to a solid is called the *heat of solidification* (H_{solid}). *(Sec. 11.6)*

heat of reaction (ΔH) The difference in heat energy between the reactants and the products for a given chemical reaction. *(Sec. 16.2)*

heat of vaporization (H_{vapor}) The heat required to convert a liquid to a gas at its boiling point. Conversely, the heat released when a gas changes to a liquid is called the *heat of condensation* (H_{cond}). *(Sec. 11.6)*

Henry's law The principle that the solubility of a gas in a liquid is proportional to the partial pressure of the gas above the liquid. *(Sec. 13.1)*

heterogeneous equilibrium A type of equilibrium in which all of the participating species are not in the same physical state; for example, an equilibrium between an insoluble precipitate and its ions in an aqueous solution. *(Sec. 16.4)*

heterogeneous mixture Matter having an indefinite composition and variable properties. *(Sec. 3.2)*

homogeneous equilibrium A type of equilibrium in which all of the participating species are in the same physical state; for example, an equilibrium between reactants and products in the gaseous state. *(Sec. 16.4)*

homogeneous mixture Matter having a definite composition, but variable properties from sample to sample; examples include alloys and solutions. *(Sec. 3.2)*

hydrate A substance that contains a specific number of water molecules in a crystalline compound. *(Sec. 11.9)*

hydrocarbon A compound that contains only hydrogen and carbon. *(Sec. 19.1)*

hydrocarbon derivative A compound that contains carbon, hydrogen, and another element such as oxygen, nitrogen, or a halogen. *(Sec. 19.5)*

hydrogen bond An intermolecular attraction based on permanent dipoles involving a H atom bonded to an O or N atom. *(Sec. 11.9)* The attraction between a H atom bonded to an O or N atom, and a nonbonding electron pair on an electronegative atom in another molecule. *(Sec. 12.2)*

hydronium ion (H_3O^+) The ion that results when a hydrogen ion attaches to a water molecule by a coordinate covalent bond. The hydronium ion is the predominant form of the hydrogen ion in an aqueous acid solution. *(Sec. 14.2)*

hydroxyl group (—OH) The —OH group, which is present in alcohols and phenols. *(Sec. 19.7)*

hypothesis An initial, tentative proposal of a scientific principle that attempts to explain the meaning of a set of data collected in an experiment. *(Sec. 1.1)*

I

ideal gas A theoretical gas that obeys the kinetic theory under all conditions of temperature and pressure. *(Sec. 10.10)*

ideal gas constant (R) The proportionality constant R in the equation $PV = nRT$. *(Sec. 10.11)*

ideal gas law The principle stated by the relationship $PV = nRT$; also called the *ideal gas equation*. *(Sec. 10.11)*

immiscible A term that refers to liquids that do not dissolve in one another and separate into two layers. *(Sec. 13.2)*

inner transition elements The elements in the lanthanide and actinide series. *(Sec. 5.3)*

inorganic chemistry The study of chemical substances that do not contain the element carbon. *(Sec. 1.2)*

inorganic compound A compound that does not contain carbon. *(Sec. 6.1)*

instrument A device for recording a measurement such as length, mass, volume, time, or temperature. *(PSS.1)*

International System (SI) A sophisticated system of measurement that is more comprehensive than the metric system and has seven base units. *(Sec. 2.1)*

inversely proportional A relationship between two variables that have an inverse relationship; for example, if one variable doubles, the other variable is halved. *(Sec. 10.4)*

ion An atom (or group of atoms) that has a negative or a positive charge as the result of gaining or losing valence electrons. *(Sec. 5.9)*

ionic bond A bond resulting from the attraction between a positively charged cation and a negatively charged anion. *(Sec. 12.1)*

ionic charge A term for the positive charge on a metal atom that has lost electrons, or the negative charge on a nonmetal atom that has gained electrons. *(Sec. 5.10)*

ionic solid A crystalline solid composed of ions that repeat in a regular pattern. *(Sec. 11.5)*

ionization The process of a polar compound dissolving in water and forming positive and negative ions; for example, HCl dissolves in water to give hydrogen ions and chloride ions. *(Sec. 14.2)*

ionization constant of water (K_w) A constant that equals the product of the molar hydrogen ion concentration and the molar hydroxide ion concentration in water; $K_w = 1.0 \times 10^{-14}$ at 25 °C. *(Sec. 14.7)*

ionization energy The amount of energy necessary to remove an electron from a neutral atom in the gaseous state. *(Sec. 5.9)*

ionization equilibrium constant (K_i) A constant that expresses the molar equilibrium concentrations of ions in an aqueous solution for a slightly ionized acid or base. *(Sec. 16.6)*

isoelectronic A term for two or more ions (or ions and an atom) with the same electron configuration; for example, Na^+ and F^- each have 10 electrons, and their electron configurations are identical to the noble gas neon. *(Sec. 5.10)*

isomers Compounds with the same molecular formula, but with different structural formulas. Isomers have different physical and chemical properties. *(Sec. 19.2)*

isotopes Atoms with the same atomic number, but a different mass number; atoms of the same element that differ by the number of neutrons in the nucleus. *(Sec. 4.4)*

IUPAC nomenclature The system of rules for naming chemical compounds set forth by the International Union of Pure and Applied Chemistry. *(Sec. 6.1)*

J

joule (J) A unit of energy in the SI system; 1 cal = 4.184 J. *(Sec. 2.10)*

K

Kelvin unit (K) The basic unit of temperature in the SI system. *(Sec. 2.9)*

kinetic energy (KE) The energy associated with the motion of particles; the energy associated with the mass and velocity of a particle. *(Sec. 3.9)*

kinetic theory A theoretical description of gas molecules demonstrating ideal behavior; also referred to as the *kinetic molecular theory*. *(Sec. 10.10)*

L

lanthanide series The elements with atomic numbers 58–71. *(Sec. 5.3)*

Latin system A system for naming ionic compounds that designates the variable charge on a metal cation with an *–ic* or *–ous* suffix attached to the stem of the Latin name. *(Sec. 6.2)*

law See *natural law*.

law of chemical equilibrium The principle that the molar concentrations of the products in a reversible reaction divided by the molar concentrations of the reactants (each raised to a power corresponding to a coefficient in the balanced equation) is equal to a constant. The law of chemical equilibrium can be written mathematically as $K_{eq} = [C]^a [D]^d / [A]^a [B]^b$. *(Sec. 16.3)*

law of combining volumes The principle that volumes of gases that combine in a chemical reaction, at the same temperature and pressure, are in the ratio of small whole numbers; also called *Gay-Lussac's law of combining volumes*. *(Sec. 9.6)*

law of conservation of energy The principle that states energy can neither be created nor destroyed, but can be changed from one form to another; for example, nuclear energy to heat energy. *(Sec. 3.10)*

law of conservation of mass The principle that states matter can neither be created nor destroyed. *(Sec. 3.8)* The statement that mass is neither gained nor lost during a chemical reaction. *(Sec. 9.1)*

law of conservation of mass and energy The principle that states the total mass and energy in the universe is constant. The statement that the total mass and energy, before and after a chemical change, is constant. *(Sec. 3.10)*

law of definite composition The principle that states a compound always contains the same elements in the same proportion by mass; also called the *law of definite proportion*. *(Sec. 3.5)*

law of multiple proportions The principle that two elements that can form more than one compound combine in the ratio of small whole numbers; for example, CO and CO_2. *(Sec. 4.1)*

Le Chatelier's principle The statement that any reversible reaction at equilibrium when stressed by a change in concentration, temperature, or pressure, shifts to relieve the stress. *(Sec. 16.5)*

Lewis structure See *electron dot formula*.

light A specific term that refers to visible radiant energy; that is, violet to red. A general term that refers to both visible and invisible radiant energy. *(Sec. 4.6)*

like dissolves like rule The general principle that solubility is greatest when the polarity of the solute and solvent are similar. *(Sec. 13.2)*

limiting reactant The substance in a chemical reaction that controls or limits the maximum amount of product formed. *(Sec. 9.7)*

line spectrum See *emission line spectrum*.

lipid A biological compound such as a fat, oil, wax, or steroid that is insoluble in water. *(Sec. 20.1)*

liter (L) The basic unit of volume in the metric system equal to the volume of a cube 10 cm on a side. *(Sec. 2.1)*

lock-and-key model A theory that explains enzyme catalysis; the theory states that the shape of the substrate molecule must fit the contour of the active site on an enzyme. (Sec. 20.3)

M

main-group elements See *representative elements*.

malleable The property of a metal that allows it to be hammered or machined into a foil. (Sec. 3.4)

mass The quantity of matter in an object that is measured by a balance. (PSS.1)

mass/mass percent (m/m %) A solution concentration expression that relates the mass of solute in grams dissolved in each 100 g of solution. (Sec. 13.8)

mass–mass problem A type of stoichiometry calculation that relates the masses of two substances according to a balanced equation. (Sec. 9.3)

mass number (A) A value that indicates the number of protons and neutrons in the nucleus of a given atom. (Secs. 4.4 and 18.2)

mass–volume problem A type of stoichiometry calculation that relates the mass of a substance to the volume of a gas according to a balanced equation. (Sec. 9.3)

measurement A numerical value with an attached unit that expresses a physical quantity such as length, mass, volume, time, or temperature. (PSS.1)

metal An element that is generally shiny in appearance, has a high density, high melting point, and is a good conductor of heat and electricity. (Sec. 3.4)

metal oxide A compound that reacts with water to form an alkaline solution; also termed a *basic oxide*. (Sec. 11.9)

metallic solid A crystalline solid composed of metal atoms that repeat in a regular pattern. (Sec. 11.5)

metalloid See *semimetal*.

meter (m) The basic unit of length in the metric system of measurement. (Sec. 2.1)

metric system A decimal system of measurement using prefixes and a basic unit to express physical quantities such as length, mass, and volume. (Sec. 2.1)

milliliter (mL) A common unit of volume in the metric system equal to one-thousandth of a liter. (PSS.1)

miscible A term that refers to liquids that dissolve completely in one another. (Sec. 13.2)

molar mass (MM) The mass of 1 mol of substance expressed in grams. (Secs. 8.3 and 9.1)

molar volume The volume occupied by 1 mol of gas at STP; at 0 °C and 1.00 atm the volume of 1 mol of gas is 22.4 L. (Secs. 8.5 and 9.5)

molarity (M) A solution concentration expression that relates the moles of solute dissolved in each liter of solution. (Sec. 13.9)

mole (mol) The amount of substance that contains Avogadro's number of particles; that is, an amount of substance that contains 6.02×10^{23} particles. (Sec. 8.2)

mole ratio The ratio of moles of reactants and products according to the coefficients in the balanced chemical equation. (Sec. 9.1)

molecular formula A chemical formula that expresses the actual number of atoms of each element in a molecule. (Sec. 8.9)

molecular shape The geometric shape formed by the atoms bonded to the central atom in a molecule; also called *molecular geometry*. (Sec. 12.10)

molecular solid A crystalline solid composed of molecules that repeat in a regular pattern. (Sec. 11.5)

molecule A single particle composed of nonmetal atoms. (Sec. 3.5) The simplest representative particle in a compound composed of nonmetals. (Sec. 6.7) The simplest particle in a substance held together by covalent bonds. (Sec. 12.1)

monoatomic ion A single atom that has a negative or positive a charge as the result of gaining or losing valence electrons. (Secs. 6.1 and 12.5)

monomer A small molecule that bonds to itself repeatedly to form a long, continuous chain. (Sec. 19.3)

monosaccharide A carbohydrate composed of a simple sugar molecule. A simple sugar is characterized by an aldehyde or ketone functional group and usually several hydroxyl groups. (Sec. 20.4)

N

natural law An extensively tested proposal of a scientific principle that states a measurable relationship under different experimental conditions. A natural law is often expressed as an equation; for example, $P_1V_1 = P_2V_2$. (Sec. 1.1)

net dipole The overall direction of partial negative charge in a molecule with two or more dipoles. (Secs. 11.7 and 13.2)

net ionic equation A chemical equation that results from canceling spectator ions in a total ionic equation. (Sec. 14.11)

neutralization reaction A type of reaction in which an acid and a base produce a salt and water. (Sec. 7.4)

neutron (n^0) A neutral subatomic particle with a mass of 1 amu, which is approximately equal to the mass of a proton. (Sec. 4.3)

noble gases The relatively unreactive Group VIIIA/18 elements. (Sec. 5.3)

nonbonding electrons The valence electrons in a molecule that are not shared; also referred to as *lone pairs*. (Sec. 12.4)

nonmetal An element that is generally dull in appearance, has a low density, low melting point, and is not a good conductor of heat and electricity. (Sec. 3.4)

nonmetal oxide A compound that reacts with water to form an acidic solution; also termed an *acidic oxide*. (Sec. 11.9)

nonpolar bond A covalent bond in which one or more pairs of electrons are shared equally. (Sec. 12.7)

nonpolar solvent A dissolving liquid composed of nonpolar molecules. (Sec. 13.2)

nonsignificant digits The digits in a measurement that exceed the certainty of the instrument. (PSS.3)

nuclear equation A shorthand representation using atomic notation to describe a nuclear reaction. (Sec. 18.2)

nuclear fission A nuclear reaction in which a heavy nucleus splits into two or more lighter nuclei and releases energy. (Sec. 18.7)

nuclear fusion A nuclear reaction in which two light nuclei combine into a single heavy nucleus and releases energy. (Sec. 18.8)

nuclear reaction A high-energy change involving the atomic nucleus. (Sec. 18.2)

nucleic acid A biological polymer compound that carries genetic information. (Sec. 20.1)

nucleotide A repeating unit in a nucleic acid composed of a sugar, a base, and phosphoric acid. (Sec. 20.6)

nucleus See *atomic nucleus*.

nuclide A specific atom with a designated number of protons and neutrons in its nucleus. (Sec. 18.2)

O

octet rule The statement that an atom tends to bond in such a way so as to acquire eight valence electrons. A hydrogen atom is an exception to the rule and acquires only two valence electrons. (*Sec. 12.1*)

oil A triglyceride from a plant source that contains mostly unsaturated fatty acids. (*Sec. 20.5*)

orbital A region in space surrounding the nucleus of an atom in which there is a high probability (~ 95) of finding an electron with a given energy. (*Sec. 4.11*)

organic chemistry The study of chemical substances that contain the element carbon. (*Sec. 1.2*) The study of carbon-containing compounds. (*Sec. 19.1*)

oxidation A chemical process characterized by the loss of electrons. A process in which a substance undergoes an increase in oxidation number. (*Sec. 17.2*)

oxidation number A positive or negative value assigned to an atom in a substance according to a set of rules; a value that indicates whether an atom is electron-poor or electron-rich compared to the free atom. (*Sec. 17.1*)

oxidation–reduction reaction See *redox reaction.*

oxidizing agent A substance that causes the oxidation of another substance in a redox reaction; the substance that is reduced in a redox reaction. (*Sec. 17.2*)

oxyanion A polyatomic anion that contains one or more elements combined with oxygen; for example, NO_3^- and SO_4^{2-}. (*Sec. 6.3*)

P

parent–daughter nuclides A term for a decaying nuclide and the resulting nuclide that is produced. (*Sec. 18.3*)

partial pressure The pressure exerted by an individual gas in a mixture of two or more gases. (*Sec. 10.9*)

peptide linkage An amide bond that joins two amino acid molecules in a small peptide, polypeptide, or protein. (*Sec. 20.2*)

percent (%) An expression for the amount of a single quantity compared to an entire sample; an expression of parts per hundred parts. (*Sec. 2.5*)

percent composition A list of the mass percent of each element in a compound. (*Sec. 8.7*)

percent yield The actual yield compared to the theoretical yield expressed as a percent. (*Sec. 9.9*)

period A horizontal row in the periodic table; a series of elements with properties that vary from metallic to nonmetallic. (*Sec. 5.3*)

periodic law The properties of the elements recur in a repeating pattern when arranged according to increasing atomic number. (*Sec. 5.2*)

periodic table A chart that arranges elements according to their properties and includes metals, nonmetals, and semimetals. (*Sec. 3.4*)

pH The molar concentration of hydrogen ions expressed on an exponential scale; the negative logarithm of the molar hydrogen ion concentration. (*Sec. 14.8*)

phenyl group The part that remains after a hydrogen atom is removed from a benzene molecule. (*Sec. 19.2*)

phospholipid A lipid that has two fatty acids and phosphoric acid joined to glycerol by ester bonds. (*Sec. 20.5*)

photon A particle of radiant energy. (*Sec. 4.7*)

physical change A modification of a substance that does not alter its chemical composition; for example, a change in physical state. (*Sec. 3.7*)

physical property A characteristic of a substance that can be observed without changing its chemical formula. (*Sec. 3.6*)

physical state The condition of matter existing as a solid, liquid, or gas. (*Sec. 3.1*)

polar bond A covalent bond in which one or more pairs of electrons are shared unequally. (*Sec. 12.6*)

polar solvent A dissolving liquid composed of polar molecules. (*Sec. 13.2*)

polyatomic ion A group of atoms bound together that bears an overall negative or positive charge. (*Sec. 6.1*) A group of atoms held together by covalent bonds that bears an overall negative or positive charge. (*Sec. 12.5*)

polymer A giant molecule composed of small molecules bonded together repeatedly in a long, continuous chain. (*Sec. 19.3*)

polypeptide A large molecule composed of 10–50 amino acids joined by amide bonds. (*Sec. 20.2*)

polysaccharide A carbohydrate polymer composed of simple sugar molecules joined by glycoside linkages. (*Sec. 20.4*)

positron (β^+ or $_{+1}^{0}e$) A nuclear radiation identical in mass, but opposite in charge, to that of an electron. The term *positron* is derived from "positive electron." (*Sec. 18.2*)

potential energy (PE) The stored energy that matter possesses owing to its position or chemical composition. (*Sec. 3.9*)

power of 10 A positive or negative exponent of 10. (*PSS.6*)

precipitate An insoluble solid substance produced by a chemical reaction in an aqueous solution. (*Sec. 7.1*)

product A substance resulting from a chemical reaction. (*Sec. 7.2*)

protein A biological compound that is a polymer composed of amino acids joined by peptide linkages. (*Sec. 20.1*)

proton (p^+) A positively charged subatomic particle with a mass of 1 amu, which is approximately 1836 times the mass of an electron. (*Sec. 4.2*)

proton acceptor A term for a Brønsted–Lowry base, which is a synonym for hydrogen ion acceptor. (*Sec. 14.3*)

proton donor A term for a Brønsted–Lowry acid, which is a synonym for hydrogen ion donor. (*Sec. 14.3*)

pure substance See *substance.*

Q

quantum level See *energy level.*

quantum mechanical atom A model of the atom that describes an electron in terms of its probability of being found in a particular location around the nucleus. (*Sec. 4.11*)

R

radiant energy spectrum A range of light energy extending from short-wavelength gamma rays to long-wavelength microwaves. (*Sec. 4.6*)

radioactive decay series The stepwise disintegration of an unstable nuclide until a stable nucleus is reached; also called *decay series.* (*Sec. 18.3*)

radioactivity The emission of particles or energy from an unstable atomic nucleus. *(Sec. 18.1)*

radionuclide An atom whose nucleus is unstable and decays radioactively. *(Sec. 18.5)*

rare earth elements The elements with atomic numbers 21, 39, 57, and 58–71. *(Sec. 5.3)*

rate of reaction The rate at which the concentrations of reactants decrease, or the concentrations of products increase, per unit time. *(Sec. 16.3)*

reactant A substance undergoing a chemical reaction. *(Sec. 7.2)*

reaction profile A graph of the energy of reactants and products as a reaction progresses. *(Sec. 16.2)*

real gas A gas that deviates from ideal behavior at a low temperature and a high pressure. *(Sec. 10.10)*

reciprocal The relationship between a fraction and its inverse; for example, 1 yard/3 feet and 3 feet/1 yard. *(Sec. 2.2)*

redox reaction A chemical reaction that involves electron transfer between two reacting substances. *(Sec. 17.2)*

reducing agent A substance that causes the reduction of another substance in a redox reaction; the substance that is oxidized in a redox reaction. *(Sec. 17.2)*

reduction A chemical process characterized by the gain of electrons. A process in which a substance undergoes a decrease in oxidation number. *(Sec. 17.2)*

reduction potential The relative ability of a substance to undergo reduction; the relative strength of an oxidizing agent. *(Sec. 17.5)*

replication The process by which a DNA molecule synthesizes an identical molecule of DNA. *(Sec. 20.6)*

representative elements The Group A (1, 2, and 13–18) elements in the periodic table; also termed *main-group elements*. *(Sec. 5.3)*

reversible reaction A reaction that proceeds simultaneously in both the forward direction toward products and the opposite direction toward reactants. *(Sec. 16.3)*

rounding off The process of eliminating digits that are not significant. *(PSS.3)*

S

salt An ionic compound produced by an acid–base reaction; the product of a neutralization reaction in addition to water. *(Secs. 7.11 and 14.2)*

salt bridge A porous device that allows ions to travel between two half-cells to maintain an ionic charge balance in each compartment. *(Sec. 17.6)*

saponification A chemical reaction of a fat or oil with sodium hydroxide to produce soap and glycerol. *(Sec. 20.5)*

saturated hydrocarbon A hydrocarbon that contains only single bonds. *(Sec. 19.1)*

saturated solution A solution that contains the maximum solute that can dissolve at a given temperature. *(Sec. 13.7)*

science The methodical exploration of nature and the logical explanation of the observations. *(Sec. 1.1)*

scientific method A systematic investigation that involves performing an experiment, proposing a hypothesis, testing the hypothesis, and finally, stating a theory or law that explains a scientific principle. *(Sec. 1.1)*

scientific notation A method for expressing numbers by moving the decimal place after the first significant digit and indicating the number of decimal moves by a power of 10. *(PSS.7)*

second (s) The basic unit of time in the metric system. *(Sec. 2.1)*

semimetal An element that is generally metallic in appearance and has properties midway between those of a metal and a nonmetal; also called a *metalloid*. *(Sec. 3.4)*

SI See *International System*.

significant digits The digits in a measurement known with certainty plus one digit that is estimated; also referred to as *significant figures*, or simply, *"sig figs."* *(PSS.2)*

single bond A bond composed of one electron pair shared between two atoms. A single bond is represented by a dash between the symbols of the two atoms. *(Sec. 12.4)*

single-replacement reaction A type of reaction in which a more active element displaces a less active element from a solution or compound. *(Sec. 7.4)*

soft water Water that contains sodium cations, Na^+, and a variety of anions such as CO_3^{2-}, SO_4^{2-}, and PO_4^{3-}. *(Sec. 11.7)*

solubility The maximum amount of solute that can dissolve in a solvent at a given temperature; usually expressed in grams of solute per 100 g of solvent. *(Sec. 13.6)*

solubility product equilibrium constant (K_{sp}) A constant that expresses the molar equilibrium concentrations of ions in an aqueous solution for a slightly dissociated ionic compound. *(Sec. 16.8)*

solute The component of a solution that is the lesser quantity. *(Sec. 13.2)*

solution The general term for a solute dissolved in a solvent. A solution is an example of a homogeneous mixture. *(Sec. 13.2)*

solvent The component of a solution that is the greater quantity. *(Sec. 13.2)*

solvent cage A cluster of solvent molecules surrounding a solute particle in a solution. *(Sec. 13.4)*

specific gravity (sp gr) The ratio of the density of a liquid compared to the density of water at 4 °C; a unitless expression. *(Sec. 2.8)*

specific heat The amount of heat required to raise the temperature of 1 g of any substance 1 °C; the specific heat of water is 1.00 cal/(g × °C). *(Secs. 2.10, 11.6)*

spectator ions Those ions in aqueous solution that do not participate in a reaction, and do not appear in the net ionic equation. *(Sec. 14.11)*

standard conditions See *standard temperature and pressure (STP)*.

standard solution A solution whose concentration has been established accurately (usually by titration to 3 or 4 significant digits). *(Sec. 14.6)*

standard temperature and pressure (STP) A temperature of 0 °C and a pressure of 1 atm. *(Secs. 8.5 and 9.5)* A temperature of 273 K and a pressure of 760 mm Hg for a gas. *(Sec. 10.7)*

steroid A lipid hormone composed of four rings of carbon atoms fused into a single molecular structure. *(Sec. 20.5)*

Stock system A system for naming ionic compounds that designates the variable charge on a metal cation with Roman numerals in parentheses. *(Sec. 6.2)*

stoichiometry The relationship of quantities (i.e., mass of substance or volume of gas) in a chemical reaction according to the balanced chemical equation. *(Sec. 9.3)*

strong electrolyte An aqueous solution that is a good conductor of electricity; for example, strong acids, strong bases, and soluble salts. *(Sec. 14.10)*

structural formula A diagram of a molecule or polyatomic ion that shows the chemical symbol of each atom and a dash representing each pair of bonding electrons. *(Sec. 12.4)* A chemical formula that shows the arrangement of atoms in a molecule. *(Sec. 19.2)*

sublimation A direct change of state from a solid to a gas without forming a liquid. *(Sec. 3.1)*

subscript A digit in a chemical formula that represents the number of atoms or ions occurring in the substance. *(Sec. 7.3)*

substance Matter with a definite composition and constant properties; examples include elements and compounds. It is also referred to as *pure substance*. *(Sec. 3.2)*

supersaturated solution A solution with more than the maximum solute that can dissolve at a given temperature. *(Sec. 13.7)*

surface tension The resistance of a liquid to spread out, and its tendency to form spherical drops with minimum surface area. *(Sec. 11.3)*

T

temperature The average energy of molecules in motion. *(Sec. 2.9)*

ternary ionic compound A compound that contains three elements, including at least one metal. *(Sec. 6.1)*

ternary oxyacid A compound that contains hydrogen, a nonmetal, and oxygen dissolved in water. *(Sec. 6.1)*

theoretical yield The amount of product that is calculated to be obtained from given amounts of reactants. *(Sec. 9.9)*

theory An extensively tested proposal of a scientific principle that explains the behavior of nature. A theory offers a model, for example the atomic theory, to describe nature. *(Sec. 1.1)*

titration A laboratory procedure for delivering a measured volume of solution using a buret. *(Sec. 14.5)*

torr A unit of gas pressure equal to 1 mm Hg. *(Sec. 10.2)*

total ionic equation A chemical equation that shows ionized substances in solution as ions and slightly ionized substances as nonionized. *(Sec. 14.11)*

transcription The process by which a DNA molecule synthesizes a complementary single strand of RNA. *(Sec. 20.6)*

transition elements The Group B (3–12) elements in the periodic table. *(Sec. 5.3)*

transition state The highest point on the reaction profile at which there is the greatest potential energy. *(Sec. 16.2)*

transmutation The conversion of one element to another by inducing a nuclear reaction using particle bombardment. *(Sec. 18.6)*

transuranium elements The elements with atomic numbers beyond 92. All of the elements following uranium are synthetic. *(Sec. 5.3)*

triglyceride A lipid that has three fatty acids joined to glycerol by ester bonds; also called a *triacylglycerol*. *(Sec. 20.5)*

triple bond A bond composed of three electron pairs shared between two atoms. A triple bond is represented by three dashes between the symbols of the two atoms. *(Sec. 12.4)*

tritium (^3_1H) The nuclide of hydrogen with two neutrons in the nucleus. *(Sec. 18.8)*

Tyndall effect The phenomenon of scattering a beam of light by colloid particles. *(Sec. 13.3)*

U

uncertainty The degree of inexactness in a measurement obtained from an instrument. *(PSS.1)*

uncertainty principle The statement that it is impossible to precisely measure both the location and energy of a particle at the same time. *(Sec. 4.11)*

unit analysis method A systematic procedure for solving problems that converts the units in a given value to the units in the answer; also referred to as *dimensional analysis* or *factor label method*. *(Sec. 2.3)*

unit equation A statement that relates two values that are equivalent; for example, 1 ft = 12 in. and 1 in. = 2.54 cm. *(Sec. 2.2)*

unit factor A ratio of two quantities that are equivalent and can be applied to convert from one unit to another; for example, 1 m/100 cm. *(Sec. 2.2)*

unsaturated hydrocarbon A hydrocarbon that contains a carbon-carbon double bond or triple bond. *(Sec. 19.1)*

unsaturated solution A solution that contains less than the maximum solute that can dissolve at a given temperature. *(Sec. 13.7)*

V

vacuum A volume of space that does not contain gas molecules. *(Sec. 10.2)*

valence electrons The electrons that occupy the outermost *s* and *p* sublevels of an atom. *(Sec. 5.7)* The electrons in the outermost *s* and *p* sublevels of an atom that undergo reaction and form chemical bonds. *(Sec. 12.1)*

valence shell electron pair repulsion See *VSEPR theory*.

vapor pressure The pressure exerted by gaseous vapor above a liquid in a sealed container when the rates of vaporization and condensation are equal. *(Secs. 10.8 and 11.3)*

viscosity The resistance of a liquid to flow. *(Sec. 11.3)*

visible spectrum A range of light energy observed as violet, blue, green, yellow, orange, or red; the wavelengths of light from 400–700 nm. *(Sec. 4.6)*

voltaic cell An electrochemical cell in which a spontaneous redox reaction occurs and generates electrical energy; also called a *galvanic cell*. *(Sec. 17.6)*

volume by displacement A technique for determining the volume of a solid or a gas by measuring the volume of water it displaces. *(Sec. 2.7)* A technique for determining the volume of a gas by measuring the volume of water it displaces. *(Sec. 10.9)*

volume–volume problem A type of stoichiometry calculation that relates the volumes of two gases (at the same temperature and pressure) according to a balanced equation. *(Sec. 9.3)*

VSEPR theory A model that explains the shapes of molecules as a result of bonding and nonbonding electron pairs around the central atom repelling each other. *(Sec. 12.10)*

W

water of hydration The number of water molecules bound to a formula unit in a hydrate; also called the *water of crystallization*. *(Sec. 11.10)*

wavelength The distance a light wave travels to complete one cycle. *(Sec. 4.6)*

wax A lipid that contains a fatty acid joined to an alcohol by an ester linkage. *(Sec. 20.5)*

weak electrolyte An aqueous solution that is a poor conductor of electricity; for example, weak acids, weak bases, and slightly soluble salts. *(Sec. 14.10)*

Photo Credits

Chapter 1: Page 1 Dorling Kindersley Media Library (L); NASA (R) **Page 2** Pumkinpie/Alamy **Page 3** Gary J. Shulfer/C. Marvin Lang **Page 4** Gary J. Shulfer/C. Marvin Lang **Page 5** Eric Broder Van Dyke/Shutterstock **Page 6** Alcoa Technical Center

PSS: Page 11 Charles D. Winters/Photo Researchers, Inc. **Page 12** United States Mint Headquarters **Page 14** Mettler Toledo North America (BR); Ohaus Corporation (T) (BL) **Page 17** Felix Mizioznikov/iStockphoto (T) (BR); Texas Instruments Incorporated (B) **Page 21** NASA (T); Centers for Disease Control (B) **Page 26** NASA

Chapter 2: Page 28 Ira Block/Shutterstock **Page 30** National Institute of Standards and Technology **Page 31** National Institute of Standards and Technology **Page 35** Bork/Shutterstock **Page 37** Charles H. Corwin **Page 38** Charles H. Corwin **Page 39** AFP/Getty Images/Newscom (T) (B) **Page 40** Inger Anne Hulbækdal/Shutterstock **Page 41** Corbis **Page 43** Clive Streeter/Dorling Kindersley **Page 44** Pearson Education/Eric Schrader **Page 45** BMW Group Press Club **Page 48** Harry Taylor/Dorling Kindersley **Page 52** Australian Postal Service/National Standards Commission **Page 53** Andraž Cerar/Shutterstock **Page 54** ggw1962/Shutterstock **Page 61** Luca di Filippo/iStockphoto.com (T); Spike Mafford/Getty Images (B) **Page 62** goldenangel/Shutterstock

Chapter 3: Page 63 Mikael Damkier/Fotolia **Page 64** Alex Staroseltsev/Shutterstock (L); Adisa/Shutterstock (M); Can Balcioglu/Shutterstock (R) **Page 65** Richard Megna/Fundamental Photographs **Page 67** Richard Megna/Fundamental Photographs (T); Pearson Education/Tom Bochsler Photography Limited (B) **Page 68** Filipe Varela/iStockphoto (L); Daniel Timiraos/iStockphoto (2nd from L); Mustafa Deliormanli/iStockphoto (3rd from L); Achim Prill/iStockphoto (R) **Page 71** Ann Steer/iStockphoto **Page 78** Ryan McVay/Getty Images (M); Eric Foltz/iStockphoto (R); Yellowj/Shutterstock (L) **Page 79** Aga & Miko (arsat)/Shutterstock **Page 81** Dorling Kindersley (TL); Charles D. Winters/Photo Researchers, Inc. (TR); Richard Megna/Fundamental Photographs (M); Nadezda Boltaca/Shutterstock (B) **Page 83** Pearson Education/Eric Schrader (L); Richard Megna/Fundamental Photographs (M) (R) **Page 84** Alexander Zhiltsov/iStockphoto (T); Pearson Education/ Donald Clegg and Roxy Wilson (B) **Page 87** Michael T. Sedam/Corbis **Page 90** kabby/Shutterstock (T); Gary J. Shulfer/Marvin C. Lang (B) **Page 93** mikeledray/Shutterstock **Page 95** Richard Megna/Fundamental Photographs **Page 98** Melissa Carroll/iStockphoto (T); Pearson Education/Eric Schrader (B)

Chapter 4: Page 99 www.images-of-elements.com/hydrogen.php **Page 100** Library of Congress **Page 106** Michael Dalton/Fundamental Photographs **Page 108** REUTERS/Kai Pfaffenbach **Page 114** Gary J. Shulfer/Marvin C. Lang **Page 116** Charles H. Corwin **Page 117** Phillip Slawinski (5) **Page 122** Paul Ehrenfest/AIP Emilio Segre Visual Archives, Ehrenfest Collection **Page 128** Charles H. Corwin **Page 130** Matthew Pasant (BL); Charles H. Corwin (BR)

Chapter 5: Page 131 Dorling Kindersley **Page 133** Visual Arena **Page 142** Richard Megna/Fundamental Photographs **Page 152** NASA **Page 155** La Sociedad Estatal Correos y Telegrafos S.A./Professor Gabriel Pinto, Department of Chemistry, University of Madrid **Page 159** Pearson Education/Tom Bochsler Photography Limited

Chapter 6: Page 160 Richard Megna/Fundamental Photographs **Page 162** Diane Diederich/iStockphoto **Page 163** Richard Megna/Fundamental Photographs **Page 164** Jacques-Louis David **Page 169** J Duggan/Shutterstock **Page 170** Alex Kosev/Shutterstock **Page 171** Richard Megna/Fundamental Photographs **Page 172** Raimond Spekking/Wikimedia Commons/CC-BY-SA-3.0 & GDFL (T); Rob Lavinsky/iRocks.com (B) **Page 173** Melissa Carroll/iStockphoto **Page 175** Yuri Yavnik/Shutterstock **Page 177** Reika/Shutterstock (T); Stacey Newman/iStockphoto (B) **Page 178** Richard Megna/Fundamental Photographs **Page 179** Pearson Education/Eric Schrader **Page 180** Richard Megna/Fundamental Photographs **Page 184** Pearson Education/Tom Bochsler Photography Limited (L); Rob Lavinsky/iRocks.com (R) **Page 186** Parent Géry **Page 187** Richard Megna/Fundamental Photographs

Chapter 7: Page 188 Richard Megna/Fundamental Photographs (L) (R) **Page 189** Vakhrushev Pavel/Shutterstock (L); H. Eugene LeMay, Jr. (R) **Page 190** Pearson Education/Eric Schrader (L); Richard Megna/Fundamental Photographs (M) (R) **Page 194** Richard Megna/Fundamental Photographs **Page 195** Pearson Education/Eric Schrader **Page 198** Pearson Education/Tom Bochsler Photography Limited **Page 199** Pearson Education/Tom Bochsler Photography Limited **Page 200** Pearson Education/Tom Bochsler Photography Limited **Page 202** Richard Megna/Fundamental Photographs **Page 204** Pearson Education/Tom Bochsler Photography Limited **Page 205** Pearson Education/McCracken Photographers **Page 206** Pearson Education/Tom Bochsler **Page 207** Pearson Education/Eric Schrader **Page 208** Pearson Education/McCracken Photographers **Page 209** Pearson Education/McCracken Photographers **Page 210** Richard Megna/Fundamental Photographs **Page 211** Pearson Education/Eric Schrader **Page 215** George Resch/Fundamental Photographs (L); Pearson Education/Tom Bochsler Photography, Ltd. (R) **Page 217** Pearson Education/Tom Bochsler Photography (RT); Richard Megna/Fundamental Photographs (RM) **Page 220** Richard Megna/Fundamental Photographs (L (3)); Pearson Education (R (3))

Chapter 8: Page 221 hosha/Shutterstock **Page 225** Richard Megna/Fundamental Photographs **Page 227** Pearson Education/Tom Bochsler Photography **Page 231** Charles H. Corwin (T); Lars Christensen/Shutterstock (B) **Page 232** Richard Megna/Fundamental Photographs **Page 247** Richard Megna/Fundamental Photographs

Chapter 9: Page 249 Lee Prince/Shutterstock **Page 250** Deborah Davis/Photonica/Getty Images **Page 254** JinYoung Lee/Shutterstock **Page 255** Richard Megna/Fundamental Photographs **Page 256** Pearson Education/McCracken Photographers **Page 257** Pearson Education/McCracken Photographers/**Page 259** Dmitry Vereshchagin/Fotolia **Page 260** Pearson Science/Eric Schrader **Page 262** Richard Megna/Fundamental Photographs **Page 263** Denton Rumsey/Shutterstock **Page 264** Pearson Education/Tom Bochsler Photography Limited/**Page 265** Richard Megna/Fundamental Photographs **Page 268** Bogdan Vasilescu/Fotolia **Page 270** Pearson Education/McCracken Photographers (T) (B) **Page 274** Richard Megna/Fundamental Photographs **Page 275** Pearson Education/Eric Schrader (T); Bryn Lennon/Getty Images (B)

Chapter 10: Page 279 CC-by-3.0 license/Images-of-elements.com **Page 280** Jeff Schultes/Shutterstock **Page 283** Sylbia Schug/iStockphoto **Page 288** Pictorial Press Ltd/Alamy **Page 289** Richard Megna/Fundamental Photographs **Page 297** Jim Sugar/Corbis **Page 307** weareadventurers/iStockphoto (L); Slobo Mitic/iStockphoto (R) **Page 309** Simon Podgorsek/iStockphoto

Chapter 11: Page 312 Chip Clark/Fundamental Photographs **Page 313** Pearson Education Corporate Digital Archive **Page 318** Kristen Brochmann/Fundamental Photographs (T); wiklander/Shutterstock (B) **Page 319** Richard Megna/Fundamental Photographs **Page 320** Pearson Education/Eric Schrader **Page 321** Parent Géry (T); npix/iStockphoto (M); James Steidl/Shutterstock (B) **Page 327** Doc. RNDr. Josef Reischig, CSc., used under a Creative Commons license. http://creativecommons.org/licenses/by/3.0/deed.en **Page 328** Richard Megna/Fundamental Photographs (L) (M) (R) **Page 329** aist1974/Shutterstock **Page 330** Richard Megna/Fundamental Photographs **Page 333** Charles H. Corwin **Page 336** Heidi Kristensen/iStockphoto **Page 339** Paul Silverman/Fundamental Photographs **Page 340** Richard Megna/Fundamental Photographs

Chapter 12: Page 341 Mark A. Schneider/Photo Researchers, Inc. **Page 343** Susan Trigg/iStockphoto (L); Amir Kaljikovic/Fotolia (R) **Page 359** Prasad Photography **Page 366** General Electric Corporate Research & Development Center

Chapter 13: Page 375 Lucenet Patrice/Oredia Eurl/SuperStock **Page 377** cbpix/Shutterstock **Page 379** Kamran Jebreili/Associated Press **Page 381** Richard Megna/Fundamental Photographs **Page 383** Richard Megna/Fundamental Photographs **Page 386** Pearson Education/Eric Schrader (B); Richard Megna/Fundamental Photographs (T (3)) **Page 388** Pearson Education (T); Andrew Gentry/iStockphoto (B) **Page 390** Pearson Education (T (3)) **Page 391** Pearson Education/Eric Schrader **Page 392** Pearson Education/Eric Schrader (T); Pearson Education/Tom Bochsler Photography Limited (B) **Page 397** Pearson Education/Eric Schrader (L) (R)

Chapter 14: Page 403 Richard Megna/Fundamental Photographs **Page 404** Pearson Education/Eric Schrader **Page 405** Sabine Kappel/Shutterstock (T); Edyta Linek/iStockphoto (B) **Page 406** Eric Schrader/Fundamental Photographs **Page 407** Simon Bratt/Sutterstock (T); Richard Megna/Fundamental Photographs (B) **Page 408** Pearson Education/Eric Schrader **Page 409** Photos.com **Page 411** Pearson Education/Tom Bochsler Photography Limited (L) (M) (R) **Page 413** Richard Megna/Fundamental Photographs (T (3)) **Page 420** Richard Megna/Fundamental Photographs **Page 421** Pearson Education/Eric Schrader (T) (B) **Page 423** Pearson Education/Eric Schrader **Page 424** NYC Parks Photo Archive/Fundamental Photographs (L); Kristen Brochmann/Fundamental Photographs (R); National Atmospheric Deposition Program (B) **Page 433** Richard Megna/Fundamental Photographs **Page 434** Pearson Education/Tom Bochsler Photography Limited

Index